Electrophoresis '84

Editor:
Volker Neuhoff

Electrophoresis '84

Editor:
Volker Neuhoff

Proceedings
of the Fourth Meeting
of the International Electrophoresis Society

Göttingen 1984

Weinheim
Deerfield Beach, Florida
Basel

Prof. Dr. Volker Neuhoff
Max-Planck-Institut für
experimentelle Medizin
Forschungsstelle Neurochemie
Hermann-Rein-Straße 3
D-3400 Göttingen

ISBN 3-527-26074-9 (Verlag Chemie)
ISBN 0-89573-227-0 (Verlag Chemie International)

Production Manager: Peter J. Biel
Cover design: Studio Fladt, D-6700 Ludwigshafen
Printing and Bookbinding: Zechnersche Buchdruckerei, D-6720 Speyer
Printed in the Federal Republic of Germany

Preface

The analytical and preparative potential of electrophoretic separation was recognized at an early date, and not least in the biological sciences, where the introduction of electrophoretic methods of separation using different supporting media constituted a major breakthrough. These methods have helped to solve many scientific problems, and their development is still going on, as can be seen from the success and wide circulation of *Electrophoresis,* a young journal devoted solely to the subject. Nowadays, a wide variety of such methods is available, clearly demonstrating that no one method in itself is capable of solving all the separation problems for the many types of biological materials. This means that the experimentalist must have a whole repertoire of electrophoretic techniques at his disposal, or at least be fully aware of the latest trends and developments relevant to his particular area of research.

Meetings of national electrophoresis societies and the International Electrophoresis Society are now being convened at regular intervals so as to promote the exchange of information and to give experts the chance of discussing their problems with other experts working in the same field. In this connection it is interesting to note that the national electrophoresis societies were founded only recently and that their meetings are being well attended. Several books covering the papers presented at previous national and international meetings have already been published, any they all have been well received by the scientific community.

Electrophoresis '84 is unique in that it constitutes a collection of all the invited speakers' papers and all poster abstracts submitted to the fourth meeting of the International Electrophoresis Society that is available in book form prior to the convening of the congress. This has been achieved through the thoughtful cooperation of all the authors and through Verlag Chemie's readiness to print this volume at only a few weeks notice. Such a timely publication of all the latest trends and developments, new methods, and recent results in the field of electrophoresis is regarded as a further attempt not only to prepare a firm foundation for the discussion and exchange of scientific facts during the congress, but also to promote and stimulate the development of new ideas, however vague they may initially be. For this reason the present program committee, consisting of R.C. Allen (USA), M. Dunn (UK), K. Felgenhauer (FRG), T. Klose (FRG), V. Neuhoff (FRG), and B.T. Radola (FRG) - planned only a limited number of invited lectures, dispensing with the parallel sessions commonly included in the programs at comparable meetings, so as to ensure that participants will actually be able to assimilate all new information relevant to their particular fields of interest, yet leaving them time to explor other fields.

Further progress in the broad field of electrophoresis will either be inhibited by egocentric seclusion or be stimulated by the open exchange of information on new developed methods and the crucial "tricks" involved therein. It is my sincere wish that *Electrophoresis '84,* as the proceedings of the fourth meeting of the International Electrophoresis Society, will serve to further international collaboration. Obviously, the subjects chosen for *Electrophoresis '84* in no way cover all aspects of electrophoresis. They were expressly selected by the members of the program committee responsible for this particular congress. Further subjects are bound to be selected by future program committees, thus ensuring a continuity of purpose in our proceedings.

I take great pleasure in thanking the members of the present program committee and all my coworkers for their cooperative efforts and sustained help. Without financial support from the Deutsche Forschungsgemeinschaft and from the Niedersächsische Minister for Wissenschaft and Kunst, as well as from numerous German firms through the Stiftverband für die Deutsche Wissenschaft, the convening of this congress would have been impossible. On behalf of the International Electrophoresis Society, the program committee and all participants I extend my sincere gratitude to these sponsors. Their funds will be productively invested; they will not only help the dissemination of information about new methods and techniques but also foster their application in many different fields, including basic research as well as clinical analysis.

Göttingen, July 1984 Volker Neuhoff

Contents

Symposium

New Developments

Chairmen: *S. Hjertén* and *B. J. Radola*

Poster Abstracts

Poster Abstracts

Symposium

Application – Clinical and Genetic

Chairmen: *K. Felgenhauer, C. A. Saravis* and *K. Taketa*

Poster Abstracts

Symposium

New Developments

Chairmen:
S. Hjertén and B. J. Radola

RECENT DEVELOPMENTS IN BUFFER ELECTROFOCUSING

Andreas Chrambach

Laboratory of Theoretical and Physical Biology, National Institute of Child Health and Human Development, National Institutes of Health, Bethesda MD, USA

SUMMARY

Buffer electrofocusing (BEF) presently provides a) a limited selection of practical pH gradients at low cost; b) computer simulation of pH gradients composed of 13 acidic, 16 basic or any higher number of constituents within negligible computer time, using a moving boundary model, which avoids the workload of empirical pH gradient engineering; c) a theory-aided selection of measures for pH gradient stabilization; d) an electrofocusing system relatively free from artifactual interaction products with proteins; e) easy separation of isolated proteins from carrier constituents. Problems associated with the present rudimentary method which lie in the way of its development to a widely useful separation method are outlined and remedies for these problems are suggested. The pro's and con's of BEF against the background of competing electrofocusing methods are outlined.

1 INTRODUCTION

Electrofocusing in mixtures of simple buffers preceded the synthesis of carrier ampholyte mixtures by Vesterberg (1), and was supplanted by it since the pH gradients formed by synthetic carrier ampholyte mixtures (designated SCAMs) were more linear, comprised wider pH ranges and were more effortlessly produced since SCAMs became commercially available. A literature review of these early buffer electrofocusing separations is provided by (2). Of importance is that all of these early BEF experiments were conducted with buffer mixtures consisting at least in part of amphoteric buffers, and could therefore be reconciled with the concept that pH gradients form by an alignment of isoelectric ampholytes in the order of their pI values. This concept is erroneously ascribed to the theoretical treatment of electrophoretic migration and condensation (focusing) of ampholytes in a pre-existing pH gradient developed by Rilbe (3).

2 THE IMPACT OF BEF ON THE THEORETICAL UNDERSTANDING OF PH GRADIENT FORMATION

In a meaningful sense, BEF dates from 1976. In that year, Nguyen and the author described a pH gradient formed naturally from a mixture of 10 non-amphoteric organic bases (Fig.1, right) at 3 concentrations, 0.001 to 0.1 M each, and followed the genesis and maintenance of this gradient as a function of time (4). It was an incredibly poor-looking pH 4 to 10 gradient, wiggly and even violating the law of pH monotony, but it had formed nonetheless naturally, without any doubt, with time in the electric field and necessarily by a mechanism which did not involve an isoelectric condensation. Parenthetically, the worst cosmetic features of this pH gradient could remedied later once it was realized that the basic carrier constituents gave rise to polyacrylamide with a low average chain length and therefore little mechanical stability, and that this effect could be counteracted by coating of the glass walls of the gel container with linear polyacrylamide (5,6).

3 EMPIRICAL BUFFER PH GRADIENTS - AN UNPROMISING APPROACH

Viewed in 1976, the promise of BEF for practical separations did not lie with the curious non-amphoteric pH gradient, but rather with the far better-behaved 9-component pH gradient made mostly of amphoteric constituents (Fig.1,left). This promise appeared fourfold: i) There was a biochemical advantage in exposing the species of interest to chemically defined compounds with known functional groups, at known concentrations, compared to the inconcisely defined components of SCAMs. ii) The cost of buffer mixtures compared to the price of SCAMs was lower by two orders of magnitude or more, thus enabling economically disadvantaged laboratories to electrofocus. iii) It appeared likely that small molecular weight buffers would exhibit fewer interactions with proteins than larger and multivalent synthetic carrier ampholytes. iv) It appeared readily possible to tailor pH gradients to one's needs by the mere addition or subtraction of buffer constituents from the mixture. It is this part of the promise that empirical BEF was unable to fulfill with sufficient ease and precision. The simple fact is that from a knowledge of the pKs alone it is possible to design acidic, basic and neutral pH gradients (Fig.2) but it is not possible to arrive at a particular desired pH range without a great many experimental trials. The most convincing example in that regard is the pH 2.5-11 buffer gradient elaborated and characterized by Cuono (2). It was generated by more than 100 trials in which constituents were exchanged, added or subtracted. The resulting pH gradient is stable over a period of 6 hours at 100 V/cm, on a slab gel 1mm thick, which is sufficient for ferritin (MW 450K) to reach its pI-position in a gel of 5 %T, 2.5 $\%C_{Bis}$. The conductance profile at the steady state is similar to that found with SCAMs. Undoubtedly, it is this empirical 47-buffer mixture (Fig.3) which still represents the most widely practical BEF system. A 13-buffer system, consisting nearly entirely of acidic Good's buffers (Fig.4, top), is useful over a more narrow pH-range which, however, does encompass the pH 5 region in which many proteins are isoelectric (Fig.5). Its preparation is, of course, much simpler than that of the wide pH-range buffer: All 13 buffers were mixed to a final concentration of 0.04 M each in a Sephadex G-75 gel (13). Final concentrations within the aligned phases were of the order of 0.5 M. Under these conditions, this empirical pH gradient exhibits a striking stability.

In addition to the laboriousness in pH gradient engineering, the empirical design of BEF gradients suffers from ignorance of the position of buffer constituents along the pH gradient. Computer simulation has taught us (see below) that in view of the regulated, constant concentration of each of the buffer constituents, the fraction of the gradient length occupied by each of the buffers at the steady state varies from one buffer to the next in proportion to its load (moles). Moreover, in the empirically designed pH gradients developed to date no assurance exists that they have reached the steady state, in particular when non-amphoteric buffers are admixed to amphoteric ones. This is due to the fact that non-amphoteric buffers can only migrate uni-directionally, and that therefore their steady state alignment, presumably by way of backward diffusion, is slow compared to amphoteric buffers. It should be noted, however, that this problem in the application of non-amphoteric constituents, in either the empirical or the computer simulation design of pH gradients, is one of experimental technique and not of principle. A way to possibly avoid this problem will be discussed in section 5. A further retarding factor in the attainment of the steady state is the interaction, by electrostatic and/or hydrophobic forces, between carrier constituents, which we will deal with extensively further below. Again, this problem in the recognition of the steady state is not one limited to empirically designed buffer pH gradients.

4 COMPUTER SIMULATION OF PH GRADIENTS

The demonstration of a natural pH gradient made from a few non-amphoteric constituents does not, by itself, teach us a great deal concerning the mechanism of pH gradient genesis in electrofocusing. It certainly does not prove that all of electrofocusing necessarily involves a mechanism of non-isoelectric alignment of constituents. The mere insight that in this rather odd case a pH gradient forms non-isoelectrically is a curiosity for the methodologist in the field of focusing, but at first sight seems without any practical interest for most of us involved in practical separations by EF.

The above-stated claim that BEF, in a meaningful sense, started with that modest gradient made of 10 bases, rests on the fact that it led to the application of moving boundary theory to the computer simulation of practical pH gradients for EF, made of 15 to potentially at least 50 simple and chemically characterized buffers. Such computer simulations again proved of crucial importance for the practice of electrofocusing in view of the intolerable amount of labor involved in the empirical development of pH gradients and their tailoring to one's specific needs. There exist at present two computational approaches for the simulation of pH gradients and their time course. The approach of Bier et al. (14) may be the more rigorous one of the two, being based on a consideration of the sum of physical processes involved in pH gradient genesis - diffusion as well as electrophoresis; it treats the transient and steady states alike. This approach has to date not been able to simulate pH gradients over a wide pH range, or comprising more than 3 or 4 constituents, for at least two reasons: It requires a great deal of computer time so that the computation of even as limited a system as one consisting of 13 or 16 components would be prohibitively expensive and time consuming. Secondly, it requires as input parameters the pKs and ionic mobilities of all of the ionic forms of a molecule, and these, of course are not available.

From a practical point of view, the less rigorous approach taken by Hjelmeland and the author (15,12) is therefore preferable, since it does allow one to predict buffer pH gradients and their dynamics with time within negligible computing time and with any desired number of carrier constituents. Examples for pH gradient simulation by the Hjelmeland program will be discussed in detail which employ either 13 acidic or 16 basic buffers, both amphoteric and non-amphoteric (Fig.4).

The Hjelmeland program applies steady state moving boundary (isotachophoretic) theory to multiple sequential moving boundaries, set up by multiple trailing constituents, and calculates the regulated, operative pH within each of the boundaries. Since at the steady state boundaries in such a system align in order of the net mobilities of the trailing constituents, a monotonic step function of pH across the multiple boundaries ensues. In practice, this step function smoothes out into a continuous pH gradient either due to diffusion in the electric field (which in this treatment is neglected) and/or during the interval between termination of electrophoresis and pH measurement. The crucial insight for electrofocusing (15,16) is that this pH gradient across multiple moving boundaries is arrested in its electrophoretic displacement to the degree that the common counter ion of leading and trailing constituents is replaced by the proton and hydroxyl ion as the sole counterions. This requirement for a common ion concentration of 0 principally distinguishes the application of the Hjelmeland program from a previous application of the Routs program for the same purpose (17).

Multiplicity of carrier constituents is limited only by the input requirement for the ionic mobility of either the cationic or the anionic species used in the design of the pH gradient, at the temperature and ionic strength of that gradient. The program is limited to monovalent acids, bases and biprotic ampholytes and has as the only additional input requirement the pKs of these species. These, however, in contrast to the ionic mobilities, are well known at least for one particular set of temperature and ionic strength. Correction of pK values to a desired ionic strength and temperature can be made according to the equations and correction factors shown in the figure at least for a limited number of constituents (Fig.6). The big hold-up on the general applicability of the Hjelmeland program for the simulation of pH gradients in general practice of BEF is our ignorance of the ionic mobilities of buffer constituents. The values known to the author are derived either from conductimetric analysis in the author's laboratory [Fig.4 of (18)] the documentation of which is unpublished, or from a recent compilation (19) which, however, does not refer to most of the amphoteric "Good's buffers" (20) which constitute the bulk of practical BEF constituents at this time. It is important to note that a) the extension of this presently available list to larger numbers of constituents, with values for 0^{0} well as for 25^{0} C, b) the physical-chemical treatment of ionic mobility for ampholytes with narrowly adjacent pKs (21), and c) the synthesis of amphoteric compounds with pI values 6 to 8 represent unsolved problems which still stand in the way of a widespread practical application of pH gradient simulation. Nonetheless, the method appears sufficiently important to warrant a detailed explanation on how to use the Hjelmeland program for pH gradient simulations.

Fig.7 lists the program as applied to a system of 13 acids. The input parameters are: i) ionic mobilities, relative to Na^+, lines 6-18; ii) pK_1, lines 19-31; iii) pK_2, lines 32-44; iv) molarity of the leading phase, line 45. When more than 13 constituents are used, input sections i), ii) and iii) are expanded to the desired number. The output format is given by Fig.8. The first two lines, and column 1 of the third line, restate the input parameters. The rows state the molar concentrations, pHs, trailing ion net mobilities relative to Na^+ (r), and conductances (κ) within contiguous zones occupied by the selected constituents at the steady state. It is seen that both pHs and trailing ion net mobilities decrease monotonically. The boundary displacement rate, ν, serves as a measure of pH gradient decay, as does the boundary velocity, v, computed for a regulated current of 4 mA/cm^2, 0°C. These computed measures of boundary displacement are indicative of substantial gradient stability; the experimentally observed (Buzas, Zs. and the author, unpublished data) much greater instability (Fig.9) is presumably due to perturbing factors in a milieu of exceedingly low conductance (ranging from 1 to 9 x 10^{-5} µmhos/cm) and no buffering capacity, in view of a pI-pK difference of the buffers used of 3 or more pH units (3) in most cases (Fig.4), or possibly due to electrolysis products formed in the electrolyte chambers.

It is noteworthy that the alignment of either acidic or basic constituents in order of net mobility, as postulated by the moving boundary theory, leads necessarily to steady state pHs in the sequential buffer compartments which are approximately isoelectric (Fig.4). Therefore, the known isoelectric alignment of proteins in a preformed pH gradient in no way counterindicates the hypothesis that pH gradients form, and proteins are aligned by, a moving boundary mechanism (15).

5 PERFORMANCE OF BUFFER PH GRADIENTS

5.1 The experimental setup of computer simulated pH gradients

In practice, it appears desirable to set up equal length compartments for the desired number of buffer constituents across the pH gradient. The number of moles of each constituent to give, for instance, a 1 cm long zone in a gel tube of 6 mm ID (0.27 cm^2 cross-sectional area) is calculated as concentration (mmoles/ml) given in the output (Fig.8) multiplied by 0.27 (ml of a 1 cm gel segment). This value is further multiplied by the dilution which the constituent suffers upon being incorporated into a gel. If, as is convenient, a polyacryamide gel is prepared by mixing buffer, monomer stock solution and catalyst mixture in a 1:2:1 volume ratio (22), i.e. the buffer is 4-fold diluted, the constituent would have to be weighed into the buffer mixture in an amount given by concentration x 0.27 x 4.

Amphoteric buffers, capable of migrating bidirectionally, can be combined in the requisite amounts given by the output (Fig.8) into a single gel buffer mixture. However, non-amphoteric compounds other than the leading ion when added to such a mixture should considerably slow down the attainment of a steady state alignment since they can only migrate unidirectionally and must be assumed to move backward by either diffusion or electroendosmosis. It is therefore suggested to apply non-amphoterics in the catholyte or anolyte outside the gel, and to provide for their entrance into the gel by admixing to the gel buffer an equivalent amount of K^+ or Cl^- counterion for the amphoteric species. This procedure, however, remains untested to date.

It appears from work with acidic buffer pH gradients of the type shown in Fig.9 that the mechanical stability of "non-restrictive" polyacrylamide gels during BEF is progressively deteriorating during electrofocusing with formation of bubbles and cracks under the conditions of BEF given in the Legend to Fig.9, irrespective of whether the leading ion concentration is 0.1 or 1.0 M. That instability is not observed in the very similar 13-component empirical system (Fig.5) applied on Sephadex G-75 gels. This suggests that the low conductance of the 13-component mixture (see section 4) gives rise to local Joule heat in excess of the heat dissipation capacity of the apparatus, causing pertubations in polyacrylamide, but not in the much more robust Sephadex gel. If this interpretation is correct, a lowering of the voltage in combination with relatively high (about 0.5 M) concentrations of the constituents at the steady state should help to eliminate regions of excessive resistance across the pH gradient to the point where local Joule heating can be dissipated.

The basic pH gradient referred to in Fig.3 was nonetheless computed with an even lower leading ion concentration of 0.01 M to bring the pH values between non-amphoteric and amphoteric constituents more closely together. The gel stability under these conditions remains to be tested with agarose, since polyacrylamide when formed in basic constituents tends to polymerize poorly, presumably in view of insufficient average chain length (excessive catalysis).

It is also not clear as yet whether there is an advantage to maintaining constituents with rather similar properties in the mixture, or whether one should rationalize the mixture to provide amphoteric constituents about equally spaced in pI. Thus, the 13 constituent mixture shown in Fig.4 can easily be simplified by restriction to 9 truly different constituents. Preliminary data do suggest, however, that such reduction in the number of constituents reduces the range of the pH gradient at the neutral region and is not beneficial to gradient stability (Buzas, Zs. and the author, unpublished data). It appears likely, therefore, that for the practice of BEF, it is best to utilize the highest possible multiplicity of constituents, as was done in the design of the empirical 47-component mixture.

It appears that the stability of buffer pH gradients improves if they are restricted to one or the other side of neutrality. The pH gradient shown in Fig.5 becomes increasingly unstable when the trailing ion glycine is replaced by first histidine, then lysine (13). The possible reasons for stabilization on either side of neutrality are discussed in section 7.

5.2 Transient and steady state current density

Steady state currents in BEF are somewhat higher than in electrofocusing with SCAMs but are still barely detectable at the milliampere scale; a value of 1.0 mA/cm^2 of gel appears representative at 20 V/cm. By contrast, transient state current density can be very high and poses a serious heat dissipation problem. Representative initial current values in BEF are 20 to 40 mA/cm^2 at a regulated voltage of 20 V/cm. Thus, current control at acceptable values (e.g. 4 mA/cm^2 at 0°C) is required until such a time that the voltage has increased to 20 V/cm. Thereafter, voltage control at the usual level of 20 V/cm (0°C, 6 mm diameter gel tubes surrounded by agitated electrolyte) is acceptable. In practice, prefocusing overnight at constant current is the most convenient way to prepare gels for BEF. Longer times are required for wide diameter preparative gels (see Fig.10). A representative prefocusing time for 1 mm gel slabs appears the value of 40 min at a regulated power of 20 Watts applied in the 47-buffer mixture (2) under conditions of relatively efficient heat dissipation at 5°C.

5.3 Equiconductance

One of the hitherto unfulfilled promises of BEF is the possibility, in this method, to achieve a uniform conductance across the pH gradient by choice of neutral amphoteric constituents with high conductivity at the pI, i.e. relatively small pI-pK differences [Table 1.2 of (23)] while employing less conductive species with larger pI-pK values at the extremes of pH. Note that the same goal cannot be achieved by adding greater amounts of neutral constituents to the mixture, since the concentrations are regulated at the steady state; greater amounts would therefore simply widen the zone occupied by a constituent, but not change its conductance properties. The handicap to that approach is that the ionic mobilities of constituents with small pI-pK values are not known, and that the theoretical solution to the evaluation of ionic mobilities under these conditions (21) has not as yet been transformed into a computerized, easy-to-use laboratory approach. Therefore, the judicious distribution of constituents with high and low pI-pK values remains an empirical problem to date which has not been tackled by anyone in view of the laboriousness of the empirical approach.

Conductance of the 47-buffer mixture has been reported [Fig.4 of (2)]. It appears rather uniform across the center of the pH gradient, and not significantly different from the conductance profiles reported for SCAMs at some arbitrary optimal timepoint [Fig.1.20 of (23)]. The dynamics of the conductance profile with BEF time have not been reported to date.

5.4 Neutralization reactions between carrier constituents and other problems of crossed multiple sequential moving boundaries

There is evidence from 2 investigations showing presumably ionic interaction between anionic and cationic constituents under conditions where a train of anionic sequential moving boundaries is superimposed on a cationic one, such as is necessarily the case with pH gradients spanning widely across neutrality, as in the 47-buffer mixture (2). It shows that the addition of cationic constituents to the mixture causes alkalinization in the acidic part of the pH gradient [Fig.9 of (2), and similar effects upon the addition of arg under the conditions of Fig.10].

Crossed multiple sequential moving boundary systems, consisting of an anionic and a cationic stack, have only been assembled once to date and remain to be carefully studied. In the single case, a 6 component mixture of acids was combined with a 6 component mixture of bases. The resulting pH gradient, very steep at the neutral center, appeared to roughly simulate the individual pH gradients of its two parts [compare Fig.6 at 72 to 155 h with Fig.3, 212-286 h and Fig.4 of (12)]. The instability problem associated with these systems due to the passage of protons from the anolyte to the leading phase of the cationic stack, and the corresponding perturbance of the steady state alignment of the anionic train by hydroxyl ions from the catholyte will be discussed in section 7.

6 ELECTROFOCUSING OF PROTEINS

6.1 Is electrofocusing isoelectric?

In theory, proteins like any other constituents should align in order of their net mobility at the steady state in contiguous fashion. One would expect therefore that proteins are separated but unresolved at the steady state of BEF unless the buffer constituents possess intermediate net mobilities between the proteins. Such spacing is extremely unlikely if the multiplicity of proteins exceeds that of the buffer constituents. Even in that case, most proteins have been shown to possess net mobilities even in "non-restrictive" gels far less than most simple organic compounds (24). This difference in the net mobilities between macromolecules and simple buffers is vanishing at the steady state in an arrested pH gradient (common ion concentration zero) where, as Fig.4 shows, amphoteric buffer constituents are isoelectric, and macromolecules also approach their isoelectric pHs. Thus, for amphoteric buffers or proteins, the mechanism of isoelectric condensation underlying the Svensson theory (3) appears equivalent and, in its result, interchangeable with the moving boundary mechanism of pH gradient formation, in spite of the differences in the mathematical construct by which this result is achieved. The sole distinction between the 2 ways of achieving an isoelectric alignment of constituents remains the ability of the moving boundary mechanism to explain the formation of natural pH gradients by non-amphoteric constituents. Furthermore, it has the advantage of being able to provide easy computer simulation of operative conditions within the phases at the steady state and of pH gradient instability (section 7) which the alternative theoretical treatments (3,16) have not provided to date.

Since alignment of amphoteric buffers even by a moving boundary mechanism is isoelectric it is not surprising that proteins locate in the pH gradient in their isoelectric positions as well and separate accordingly at pHs indistinguishable from those in electrofocusing in SCAMs (Fig.9,10). What is remarkable is the fact that the isoelectric positions of the proteins in a (at least theoretically) well-defined 13-component pH gradient (Fig.9) are not limited to the interfaces between the buffer phases: The protein peak positions lie well within the calculated "buffer compartments" and are obviously not limited to the narrow space between them. Therefore, protein resolution in BEF may depend on the non-ideal concentration profiles with overlapping phase boundaries due to either diffusion or chemical interactions between constituents.

Protein fractionations by BEF aiming at the purification and characterization by pI of single proteins [e.g. (8)] provide no comparable mechanistic information but have been valuable as a check on pIs (Table 1) and degree of homogeneity unaffected by interactions with SCAMs (see section 6.2), as well as for preparative purposes (Fig.10). Here, BEF has the particular advantage that the protein can be separated from the carrier constituents by simple dialysis or gel filtration.

6.2 Binding artifacts

One of the promising aspects of BEF has been the absence of protein interactions with simple buffers, in contradistinction to those with larger and in part more highly hydrophobic SCAMs. Two studies show that this expectation was justified but that the differences in binding between SCAMs and simple buffers are merely quantitative and not absolute. In the first of these studies (25) a synthetic, polydisperse macromolecular amphoteric dye was subjected to electrofocusing in a buffer mixture and in SCAMs to measure H-bond, hydrophobic and ionic interactions by the effect on the dye pattern of 8 M urea, detergents and high ionic strength respectively. The result was that all of the three interactions could be detected in SCAM electrofocusing, while only ionic interactions persisted in the buffer mixture. The second study (Ben-Or, S. and the author, unpublished) used pI-shifts of glucocorticoid receptor as a measure of SCAM or buffer binding. The result (Table 1) was that pI-range 8-10 SCAMs (added to the protein load to enhance its degree of ionization and electrophoretic entrance rate into the gel) bound to the receptor. The effect was augmented when the SCAMs were aged and presumably aggregated. However, arginine added to the sample prior to BEF, also shifted the pI upward indicating an interaction which presumably was again ionic.

7 A NEW UNDERSTANDING OF PH GRADIENT INSTABILITY AND ITS CONTROL IN THE LIGHT OF THE HYPOTHESIS THAT PH GRADIENTS FORM BY A MOVING BOUNDARY MECHANISM

The interconvertibility of sequential moving boundary systems giving rise to either moving or stationary pH gradients, depending on the choice of anolyte and catholyte (17), and the possibility to produce natural pH gradients with exclusively non-amphoteric buffer mixtures (4) gave rise to the hypothesis that pH gradients formed by a moving boundary mechanism. This hypothesis was strengthened by the realization that sequential moving boundary systems could be arrested by reducing the common counterion concentration to zero (15,16). Under those conditions, the moving boundary theory, incorporated into a suitable program, is able to confirm a number of previously made empirical observations with regard to pH gradient stabilization. This confirmation further strengthens the hypothesis, and it also must strengthen the confidence with which the user of any electrofocusing method can avail himself of the various tools for pH gradient stabilization which are rationalized by the moving boundary hypothesis. These are: a) Stabilization by control of the pH of the anolyte and catholyte and the pH range of the gradient (26-28). The more neutral the pH of anolyte and catholyte, the less ionization of the constituents aligned at the steady state, and therefore the less boundary displacement (pH gradient instability). Also, in pH gradients crossing neutrality, continuous passage of protons from the trailing to the leading phase of the cationically aligned constituents, and the corresponding passage of hydroxyl ions from the trailing to the leading phase of anionic constituents, increases the degree of ionization and perturbs the steady state and therefore causes instability of the pH gradient. b) Stabilization in proportion to the concentration of catholyte and anolyte (29). The boundary displacement, ν (Fig.8) is reduced in proportion to the concentration of the leading phase. Since the leading phase is the catholyte (for cationic constituents) or anolyte (for anionic constituents), their increased concentration must lead to stabilization. c) Strongly basic catholytes and acidic anolytes destabilize pH gradients. This is accounted for by the mechanism detailed in section a). d) The catholyte can be an acid, the cathodic pH below 7 (10). This condition conforms to the requirement of an alignment of acids between a leading and a trailing acid. e) The drift is anodic when a strongly basic catholyte and a weakly acidic anolyte are used (29). Otherwise it is cathodic. The cathodic drift is explained by the fact that cationic carrier constituents have ionic mobilities higher, in general, than anionic constituents. Thus, the cationic alignment of constituents is displaced at a more rapid rate than the anionic one, and the net displacement is cathodic. When the leading ions of the two opposing stacks of constituents are a strong base and a weak acid respectively, the cationic constituents are relatively highly ionized and mobile, and a relatively high displacement rate for that stack arises. Under those conditions, it may be higher than than of the anionic train, thus reversing the usual direction of net boundary displacement.

8 AGENDA AND PROGNOSIS FOR BEF, AND ITS PLACE AMONG THE COMPETING ELECTROFOCUSING METHODS

Clearly, BEF is not a widely useful electrofocusing method as yet. Many more buffer constituents with measured ionic mobility values for at least 0 and 25°C are needed. Ionic mobility determinations are particularly lacking for buffers with pI - pK values less than 2. Also, not enough compounds in that category are known. Their design and synthesis represents a necessary future task for the organic chemist if BEF is ever to become a widely applicable method. For the physical chemist, there remains the task of adapting available buffer theory (21) to a method by which amphoteric compounds with small pI - pK values can be assigned ionic mobility values. Given more and better constituents and ionic mobility values, the moving boundary program is capable of predicting pH gradients and their dynamics readily. For the methodologist, there remains the task of verifying predicted constituent positions in the pH gradient, using radioactively labeled constituents. Conductivity across BEF pH gradients needs to be evaluated as a function of electrofocusing time. Maximal wattage values need to be found which provide gel stability within the heat dissipation capacity of given apparatus forms. Possibly, media other than polyacrylamide must be found which are more tolerant to Joule heat and more convenient to use than Sephadex. Finally, the question remains to be answered whether BEF systems crossing neutrality and providing pH gradients between acid and base can be set up with a stability similar to those across one half the pH scale. To date, that does not appear to be the case. Accordingly, BEF may remain limited to relatively narrow pH ranges, and share this limitation with both Immobiline pH gradients (30) and those made of monosaccharide-borate complexes (31).

Among practical electrofocusing methods, BEF and electrofocusing in monosaccharide-borate complexes (31) alone excel in low cost, assuming that buffer mixtures are prepared in the laboratory. Compared to electrofocusing in SCAMs, BEF exhibits as yet a rather poor armory of pH gradients (Fig.2) and less perfect pH gradient linearity. However, it compares favorably with electrofocusing in SCAMs from the viewpoint of its relatively diminished tendency to form interaction products with proteins which are irreversible during the time allotted for practical separations. It also excels in the ease with which carrier constituents can be removed from the protein after isolation. It allows for pH gradient engineering by rapid and effortless computer simulation, rather than tedious trial-and-error experimentation, just like the Immobiline method (32), and in contrast to electrofocusing in SCAMs or monosaccharide-borate complexes.

For all of these reasons, further work on developing BEF from its present stage of infancy to a widely practical separation method along the lines indicated above appears justified.

9 REFERENCES

(1) O. Vesterberg in N. Catsimpoolas (Ed.) Isoelectric Focusing, Academic Press, New York NY 1976, pp. 53-76.

(2) C. B. Cuono, G. A. Csapo, Electrophoresis 3 (1982) 65-75.

(3) H. Svensson, Acta Chem. Scand. 16 (1962) 456-466.

(4) N. Y. Nguyen, A. Chrambach, Anal. Biochem. 74 (1976) 145-153.

(5) A. Chrambach, N. Y. Nguyen in B. J. Radola and D. Graesslin (Eds.) Electrofocusing and Isotachophoresis, de Gruyter, Berlin 1977, pp. 51-58.

(6) B. C. An der Lan, A. Chrambach in B. D. Hames and D. Rickwood (Eds.) Gel Electrophoresis of Proteins: A Practical Approach, Information Retrieval Ltd. Press, London (1981) pp. 157-187.

(7) R. L. Prestidge, M. T. W. Hearn, J. Separation Purif. Methods 10 (1981) 1-28.

(8) M. T. W. Hearn, R. L. Prestidge, J. F. T. Griffin, G. W. Mhlanga, Prep. Biochem. 11 (1981) 191-200.

(9) B. E. Chidakel, N. Y. Nguyen, A. Chrambach, Anal. Biochem. 77 (1977) 216-225.

(10) N. Y. Nguyen, A. Chrambach, Electrophoresis 1 (1980) 14-22.

(11) N. Y. Nguyen, A. Salokangas, A. Chrambach, Anal. Biochem. 78 (1977) 287-294.

(12) Zs. Buzas, L. M. Hjelmeland, A. Chrambach, Electrophoresis 4 (1983) 27-35.

(13) C. Auzan, A. Michaud, A. in G. Peltre (Ed.) Electrophorese-Paris-82, Institut Pasteur, Paris (1982), progr. p.1.

(14) M. Bier, O. A. Palusinski, R. A. Mosher, D. A. Saville, Science 219 (1983) 1281-1287.

(15) L. M. Hjelmeland, A. Chrambach, Electrophoresis 4 (1983) 20-26.

(16) C. Schafer-Nielsen, P. J. Svendsen, Anal. Biochem. 114 (1981) 244-262.

(17) N. Y. Nguyen, D. Rodbard, P. J. Svendsen, A. Chrambach, Anal. Biochem. 77 (1977) 39-55.

(18) T. M. Jovin, Ann. N.Y. Acad. Sci. 209 (1973) 477-496.

(19) T. Hirokawa, M. Nishino, N. Aoki, K. Yoshiyuki, Y. Sawamoto, T. Yagi, J.-I. Akiyama, J.-I., J. Chromatography 271 (1983) D1-D106.

(20) N. E. Good, G. D. Winget, W. Winter, T. N. Connolly, S. Izawa, R. M. M. Singh, Biochemistry 5 (1966) 467-477.

(21) H. Rilbe in N. Catsimpoolas (Ed.) Isoelectric Focusing, Academic Press, New York, NY (1976), pp. 13-52.

(22) A. Chrambach, D. Rodbard, in D. B. Hames and D. Rickwood (Eds.) Gel Electrophoresis of Proteins: A Practical Approach, Information Retrieval Limited Press, London (1981) pp. 93-144.

(23) P.-G. Righetti, Isoelectric Focusing: Theory, Methodology and Applications, Elsevier Biomedical Press, Amsterdam 1983, pp. 1-386.

(24) N. Y. Nguyen, A. Chrambach, Anal. Biochem. 94 (1979) 202-210.

(25) C. B. Cuono, G. A. Chapo, A. Chrambach, L. M. Hjelmeland, Electrophoresis 4 (1983) 404-407.

(26) B. An der Lan, A. Chrambach, Electrophoresis 1 (1980) 23-27.

(27) N. Y. Nguyen, A. Chrambach, Anal. Biochem. 82 (1977) 54-62.

(28) N. Y. Nguyen, A. Chrambach, Anal. Biochem. 82 (1977) 226-235.

(29) N. Y. Nguyen, A. Chrambach, Anal. Biochem. 79 (1977) 462-469.

(30) B. Bjellqvist, K. Ek, P. G. Righetti, E. Gianazza, A. Gorg, R., R.

Westermeier, W. Postel, J. Biochem. Biophys. Methods 6 (1982) 317-340.

(31) G. V. Troitsky, V. P. Zav'yalov, V. M. Abramov, Doklady Akademii Nauk SSSR 214 (1974) 955-958.

(32) G. Dossi, F. Celentano, E. Gianazza, P. G. Righetti, J. Biochem. Biophys. Methods 7 (1983) 123-142.

(33) Biochemists' Handbook, C. Long (Ed.), Van Nostrand Co., Princeton NJ (1961), pp. 43-44. (34) B. An der Lan, S. Ben-Or, S. Allenmark, J. V. Sullivan, P. Fitze, A. Jackiw, Electrophoresis, in press.

BUFFER ELECTROFOCUSING

AMPHOTERIC — BEF — NON-AMPHOTERIC

BUFFER	pK_2
MES	6.4
MOPS	7.2
ACES	7.3
TES	8.0
TRICINE	8.6
BICINE	8.7
TAURINE	9.7
GLYCINE	10.5
GABA	11.3

⊖

⊕

BUFFER	pK_2
PYRIDINE	5.5
4-PICOLINE	6.2
BISTRIS	6.9
LUTIDINE	7.0
IMIDAZOLE	7.5
HEM	7.2
NEM	8.0
TEA	8.4
TRIS	8.8
MEA	10.4

Fig.1. BEF constituent mixtures in 1976.

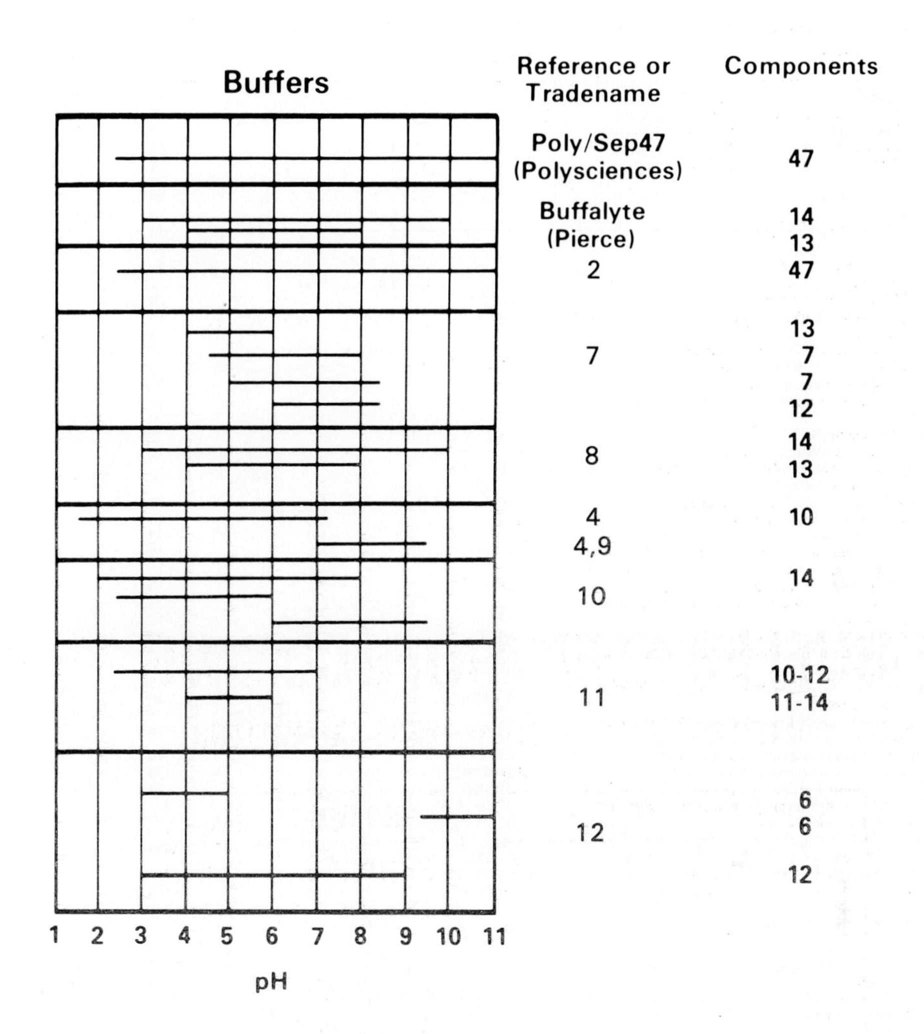

Fig.2. pH ranges of reported BEF systems.

Amphoteric constituents		Abbreviation	pI[a)]	pK_2[a)]	pK_1[a)]	Concentration mM	Supplier[b)]
1	L-Glutamic Acid		3.0			10	S
2	2-Pyridine Carboxylic Acid (Picolinic Acid)		3.2			10	S
3	4-Pyridine Carboxylic Acid (Isonicotinic Acid)		3.3			10	S
4	3-Pyridine Carboxylic Acid (Nicotinic Acid)		3.4			10	S
5	2-Aminoethane Sulfonic Acid (Taurine)		5.1			20	S
6	D,L-Threonine		5.6			10	S
7	Glycylglycine		5.7			10	S
8	Glycine		6.0			20	S
9	N-Methylglycine (Sarcosine)		6.1			20	S
10	L-Proline		6.3			10	S
11	Iminodiacetic Acid		6.4			20	S
12	Creatine		6.8			20	S
13	γ-Amino-n-Butyric Acid	GABA	7.3			20	S
14	ε-Amino-n-Caproic Acid	EACA	7.6			10	S
15	L-Histidine		7.7			10	S
16	Guanidoacetic Acid (Glycocyamine)		8.0 est.			20	S
17	N-β-Alanyl-histidine (Carnosine)		8.2			20	S
18	L-Lysine monohydrochloride		9.7			20	S
19	L-Ornithine monohydrochloride		9.7			20	S
20	L-Arginine		10.7			10	S
21	L-Asparagine		10.7			20	S
22	Glycine betaine (Lycin; Betaine)				1.8	20	S
23	γ-Amino-β-hydroxybutyric acid betaine (D,L-carnitine hydrochloride)				3.9 est.	20	S
24	2-(N-Morpholino)ethane sulfonic acid	MES		6.1		20	S
25	N-(2-Acetamido)-iminodiacetic acid	ADA		6.6		10	S
26	N-(2-Acetamido)-2-aminoethane sulfonic acid	ACES		6.8		20	S
27	3-(N-Morpholino)-2-hydroxypropane sulfonic acid	MOPSO		6.9		10	R
28	N,N-Bis(2-hydroxyethyl)-2-aminoethane sulfonic acid	BES		7.1		10	S
29	3-(N-Morpholino)-propane sulfonic acid	MOPS		7.2		10	R
30	N-Tris(hydroxymethyl)methyl-2-aminoethane sulfonic acid	TES		7.4		20	S
31	N-2-Hydroxyethylpiperazine-N'-2-ethane sulfonic acid	HEPES		7.5		20	S
32	3-[N-bis(Hydroxyethyl)-amino]-2-hydroxypropane sulfonic acid	DIPSO		7.5		[illegible]	R
33	3-[N-(Tris-hydroxymethylamino]-2-hydroxypropane sulfonic acid	TAPSO		7.6		20	R
34	N-Hydroxyethylpiperazine-N'-2-hydroxypropane sulfonic acid	HEPPSO		7.8		10	R
35	N-2-Hydroxyethylpiperazine propane sulfonic acid	EPPS		8.0		10	S
36	N-Tris(hydroxymethyl)methyl glycine	TRICINE		8.1		20	S
37	N,N bis(2-hydroxyethyl) glycine	BICINE		8.3		20	S
38	N-Tris(hydroxymethyl)methyl-3-aminopropane sulfonic acid	TAPS		8.4		10	S
39	3-[N-(α, α-Dimethyl hydroxyethyl)-Amino]-2-hydroxypropane sulfonic acid	AMPSO		9.1		10	S
40	2-(N-Cyclohexylamino) ethane sulfonic acid	CHES		9.5		10	S
41	Cyclohexylaminopropane Sulfonic Acid	CAPS		10.4		10	S
Non-Amphoteric constituents							
42	Malic Acid				3.4	10	S
43	Lactic Acid				3.9	10	S
44	Acetic Acid				4.8	10	B
45	Propionic Acid				4.9	10	S
46	Benzamidine				11.6	20	F
47	Biguanide			13.2	3.1	10	A[c)]

a) At 25 °C as reported in the literature [11–16]

b) A: Aldrich Chemical Co., Milwaukee, WI
B: Baker Chemical Co., Phillipsburg, NJ
F: Fluka/Tridom Chemical Inc., Hauppauge, NY
R: Research Organics, Inc., Cleveland, OH
S: Sigma Chemical Co., St. Louis, MO

c) Synthesized from biguanide sulfate; see section 2.2

Fig.3. Composition of the 47-component BEF system (2).

No.	Compound	pK(1)0°C	pK(2)0°C	r(0°C)	pI (0°C)	Steady-state pH	$\bar{r}$	I (M)	Ref.
1	HOAc	4.74		0.790		2.87	3.37×10^{-3}	1.0	J
2	MES	0.5	6.41	0.440	3.46	3.86	2.14×10^{-4}		J
3	ACES	0.5	7.34	0.470	3.92	4.31	7.45×10^{-5}		J
4	MOPS	0.5	7.41	0.43 est.	3.96	4.36	6.75×10^{-5}		G
5	HEPES	0.5	7.85	0.280	4.18	4.66	3.68×10^{-5}		J
6	TES	0.5	7.96	0.410	4.23	4.65	3.54×10^{-5}		J
7	HEPPS	0.5	8.40	0.43 est.	4.45	4.86	2.16×10^{-5}		G
8	TAPS	0.5	9.07	0.455	4.79	5.20	9.87×10^{-6}		H
9	Tricine	2.3	8.60	0.320	5.45	5.47	2.65×10^{-6}		J
10	Bicine	2.3	8.74	0.690	5.52	5.53	2.35×10^{-6}		J
11	Serine	2.30	9.91	0.70 est.	6.13	6.14	0.61×10^{-7}		B
12	OH-prol	1.9	10.30	0.57 est.	6.10	6.15	0.61×10^{-7}		J
13	gly	2.48	10.46	0.740	6.47	6.44	0.29×10^{-7}		J
1	monoethanolamine		10.35	0.860		11.68	1.29×10^{-1}	0.01	J
2	Ammediol		9.56	0.430		11.15	3.50×10^{-2}		J
3	morpholine		8.85	0.730		10.90	2.08×10^{-2}		J
4	Tris		8.84	0.410		10.78	1.49×10^{-2}		J
5	tri-Ethanolamine		8.35	0.550		10.59	9.95×10^{-3}		J
6	NEM		8.03	0.620		10.46	7.37×10^{-3}		J
7	imidazole		7.46	0.970		10.25	4.96×10^{-3}		J
8	HEM		7.19	0.610		10.03	2.78×10^{-3}		J
9	lut		7.00	0.600		9.93	2.21×10^{-3}		J
10	pico		6.21	0.710		9.57	9.79×10^{-4}		J
11	pyr		5.50	0.860		9.25	4.84×10^{-4}		J
12	creatinine		5.21	0.716		9.05	2.97×10^{-4}		H
13	eps-NH2-caproic	4.42	11.71	0.55	8.10	8.07	6.03×10^{-5}		H
14	GABA	4.13	11.33	0.64	7.73	7.73	3.3×10^{-6}		J
15	his	6.35	9.18	0.490	7.64	7.77	1.96×10^{-6}		J
16	beta-ala	3.69	11.0	0.59	7.35	7.35	7.94×10^{-7}		J

Fig.4. Composition of representative acidic and basic BEF systems for generation of computer simulated pH gradients, and some of their properties (Zs. Buzas, L. M. Hjelmeland and A. Chrambach, in preparation).

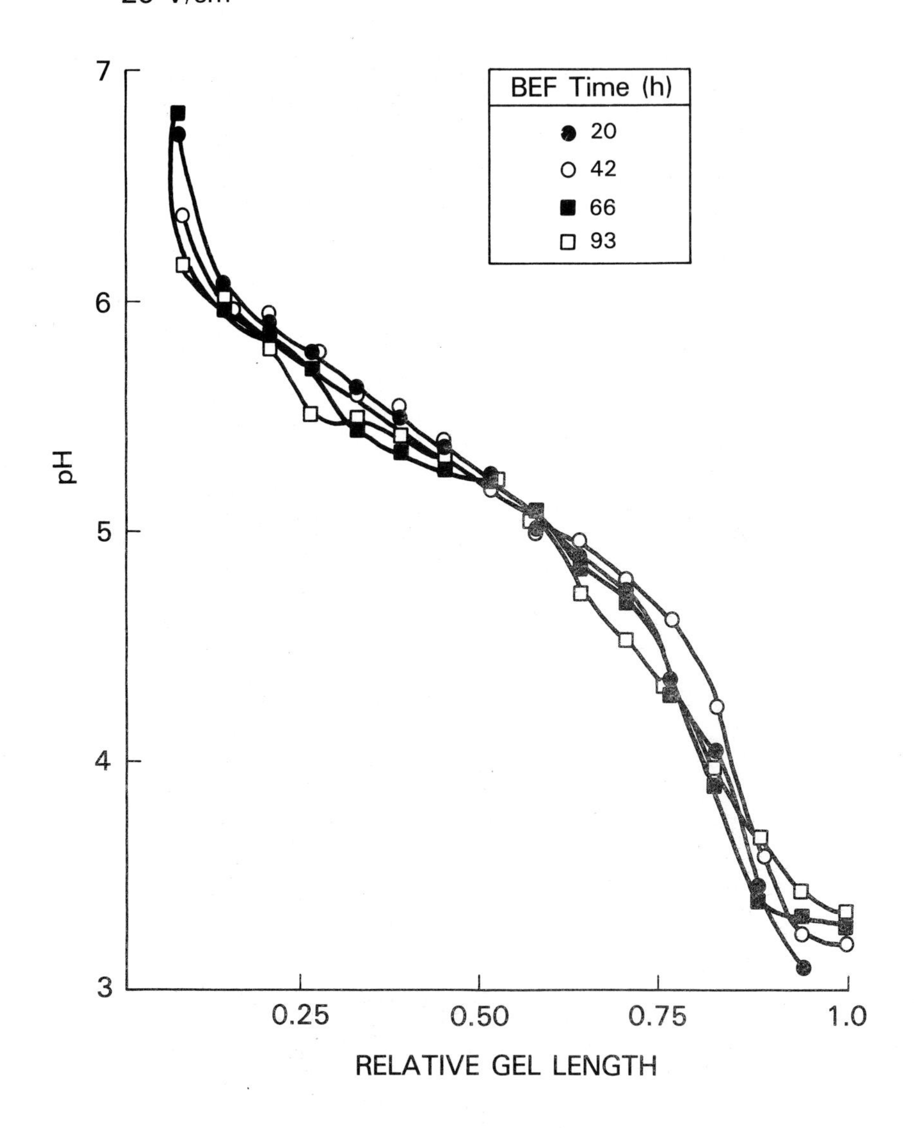

Fig.5. Empirical pH gradient in BEF and its stability. Composition: 13 acidic buffers listed in Fig.4, 0.04 M each. Matrix: Sephadex G-75 (13).

Thermodynamic acid dissociation constants of some weak acids

$$pK = A/T - D + CT, \text{ where } T \text{ is the absolute temperature}$$

$$pK' = pK - \frac{(-2z_A + 1)A\,I^{\frac{1}{2}}}{1 + 1{\cdot}6\,I^{\frac{1}{2}}}$$

Name	n	$pK_{0°}$	$pK_{25°}$	A	D	C
Acetic acid	−1	4·781	4·756	1170·48	3·1649	0·013399
α-Alanine, K_1	+1	2·431	2·348	1383·06	6·3639	0·013662
α-Alanine, K_2	−1	10·616	9·867	2941·55	1·8171	0·006095
β-Alanine, K_1	+1	3·654	3·551	1231·71	3·8478	0·010957
β-Alanine, K_2	−1	10·997	10·234	2589·55	−1·1712	0·001269
*allo*Threonine, K_1	+1	2·183	2·108	1111·7	4·7982	0·010657
*allo*Threonine, K_2	−1	9·805	9·097	2764·3	1·8531	0·005631
α-Amino-*n*-butyric acid, K_1	+1	2·338	2·290	1174·74	5·3735	0·012487
α-Amino-*n*-butyric acid, K_2	−1	10·561	9·830	2879·31	1·6446	0·006095
α-Amino-*iso*butyric acid, K_1	+1	2·422	2·357	1344·95	6·3053	0·013924
α-Amino-*iso*butyric acid, K_2	−1	10·990	10·204	3010·95	1·5404	0·005520
γ-Aminobutyric acid, K_1	+1	4·087	4·031	1209·07	3·7820	0·012605
γ-Aminobutyric acid, K_2	−1	11·369	10·556	2804·84	−0·5879	0·001880
ε-Aminocaproic acid, K_1	+1	4·424	4·373	1803·5	7·6874	0·020166
ε-Aminocaproic acid, K_2	−1	11·707	10·807	2708·6	−2·5445	−0·002757
2-Amino-ethylphosphoric acid, K_2	−1	5·842	5·838	1228·34	2·7328	0·01493
2-Amino-ethylphosphoric acid, K_3	−3	11·394	10·638	2998·17	1·3841	0·006596
2-Amino-ethylsulphuric acid, K_2	−1	9·924	9·182	2530·12	−0·2782	0·001402
α-Amino-*n*-valeric acid, K_1	+1	2·379	2·318	1222·02	5·5238	0·012553
α-Amino-*n*-valeric acid, K_2	−1	10·537	9·805	2618·57	−0·1669	0·002869
Ammonium ion	+1	10·084	9·245	2835·76	0·6322	0·001225
Arginine, K_1	+3	1·911	1·823	1087·58	4·7526	0·009819
Arginine, K_2	+1	9·718	8·991	2643·57	0·8783	0·003363
Aspartic acid, K_1	+1	2·129	1·992	1109·6	4·1563	0·008138
Aspartic acid, K_2	−1	4·012	3·901	1706·3	6·7436	0·016506
Aspartic acid, K_3	−3	10·634	10·004	2880·3	2·6890	0·010173
Benzoic acid	−1	4·249	4·202	1590·2	6·394	0·01765
Boric acid	−1	9·500	9·235	2237·94	3·305	0·016883
Bromo-acetic acid	−1	2·850	2·902	975·25	4·5525	0·014031
*iso*Butyric acid	−1	4·824	4·848	950·93	2·1074	0·012632
n-Butyric acid	−1	4·804	4·820	1033·39	2·6215	0·013334
Carbonic acid, K_1	−1	6·576	6·352	3404·71	14·8435	0·032786
Carbonic acid, K_2	−3	10·626	10·329	2902·39	6·4980	0·02379
Chloro-acetic acid	−1	2·831	2·868	1270·32	6·4805	0·017063
Citric acid, K_1	−1	3·222	3·128	1255·6	4·5635	0·011673
Citric acid, K_2	−3	4·837	4·761	1585·2	5·4460	0·016399
Citric acid, K_3	−5	6·394	6·396	1814·9	6·3664	0·022389
Creatinine	+1	5·176	4·828	1109·71	−1·1922	−0·000289
Diethyl-acetic acid	−1	4·623	4·734	491·81	0·0428	0·010490
Diethylammonium ion	+1	11·54	10·99	−1228·7	−26·221	−0·03726
5 : 5-Diethylbarbituric acid	−1	8·399	7·982	2324·47	3·3491	0·011856
Dimethylammonium ion	+1	11·552	10·774	1932·6	−6·495	−0·007389
N-Dimethylglycine, K_2	−1	10·442	9·940	1209·07	−7·4407	−0·005217
(−)Ephedrinium ion	+1	10·252	9·543	1833·50	−5·1505	−0·005804
(+)ψ-Ephedrinium ion	+1	10·430	9·706	1688·44	−6·4744	−0·008151
Ethylenediammonium ion, K_1	+3	7·564	6·849	1819·10	−2·6111	−0·006247
Ethylenediammonium ion, K_2	+1	10·712	9·927	2277·4	−3·3073	−0·003415
Fluoroacetic acid	−1	2·520	2·586	762·69	3·5518	0·012007
Formic acid	−1	3·785	3·752	1342·85	5·2743	0·015168
Glucose 1-phosphoric acid, K_2	−3	6·514	6·504	1432·16	3·4213	0·017177
Glycerol 1-phosphoric acid, K_2	−3	6·646	6·656	1411·37	3·3605	0·017718
Glycerol 2-phosphoric acid, K_1	−1	1·207	1·335	1891·91	13·4799	0·02841
Glycerol 2-phosphoric acid, K_2	−3	6·668	6·650	1667·40	4·8394	0·01978
Glycine, K_1	+1	2·443	2·350	1332·17	5·8870	0·012643
Glycine, K_2	−1	10·496	9·778	2666·84	0·3648	0·004018
Glycollic acid	−1	3·875	3·831	1303·26	4·7845	0·014236
Glycylalanine, K_1	+1	3·137	3·153	691·79	1·8996	0·009166
Glycyl α-amino-*n*-butyric acid, K_1	+1	3·131	3·155	727·94	2·2214	0·009840
Glycylasparagine, K_1	+1	2·981	2·942	1176·54	4·8520	0·012907
Glycylglycine, K_1	+1	3·167	3·140	1003·35	3·5670	0·011207
Glycylglycine, K_2	−1	8·975	8·253	2902·3	3·4932	0·006749
Glycyl-leucine, K_1	+1	3·151	3·180	718·40	2·1910	0·009929
Glycylserine, K_1	+1	3·020	2·981	1090·92	4·1993	0·011807
Hexamethylenediammonium ion, K_1	+3	10·762	9·841	2773·65	−1·3649	−0·002771
Hexamethylenediammonium ion, K_2	+1	11·857	10·931	2795·01	−2·3746	−0·002744
*iso*Hexanoic acid	−1	4·826	4·845	933·68	1·9289	0·012215
n-Hexanoic acid	−1	4·839	4·857	966·67	2·1292	0·012556
Hydroxyproline, K_1	+1	1·903	1·818	1156·7	5·2753	0·010777
Hydroxyproline, K_2	−1	10·299	9·662	2442·9	−0·1266	0·004500
Iodoacetic acid	−1	3·108	3·175	770·36	3·0336	0·012158
Lactic acid	−1	3·885	3·860	1286·49	4·8607	0·014776
Leucine, K_1	+1	2·385	2·329	1283·60	6·0027	0·013505
Leucine, K_2	−1	10·482	9·745	2819·38	1·2396	0·005127
Isoleucine, K_1	+1	2·368	2·318	1298·09	6·1967	0·013959
Isoleucine, K_2	−1	10·488	9·752	2933·52	2·0479	0·006578
Malonic acid, K_1	−1	—	2·855	—	—	—
Malonic acid, K_2	−3	5·668	5·696	1703·31	6·5810	0·022014
Monoethanolammonium ion	+1	10·307	9·498	2677·91	−0·3869	0·000428
Monoethylammonium ion	+1	11·31	10·67	−270·8	−20·240	−0·02907
Monomethylammonium ion	+1	11·495	10·624	2568·3	−2·990	−0·003285
Norleucine, K_1	+1	2·397	2·335	1193·30	5·2850	0·012130
Norleucine, K_2	−1	10·577	9·832	2851·80	1·2891	0·005218
Oxalic acid, K_1	−1	—	1·271	—	—	—
Oxalic acid, K_2	−3	4·201	4·266	1423·8	6·5007	0·020095
p-Phenolsulphonic acid, K_2	−3	9·352	9·053	1961·2	1·1436	0·012139
Phosphoric acid, K_1	−1	2·057	2·148	799·31	4·5535	0·013486
Phosphoric acid, K_2	−3	7·312	7·200	1979·5	5·3541	0·019840
o-Phthalic acid, K_1	−1	2·925	2·950	561·57	1·2843	0·007883
o-Phthalic acid, K_2	−3	5·433	5·408	2175·83	9·5508	0·025694
Piperidinium ion	+1	11·963	11·123	2105·6	−6·3535	−0·0076865
Pivalic acid	−1	5·015	5·032	1044·56	2·4936	0·013489
Proline, K_1	+1	2·012	1·952	1512·6	7·9217	0·016094
Proline, K_2	−1	11·327	10·643	2230·4	−3·1592	0·000010
Propionic acid	−1	4·895	4·874	1213·26	3·3860	0·014055
Sarcosine, K_2	−1	10·852	10·200	2213·06	−2·4514	0·001094
Serine, K_1	+1	2·301	2·186	1311·2	5·6397	0·011496
Serine, K_2	−1	9·911	9·208	2594·1	0·6031	0·003725
Succinic acid, K_1	−1	4·284	4·207	1206·25	3·3266	0·011697
Succinic acid, K_2	−3	5·675	5·638	1679·13	5·7043	0·019153
Sulphamic acid	−1	1·111	0·988	3792·8	24·122	0·041544
Sulphanilic acid	−1	3·521	3·228	1143·71	1·2979	0·002314
Tartaric acid, K_1	−1	3·118	3·033	1525·59	6·6558	0·015336
Tartaric acid, K_2	−3	4·427	4·367	1765·35	7·3015	0·019276
Taurine, K_2	−1	9·739	9·061	2458·49	0·0997	0·003069
Threonine, K_1	+1	2·204	2·088	1716·1	8·5867	0·016504
Threonine, K_2	−1	9·776	9·099	2631·1	1·2866	0·005237
Triethylammonium ion	+1	11·19	10·67	−1395·6	−26·592	−0·03770
Trimethylammonium ion	+1	10·352	9·798	541·4	−12·611	−0·015525
*iso*Valeric acid	−1	4·726	4·780	769·09	1·2592	0·011605
n-Valeric acid	−1	4·823	4·842	909·71	1·7787	0·011973
Valine, K_1	+1	2·322	2·286	1245·31	6·0251	0·013868
Valine, K_2	−1	10·442	9·716	2776·46	1·1033	0·005056

Fig.6. pK values at 0 and 25°C, and expressions for their change with temperature and ionic strength (I). Table 6 of (33).

```
  1.   //ACCAMPHO    JOB   (JPV1,675,A),CHRAMBACH
  2.   //S1   EXEC    FORVCOMP
  3.   //COMP.SYSIN   DD   *
  4.         DIMENSION X(13,11) ———————————————— n
  5.         COMMON X,I
  6.         X(1,1)  =   -0.790
  7.         X(2,1)  =   -0.440
  8.         X(3,1)  =   -0.470
  9.         X(4,1)  =   -0.430
 10.         X(5,1)  =   -0.280
 11.         X(6,1)  =   -0.41
 12.         X(7,1)  =   -0.43
 13.         X(8,1)  =   -0.41
 14.         X(9,1)  =  -0.320
 15.         X(10,1)  =   -0.690
 16.         X(11,1)  =   -0.70
 17.         X(12,1)  =   -0.570
 18.         X(13,1)  =   -0.740
 19.         X(1,2)  =    4.74
 20.         X(2,2)  =    0.5
 21.         X(3,2)  =    0.5
 22.         X(4,2)  =    0.5
 23.         X(5,2)  =    0.5
 24.         X(6,2)  =    0.5
 25.         X(7,2)  =    0.5
 26.         X(8,2)  =    0.5
 27.         X(9,2)  =    2.3
 28.         X(10,2)  =    2.3
 29.         X(11,2)  =    2.3
 30.         X(12,2)  =   1.9
 31.         X(13,2)  =    2.4
 32.         X(1,11)  = 0.0
 33.         X(2,11)  = 6.41
 34.         X(3,11)  = 7.34
 35.         X(4,11)  = 7.41
 36.         X(5,11)  = 7.85
 37.         X(6,11)  = 7.96
 38.         X(7,11)  = 8.40
 39.         X(8,11)  = 9.07
 40.         X(9,11)  = 8.60
 41.         X(10,11)  = 8.74
 42.         X(11,11)  = 9.91
 43.         X(12,11)  = 10.30
 44.         X(13,11)  = 10.46
 45.         X(1,3)  =    1.0 ———————————————— I
 46.         DO 10 I = 1 , 12 ———————————————— n-1
 47.         X(I+1,3)  = X(I,3)*(1-(8.49/X(I,1)))/(1-(8.49/X(I+1,1)))
 48.    10   CONTINUE
 49.         DO 20 I = 1 , 13 ———————————————— n
 50.          IF (X(I,11).NE.0.0) GO TO 15
 51.         X(I,4)=  (X(I,2)-ALOG10(X(I,3)))/2
 52.         X(I,5)=10.0**(X(I,4)-X(I,2))
 53.        GO TO 18
 54.     15   CALL AMPHO (DUMMY)
 55.      18 X(I,6)=X(I,1)*X(I,5)
 56.         X(I,7)=(27.4E-5)*96.5*(10.0**(-X(I,4)))*(8.49-X(I,1))
 57.         X(I,8)=X(I,5)*X(I,1)*(27.4E-5)/X(I,7)
 58.         X(I,9)=(1.0E-3)*X(I,8)/(0.27)
 59.    20   CONTINUE
 60.         DO 30 I = 1,12 ———————————————— n-1
 61.         X(I,10)=(((9074.52)*27.4E-5)*X(I,6)*X(I+1,6))
 62.       1 /(X(I,9)*(96500.0)*(X(I,6)-X(I+1,6)))
 63.    30   CONTINUE
 64.         WRITE (15,100) X
 65.    100  FORMAT (13E10.4) ———————————————— n
 66.         RETURN
 67.         END
 68.        SUBROUTINE AMPHO
 69.   C PROGRAM TO EVALUATE THE PH OF A SOLUTION OF A PURE AMPHOLYTE
 70.   C
 71.        INTEGER IMAX
 72.        REAL C, PK1, PK2, K1, K2, PI, PH, H1, H2, PH,
 73.       1Z, N2, CZERO, CPLUS, CMINUS, DELTA
 74.        DIMENSION X(13,11) ———————————————— n
 75.        COMMON X,I
 76.        PK1 = X(I,2)
 77.        PK2 = X(I,11)
 78.        K1 = 10.0 ** (-PK1)
 79.        K2 = 10.0 ** (-PK2)
 80.        PI = (PK1 + PK2)/ 2
 81.        HI = 10.0 ** (-PI)
 82.        Z  = K1 * (((10.0 ** (-14))/ HI) ** 2)
 83.        C =  X(I,3)
 84.        H2 = (HI + (10.0 ** (-7)))/2
 85.        IMAX = 0
 86.     10 H1 = H2
 87.        IMAX = IMAX + 1
 88.        N2 = (H1 ** 2) + (H1 * K1) + (K1 * K2)
 89.        CZERO = (H1 * K1 * C)/ N2
 90.        H2 = SQRT ((HI ** 2)*((CZERO + Z)/(CZERO + K1)))
 91.        DELTA = ABS (ALOG10 (H2) - ALOG10 (H1))
 92.        IF (DELTA .LT. 0.01) GO TO 20
 93.        GO TO 10
 94.     20 CPLUS = (H2 * H2 * C)/ N2
 95.        CMINUS = (K1 * K2 * C)/ N2
 96.        PH = -ALOG10 (H2)
 97.        X(I,4) = PH
 98.        X(I,5) = (CMINUS-CPLUS)/X(I,3)
 99.     40 CONTINUE
100.        RETURN
101.        END
102.   //   EXEC FORVLKGO
103.   //GO.FT01F001  DD   DSN=JBK1ACC.AMPHO.DATA,
104.   //       VOL=SER=FILE30,DISP=SHR,
105.   //          UNIT=FILE
106.   /*
```

Fig.7. Program for the computation of pH gradients in BEF, using moving boundary theory (15).

	Acetic A.	MES	ACES	MOPS	HEPES	TES	HEPPS	TAPS	Tricine	Bicine	OH-prol	ser	gly
r	-.7900E+00	-.4400E+00	-.4700E+00	-.4300E+00	-.2800E+00	-.4100E+00	-.4300E+00	-.4100E+00	-.3200E+00	-.6900E+00	-.7000E+00	-.5700E+00	-.7400E+00
pK	0.4740E+01	0.5000E+00	0.5000E+00	0.5000E+00	0.5000E+00	0.5000E+00	0.5000E+00	0.5000E+00	0.2300E+01	0.2300E+01	0.2300E+01	0.1900E+01	0.2400E+01
conc (M)	0.1000E+01	0.5788E+00	0.6162E+00	0.5663E+00	0.3750E+00	0.5411E+00	0.5663E+00	0.5411E+00	0.4267E+00	0.8829E+00	0.8943E+00	0.7399E+00	0.9412E+00
pH	0.2370E+01	0.3550E+01	0.4010E+01	0.4051E+01	0.4308E+01	0.4339E+01	0.4546E+01	0.4555E+01	0.5453E+01	0.5521E+01	0.6106E+01	0.6104E+01	0.6431E+01
ϕ	0.4266E-02	0.4872E-03	0.1586E-03	0.1569E-03	0.1313E-03	0.8644E-04	0.5019E-04	0.2409E-04	0.8275E-05	0.3411E-05	0.8763E-06	0.1065E-05	0.3947E-06
$\bar{r}$	-.3370E-02	-.2144E-03	-.7454E-04	-.6746E-04	-.3675E-04	-.3544E-04	-.2158E-04	-.9875E-05	-.2648E-05	-.2353E-05	-.6134E-06	-.6077E-06	-.2921E-06
κ(μmhos/cm)	0.1047E-02	0.6657E-04	0.2315E-04	0.2095E-04	0.1141E-04	0.1101E-04	0.6703E-05	0.3067E-05	0.8217E-06	0.7310E-06	0.1903E-06	0.1375E-06	0.9048E-07
ν(ml/Coulomb)	-.8822E-03	-.8822E-03	-.8822E-03	-.8822E-03	-.8822E-03	-.8822E-03	-.8822E-03	-.8822E-03	-.8830E-03	-.8822E-03	-.8834E-03	-.8825E-03	-.8845E-03
v(cm/day)	-.3267E-05	-.3268E-05	-.3267E-05	-.3267E-05	-.3267E-05	-.3267E-05	-.3267E-05	-.3267E-05	-.3270E-05	-.3267E-05	-.3272E-05	-.3269E-05	-.3276E-05

Fig.8. Representative computer output of the program depicted in Fig.7, using the 13 acidic constituents listed in Fig.4. The parameter r designates the ionic mobility relative to Na^+, $\bar{r}$ the relative net mobility. r designates the ratio of ionized to non-ionized forms of the constituent. Specific conductance, κ, is given in μmhos/cm. Boundary displacement is given in terms of ν and v.

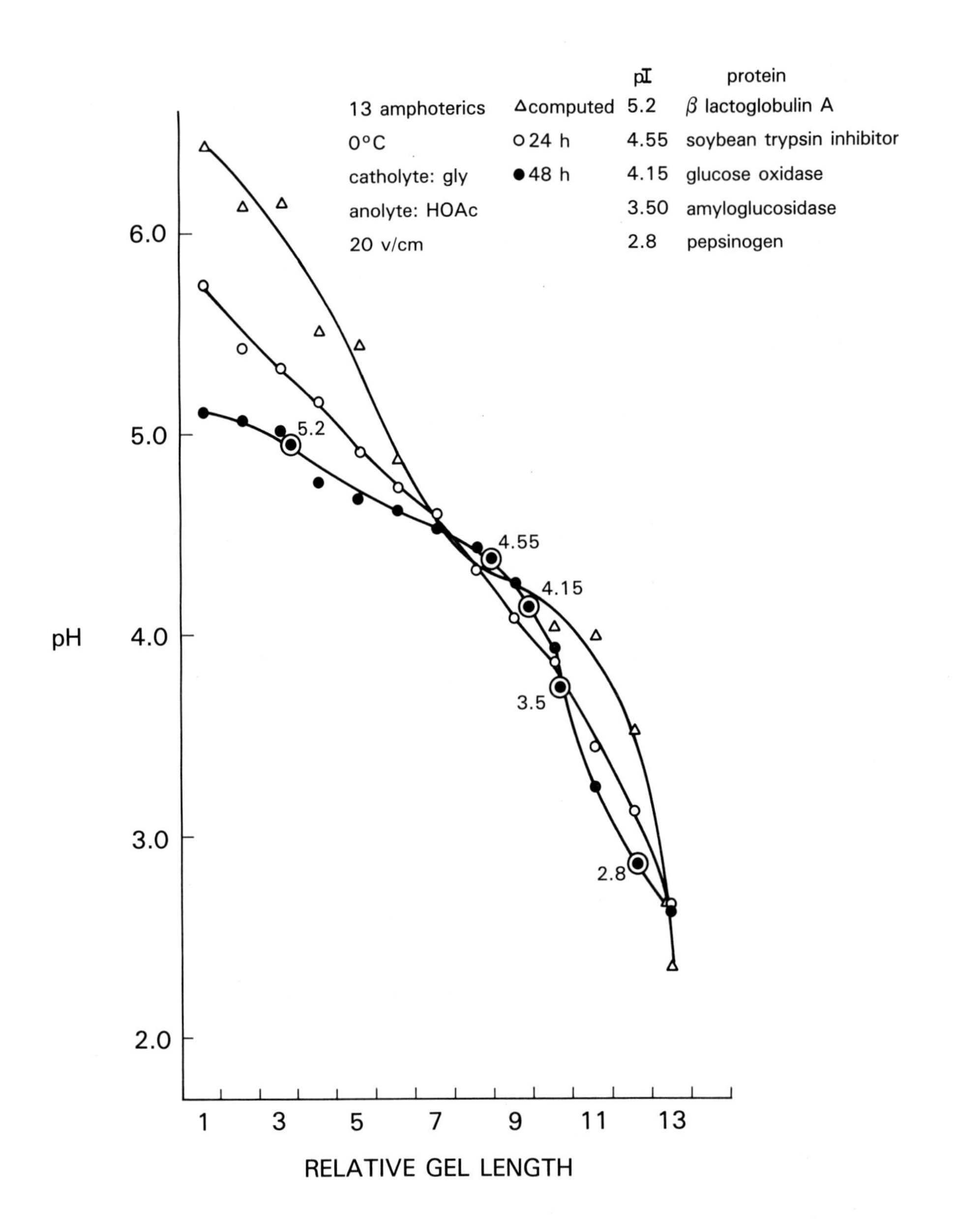

Fig.9. Computed and experimental pH gradients of the composition given in Fig.4 (top), Fig.7 and Fig.8.

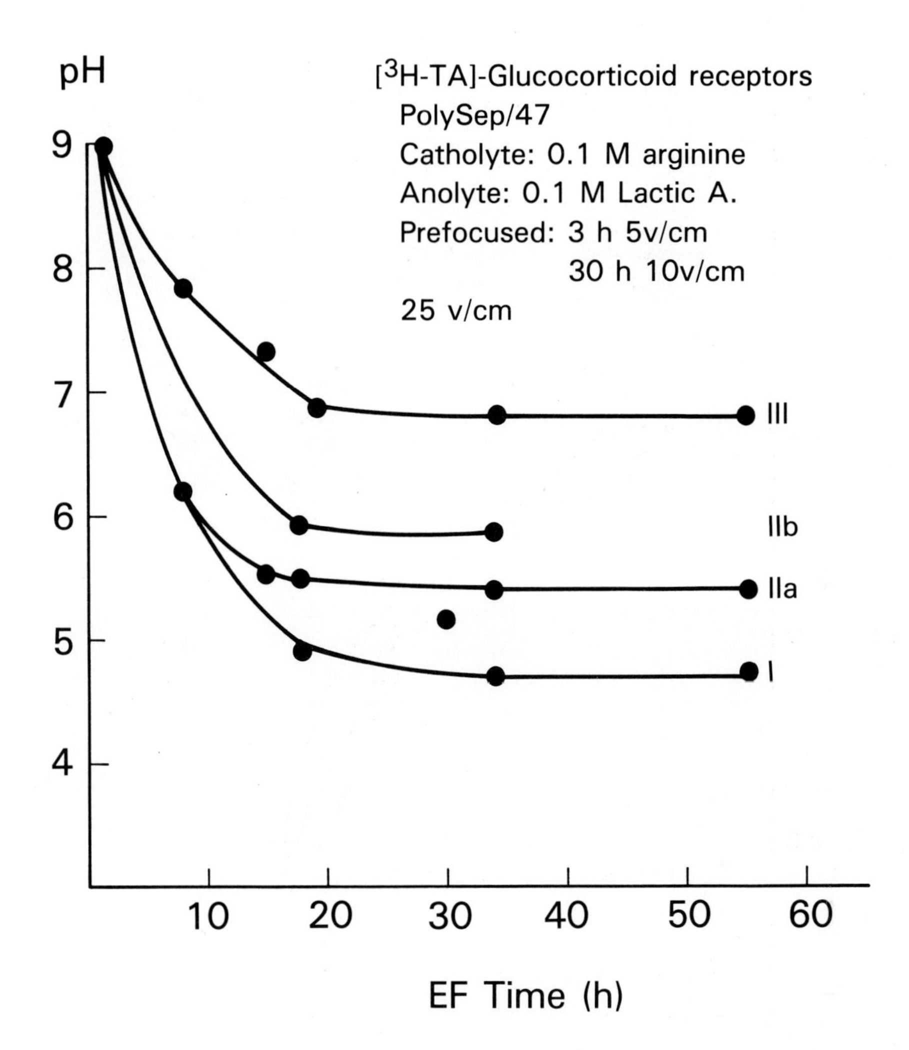

Fig.10. Isoelectric points determined for 4 components of the glucocorticoid receptor of embryonic chick retina, using the 47-component buffer mixture, Sephadex G-75 in 18 mm diameter tubes (34), -4°C (S. Ben-Or and A. Chrambach, in preparation).

Table 1. pI' values of glucocorticoid receptor species as a function of the addition of basic constituents to the sample prior to electrofocusing

Experiment	Type of EF	Addition	pI'	Receptor species
	pI-range 5-8 SCAMs	pI-range 8-10 SCAMs		
A	Aged	Aged	4.8 ± 0.1	I
			5.4 ± 0.3	IIA
			6.5 ± 0.2	IIB
			7.6 ± 0.5	III
B	Fresh	Fresh	4.7 ± 0.1	I
			5.4 ± 0.3	IIA
			6.1 ± 0.1	IIB
			6.7 ± 0.1	III
C	Fresh	-	4.8 ± 0.1	I
			5.7 ± 0.005	II
			6.2 ± 0.005	III
D	Poly/Sep 47		4.9	I
			5.7	II
			6.5	III
E	Poly/Sep 47	0.1 M arg	-	I
			5.6, 5.9	II
			8.2-9.0	III

IMMOBILIZED pH GRADIENTS: ANALYTICAL AND PREPARATIVE ASPECTS

Pier Giorgio Righetti, Elisabetta Gianazza and Cecilia Gelfi

Chair of Biochemistry, Faculty of Pharmacy and Department of Biomedical Sciences and Technology, University of Milano, Via Celoria 2, Milano 20133, Italy

SUMMARY

The analytical and preparative aspects of immobilized pH gradients (IPG) are reviewed. Three analytical parameters are evaluated: a) the polymerization kinetics; b) the generation of extended pH gradients (from 2 to 6 pH units) with automatic optimization of pH gradient linearity, β power, ionic strength by computer modelling; c) sources of artefacts (binding of histones and basic nuclear proteins to the Immobiline matrix). At the preparative level, the following aspects are described: a) theoretical prediction of acceptable protein loads in IPGs; b) optimization of environmental parameters; c) protein detection; d) electrophoretic protein recovery in composite agarose-HA gels; e) protein elution from HA beads; f) protein load as a function of %T. In the conclusions, some possible future developments of the IPG technique are discussed.

1 INTRODUCTION

Immobilized pH gradients (IPG) (1) represent a quantum jump in electrophoretic techniques. Why was it necessary to resort to IPGs? Conventional isoelectric focusing (IEF), the 23-year-old pupil of Svensson-Rilbe (2) had begun to show the crippling diseases of age, such as: a) instability of pH gradient with time (cathodic drift); b) lack of even conductivity and buffering capacity (β); c) extremely low and unknown ionic strength and d) limited load capacity, mostly due to isoelectric

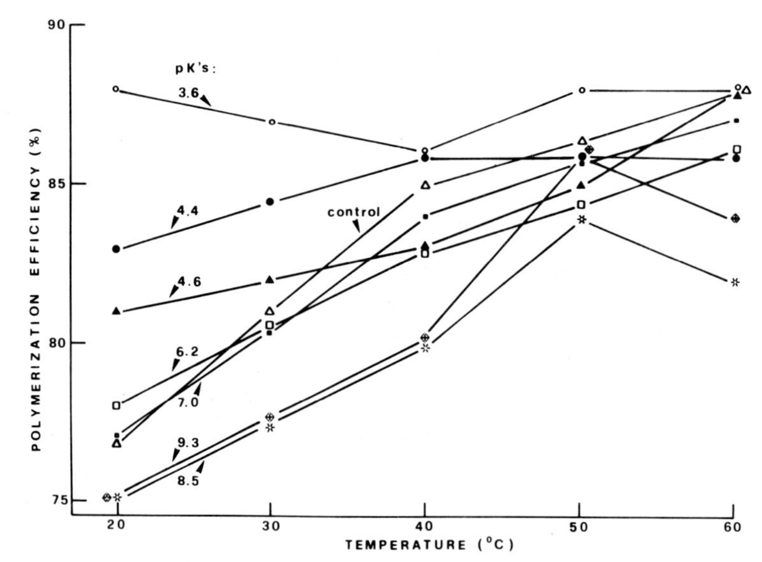

Fig. 1. Incorporation efficiency of the seven Immobiline chemicals as a function of temperature, from 20 to 60°C. Conditions: 10 mM each Immobiline in a 5%T, 4%C, pH 8.0 gelling solution, 1 hour reaction time, 0.047% TEMED and 0.033% AP. The disappearance of double bonds was followed at 285 nm in a Cary 219 spectrophotometer with a 2A full scale. The best convergence (similar reactivity ratios) is only obtained at 50°C (from Righetti et al., see ref. 11).

precipitation caused by the low ionic strength environment. Grafted pH gradients, as the reader will appreciate, have completely solved all these problems.

The outline of the present review: since the early findings have been dealt with in (1) and presented at the Athens (3-5) and Tokyo's meetings (6, 7), we will discuss here recent developments from our laboratory. There will be two main sections: one on analytical and one on preparative aspects.Their content has been outlined in the summary.

2 ANALYTICAL ASPECTS

2.1 Polymerization kinetics

In copolymerization chemistry, it is often described that the composition of the copolymer formed differs from the initial input composition due to the fact that the monomers differ in reactivity towards free radical addition (8). Thus, with less than 100% incorporation of monomers into the polymer, there exists the possibility that the concentration ratios between the Immobilines built into the gel will differ from the ratios in the starting solution: this could have serious consequences on the pH gradient generated, e.g. by changing its slope and the theoretically computed pH interval. With techniques described by Gelfi and Righetti (9, 10), we have studied the effects of the following parameters on the Immobiline gels: a) levels of persulphate: from 0.015 to 0.058%; b) levels of TEMED: for 0.024% to 0.094%; c) temperature range: from 20 to 60°C. The optimum in polymerization efficiency (in the range 84-88% incorporation for all the seven Immobiline chemicals) was found at the following values: 0.047% TEMED; 0.033% persulphate, 50°C and at pH >7. Fig. 1 gives an example of the effect of temperature on the extent and rate of reaction of Immobilines: as the temperature is lowered, the reactivity rate diverges greatly for the different Immobiline chemicals, with a consequent lowering of the incorporation levels in the gel matrix. 1 hour polymerization at 50°C appears to be just the right solution: all Immobilines seem to come to a confluence point, by exhibiting very similar reactivity ratios and incorporation efficiencies (11). Another important lesson has been learned from these experiments: when casting extended pH gradients (e.g. pH 3.5-9.5, the widest possible with Immobiline chemicals) it is imperative that the acidic end of the pH gradient be titrated (with NaOH) at least around pH 8, so as to ensure a uniform reactivity ratio between the two pH extremes. If a better than 84-88% incorporation efficiency is required (e.g. 95%) for some special experiments, this can be achieved by completely excluding the oxygen from the polymerization mixture. We have obtained that by building a gradient mixer which provides for anaerobic conditions, but the experimental manipulations become more complex.

2.2 Extended pH gradients

In order to obtain wider pH ranges than covered by the buffering power (β) of a single Immobiline, with the most linear pH gradient course and the smoothest possible β and ionic strength profiles, we have defined both a theoretical framework for the combination of several Immobilines and a computational tool for the simulation and automatic optimization of the results.

2.2.1 Computer program

The program "buffer systems and pH gradient simulator", written by G. Dossi and F. Celentano, allows: a) to compute the pH of a mixture of buffers; b) to titrate such mixture to any desired pH by the addition

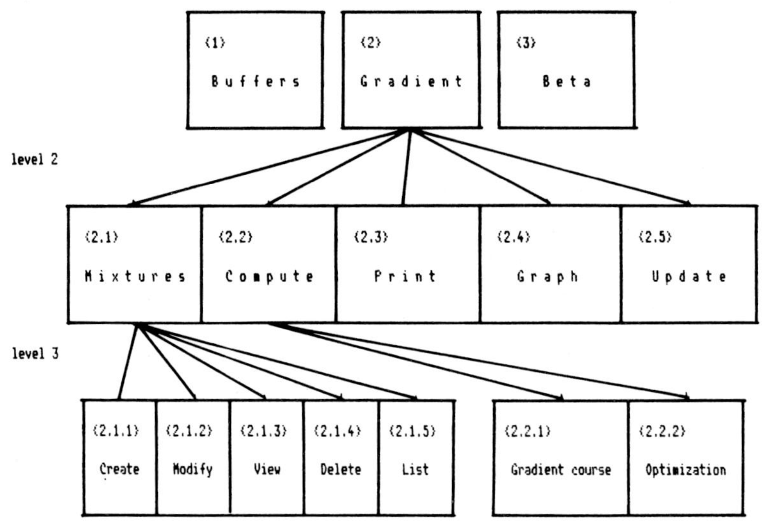

Fig. 2. Diagram of the computer program "buffer systems and pH gradient simulator". The main options within the block "Gradient" are only reported. Procedures of different levels are connected with one another in a tree-like structure, typical of the Pascal language, and may be activated according to their sequence number (top-down, left-rigth sequence). Details in the text.

of an acid, or of a base; c) to figure for a set of buffers the optimal concentration for generating a linear pH gradient; d) to compute the course of: pH (and its deviation from linearity), β and ionic strength from the linear mixing (in series) between 2 to 5 solutions of buffers and titrants. Its language and operating system is the UCSD-Pascal. Fig. 2 sketches its general structure.

The program includes 3 blocks. Within their archive {1} the buffers are identified by an index number. Each record (Fig. 3A) files two essential parameters for the computation: the kind of buffer - whether an acid or a base - and its pK, together with further informations of interest to the user: chemical and common name, manufacturer, etc. The block "Gradient" {2} contains the archive of the buffer mixtures {2.1}. Each component within this file may be: created, modified, deleted, displayed on a video screen or hard-copied by a printer {2.1.1 to 2.1.5; similar procedures operate on the buffer archive}. The various fields of a mixture record (Fig. 3B) correspond to: name, number of mixer chambers (1 to 5 solutions), volume of each chamber and volume of each step (these parameters set the simulation definition), the gradient extremes (the gradient deviation is referred to the linear regression between these two va-

```
Page   1 of the list of the Buffers

Buffer number  13
   Name          : Imm. pK 4.6 8M urea
   Code          :
   Manufact by   : LKB
   Catalog n.    : 1819
   Kind          : Acid
   pK            :    5.310
   Notes         : pK at 10*C in a gel phase with 8M urea
```

```
Mixture number  200
 Name               : 4.5-9.5, 8M urea
 $ of chambers      : 2
 Volume each cham.  : 7.00000
 Volume each step   : 1.00000
 Date               : 10/01/1984
 Initial pH         :    4.500
 Final pH           :    9.500
 Notes              : pH at 25*C in solution: 3.69-9.00 (mixture = 7.85)
Buffer concentrations

n. 1 pK  0.80   Cham 1   11.375   Cham 2    0.000
n.12 pK  4.47   Cham 1    2.761   Cham 2    2.761
n.13 pK  5.31   Cham 1    3.849   Cham 2    3.849
n.14 pK  6.71   Cham 1    3.333   Cham 2    3.333
n.15 pK  7.53   Cham 1    2.994   Cham 2    2.994
n.16 pK  8.87   Cham 1    4.139   Cham 2    4.139
n.17 pK  9.94   Cham 1    2.874   Cham 2    2.874
n. 8 pK 12.00   Cham 1    0.000   Cham 2    3.690
```

```
Page   1 of the list of Mixture(Grad) n. 200

Step  0  pH grad =  4.500  Dev = -0.0002  Beta =  2.675  Ion str =  13.332
Step  1  pH grad =  4.866  Dev =  0.0089  Beta =  3.149  Ion str =  13.556
Step  2  pH grad =  5.198  Dev = -0.0164  Beta =  3.280  Ion str =  13.756
Step  3  pH grad =  5.534  Dev = -0.0370  Beta =  3.062  Ion str =  13.892
Step  4  pH grad =  5.909  Dev = -0.0193  Beta =  2.713  Ion str =  13.865
Step  5  pH grad =  6.308  Dev =  0.0219  Beta =  2.780  Ion str =  13.532
Step  6  pH grad =  6.673  Dev =  0.0301  Beta =  3.109  Ion str =  12.933
Step  7  pH grad =  7.009  Dev =  0.0089  Beta =  3.259  Ion str =  12.214
Step  8  pH grad =  7.341  Dev = -0.0164  Beta =  3.196  Ion str =  11.446
Step  9  pH grad =  7.689  Dev = -0.0250  Beta =  2.957  Ion str =  10.655
Step 10  pH grad =  8.070  Dev = -0.0011  Beta =  2.735  Ion str =   9.853
Step 11  pH grad =  8.456  Dev =  0.0275  Beta =  2.913  Ion str =   9.046
Step 12  pH grad =  8.807  Dev =  0.0213  Beta =  3.190  Ion str =   8.237
Step 13  pH grad =  9.143  Dev =  0.0006  Beta =  3.148  Ion str =   7.429
Step 14  pH grad =  9.500  Dev =  0.0001  Beta =  2.871  Ion str =   6.626
```

Fig. 3. Computer printout. (a): buffer record list; (b): mixture record list; (c): gradient course print.

lues), and the buffer concentrations. For up to 10 components the buffer index is entered (which prompts the buffer pK to be displayed) together with its concentration (with a precision of 3 decimal figures) in each of the mixer chambers. For the computation {2.2} of the gradient course {2.2.1}, the concentration of each buffer (C_i) in the output flow is calculated with the Peterson and Sober equation (12). pH values are then obtained by solving (with the Newton's approximation) a general Henderson-Hasselbalch equation ($C_i=B_j$ for any of the l bases or A_i for any of the m acids):

$$\sum_{1}^{l} [B_j^+] \frac{[H^+]}{[H^+] + K_j} - \sum_{1}^{m} [A_i^-] \frac{K_i}{[H^+] + K_i} = 0$$

β and ionic strength are computed as detailed in (13). The parameters of the gradient (pH, deviation from linearity, β, ionic strength) may be either listed {2.3} (from step 0=conditions as in the first limiting solution, to step (volume of each chamber x number of chambers / volume of each step) = conditions as in the last limiting solution) by the printer (Fig. 3C) or drawn in a graph {2.4}.

If the results thus obtained are found unsatisfactory, the procedure "Optimization" {2.2.2} may be invoked. The value of the maximal deviation from linearity, and the pH where it occurs, and SD(pH) (standard deviation along the pH course) are first computed and displayed. The procedure is then started by entering the selection of the buffers whose concentration is to be optimized (usually not more than 4 components, with pKs close to the pH of maximal deviation). The search for the buffer concentrations that allow for a better linearity of the pH course is guided by the "steepest descent principle" (Fig. 4). The concentrations of the selected buffers are slightly modified around the starting conditions, and the new SD(pH) calculated; further steps are taken along the direction that results in the fastest decrease of SD(pH). The algorithm stops whenever a local minimum of SD(pH) is found. A new optimization cycle may then be started, with a different selection of components to be dealt with. In order to approach the absolute minimum, different starting conditions are sometimes to be tried - which are suggested by the scans of β and ionic strength courses (to get over SD ridges, see Fig. 4). The optimal concentrations are eventually updated in the mixture archive {2.5}.

2.2.2 Experimental approaches to the formation of extended pH ranges

We have described three procedures for casting 2 to 6 unit wide pH gradients. Peak concentrations of various Immobilines may be sequentially eluted from a gradient mixer with many chambers connected in series, each containing one of the buffering species in order of increasing (or

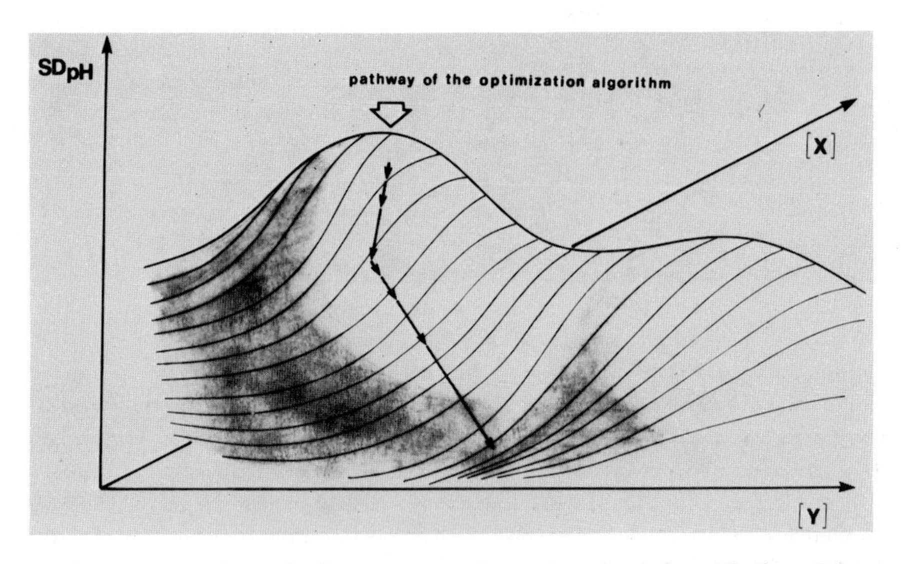

Fig. 4. Illustration of the steepest descent principle. If the concentration of the two buffers, X and Y, has to be optimized in order to give the most linear pH gradient, i.e. the lower standard deviation of pH, the pH course, and its SD are calculated for the starting conditions. The concentrations are then slightly altered, the new SD is compared with the previous result. The trial is repeated till a decreasing deviation is found; further variations are then tested while doubling the concentration change every time. A new direction is sought for when no more decrease of SD can be obtained along the former one.

decreasing) pK (the concentration profiles are described by the Peterson and Sober equation) (12). The mathematics of this approach are complex and not amenable to an automatic optimization procedure; trial and error is left as the only alternative. A special apparatus is required, with a large dead volume (inherent to the multiple chamber-to-chamber connections): only thick gels, or a stack of thin ones, can thus be polymerized at once. Several solutions have to be prepared: the check on the pH of each is simple and corrections effective - typically only one buffer and a counterion are present. However, there is no possibility of cross-control among different solutions. To compensate for these complications, this method allows for the lowest consumption of buffers (concentration is minimal at pHs remoted from pK, where their buffering contribution is negligible). Moreover, no strongly acidic or basic Immobilines (as yet not commercially available) are required to titrate the limiting solutions to the range extremes. Examples of 3 and 5 pH unit wide gradients obtained with a 5 chamber mixer have been presented in (13) and (14).

If a standard 2 chamber mixer is used instead, several buffers are pooled in each vessel; every component is then sequentially titrated to its buffering pH range. Two alternative procedures have been devised. In one approach, the buffers are present with the same concentration in both chambers, and a gradient of strong acid and base titrates them between the range extremes. The linearity of the gradient rests upon the constancy of the β power (15); this in turns is achieved by adjusting the relative concentrations of the components, e.g. by increasing those of the vicinal buffers to compensate for large ΔpKs. In the other procedure, the concentration of each buffer may vary between the mixer chambers, which results in a shift of the apparent pK of the buffer (16). The slopes of the various concentration gradients are then chosen so as to evenly space the pK_{app}, while the buffer concentrations (at pK_{app}) may be kept close to one another. In both cases, the optimization of the mixture composition for 2-chamber mixers may be provided for by automatic computation. This is especially simple with the same concentration approach: the block "Beta" {3} of the program serves this purpose. Another major advantage with both protocols is the use of ordinary apparatus, available in any size. Common disadvantages are a 50% higher consumption of buffers over the 5-chamber system and the need, for most pH ranges, of strong titrants.

When comparing to one another the two protocols for 2-chamber mixers (16), the more flexible different-concentration approach is found to give the best linearity of the pH course: maximal deviation doesn't exceed 1%, SD(pH) is on the average 0.4% of the gradient span. On the other hand, the same-concentration approach rates better in terms of constancy of β power and ionic strength. Moreover, with the derivation of both limiting solutions from a single mixture, with the reduced number of manipulations, with the highest inertia to experimental errors, the latter is superior in terms of both, precision and reproducibility.

Formulations according to the different-concentration protocol for 2-3 pH unit ranges have been published in LKB Application Note No. 322; for wider ranges according to the same concentration method in (15) and (6) (the latter optimized to give linear pH gradients in presence of 8M urea, which causes the pK of the Immobilines to unevenly shift towards more alkaline values) (17). A complete and perfected list of recipes for twenty 2 to 6 unit gradients, according to both methods, is presented in (16).

2.3 Artefacts: asking the impossible

When describing a new technique, it is important to define the limits of its validity, within which the method behaves as predicted. Outside these borders, the method could give erroneous answers likely to lead to misinterpretation of experimental data. For instance, in conventional IEF in presence of amphoteric buffers, several types of artefacts have been reported: binding of carrier ampholytes to nucleic acids (18), to heparin

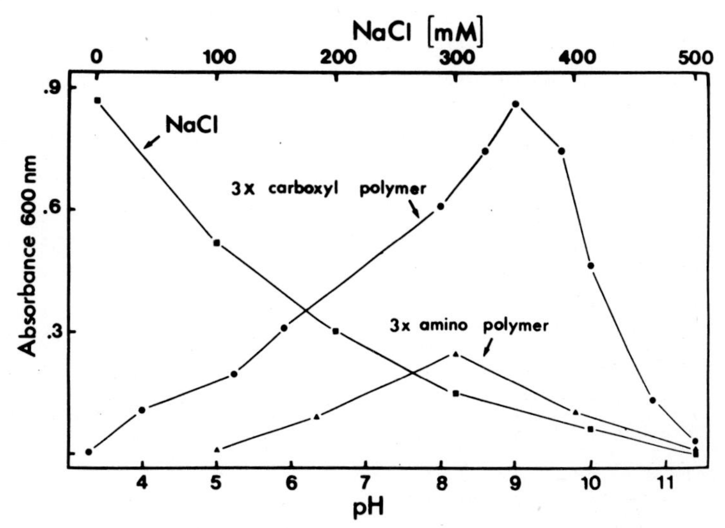

Fig. 5. Formation and disaggreagation of complexes between soluble, carboxyl and amino Immobilines and histone like (HMG) proteins. Polymers with pure carboxyl or amino surfaces, having a 3-fold higher concentration of Immobilines than standard gels (ca. 30 mM), were used in this experiment, and the stability of their complexes with HMG proteins was studied as a function of pH. With the carboxyl polymer, the disaggregation of its HMG protein complex by increasing NaCl molarities is also plotted (from Righetti et al.; see ref. 29).

(19, 20), to polyanions (21), even to dyes (22). This complex formation resulted in a multimodal sample distribution (in the case of heparin, more than 20 zones with different pIs in the pH 3.5-4.5 interval) representing the complex between the same type of macromolecule and different types of carrier ampholytes, with different pI values. The IPG technique is no exception to this rule, although artefacts will occur by a different mechanism: as the charge density of the macromolecule to be separated approaches the charge density of the matrix, a strong interaction will occur, which will result either in total sample precipitation, at the application point, or in extended smears covering a wide gel surface. We have found that IPG matrices interact strongly with at least two classes of proteins, histones and the histone-like, "high-mobility group" (HMG) chromatin proteins, forming insoluble complexes. The nature of these interactions has been demonstrated to be purely ionical: the complexes are split by high ionic strength (0.5M NaCl) and/or by altering the pH (full disaggregation being obtained at pH 5.5 and at pH 11.5). By preparing soluble homo-Immobiline polymers (polymerized in the absence of cross-linker) formed either by a pure carboxyl or by a pure amino surface, we have demonstrated (23) that histones and HMGs bind preferentially with "carboxyl" Immobiline polymers (see Fig. 5). Thus, one should not ask the impossible to the IPG technique: nucleic acids, heparin and polyanions too will not be amenable to fractionation in IPG matrices, and will precipitate at the application point. Except for these limitations, we have found IPGs to perform normally with all proteins we have tried (having pIs in the pH 3.5-10 range) but one: serum albumin (HSA). As seen in the separations of Görg et al. (24) and Cleve et al. (25), HSA produces long smears between pH 4.7 and 5.2, instead of focusing regularly. We believe that HSA recognizes as ligands pK 4.4 and 4.6 Immobilines, which are unfortunately needed as buffers in the pH region in which HSA is isoelectric. These complexes are however sensitive to 8M urea, so that practically normal patterns are obtained when running 2-D maps by the O'Farrell technique (26).

3 PREPARATIVE APPLICATIONS

We will explore now the preparative aspects of IPGs: since their inception as an analytical technique, it soon turned out that their loading capacity in preparative work was just as stricking. The load ability of IPG gels has been demonstrated to be at least 10 times higher than in conventional IEF, thus approaching or even passing the load limit of isotachophoresis (27, 28). The outline of the present section can be found in the summary.

3.1 Theoretical prediction of acceptable protein loads in IPGs

For practical preparative work an equation has been derived correlating the maximum protein load in a single zone to the pI distance (ΔpI) with the nearest contaminant, to the gel cross-sectional area and to the slope of the pH gradient. The equation is:

$$M = \left[\frac{\Delta pI}{d(pH)/dx} L\right] 2C_M A \qquad (2)$$

where:

M = protein load in a single zone (major component) in mg;

ΔpI = pI difference between major component and nearest contaminant (in pH units);

$d(pH)/dx$ = slope of the pH gradient along the separation track (pH units /cm);

L = protein free space, between the major band and the impurity, which is needed to cut the gel without loss of protein or without carrying over the impurity (in general 1 mm is an acceptable distance);

C_M = average concentration in the focused zone of the major component (mg/ml);

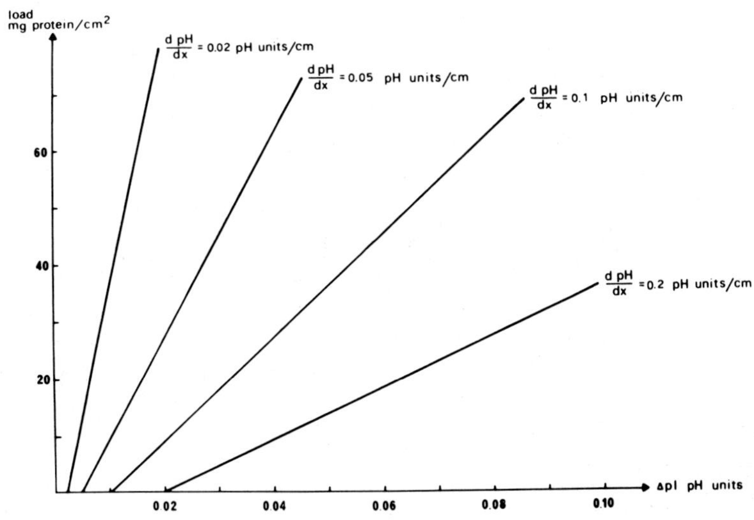

Fig. 6. Acceptable protein load as a function of ΔpI for different pH slopes plotted for a mean concentration of 45 mg/ml in the major protein zone. This is a graphical representation of Eqn. (2) (from Ek et al., see ref. 27).

A = cross-sectional area of the gel perpendicular to the focusing direction (in cm^2).

It can be seen that protein load can be maximized by increasing A (the liquid volume available to the focused zone) and by decreasing the slope of the pH gradient (i.e. by focusing in ultranarrow pH gradients). As a practical guide line, a graph has been constructed correlating these three basic experimental parameters: protein load in a single zone, ΔpI between the band of interest and nearest contaminant and slope of the pH gradient along the separation axis $|d(pH)/dx|$. Fig. 6 shows how the graph is laid out: the abscissa reports the ΔpI value (in pH units) and the ordinate the protein load (mg/cm^2) for a given A value. The ΔpI vs. protein load plane is cut by lines of different slopes representing pH gradients of different widths along the IPG gel length. It is seen that ultranarrow pH gradients (e.g. 0.02 pH units/cm) allow extremely high protein loads (up to 80 mg $/cm^2$) while still retaining a resolution better than ΔpI=0.01. At the opposite extreme, broad pH gradients (e.g. 0.02 pH units/cm) would allow a resolution of only ΔpI=0.1 with a protein load of less than 40 mg/cm^2.

3.2 Optimization of environmental parameters

We have also performed a thorough study on the optimization of environmental parameters ($\underline{I}$, gel thickness, pH gradient width) for maximizing

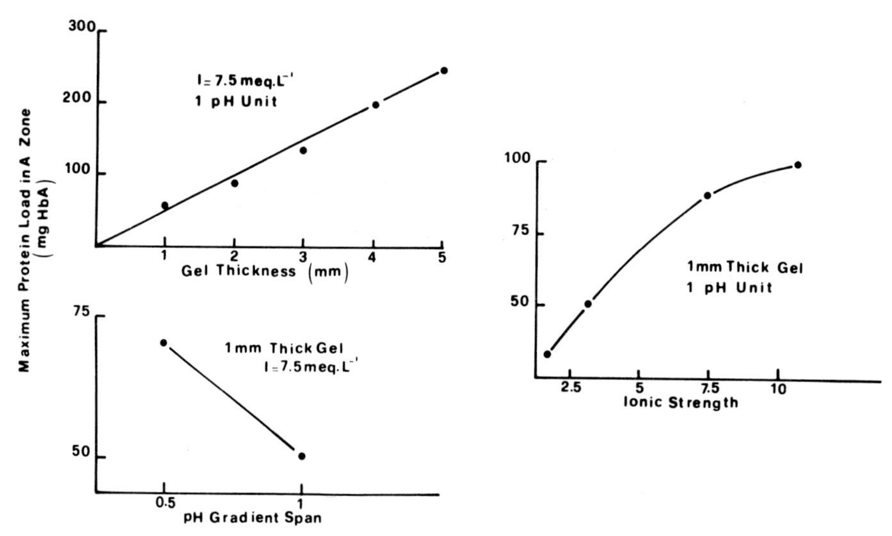

Fig. 7. Loading capacity of IPGs. The maximum load in a single protein zone is plotted: (a) as a function of ionic strength (I) at constant gel thickness (1 mm) in a 1 pH unit span; (b) as a function of gel thickness at constant I in a 1 pH unit interval; (c) as a function of pH gradient width at constant I and constant gel thickness (from Gelfi and Righetti, see ref. 28).

protein loads in Immobiline matrices. These aspects are summarized in Fig. 7. By increasing the ionic strength (I) of the gel from 1.25 to 7.5 mequiv.L^{-1} a four fold increment in load capacity is obtained; above this level, a plateau is abruptly reached around 10-12 mequiv.L^{-1}. By increasing the gel thickness from 1 to 5 mm a proportional five-fold increment in protein load ability is achieved; the system does not level off, however a 5 mm thickness seems to be optimal since thicker gels begin to develop thermal gradients in their transverse section, generating skewed zones. Finally, by progressively decreasing the width of the pH interval, there is a linear increase in protein load capability; here too the system does not reach a plateau, however, due to the very long focusing times required by narrow pH gradients, aggravated by the high viscosity of protein zones at high loads,it is suggested not to attempt to fractionate large protein amounts in pH ranges narrower than 0.5 pH units.

We have stated that IPGs have a load ability at least 10 times higher than conventional IEF. We believe this is mostly due to the strong difference in ionic strength characteristic of the two systems. At the very low I values typical of IEF (ca. 1 mequiv.L^{-1}) macromolecules will have a very low solubility minimum, and will tend to aggregate and flocculate. An increase of I, ca. 7-10 mequiv.L^{-1}, as characteristic of IPGs, is thus beneficial since, according to the Debye-Hückel equation:

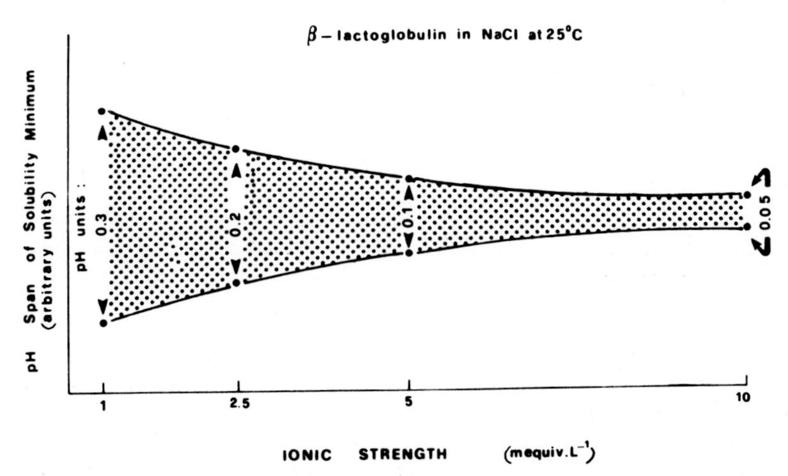

Fig. 8. Solubility of a protein in the neighborhood of its pI as a function of the ionic strength of the milieu. At 1 mequiv.L^{-1} (conditions prevailing in conventional IEF), β-lactoglobulin has a minimum of solubility over a span of 0.3 pH units; the width of the solubility funnel is markedly decreased at high $\underline{I}$ values (it is only 0.05 pH units at 10 mequiv.L^{-1}, value typical of an IPG milieu) (from Gelfi and Righetti, see ref. 28).

$$-\log \gamma = \log (S/S_o) = 0.51 \; Z^2 \sqrt{I} \qquad (3)$$

where γ is the activity coefficient of an ion of charge Z, S and S_o are the solubilities of a protein at the pI at a given $\underline{I}$ and as extrapolated to zero $\underline{I}$, respectively. Thus, as the environmental $\underline{I}$ increases, and the γ values of the ions (both in solution and in the protein) decrease, the protein solubility increases: the is the well known "salting in" effect described by Cohn (29). We are tempted to equate IPG gels to "salting in" media and IEF gels to "salting out" milieus. It might be argued that, as long as the proteins precipitate at their pI, and this material is confined in the isoelectric zone, this should not affect the load capacity in the gel matrix, since the precipitated zone is gravitationally stable. The point of the matter is that in real cases this does not quite happen. As demonstrated by Gronwall (30), the solubility of an isoionic protein, plotted against pH near the isoionic point, is a parabola, with a fairly narrow minimum at relatively high $\underline{I}$, but with progressively wider minima, on the pH axis, at decreasing $\underline{I}$ values. We have re-plotted his data in Fig. 8: it can be seen that, at the prevailing $\underline{I}$'s typical of conventional IEF (1 mequiv.L^{-1}), the solubility minimum of β-lactoglobulin spans at least a 0.3 pH unit interval, while in IPGs ($\underline{I}$=10 mequiv.L^{-1}) the pH width of solubility minima strongly decreases in a funnel-shaped fashion down to only 5/100 of a pH unit. In other words, what is detrimental in preparative IEF runs *is not isoelectric precipitation, but near-isoelec-*

tric precipitation. The precipitate is not confined at the pI position, but is usually smeared over as much as 1/2 pH unit interval, thus being completely detrimental to the resolution of adjacent species.

3.3 Protein detection

At the end of a preparative separation, we have first to reveal the focused protein zones in order to excise and elute the band of interest. In IPGs, this can be done in two ways: by Coomassie stain or by visual inspection of refractive indexes. In the former case, at the end of the IPG run, a strip is cut from each edge of the gel, parallel to the pH gradient and including part of the area where the sample was applied. The two strips are then fixed and stained so as to reveal the protein zones, while the gel slab is kept under voltage (this can be done since there is no cathodic drift, so the band position does not change with time). By putting the now stained gel strips back into their original position, the protein zone of interest is located and the gel strip containing it is cut out. Even more interesting is the second detection method: as discovered by Kolin (31), in his "artificial" pH gradients obtained by buffer diffusion, a protein zone condensed at its pI will exhibit a sufficiently steep refractive index gradient to be detected by the naked eye. This smart detection principle is lost in conventional IEF, however, since the carrier ampholytes themselves, once focused at their pI under high voltage, would give such a complex striation pattern (32), thus completely obscuring the protein position. This principle is again fully operative in Immobiline gels, since the buffering species cannot collect in ridges about their pI, and it can be substituted as a guideline for detecting and cutting the protein zone of interest without resorting to Coomassie stain (27).

3.4 Electrophoretic protein recovery in composite agarose/hydroxy apatite (HA) gels

Since IPGs can behave as ion-exchange matrices, protein recovery is performed electrophoretically. This step consists in the electrophoretic transport of the focused protein zone out of the IPG gel strip into a layer of hydroxyapatite (HA)-containing granulated gel, through a contact made of an agarose bed (33, 34). Electrophoresis is performed in a glass tray, of dimensions 245x120x5 mm (see Fig. 9) . Three electrofocusing strips, soaked in 100 mM Tris-Gly buffer, pH 9.1, and cut to length, are placed one on top of the other against the silicone rubber frame at the cathodic long side of the tray; three more strips, likewise treated, are placed 40 mm from and parallel to the anodic long side of the tray. Mol-

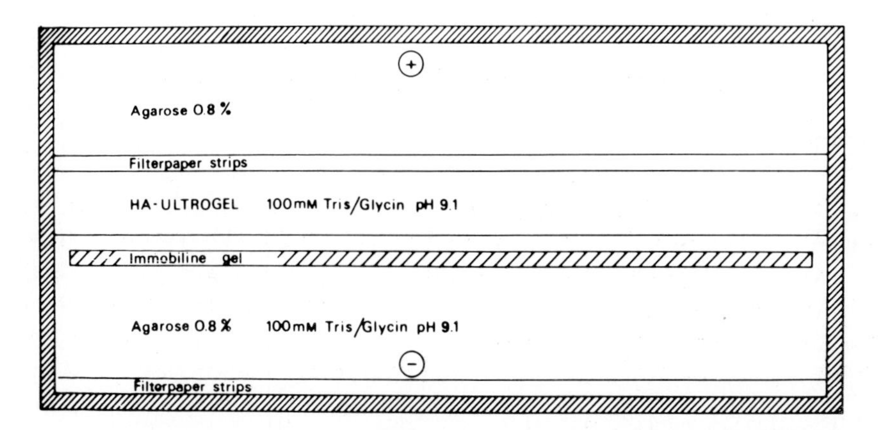

Fig. 9. Recovery of protein zones from Immobiline gels. Application of the IPG gel strip from the first step to the agarose gel of the second step. The polyacrylamide gel strip, containing the protein of interest, is cut along the contours of the main band (still supported by the Gel Bond PAG). The 0.8% agarose gel layer, 5 mm thick, was made to contain 100 mM Tris-Gly, pH 9.1. A trough was cut in the agarose gel to accomodate the polyacrylamide gel strip with a snug fit. The protein is recovered in the beads of hydroxyapatite contained in the central trough by applying 30 W constant power for 60 min (420 V initial voltage drop) at 10°C (from Ek et al., see ref. 27).

ten 0.8% agarose-M, in 100 mM Tris-glycine buffer, pH 9.1, is poured into the tray and allowed to set. A 20 mm wide agarose strip is then removed along the anodic filter paper strip and replaced by a slurry of HA Ultrogel (crystals of calcium phosphate coated with agarose). The IPG gel strip, containing the protein of interest, is now placed 5 mm away from and on the cathodic side of the HA Ultrogel. If the IPG gel strip is 0.5-1 mm thick, it can simply be laid on top of the agarose gel (with the gel side facing down and the Gel Bond PAG facing the operator). For 2-5 mm thick gels, the protein-containing IPG strip is placed in a trough of the same size cut out of the agarose gel layer, having a corresponding 2-5 mm thickness: this ensures uniform electrophoretic transport throughout the thickness of the IPG gel strip. The electric circuit is now closed with paper wicks going from the electrolyte reservoir of the Multiphor chamber to the surface of the agarose gel. The electrode buffer is 0.2 M Tris-Gly, pH 9.1, and the electrophoretic removal is performed at 30 W constant power for 1 hour at 10°C with an initial voltage of 420 V. As shown by Coomassie Blue stain, almost no protein remains behind in the IPG gel strip. There are at least two good reasons to prefer electrophoretic elution to diffusional recovery from ground gel pieces: the IPG matrix, once finely ground, would swell ominously in the elution buffer (thus re-absorbing the protein) and it would release in the superna-

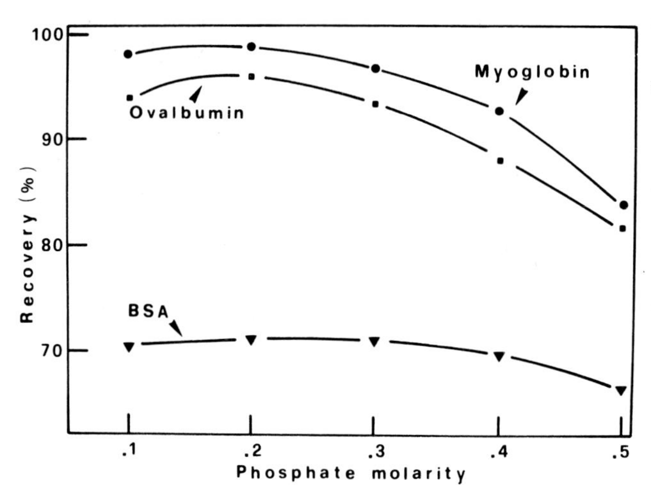

Fig. 10. Recovery of protein fractions as a function of phosphate eluant molarity. Myoglobin (●), ovalbumin (■) and BSA (▼) were separately absorbed onto HA-Ultrogel, equilibrated in 100 mM Tris-Gly buffer, pH 9.1, and eluted with increasing molarities (from 0.1 to 0.5 M) of pH 6.8 phosphate buffer (from Ek et al., see ref. 27).

tant un-cross-linked polyacrylamide-Immobiline chains (thus contaminating the sample (35).

3.5 Protein elution from HA-beads

After electrophoresis, the HA-Ultrogel is transferred with a spatula to a 25 ml plastic syringe plugged in the bottom with some cotton wool or with discs of filter paper. The protein is eluted with aliquots of 0.2M to 0.25M phosphate buffer, pH 6.8. In addition to the first fraction, 5x7 ml of buffer are normally sufficient to remove all the protein from the HA-Ultrogel. The buffer aliquots are pipetted in the syringe barrel, the beads briefly stirred with a glass rod and then the buffer eluted in a test tube with the aid of the syringe piston: this helps to squeeze out all the liquid from the HA crystals. The HA beads can then be regenerated for subsequent use by washing in 1M phosphate, pH 6.8, as described above.

The recovery from HA beads has been tested for six different proteins: hemoglobin (Hb), myoglobin, bovine serum albumin (BSA), carbonic anhydrase, ovalbumin and human transferrin. Recoveries range from 76% (BSA) up to 98% (Hb and myoglobin), typical values being of the order of 85%. These yields from Immobiline matrices are of the same order of magnitude as protein recoveries from Sephadex beads run in conventional IEF by the Radola technique (36). Recoveries are optimized by working in a range of 0.2-0.25 M phosphate molarities (see Fig. 10): at lower (0.1 M) and higher values (0.5M) there is a loss of protein, in the first case due to ion bonding, in the second case, most probably, due to hydrophobic interaction with the HA-matrix.

3.6 Protein load as a function of %T

It turns out that the situation, in preparative runs, is a bit more complex than

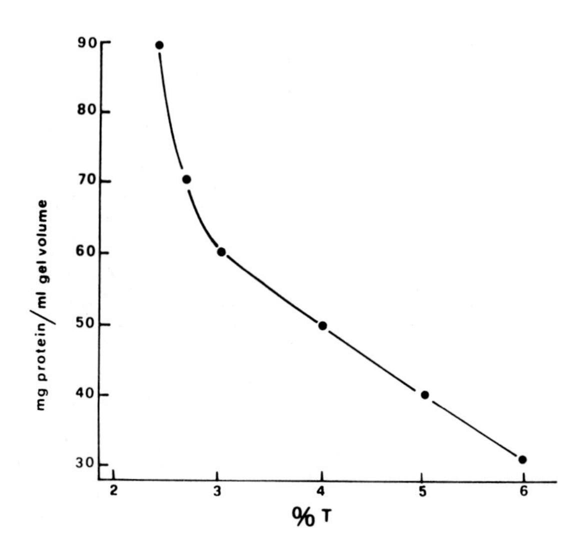

Fig. 11. Relation between loading capacity (in terms of mg protein/ml gel volume) and %T (T = grams of acrylamide and cross-linker per 100 ml gel volume) value of the gel matrix. Notice that, while in the range 3% to 6%T the protein load decreases linearly, in softer gels (3% T and lower) it increases exponentially (from Righetti and Gelfi, see ref. 37).

what we have described. We have seen that, no matter how the experimental conditions are optimized, and the ionic strength is increased, a common upper load limit for all proteins investigated has been found, of 40-45 mg protein/ml gel solution. We have been intrigued by this barrier and have tried to carry our IPG system through this "wall". The key to this apparent "solubility limit" is to be found in Fig. 11: the amount of protein accepted by a gel matrix is directly related to its composition (%T). The limit of 40 mg protein/ml gel is only valid for a 5%T polyacrylamide matrix: as the amount of fibers in the gel is decreased, progressively more protein can be loaded in the system, so that in a 2.5%T gel as much as 90 mg protein/ml gel can be applied. This has been interpreted as a competition for the available water between the two polymers, the polyacrylamide coils and the protein to be fractionated. This is an extraordinary amount of material to be carried by a gel phase, and renders IPG by far the leading technique in any electrophoretic fractionation. However, such soft gels are quite difficult to handle: for easier manipulations, we have described a two-step casting procedure, based on the formation of a %T step and a pH plateau around the application trench (to prevent collapse of the trench walls and to speed up the electrophoretic migration of the protein out of the application zone). We have also described a new method for electrophoretic recovery from IPG gel strips, based on embedding on low gelling (37°C) agarose instead of forcing the IPG strip into a trench cut into a pregelled agarose layer (37).

4 CONCLUSIONS

With the new developments described in the present review, we believe that the IPG methodology is now quite well established, so that it should rapidly become a standard technique to be added to the armamentarium of a biochemical laboratory (beware, it might turn out to be the most powerful weapon in your panoply!). At the analytical level, the long list of tables we have just published (16), covering any possible 2-6 pH unit range, with any possible formulation, and with the possibility of interpolating any narrow range therefrom, will render the preparation of Immobiline gels just as easy as manipulating a new concoction from a recipe in a cook-book. In the preparative counterpart (27, 28), the recent discovery of the very high protein loading ability of diluted polyacrylamide matrices (37), has enabled biochemists to grasp for the first time both horns of the dilemma: how to load large amounts of protein in the preparative scale while still maintaining the resolution obtained in analytical runs. This could very well mark the beginning of a new era in separation techniques.

Of course, there are some developments which are highly desirable: one would be the preparation of highly porous gel matrices, for IEF of large proteins, the other the casting of IPG gels onto porous supports, for subsequent electroblot analysis. At the moment, we have failed in both: in the first case, large pore gels are not obtainable by drastically lowering %T (down to 2.2%). They are obtained when greatly increasing %C (30% and higher) but they are totally useless: the matrix collapses by exuding water and the Immobilines are only poorly grafted to the polyacrylamide chains (Righetti, Gelfi and Gianazza, unpublished). In the second case, we have tried several potential candidates: denitrated cellulose nitrate, cellulose acetate (including the best IEF brands), cellophane, porous polyethylene, zeta probe, Pall Biodyne, you name it: the results have been disastrous, due to a strong electro-osmotic flow (Righetti and Gelfi, unpublished).

Acknowledgements

Supported in part by a grant from Consiglio Nazionale delle Ricerche, Progetto Finalizzato "Chimica Fine e Secondaria", sottoprogetto "Tecnologie di Supporto" (Roma, Italy). E. G. is the recipient of a 3-year fellowship from the Medical Research Council.

5 REFERENCES

(1) B. Bjellqvist, K. Ek, P.G. Righetti, E. Gianazza, A. Görg, W. Postel and R. Westermeier, J. Biochem. Biophys. Methods 6 (1982) 317-339

(2) H. Svensson, Acta Chem. Scand. 15 (1961) 325-341; ibid. 16 (1962) 456-466

(3) B. Bjellqvist, K. Ek, P.G. Righetti, E. Gianazza, A. Görg and W. Postel, in D. Stathakos (Ed.) Electrophoresis '82, de Gruyter, Berlin 1983, pp. 61-72

(4) P.G. Righetti, E. Gianazza, B. Bjellqvist, K. Ek, A. Görg and R. Westermeier, in D. Stathakos (Ed.) Electrophoresis '82, de Gruyter, Berlin 1983, pp. 75-82

(5) A. Görg, W. Postel, R. Westermeier, B. Bjellqvist, K. Ek, E. Gianazza and P.G. Righetti, in D. Stathakos (Ed.) Electrophoresis '82, de Gruyter; Berlin 1983, pp. 353-361

(6) P.G. Righetti, E. Gianazza, G. Dossi, F. Celentano, B. Bjellqvist, K. Ek, B. Sahlin and C. Eklund, in H. Hirai (Ed.) Electrophoresis '83, de Gruyter, Berlin 1984, pp. 533-540

(7) K. Ek, B. Bjellqvist and P.G. Righetti, in H. Hirai (Ed.) Electrophoresis '83, de Gruyter, Berlin 1984, pp. 541-548

(8) L. Aggarwal, Polymer 17 (1976) 938-956

(9) C. Gelfi and P.G. Righetti, Electrophoresis 2 (1981) 213-219

(10) C. Gelfi and P.G. Righetti, Electrophoresis 2 (1981) 220-228

(11) P.G. Righetti, K. Ek and B. Bjellqvist, J. Chromatogr. 291 (1984) 31-42

(12) E.A. Peterson and H.A. Sober, Anal. Chem. 31 (1959) 857-862

(13) G. Dossi, F. Celentano, E. Gianazza and P.G. Righetti, J. Biochem. Biophys. Methods 7 (1983) 123-142

(14) P.G. Righetti, E. Gianazza and B. Bjellqvist, J. Biochem. Biophys. Methods 8 (1983) 89-109

(15) E. Gianazza, G. Dossi, F. Celentano and P.G. Righetti, J. Biochem. Biophys. Methods 8 (1983) 109-133

(16) E. Gianazza, F. Celentano, B. Bjellqvist and P.G. Righetti, Electrophoresis 5 (1984) 88-97

(17) E. Gianazza, G.F. Artoni and P.G. Righetti, Electrophoresis 4 (1983) 321-326

(18) E. Galante, T. Caravaggio and P.G. Righetti, Biochim. Biophys. Acta 442 (1976) 309-315

(19) P.G. Righetti, R.P. Brown and A.L. Stone, Biochim. Biophys. Acta 542 (1978) 232-244

(20) P.G. Righetti and E. Gianazza, Biochim. Biophys. Acta 532 (1978) 137-146

(21) E. Gianazza and P.G. Righetti, Biochim. Biophys. Acta 540 (1978) 357-364

(22) P.G. Righetti, E. Gianazza, O. Brenna and E. Galante, J. Chromatogr. 137 (1977) 171-181

(23) P.G. Righetti, M. Delpech, F. Moisand, J. Kruh and D. Labie, Electrophoresis 4 (1983) 393-398

(24) A. Görg, W. Postel, J. Weser, S. Weidinger, W. Patutschnick and H. Cleve, Electrophoresis 4 (1983) 153-157

(25) H. Cleve, W. Patutschnick, W. Postel, J. Weser and A. Görg, Electrophoresis 3 (1982) 342-345

(26) E. Gianazza, A. Frigerio, A. Tagliabue and P.G. Righetti, Electrophoresis (1984) in press

(27) K. Ek, B. Bjellqvist and P.G. Righetti, J. Biochem. Biophys. Methods 8 (1983) 135-155

(28) C. Gelfi and P.G. Righetti, J. Biochem. Biophys. Methods 8 (1983) 157-172

(29) J.E. Cohn, Chem. Rev. 19 (1936) 241-255

(30) A. Gronwall, Com. Rend. Lab. Carlsberg, Ser. Chim., 24 (1942) 185-195

(31) A. Kolin, J. Chem. Phys. 22 (1954) 1628-1629

(32) P.G. Righetti, M. Pagani and E. Gianazza, J. Chromatogr. 109 (1975) 341-356

(33) B.R. Ziola and D.G. Scraba, Anal. Biochem. 72 (1976) 366-371

(34) J. Guevara, E.A. Chiocca, L.F. Ckayton, A.L. von Eschenback and J.J. Edwards, Clin. Chem. 28 (1982) 756-758

(35) E. Gianazza, F. Chillemi, M. Duranti and P.G. Righetti, J. Biochem. Biophys. Methods 8 (1983) 339-351

(36) B.J. Radola, Biochim. Biophys. Acta 386 (1974) 181-195

(37) P.G. Righetti and C. Gelfi, J. Biochem. Biophys. Methods 9 (1984) in press

PROTEINBLOTTING

Ulrike Beisiegel, Wilfried Weber* and Gerd Utermann*

Universitätskrankenhaus Eppendorf, 1. Medizinische Klinik, Martinistrasse 52, D-2000 Hamburg 20, West-Germany
*Institut für Humangenetik, Bahnhofstrasse 7a, D-3550 Marburg, West-Germany.

SUMMARY

The blotting technique, first described 1979 by Renart (1) and Towbin (2), became an important tool increasing our ability to analyse proteins fractionated on gels. The term blotting, here, stands for the process of transferring proteins from gels to immobilizing matrices. It is possible by the protein blotting, to combine all kinds of high resolution gel electrophoresis, including isoelectric focusing and two-dimensional systems with the versatility of a matrix binding assay.
The protein blotting does not need a lot of technical equipment and is extremely easy to perform.

This review will discuss the different ways in which blotting experiments can be done. The choice of apparatus, immobilizing matrices and the variety of detective systems, as well as possibilities to "re-use" gels and matrices. Moreover examples for the wide range of application will be given.
The wide spread use of electrophoresis in all areas of medical and natural sciences and the versatility of this technique certainly will prove the blotting to be a method of choice for a lot of questions in protein chemistry in the future.

Abbreviations: NC: Nitrocellulose; IEF: Isoelectric focussing; BSA: Bovine serum albumin; PO: Peroxidase; DBM: Diazobenzyl-oxymethyl-paper; DPT: Diazophenyl-thioether-paper; 2-D: Two dimensional; GAR: goat anti rabbit.

1 INTRODUCTION

The protein blotting has been developed from the DNA blotting technique which became known under the term "Southern blotting", described by E.M. Southern in 1975 (3). Today the Southern blotting isan irreplacable tool in DNA and RNA research.
The use of blotting techniques in protein analysis was introduced by Renart (1) and then modified by several laboratories. Towbin (2), who first used horizontal electroelution for the transfer and Burnette (4), who gave with his modifications in 1981 further stimulating impulses to the use of protein blotting, play the most important role in the development of this technique. Today immobilized proteins can be detected specificly in picogramm amounts by sensitive immunological systems after blotting experiments.

The number of laboratories using the blotting for various kinds of proteins is increasing and the variety of modifications certainly did not yet reach its limitation.

2. EXPERIMENTAL 'SET UP'

2.1 Apparatus

All known flat-gel-systems for electrophoretic analysis of proteins can be used as seperation step before the transfer to the matrix. The gel can be set in the blotting apparatus immediately after the run or, depending on the system, has to be washed or soaked in the blotting buffer.
As blotting assemblies four general "set ups" are used, defined by the driving forces achieving the transfer:
(a) simple diffusion (5)
(b) capillary pressure (Fig. 1)
(c) negative pressure (vacuum blotting (6))
(d) electrophoretic forces (Fig. 2)
Southern, in his DNA blotting experiments, used capillary pressure and it is still used frequently in molecular biology. For the protein blotting the "electroblot" became the most useful technique, since it has a good transfer efficiency also for high molecular weight proteins. Polypeptides and small proteins, however, can be transferred with good efficiency also by capillary pressure. As well as the transfer out of agarose gels and PAGE with large pore size can be done with this assembly.

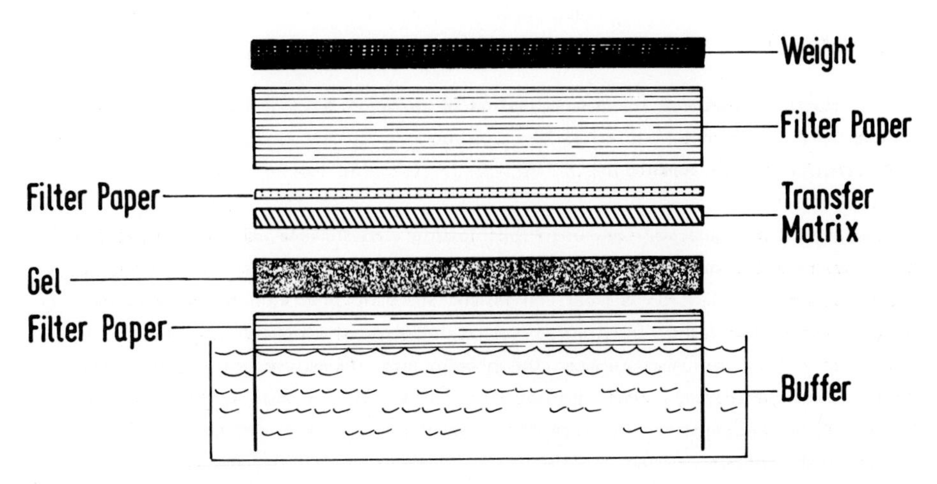

Fig. 1: "Set up" for Capillary Blotting. The buffer is sucked through the gel and the matrix by the pannel of dry filter paper on top. By the buffer flow the proteins are transferred.

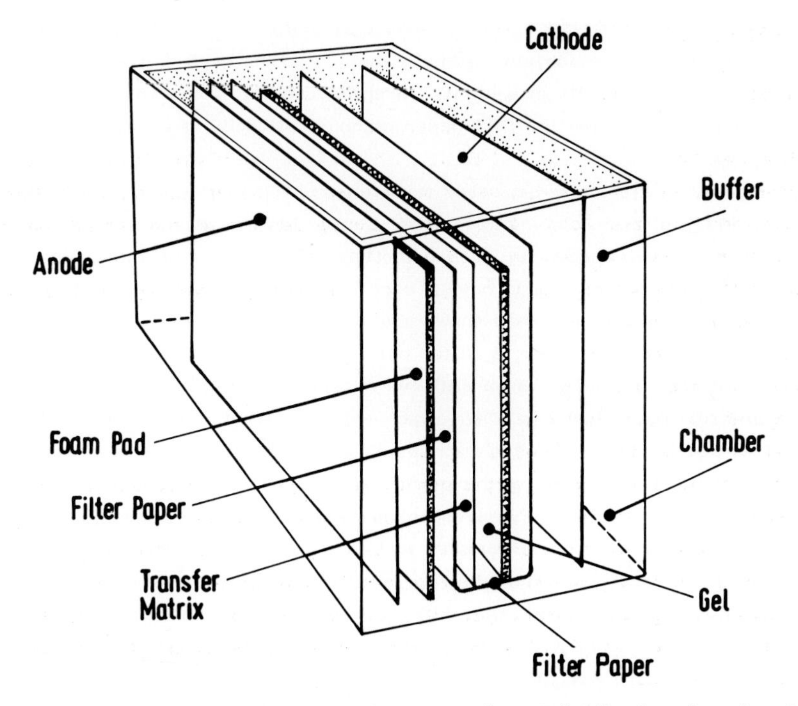

Fig. 2: "Set up" for Electroblotting. The "sandwich" of gel and matrix is held by a plastic grid and placed between the electrodes. A second foam pad at the cathodic side is often used.

2.2 Immobilizing Matrices

The matrices used for the immobilization of proteins have to be capable of binding high amounts of protein per area. The binding has to be irreversible and it should not denature the macromolecules.

The most important matrices used for blotting experiments are nitrocellulose (NC) and diazobenzyloxymethyl-paper (DBM-paper).
The use of unmodified NC is most convenient since no pretreatment is necessary. NC binds proteins rather tight and none of the original resolution is lost on the paper. But the interaction between the protein and the matrix is not fully understood. Gershoni (7) discusses hydrophobic interactions. A small poresize (0.2 µm) of the NC is important for the transfer of small proteins (8). NC can easily be stained with various common protein dyes. It is reported that pure NC (cellulose nitrate) has the highest binding capacity, which is reduced by addition of cellulose acetate.

DBM-paper has the advantage of covalently binding the proteins, but thereby the disadvantage of the need for special pretreatment before each run, namely the diazotization of the aminobenzyloxymethyl-group (9). The need of fresh diazotization for each experiment results in a higher unreproducebility. The same principle as for the DBM-paper is true for the DPT-paper which occasionally is used.

Other matrices are the nylon based membranes called Gen-Screen (NEN) New England Nuclear) (10) and Zetabind (11) (AMF-Cuno), both developed for DNA blotting first, but now also proposed for protein blotting. The nylon membranes bind through electrostatical interaction and do have a very high binding capacity, particular for small proteins. Gershoni (11) has shown that with the nylon matrix more protein is retained on the filter and more is eluted out of the gel. The high elution efficiency is due to the fact that there is no methanol necessary in the blotting buffer. In case of the NC 20% methanol is added which enhances the binding to the matrix.
A disadvantage is, that the nylon matrices also bind the common anionic protein dyes so that the visualisation of the protein pattern after the transfer is not possible by simple staining. Recently, however, an immunostain was developed (12) which can be used on the nylon membranes as well as on other matrices.
Seldom used, but certainly interesting for special problems are the cyanogen-bromide-activated acetate membranes with covalent binding (13) and the DEAE-paper (Diethylaminoethyl-paper) which binds with ionic interaction. But those should not be discussed here any further.

2.3 Transfer Conditions

The transfer systems are different for the two matrices. For NC in combination with urea gels an acidic buffer is used and the NC placed on the cathodic side (15) (2). SDS gels are generally blotted in tris/glycine buffers with methanol, pH 8.3. Here the NC has to face the anode. After the transfer the NC can be stained directly with a protein dye or has to be incubated in a tris/NaCl buffer containing blocking agents like BSA, animal serum or Tween 20 (16). Following this first incubation the specific probe can be added to detect the protein.
The transfer from SDS gels to DBM- paper is usually done in a sodiumphosphate buffer in the pH range 5.5-7.5. After the transfer the remaining diazogroups have to be inactivated by an incubation in tris/HCl buffer, pH 9, containing ethanolamine and gelantine.

These systems are generally used, but there are several modifications which became important to answer special questions. In general it should be kept in mind, that the pH of the modified buffer sets the direction of the transfer. And since different buffer systems influence the elution efficiency and the binding capacity of the matric, they should be tested carefully for every special case.

2.4 Detective Systems

To visualize specific proteins on the matrix, different techniques can be used:
(a) direct or indirect radioactive label
(b) indirect immunfluorescence label
(c) indirect enzyme-linked-immunlabel

(a) Ligands or specific antibodies used to recognize the particular protein, can be radiolabelled itself and then detected in autoradiography. But the jodination of ligands can decrease their binding affinity. For that reason it is more common to use a radiolabelled second antibody, directed against the ligand or the first antibody. Radiolabel is used in around 50% of the described cases of protein blotting.

(b) Antibodies can be conjugated to fluorescence-label and then visualized in UV light (17). The fluorisothiocyanate (FITC) is here the most common method. Only 3% of the blotting experiments are done with fluorescence labelling.

(c) Enzyme conjugated to antibodies are widely used for the detection of specific proteins in various assay systems (ELISA). The same technique can be applied to the immobilized proteins on the blotting matrix. Horseradish peroxidase is the most frequently used enzymeconjugate. There are different possibilities to use enzyme labelled antibodies on the matrix. The PO-label in the second antibody is the most simple one but not very sensitive. Higher sensitivity is achieved by using a PO-labelled third antibody. Another very sensitive method is the so called PAP (peroxidase-anti-peroxidase) label (18). An excess of unlabelled third antibody e.g. here, rabbit-anti-goat, has to be used and goat-anti-peroxidase is bound to the second, free, valence of this anti-goat-antibody. The antiperoxidase is preload with enzyme, which then can be detected with the common reagents (Fig. 3).

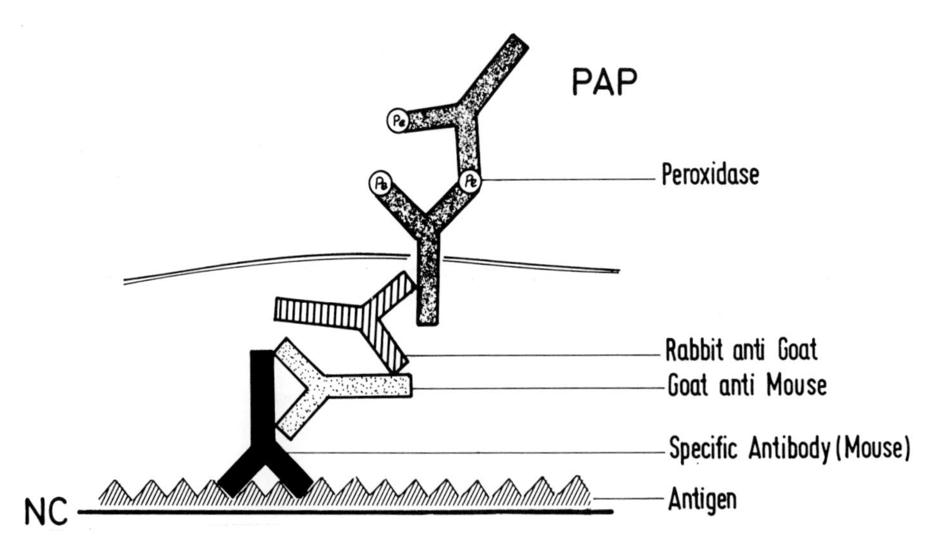

Fig. 3.: Immundetection of matrix bound antigen with the Peroxidase-Anti-Peroxidase complex.

2.5 Washing steps

Following the incubations with specific probes or the recognition systems the matrix has to be washed thoroughly to get rid of all unspecific bound substances. The washing buffers in most cases contain, next to BSA various detergents to detach the sticking proteins. The washing should be done with several changes on a rocking shaker and for a sufficient time period.

3. DOUBLE USE OF GEL AND MEMBRANES

Most of the protein blotting is done directly after the electrophoresis without a visualization of the pattern before the transfer. For several reasons, however, it can be advantageous to see the protein pattern before using it in a blotting experiment. One reason for that can be the screening for mutant proteins in genetical research. Here, only when additional bands appear in the stained pattern, their identity has to be proven immunologically on a blot. It is time and money saving in those kind of studies not to have to blot all gels. Moreover, no diffusion can occur after staining and the gels can be stored until a later transfer.
For that reason we tested the possibility to transfer apolipoproteins out of stained focussing gels. The results showed that apo E and apo A-I seperated in IEF can be efficiently eluted out of coomassie stained gels by electroblotting, just as most other tested proteins.

The next question was whether the antigenicity of the proteins was maintained. Both apo E and Apo A-I could be detected with polyclonal antibodies and J^{125} GAR on NC after transfer out of stained gels, as well as after coomassie stain of the NC. A comparison of the autoradiographic picture of "native" transfer and the transfer out of stained gels shows more distinct and clearer bands after the "stained" transfer. Probably fragments of antigen which do not focus completely, bind to the matrix while the native transfer, which are washed out in the fixing and staining procedures. Those immunological crossreacting fragments lead to a diffuse background staining on the radiograph (Fig. 4).

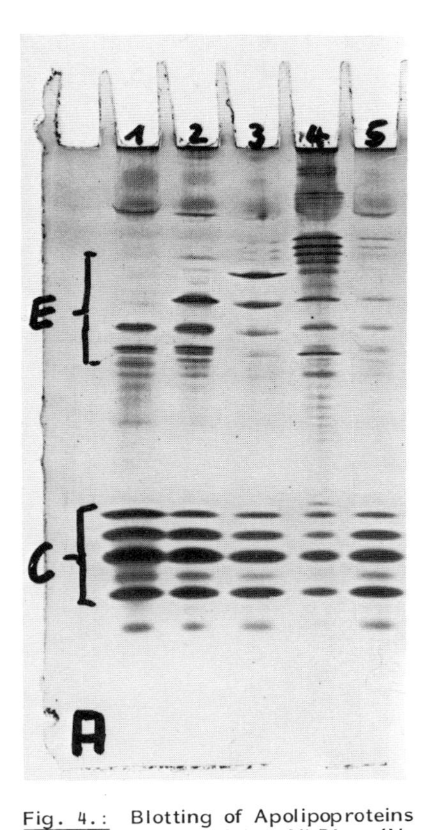

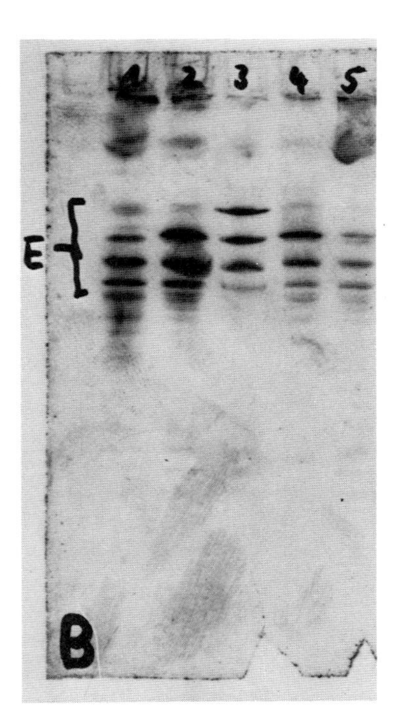

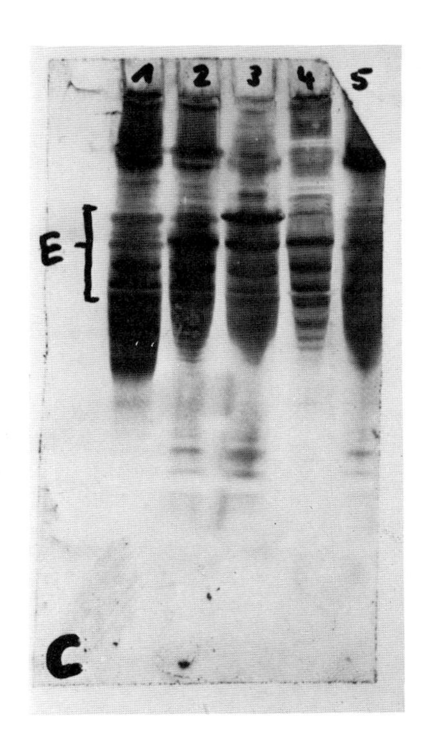

Fig. 4.: Blotting of Apolipoproteins
A. IEF (pH 4-6) of Apo VLDL's (Very-Low-Density-Lipoproteins) stained with Coomassie Blue. B. Blotting out of a stained gel: Autoradiography of the proteins transferred out of the Coomassie stained gel (A.) onto NC by electroblotting. The incubations were done in rabbit-anti-Apo E as first antibody, ^{125}J labelled goat-anti-rabbit as the second one. C. Blotting out of native gel: Equal amounts of the same Apo VLDL samples as shown in A. were applied to a parallel focussing gel. This gel was not stained and the transfer achieved by electroblotting onto NC. The autoradiography is shown after the same antibody incubation as in B.

The specific detection of proteins on immobilizing matrices has compared to other techniques of detection in the gel the advantage of the "re-use" of the antigen (19). The ligand or antibody used to recognize the protein can be eluted from the matrix, and thereby the bound protein is free for sequentially reactions. This "re-use" is particular useful for the test of series of monoclonal antibodies. The detection of several different proteins can also be done sequentially with the same label.
In our laboratory we eluted the J^{125} labelled goat anti rabbit complexed to rabbit anti apo E from apo E bound to NC and afterwards incubated the blot with rabbit anti apo A-I and J^{125} goat anti rabbit. The elution with sodium-phosphate buffer (pH 7.5), 8M urea and 0.1M ß-Mercaptoethanol, as well as 5 mg/ml BSA did not disturb the antigenic determinant of the apoproteins.

4. APPLICATIONS

The range of application for the blotting technique is extremely wide, Plasma-proteins, viral proteins, enzymes, and DNA-binding proteins have been detected by antibodies and specific ligangs, as well as cell surface antigens, immunoglobuline and translational products. It has very practical use in detecting allergens and analysing autoantibodies in their specificity. On the other side it is helpful to characterize different, immunologically crossreacting mutants, isoforms or subunits of proteins.
Here we will give only some examples from our and other peoples work.

4.1 Characterization of a receptor protein with immuno- and ligand blotting in 1- and 2-D Gelsystems

The receptor protein shown here, is the low-density-lipoprotein receptor (LDL-), a membrane protein which plays a key role in the cholesterol metabolism in men. Monoclonal and polyclonal antibodies were used for immunoblotting experiments (20). With 1- and 2-dimensional gels, followed by immunoblotting, we characterized normal and mutant receptor proteins. The mutant cell lines, we studied, derived from patients with familial hypercholesterolemia. Those patients do not express active receptor protein. With the blotting we found patients which do not have crossreactive material and those who do have structural mutated protein, which crossreact with the given antibodies.

Ligand blotting was performed with LDL, visualized with J^{125} antihuman LDL (21). Those experiments show that the protein seperated in SDS gels still has its physiological binding activity. The ligand blotting gets especially important in cases were there is no antibody available. Different possible ligands can be tested for their affinity and the receptor can be detected in species where the receptor does not crossreact with the raised antibody.

In comparison the ligand binding on the LDL-receptor has a slightly higher sensitivity than the antibody binding. But we have to be aware that this is true just for our receptor and might be totally different for other systems.

4.2 Detection of denatured enzymes via their physiological activity

In case of the LDL receptor the physiological activity was preserved after the SDS gelelectrophoresis, but this has not to be true for other binding proteins or enzymes. For the detection of inactive enzymes Van der Meer (22, 23) recently proposed a special sandwich method by which native antigen is coupled to the enzyme-bound anti-enzyme-antibody on the matrix. This can be achieved by using a great excess of antibodies in the incubation to bind one IgG to one antigen only. The second binding site will be free to bind native antigen in a subsequent incubation. The immobilized native enzyme can now mediate the physiological reaction and the reaction products are visualizing the position of the enzyme protein in the gel.

4.3 Affinity Purfication of Antibody

A very interesting application is the affinity purification of small amounts of antibody with the immunoblotting (24). A crude mixture of antibodies is used for the incubation of the NC with the immobilized known antigens. Each antibody will bind only to the band of its corresponding specific antigen. The monospecific antibody can be gained by cutting the protein band out of the NC and incubate this piece in the elution buffer which splits the antibody-antigen binding and sets the special antibody free.

5. DISCUSSION

Before the blotting technique was developed, immunological detections of proteins in gels were achieved by overlay-techniques. Overlays were used in many laboratories and can still be used, when enough antigen is available and the pore size of the gel allows the ligand or antibody to diffuse in easily. But in comparison with this method the blotting has some advantages:

- higher sensitivity
- proteins are easier and equally good accessible for all ligands
- need for smaller amounts of reagents in the incubation
- the handling of matrices is much easier than that of gels
- the processing time is reduced
- the proteins are immobilized and the matrices can be stored for long time periods

Alltogether the protein blotting is a very useful method with manifold applications. It is easy to carry out, and so every laboratory which does gel-electrophoresis can set up the blotting technique.

6 REFERENCES

(1) Renart, J., Reiser, J., Stark, G.R.:
Transfer of proteins from gels to diazobenzyloxymethyl-paper and detection with antisera: A method for studying antibody specificity and antigen structure.
Proc.Natl.Acad.Sci.USA, 76, (1979) 3116-3120.

(2) Towbin, H., Staehelin, T., Gordon, J.:
Electrophoretic transfer of proteins from polyacrylamide gels to nitrocellulose sheets: Procedure and some applications.
Proc.Natl.Acad.Sci.USA, 76, (1979) 4350-4354.

(3) Southern, E.M.:
Detection of Specific Sequences Among DNA Fragments Separated by Gel Electrophoresis.
J.Mol.Biol. 98, (1975) 503-517.

(4) Burnette, W.N.:
"Western Blotting": Electrophoretic Transfer of Proteins from Sodium Dodecyl Sulfate-Polyacrylamide Gels to Unmodified Nitrocellulose and Radiographic Detection with Antibody and Radioiodinated Protein A.
Anal.Biochem. 112, (1981) 195-203.

(5) Bowen, B., Steinberg, J., Laemmli, U.K., Weintraub, H.:
The detection of DNA-binding proteins by protein blotting.
Nucleic Acids Res. 8, (1980) 1-20.

(6) Peferoen, M., Huybrechts, R., DeLoof, A.:
Vacuum-blotting: a new simple and efficient transfer of proteins from sodium dodecyl sulfate-polyacrylamide gels to nitrocellulose.
FEBS Letters 145, (1982) 369-371.

(7) Gershoni, J.M., Palade, G.E.:
Protein Blotting: Principles and Applications.
Anal.Biochem. 131, (1983) 1-15.

(8) Lin, W., Kasamatsu, H.:
On the Electrotransfer of Polypeptides from Gels to Nitrocellulose Membranes
Anal.Biochem. 128, (1983) 302-311.

(9) Alwine, J.C., Kemp, D.J., Stark, G.R.:
Method for detection of specific RNAs in a agarose gels by transfer to diazobenzyloxymethyl-paper and hybridization with DNA probes.
Proc.Natl.Acad.Sci.USA 74, (1977) 5350-5354.

(10) Johnson et al. :
Electrophoretic transfer and detection of proteins using genescreen.
NEN Res.TIPS 1M783P-2207

(11) Gershoni, J.M., Palade, G.E.:
Electrophoretic Transfer of Proteins from Sodium Dodecyl Sulfate-Polyacrylamide Gels to a Positively Charged Membrane Filter.
Anal.Biochem. 124, (1982) 396-405.

(12) Wojtkowiak, Z., Briggs, R.C., Hnilica, L.S.:
A Sensitive Method for Staining Proteins Transferred to Nitrocellulose Sheets.
Anal.Biochem. 129, (1983) 486-489.

(13) Buhler, J.-M., Huet, J., Davies, K.E., Sentenac, A., Fromageot, P.:
Immunological Studies of Yeast Nuclear RNA Polymerases at the Subunit Level.
J.Biol.Chem. 255, (1980) 9949-9954.

(14) McLellan, T., Ramshaw, J.A.M.:
Serial Electrophoretic Transfers: A Technique for the Identification of Numerous Enzymes from Single Polyacrylamide Gels.
Biochem.Genet. 19, (1981) 647-654.

(15) Grégori, C., Schapira, F., Kahn, A., Delpech, M., Dreyfus, J.-C.:
Molecular studies of liver aldolase B in hereditary fructose intolerance using blotting and immunological techniques.
Ann.Hum.Genet. 46, (1982) 281-292.

(16) Batteiger, B., Newhall V, W.J., Jones, R.B.:
The Use of Tween 20 as a Blocking Agent in the Immunological Detection of Proteins Transferred to Nitrocellulose Membranes.
J.Immunol.Methods 55, (1982) 297-307.

(17) Ohashi, K., Mikawa, T., Maruyama, K.:
Localization of Z-Protein in Isolated Z-Disk Sheets of Chicken Leg Muscle.
J.Cell Biol. 95, (1982) 85-90.

(18) Sternberger, L.A., Petrali, J.P.:
The unlabeled antibody enzyme method immunocytochemistry of hormone receptors at target cells.
First International Symposium on Immunoenzymatic Techniques INSERM Symposium No. 2. Ed. Feldmann et al. (1976) North-Holland Publ.Co., Amsterdam, p.43-58.

(19) Erickson, P.F., Minier, L.N., Lasher, R.S.:
Quantitative electrophoretic transfer of polypeptides from SDS polyacrylamide gels to nitrocellulose sheets: A method for their re-use in immunoautoradiographic detection of antigens.
J.Immunol.Methods. 51, (1982) 241-249.

(20) Beisiegel, U., Schneider, W.J., Brown, M.S., Goldstein, J.L.:
Immunoblot Analysis of Low Density Lipoprotein Receptors in Fibroblasts from Subjects with Familial Hypercholesterolemia.
J.Biol.Chem. 257, (1982) 13150-13156.

(21) Daniel, T.O., Schneider, W.J., Goldstein, J.L., Brown, M.S.:
Visualization of Lipoprotein Receptors by Ligand Blotting.
J.Biol.Chem. 258, (1983) 4606-4611.

(22) Van der Meer, J., Dorssers, L., Zabel, P.:
Antibody-linked polymerase assay on protein blots: a novel method for identifying polymerases following SDS-polyacrylamide gel electrophoresis.
EMBO J. 2, (1983) 233-237.

(23) Muilerman, H.G., ter Hart, H.G.J., van Dijk, W.:
Anal.Biochem. 120, (1982) 46-51.

(24) Olmsted, J.B.:
Affinity Purification of Antibodies from Diazotized Paper Blots of Heterogeneous Protein Samples.
J.Biol.Chem. 256, (1981) 11955-11957.

IMMUNOSEPARATION OF PLANT PROTEINS

Jean Daussant, Danielle Bureau

Laboratoire de Physiologie des Organes Végétaux, C.N.R.S.
4 ter, route des Gardes, 92190 Meudon, France

SUMMARY

Antibodies are widely used for the separation and the identification of plant proteins at the analytical level. Immunoaffinity chromatography represents a means of separating proteins at the preparative level. The principle of the method for purifying proteinsis recalled. Different aspects of this biotechnology are examined: specificity, capacity and quality of the immunosorbents. Improvements are reported concerning the use of low affinity antibodies (polyclonal or monoclonal) and concerning desorption procedures for the recovery of biologically active proteins. Application to plant proteins are mentioned.

1. INTRODUCTION

During the two past decades antibodies have been increasingly used in plant protein and enzyme biochemistry as can be seen from recent review papers in this field (1, 2, 3, 4). Nearly all analytical techniques of modern immunochemistry were used in these studies, the first of which can be quoted already at the beginning of the century (5, 6).

One of the recent developments in immunoseparation of proteins in general, of plant proteins in particular, is the application of the immobilized immunoglobulin G (IgG) or of the antibody fractions from the corresponding immune serums for protein separation on a preparative scale. Immunosorbents can be used either in techniques of immunodepletion in order to eliminate from a protein mixture one or several components or in techniques of protein purification.

This paper deals with some aspects of immunoaffinity chromatography for the purification of proteins and its application to plant proteins. Developments concerning antigen elution are particularly emphasized.

2 PRINCIPLE OF THE IMMUNOAFFINITY CHROMATOGRAPHY FOR PROTEIN PURIFICATION

2.1. Aim

Immunoaffinity chromatography represents a very attractive tool for the purification of proteins. Three advantages of this method must be mentioned : A rapid one single step procedure of purification ; the possibility of recovering protein with their biological activity by avoiding the many and long classical procedures ; a means of purifying homologous proteins from different species when cross-reacting antibodies have been produced. The application of the method will be illustrated in section 5 by using examples provided in the field of plant proteins.

2.2. Principle

The principle of the technique (7) is shown on Fig.1.

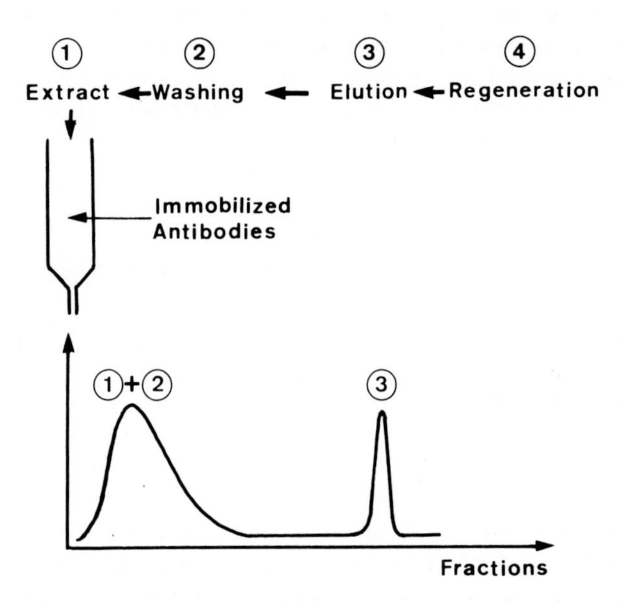

Fig. 1. Principle of immunoaffinity chromatography

IgG or the antibody fractions of an immune serum, or monoclonal antibodies are immobilized on a support, generally Sepharose or Ultrogel, and equilibrated at neutral pH. The solution of the protein mixture is passed through the column which is washed, generally with the equilibrium buffer. When no proteins are washed out anymore, desorption is carried out by using low or high pH values or by using chaotropic agents such as 3M KSCN, 4M $MgCl_2$, 8 M urea. The column is then washed again with the equilibrium buffer and can be reused a number of times.

The technique is better known as a classical means of purifying antibodies. The IgG fraction or the whole immune serum is passed on a column containing the immobilized antigen. After washing, desorption generally proceeds by using buffer at pH 2.8 (7). The desorbed fractions are immediately buffered at neutral pH for preserving their antibody activity.

However, the conditions of desorption are still an obstacle to the general application of immunoaffinity chromatography for the purification of biologically active proteins.

3 RESEARCH FOR SMOOTH CONDITIONS OF DESORPTION

Developments were made in two directions : using antibodies with low affinity and improving desorption procedures.

3.1. Use of antibodies with low affinity

The advantages of using low affinity antibodies for immunochemical purification of proteins have been underlined (8). Short immunisation procedures are known to result in antibodies with low affinity compared to those obtained after hyper-immunization (8). Thus, the use of the first bleedings as a source of antibodies for immunoaffinity chromatography has been recommended (9) although the advantage may not always be obvious (10). The chemical modification of immobilized antibodies appeared to be another and quite succesful way of reducing their affinity (11). An alternative for the choice of antibodies suitable for immunoaffinity chromatography may be found among the cross-reacting antibodies : they have indeed been reported to have lower affinity than the homologous antibodies (12). This possibility was remarkably underlined in a study on the purification of bovin α-fetoprotein (13) : A first part of the study involved the immobilized IgG fraction of an anti-rabbit α-fetoprotein immune serum, the antibodies of which are known to show low affinity against the homologous protein (14) ; the chromatography of the calf serum on the immunosorbent resulted in a retarded elution of the antigen relative to the other seric proteins. The antigen was therefore not subjected to drastic conditions of desorption. When using antibodies of such a low affinity it has to be checked whether the elution of the antigen is sufficiently delayed so that the antigenic fraction is not contaminated by tailing proteins. Moreover, a second part of the study revealed an unusual aspect of polyclonal antibodies : An anti-human α-fetoprotein immune serum was adsorbed on the immobilized bovin α-fetoprotein. Consequently, no precipitation reaction was observed by using the double diffusion test between the adsorbed immune serum and the bovin α-fetoprotein. Surprisingly however, the chromatography of the fetal calf serum on the immobilized IgG fraction of the adsorbed anti-human α-fetoprotein immune serum resulted in a retarded elution of the antigen in comparison to the other seric proteins. This study therefore indicates that immune serums may provide a choice of antibodies with various affinities, their preparation would be probably cheaper than the production of monoclonal antibodies. The chemical modification of the immunizing antigen is suggested to be a further means for preparing such cross-reacting antibodies (13).

In the past few years monoclonal antibodies aroused growing interest for their application in immunoaffinity chromatography (15, 16, 17, 18, 19, 20, 21). One main advantage is that their production does not need any preliminary preparation of highly purified antigen when a suitable screening method is available for identifying the antibodies specific for the antigens concerned. Thus, the selected antibody can be immobilized and used as a unique means of purifying the corresponding protein which otherwise could not be purified (15, 16). Another advantage of the monoclonal antibodies is that their production provides a relative large choice for selecting antibodies with the suitable avidity (16). Moreover, since a monoclonal antibody is specific for only one epitope on the antigen (with no repetitive antigenic determinants), the binding of the antigen to such an immunosorbent should, in principle, be weaker than the binding to an immunosorbent made with polyclonal antibodies (immune serum) which react with several different epitopes (22, 16). Consequently desorption should generally be easier with the first immunosorbent regardless to the choice and the use of monoclonal antibodies of particularly low avidity. Monoclonal antibodies are therefore considered as the best material for immunoaffinity chromatography. However, care must be taken in order to avoid undesirable cross-reactions : in several cases cross-reacting sites were reported when monoclonal antibodies were used on molecules in which no homology was detected by using polyclonal antibodies (23).

3.2. Improvements in smooth procedures of desorption

Attemps in different directions have been made in order to avoid the usual drastic procedures of desorption as illustrated by the following examples :

A first assay made use of the protective effect of 50 % ethylene glycol and its action in weakening hydrophobic reactions for desorbing a yeast phosphoglycerate kinase at pH 11.5 under non denaturating conditions (24).

However, most assays made use of abrupt changes in ionic environment of the immunosorbent for desorption. Such changes presumably induced a sudden decrease in the binding forces between antigen and antibodies by modifying electrostatic and hydrophobic forces. Those modifications may in turn initiate conformational changes in the immunocomplex, the result being a more or less successful release of the antigen (10, 25, 26, 27). The changes were brought about both ways, either by increasing or by decreasing the ionic strength. For instance, successful results were obtained by increasing molarity of NaCl for desorption at nearly neutral pH, with immunosorbent made of monoclonal antibodies selected for their low avidity. Moreover, a yield increase was observed by repeatedly alterning 1M and 2M NaCl solutions during elution (27). However, the procedure was judged inefficient in another study with monoclonal antibodies as immunosorbent (16). A successful desorption was reported for a plant peroxidase purified by using immobilized polyclonal antibodies ; water was used for sample application and washing of the column ; elution proceeded with 0.01M Na acetate buffer pH 5.5 (28) ; yet these adsorption conditions may favour an unspecific adsorption on the immunosorbent. Conversely, decreasing ionic strength by using hypotonic solutions (10, 29, 30) or distilled water (25) resulted in the desorption of active enzyme. However, the procedures were found not efficient when applied to other enzymes in studies involving the use of monoclonal (31) or polyclonal (26) antibodies.

Another group of studies involved the use of electrophoresis as a means of elution in immunoaffinity chromatography (32, 33, 34). These studies concerned several antigens chromatographied on the immobilized corresponding polyclonal antibodies. Electrophoresis was carried out on the immunosorbent after sample application and washing. The results clearly indicated that dissociation appeared immediately after washing - perhaps also during washing - and extended on several hours. This result is indirectly confirmed by several of the preceeding studies : indeed it was reported that the elution of the desorbed material often extends on many fractions providing sometimes too broad an elution peak (16). Thus, it appears that considerable improvements of the preceeding methods could be achieved by including an interruption during desorption. An example is given on Fig.2 with the barley β-amylase by using the immobilized IgG fraction of the corresponding immune serum. The desorption combined the use of distilled water with an interruption during the desorption. Fig.2A shows that after washing out the excess of antigen from the column, continuous desorption with distilled water did not succeed in eluting noticeable antigen amount in the fractions. However, when the desorption with distilled water was resumed after a few hours'interruption, the antigen was desorbed in one fraction. Fig. 2B indicates the influence of the length of interruption on the amount of antigen in the single fraction collected after resuming distilled water elution.

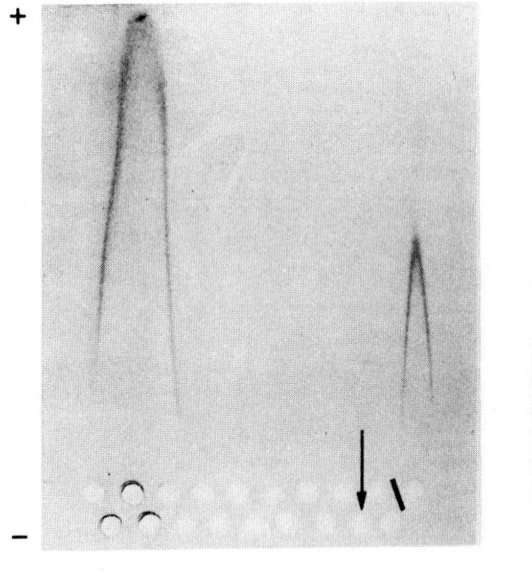

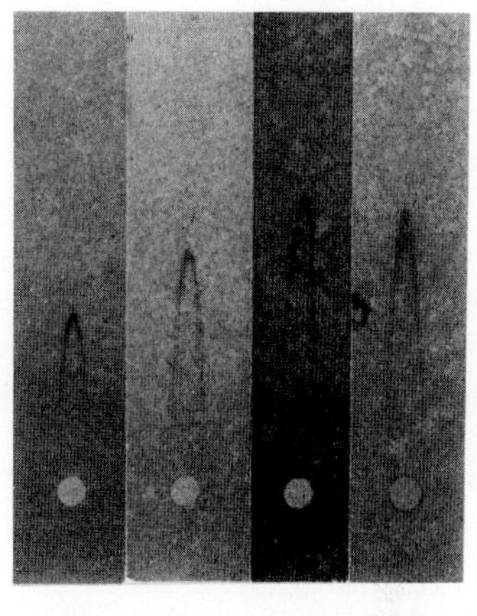

Fig. 2 A : Analysis by fused - rocket immunoelectrophoresis of fractions from an immunoaffinity chromatography. From the left to the arrow : elution and washing with the buffer. Arrow : elution with distilled water. The bar indicates the overnight interruption in the elution.

B : Rocket immunoelectrophoresis of the β-amylase fractions eluted from a same column in four runs involving different times of interruption during distilled water elution, from Bureau and Daussant, J. Immunol. Methods, 57 (1983) 205-213.

The procedure proved also to be non damaging to the barley β-amylase. The purified enzyme lost only 15 % of its molecular specific activity during purification and its important polymorphism displayed by isoelectric focusing was not modified (35). In contrast, desorption with the acidic buffer (pH 2.8) resulted in the loss of both the activity and the antigenicity of the enzyme. The interrupted elution with distilled water was then tested on five other proteins (26) : it was not applicable for one protein which was unstable in distilled water, it was useful for three others which were only poorly or not at all desorbed with the continuous elution procedure ; it proved favourable for the fifth protein which was already desorbed with the continuous elution, the interruption during elution resulting in considerably higher antigen concentration in one fraction. The examples reported (26, 36) concerned small columns containing each 1 to 3ml of immunosorbent gel. Around 5mg of the IgG fraction of the different immune serums were immobilized on 1ml support (Sepharose or Ultrogel). The columns were oversaturated with the antigens present in the protein mixtures. Generally 50 to 100μg antigen were desorbed in a single 2ml fraction which represented 65 % to 75 % of the immunoadsorbed antigen.

Conversely, the procedure can be carried out for desorbing antibodies from an immunosorbent containing the immobilized antigen : for example, an anti-barley β-amylase immune serum was passed onto an immunosorbent made of the purified enzyme immobilized on Ultrogel in unsaturated conditions. More than a third of the adsorbed antibodies were desorbed by distilled water in a procedure including a four hours' interruption during the elution : the remaining antibodies were further desorbed with continuous elution with the 0.2M glycin buffer pH 2.8. Thus, antibodies differing in their affinity for the antigen may have been separated (unpublished results).

4 OTHER IMPORTANT ASPECTS IN IMMUNOAFFINITY CHROMATOGRAPHY

4.1. Specificity

The efficiency of the immunoaffinity chromatography may be compromised by a possible non specific adsorption (16, 37, 38, 39). A detailed study on the origin of non specific adsorption which may appear was carried out by using the well known support cyanogen bromide-activated Sepharose 4B as a modell : The adsorption of different proteins, peptides and aminoacids on the unsubstituted support and on the immobilized IgG from serums of non immunized and immunized animals were investigated (40). However, the purifications achieved were often reported to be quite satisfactory by using electrophoresis, immunoelectrophoresis, crossed immunoelectrophoresis or radioisotopes for evaluating their efficiency (22, 41, 42). Fig. 3 and 4 illustrate the efficiency of the one step purification procedure carried out on β-amylase purified from a barley extract as shown on Fig.2. Polyacrylamide gel electrophoresis of the purified fraction and of several dilutions of the initial extract is reported on Fig.3 : The activity of the enzyme is well retained (A) and the protein staining indicates the disappearance of all constituents but the β-amylase in the purified fraction (B). Crossed immunoelectrophoresis of the purified fraction and of one dilution of the extract (containing the same amount of enzyme) underlines a more quantitative aspect of the purification (Fig.4) : Several major antigens other than the β-amylase (arrow) were identified in the extract (B), whereas no traces of these antigens were detected in the fraction (F) by using the same immune serum specific for several barley proteins (35). In these experiments, unspecific adsorption were avoided, as is usually recommended, by including 0.5M NaCl in the application and washing buffers. Low amounts of detergent have been also used (10, 43, 44). Some particular means for preventing undesirable adsorption may also be mentioned :

Preliminar filtration of the proteic solution on the unsubstituted support and on immobilized IgG from one non immunized animal before immunoaffinity chromatography (38) ; post-washing of the immunosorbent before desorption by using the desorbing solution at a lower concentration (16, 39). However, in the later case, depending on the affinity of the antibodies, more efficiency may have been obtained at the cost of some antigen lost.

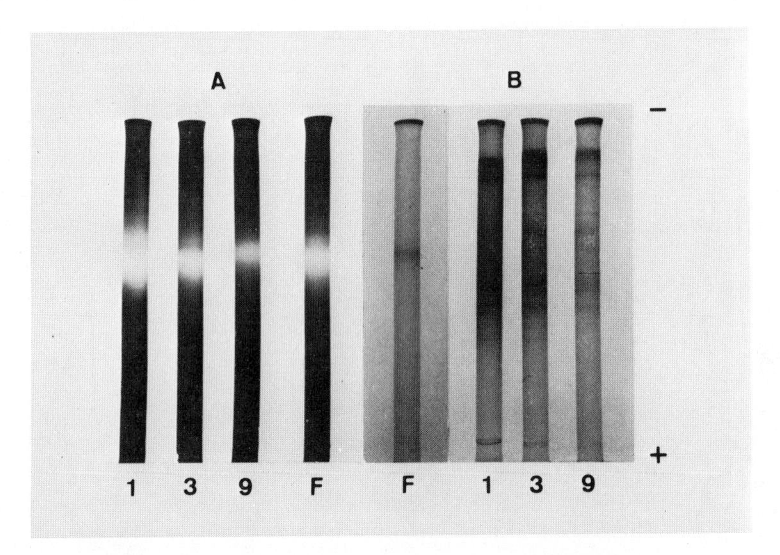

Fig.3 - Electrophoresis in 7.5 % polyacrylamide gels of a dilution series of a barley extract (1, 3, 9), of the undiluted purified fraction (F).
A : characterization for the β-amylase activity.
B : protein staining with Coomassie blue.

Another point related to the specificity of the immunoaffinity chromatography concerns the release of ligands (namely IgG) immobilized on CNBr activated Sepharose during the acidic desorption (45, 46, 47, 48, 49, 50). However in several instances - when low molecular weight antigens are concerned - desorption from such immunosorbent were used without noting any antibody leakage (cited in 48). On the other hand, the leakage of antibodies was reported to have stopped after several elution cycles of the column and therefore ceased to be a problem (51).

4.2. Capacity and longevity of the immunosorbents

In addition to the choice of low affinity antibodies and the procedure of desorption other factors play a role on the yield of antigen desorbed.

When polyclonal antibodies are used not only the saturation but also the overloading of the immunosorbent with the antigen is important in order to guarantee a maximum binding of antigens (36, 52, 53). The concentration of the antigen in the solution deposited on the immunosorbent is important : a same amount of antigen applied to the immunosorbent at a lower concentration results in a smaller amount of antigen bound (54). Overloading an immunosorbent with antigen probably reduces the possibilities of multiple binding on each antigen molecule by the polyclonal antibodies because of a high competition between the numerous antigens for the immobilized antibodies.

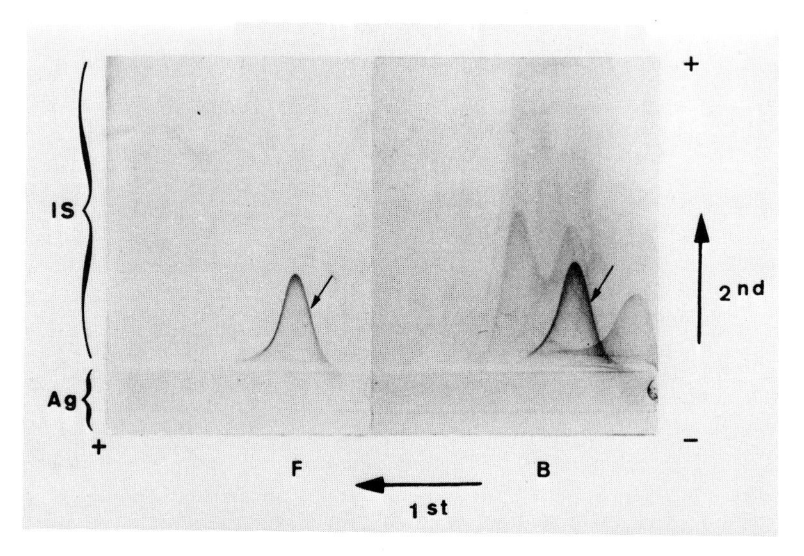

Fig. 4 - Crossed immunoelectrophoresis of the purified fraction (F) and of the barley extract (B).

(1) First dimension : electrophoresis in the agarose gel (Ag) carried out under 6.5 V/cm at 4°C for 70mn.

(2) Second dimension : eletrophoresis in the agarose gel containing an anti-barley protein immune serum (10 %) (IS) carried out under 5 V/cm at 4°C for 17h.

from Bureau and Daussant, Biochimie, 65 (1983) 361-365.

The amount of antibodies immobilized desserves also attention. A decrease in the antigen desorption yield was reported when too high a quantity of monoclonal antibody was immobilized (27). A compromise between two situations must be found : too high an amount of immobilized antibody may lead to a difficult elution and too small an amount of immobilized antibody may lead to an immunosorbent of low capacity (16).

Finally the matrix seems also to play a role in facilitating desorption. By using the same IgG preparation immobilized - according to the manufacturers'instructions -

either on Sepharose or on Ultrogel, the desorption with distilled water was faster with the second support (26). Affi-Gel 10 support was found to give an increase yield in large scale protein preparation (38). Other matrix are also available such as agarose polyacrolein microsphere beads (47) and magnetically responsive polyacrylamide agarose beads (55). They prove to be effective and specific for immunopurification of proteins.

The immunosorbents may be used repeatedly without significant loss of binding capacity for long periods of time (10, 54, 55, 56). In our laboratory several immunosorbents which are several years old and were submitted to more than 40 runs (one of them 75 cycles) are still in use. However, care must be taken in order to preserve the immunosorbents. For example, with plant extracts, irreversible attachment of phenols to proteins, namely antibodies, may rapidly inhibit the antibody activity. The experience prompted us to use seed extracts only after their filtration on Sephadex G 25. Loss of immunosorbent capacity may have different origins. For example a decrease capacity not restaured after treatment with basic, acidic buffers or with 2M guanidin chloride was attributed to the action of proteolytic enzymes in the extract (53). These enzymes may not only cleave part of the antibodies but also the covalent links between antibodies and the matrix (57). In that case the use of proteinase inhibitors during sample application and part of the washing may reduce the loss of capacity. Mild conditions of desorption may be a factor for keeping the immunosorbent in long use (10, 38). Nevertheless, insufficient desorption of the antigen may lead to a progressive decrease in the immunosorbent capacity as shown in a study on the immunopurification of the oats phytochrome : when 3M $MgCl_2$ only was used for desorption, 20 % of the column capacity was lost after each run ; when a second desorption with formic acid was carried out after the first one, no loss of immunosorption capacity was noted after several cycles (52).

5 EXAMPLES OF APPLICATION IN PLANT PROTEIN PURIFICATION

5.1. Use of immobilized monospecific antibodies

The immunoaffinity chromatography was shown to be the only means of purifying certain proteins which otherwise lose their biological activity. For instance, the phytochrome from oats'shoot is very difficult to purify by classical procedures since some proteases are co-purified and start degrading the protein ; however, by using an immunosorbent made of immobilized antibodies specific for the partially degraded protein, the phytochrome was obtained undegraded and in a high degree of purity (52). Another characteristic example is provided in a study on the 5 Aminolevulinate dehydratase an unstable enzyme which moreover exists in very small amounts in plant tissues ; the enzyme passed onto an immunosorbent made of monoclonal antibodies was proved to be very active on the immunosorbent ; however, the condition of desorption (pH 3) delivered a much less active protein ; the authors mentioned that the conditions of desorption could be improved, thus the method would be even more efficient (15). By using smooth procedures for desorption several enzymes were indeed purified still active (25, 36) and sometimes with a small loss only in the molecular specific activity (35).

The possibility of reusing the immunosorbent many times is particularly interesting in studies which involve the purification of one protein from many samples. This applies to physiological studies as it was the case for investigating the formation of two storage proteins in Pea at different steps of development (43).

Lastly it has to be mentioned that immunoaffinity chromatography is now currently used at a microscale in molecular biology : the technique aims at separating one particular antigen from a protein mixture produced in an in vitro protein synthesis system. In that case the immunosorbent is usually not reused.

5.2. Use of immobilized cross-reacting antibodies

Cross-reacting antibodies used in immunoaffinity chromatography opened new possibilities for purifying proteins from many samples without having to repeat procedures involving several time consuming steps. Several examples are provided in studies concerning comparison of homologous protein subunits from different plant species by using different types of electrophoresis : the antigenic similarities of the Ribulose bisphosphate carboxylase from a wide variety of plants was used for purifying the enzyme extracted from leaves of several plants ; antibodies specific for the enzyme from one of these plants were used as immunosorbent (58). The cross-reactivity between a storage protein, legumin, from a range of Pisum types was used in a similar study : the protein from the seed extracts of the different pea types were purified by using the immobilized antibodies specific for the legumin of one of these Pea types (59). This approach is going to be extended to other protein species, particularly to the identification and the purification of isolectins, since many of the major plant lectins are antigenically related (60).

Cross-reacting antibodies can be also used for solving other particular problems of purification as illustrated in a study concerning two α -mannosidases from Phaseolus Vulgaris. Only one of the isoenzyme could be obtained pure, antibodies were raised against this isoform ; based on the cross-reactivity between the two isoenzymes, immunoaffinity chromatography was used to purify both of them from the extract at once, the isoforms being thereafter separated by isoelectric focusing (61).

5.3. Means for obtaining monospecific antibodies

Immunoaffinity chromatography by using immobilized purified antigens found numerous applications for extracting the corresponding antibodies from an immune serum (See 4 for review) and making by the way possible the elimination of parasite antibodies which are not retained on the immobilized purified antigen. Alternately, by immobilizing the proper antigens, parasite antibodies, or cross-reacting antibodies, can be eliminated from the immune serum or from its IgG fraction (62,63). Based on that type of chromatography, a strategy for getting monospecific antibodies with use of a minimum of highly purified antigen could be defined : a relatively crude preparation of the antigen is used for immunization, the highly purified antigen is restricted to the immunoaffinity chromatography (37, 64). As already mentioned, combined use of monoclonal antibodies and immunoaffinity chromatography does not only eliminate the need of highly purified antigen for immunization, it also represents a unique means of purifying enzyme (15). In principle, no purification is necessary for immunization ; however, partial purification which increases the relative amount of the immunogen in the protein mixture will consequently increase the proportion of clones producing anti-enzyme antibodies. On the other hand, no purified enzyme is necessary for identifying these clones by using an ELISA technique : IgG produced by the different clones are specifically immobilized ; the detection among these assays of antibodies specific for the enzyme succeed by contact with the extract, followed by the enzymatic characterization after proper washing : The final purification of the enzyme can thereafter be achieved by immunoaffinity chromatography with the selected monoclonal antibodies.

6. CONCLUDING REMARK

The immunoaffinity chromatography represents a useful technique, both at the analytical and at the preparative levels. It has already proved its efficiency but remains limited in some of its applications. There is no doubt that this technique will be used increasingly since improvements are being made to get antibodies with an affinity adapted to each case and since smoother procedures of desorption are being developed.

7. REFERENCES

(1) R.B. Knox, A.E. Clarke, Electron Microscopy and Cytochemistry of Plant Cells, J.L.Hall ed., Elsevier, North-Holland, Biochemical Press 1978, pp. 149-185.

(2) J. Daussant, A. Skakoun, Isozymes : Current topics in biological and medical research, M.C. Rattazi, J.C. Scandalios, G.S. Whitt, ed., vol.5, Alan R. Liss Inc. Scientific, Medical and Scholarly Publications, New-York 1981, pp.175-218.

(3) R. Manteuffel, Encycl. Plant. Phys. : Nucleic acids and Proteins in Plants,

D. Boulter, B. Parthier, ed., Vol. 14A, Springer Verlag, Berlin 1982, pp. 459-503.

(4) J. Daussant, A. Skakoun, Seed Proteins, Annual Proceedings of the Phytochemical Society of Europe number 20, J. Daussant, J. Mossé, J. Vaughan, ed., Academic Press, London 1983, pp. 101-133.

(5) W. Magnus, Ber. Deut. Bot. Gessel, 26a (1908) 532-539.

(6) H.G. Wells, T.B. Osborne, J. Infect. Dis., 12 (1913) 341-358.

(7) C.R. Lowe, P.D.G. Dean, Affinity Chromatography, J. Wiley and Sons, ed., London 1974, pp. 150-199.

(8) E. Ruoslahti, Scand. J. Immunol. (Suppl.3) (1976) 3.

(9) R.A. Wetsel, M.A. Jones, W.P. Kolb, J. Immunol. Methods, 35 (1980) 319-335.

(10) E.M. Danielsen, H. Sjöström, O. Norén, J. Immunol. Methods, 52 (1982) 223-232.

(11) R.F. Murphy, A. Imam, A.E. Hugues, M.J. Mac Gucken, K.D. Buchanan, J.M. Conlon, D.T. Elmore, Biochim. Biophys. Acta, 420 (1976) 87-96.

(12) M.J. Crumpton, The antigens, Vol. II, M. Sela, ed., Academic Press, New-York, 1974, p.l.

(13) E. Ruoslahti, J. Immunol., 121 (1978) 1687-1690.

(14) H. Pihko, J. Lindgren, E. Ruoslahti, Immunochemistry, 10 (1973) 381.

(15) W. Liedgens, R. Grützmann, H.A.W. Schneider, Z. Naturforsch, 35 (1980) 958-962.

(16) J. Vockley, H. Harris, Biochem. J., 217 (1984) 535-541.

(17) K.H. Choo, J. Myer, R.G.H. Cotton, J. Camakaris, D.M. Danks, Biochem. J., 191 (1980) 665-668.

(18) E.M. Bailyes, A.C. Newby, K. Siddle, J.P. Luzio, Biochem. J., 203 (1982) 245-251.

(19) R.M. Denny, R.R. Fritz, N.T. Patel, C.W. Abell, Science, 215 (1982) 1400-1403.

(20) L.J. Meyer, M.A. Lafferty, M.G. Raducha, C.J. Foster, K.J. Gogolin, H. Harris,

Clin. Chim. Acta, 126 (1982) 109-117.

(21) F.K. Friedman, R.C. Robinson, S.S. Park, H.V. Gelboin, Biochem. Biophys. Research communications, 116 (1983) 859- 865.

(22) M. Heikinheimo, U.H. Stenman, B. Bang, M. Hurme, O. Mäkelä, H. Bohn, J. Immunol. Methods, 60 (1983) 25-31.

(23) D. Lane, H. Koprowski, Nature, 296 (1982) 200-202.

(24) K.K. Andersson, Y. Benyamin, P. Douzou, C. Balny, J. Immunol. Methods, 25 (1979) 375-381.

(25) J. Vidal, G. Godbillon, P. Gadal, FEBS Lett., 118 (1980) 31-34.

(26) D. Bureau, J. Daussant, J. Immunol. Methods, 57 (1983) 205-213.

(27) M. Y. Momoi, V.A. Lennon, J. Neurochem. 42 (1984) 59-64.

(28) J. Lobarzewski, R.B. Van Huystee, Plant Sci. Lett. 26 (1982) 39-46.

(29) K.M. Fukasawa, K. Fukasawa, B.Y. Hiraoka, M. Harada, Biochim. Biophys. Acta, 657 (1981) 179-189.

(30) B. Svensson, E.M. Danielsen, M. Staun, L. Jeppesen, O. Norén, H. Sjöström, Eur. J. Biochem., 90 (1978) 489-498.

(31) B.P. Morgan, R.A. Daw, K. Siddle, J.P. Luzio, A.K. Campbell, J. Immunol. Methods, 64 (1983) 269-282.

(32) P.J. Brown, M.J. Leyland, J.P. Keenan, P.D.G. Dean, FEBS Lett., 83 (1977) 256-259.

(33) M.R.A. Morgan, P.J. Brown, M.J. Leyland, P.D.G. Dean, FEBS Lett., 87 (1978) 239-243.

(34) M.R.A. Morgan, N.A. Slater, P.D.G. Dean, Analyt. Biochem., 92 (1979) 144-146.

(35) D. Bureau, J. Daussant, Biochimie, 65 (1983) 361-365.

(36) D. Bureau, J. Daussant, J. Immunol. Methods, 41 (1981) 387-392.

(37) R. Casey, Biochem. J., 177 (1979) 509-520.

(38) J.E. Mole, F. Hunter, J.W. Paslay, A.S. Bhown, J.C. Bennett, Molecular Immunology, 19 (1982) 1-11.

(39) R. Bach, J. Oberdick, Y. Nemerson, Blood, 63 (1984) 393-398.

(40) J.F. Kennedy, J.A. Barnes, J. Chromatogr., 281 (1983) 83-93.

(41) J.F. Kennedy, J.A. Barnes, J.B. Matthews, Clin. Chim. Acta, 129 (1983) 251-261.

(42) K. Levitsky, K. Chandrasekaran, P.T. Mora, D.T. Simmons, Int. J. Cancer, 32 (1983) 597-602.

(43) J. Badenoch-Jones, D. Spencer, T.J.V. Higgins, A. Millerd, Planta, 153 (1981) 201-209.

(44) T.J.V. Higgins, J.V. Jacobsen, J.A. Zwar, Plant Molecular Biology, 1 (1982) 191-215.

(45) F. Pekonen, D.M. Williams, B.D. Weintraub, Endocrinology, 106 (1980) 1327-1332.

(46) D. Dahl, Biochim. Biophys. Acta, 622 (1980) 9-17.

(47) S. Margel, FEBS Lett., 145 (1982) 341-344.

(48) H.von Schenck, R.H. Unger, Scand. J. Clin. Lab. Invest., 43 (1983) 527-531.

(49) H. Smith-Johannsen, Y.H. Tan, J. Interferon Res., 3 (1983) 473-478.

(50) J. Kohn, M. Wilcheck, Enzyme Microb. Technol., 4 (1982) 161

(51) P.R.Bukberg, N.A. Le, H.N. Ginsberg, J.C. Gibson, L.C. Goldman, W.V. Brown, J. Lipid. Res., 24 (1983) 1251-1259.

(52) R.E. Hunt, L.H. Pratt, Plant Physiol., 64 (1979) 332-336.

(53) J. Carlsen, K. Christiansen, B. Bro, Biochim. Biophys. Acta, 689 (1982) 12-20.

(54) S. Tsuchida, K. Sato, Biochim. Biophys. Acta, 756 (1983) 341-348.

(55) J.L. Guesdon, J. Courcon, S. Avrameas, J. Immunol. Methods, 21 (1978) 59-63.

(56) C.E. Carter, D.G. Colley, Molecular Immunology, 18 (1981) 219-225.

(57) G.J. Calton, Affinity Chromatography and Biological Recognition, I.M. Chaiken, M. Wilcheck, I. Parikh, ed., Academic Press, Inc., Orlando, Florida 1983, pp. 383-391.

(58) J.C. Gray, S.G. Wildman, Plant Sci. Letters, 6 (1976) 91-96.

(59) R. Casey, Heredity, 43 (1979) 265-272.

(60) C.N. Howard, J.I. Kindinger, L.M. Shannon, Arch. Biochem. Biophys., 192 (1979) 457-465.

(61) E. Paus, FEBS Lett., 72 (1976) 39-42.

(62) C.Domoney, D.R. Davies, R. Casey, Planta, 149 (1980) 454-460.

(63) I.M. Evans, R.R.D. Croy, P. Hutchinson, D. Boulter, P.I.Payne, M.E. Gordon, Planta, 144 (1979) 455-462.

(64) S. Craig, D.J. Goodchild, A. Millerd, J. Histochem. Cytochem., 27 (1979) 1312-1316.

COMPUTER SIMULATED 13-16 COMPONENT BUFFER ELECTROFOCUSING SYSTEMS

Zs. Buzas and A. Chrambach*

JATE University, Szeged, Hungary and *NIH, Bethesda MD USA

The steady-state moving boundary electrophoresis program of Hjelmeland applied to sequential boundary systems at zero common ion concentration yields near-stationary pH gradients. The number of buffer constituents making up the pH gradient is not a limiting factor in the use of this program - computing time remains negligible. Potentially, the program appears as the method of choice for pH gradient design and modification, replacing the excessively laborious trial-and-error approaches. One of the limiting factors remains our ignorance of ionic mobility values for most potential constituents, particularly those with values of pI-pK of less than 2. Within that limitation, a 13-component acidic and a 16-component basic pH gradient were computed. Buffer mixtures were designed to give equal dimensions to each of the constituents. Agreement of predicted to experimental pH gradients improved with increasing number of buffer constituents, suggesting that even buffers with large pI-pK values are applicable as long as a sufficient multiplicity acts to modify these values through constituent interactions. Variation of the leading ion concentration from 0.1 to 1.0 M changes constituent concentrations but appears to be without strong effects on pH gradient stability and the degree of approximation to predicted values. Amphoteric constituents at the steady state assumennear-isoelectric pHs. Therefore, proteins aligning in order of net mobility are also near-isoelectric, and pIs found in BEF are indistinguishable from those in conventional isoelectric focusing. The evidence that fundamentally the alignment is in order of mobility derives from natural pH gradients formed by non-amphoteric constituents. Transient state conductance and Joule heat are appreciable in BEF. Thus, to preserve poliacrylamide stability during the transient state, current control at 4 mA/cm2 or less is required until a potential of 10 V/cm is attained, with further voltage control at that value.

GENERATION OF STABLE pH GRADIENTS USING MONOVALENT BUFFERS: ANALYSIS BY COMPUTER SIMULATION

R. A. Mosher, W. Thormann, A. Graham, M. Bier

Biophysics Technology Laboratory, University of Arizona, Tucson, AZ, 85721, U.S.A.

1 INTRODUCTION

The great resolving power of analytical isoelectric focusing (IEF) has produced much interest in scaling up the process for preparative separations. However, commercial carrier ampholyte preparations, such as Ampholine, have a relatively high cost and are chemically and biologically ill-defined. These are significant limitations with regard to preparative applications, especially if the product is to be used clinically.

The concept of forming stationary pH gradients around neutrality using one weak buffer and its salt, or one weak acid and one weak base is well known. Such a gradient will be stationary to current flow because the transport numbers of the components are constant across the electrophoresis column. This concept has been used by Rilbe (1), Jonsson and Fredriksson (2) and Martin and Hampson (3) in preparative scale IEF instruments with membrane defined subcompartments.

We have recently developed a general mathematical model which describes the salient features of all the classical modes of electrophoresis, including isotachophoresis, moving boundary and zone electrophoresis and IEF (4). This work has lead to our view of the various electrophoretic techniques as being definable by their initial conditions and their boundary conditions. We have examined, by computer simulation, the conditions which must be met in order to produce pH gradients using simple monovalent buffers. We will show that when neutral membranes are used to isolate electrolytes reservoirs of constant composition from the separation column any number of components will reach a steady state at any pH interval.

2 THEORETICAL TREATMENT

The physical system under consideration is an electrophoretic column of finite length which is isolated from electrolyte reservoirs by neutral (uncharged) membranes. The composition of these reservoirs is fixed and a constant current flows through the system. The same weak buffers are present in each reservoir but at different relative concentrations so that the reservoirs have different pH values.

At the steady state, the flux of each component is everywhere equal in the column. This flux is given by

$$J_i = \mu_i C_i dV/dx - D_i dC_i/dx$$

where J_i is the flux of component i (m/M^2), μ_i is the net electrophoretic mobility of component i (M^2/V-sec), C_i is the concentration of component i (m/M^3), V is the electric field strength (V/M), D_i is the diffusion coefficient of component i (M^2/sec) and x is distance along the focusing axis (M). Eq. 1 has a different value for each component. The computation of the steady state profiles requires the solution of this equation for each component across the column, using as boundary values the specified concentration of that component in each electrolyte reservoir.

3 RESULTS

The data in Fig. 1 confirm that steady states are formed in pH regions away from neutrality. The computer predicted gradients formed with two different 2 component systems, one acidic and one basic, are presented. The pH gradients are skewed and of little use for isoelectric focusing. The profiles are shifted toward the cathode in the acidic system and toward the anode in the basic system. The currents employed are relatively low (0.2 A/M^2). Increasing the current moves the intersection of the concentration curves further away from the center of the column thus increasing the skewed nature of the curves. This is shown in Fig. 2.

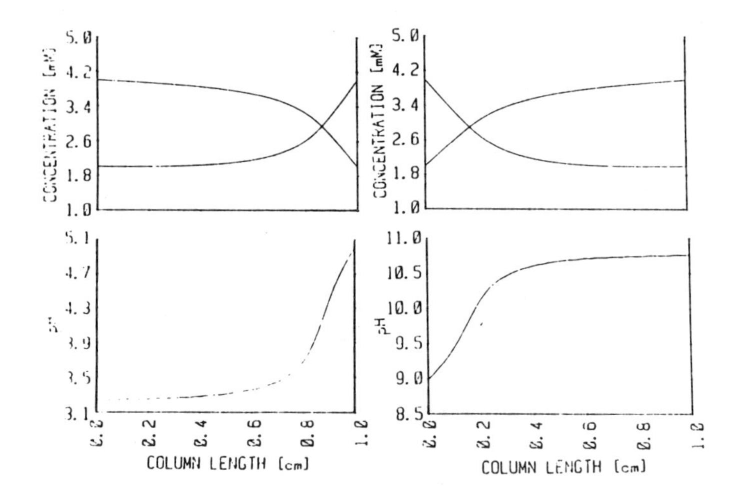

Fig. 1 Computer predicted steady state profiles produced by an acidic system (left) and a basic system (right). Acidic system: anolyte composition = 4 mM acid (pKa = 3), 2 mM base (pKa = 5); catholyte composition = 4 mM base, 2 mM acid. Component mobilities = 3.0 x 10^{-8} M^2/V-sec in both simulations. Basic system: anolyte composition = 4 mM acid (pKa = 9), 2 mM base (pKa = 11);catholyte composition = 4 mM base, 2 mM acid. Current = 0.2 A/M^2 in both simulations.

Cacodylic acid and TRIS base were employed as buffering components in the simulation data presented in Fig. 2. The pH gradients span neutrality. The solid lines depict the gradients formed with a current of 5 A/M^2. The pH profile is more nearly linear than those in Fig. 2 and would be much more useful experimentally. The effect of the current is shown by the dashed lines. This system is slightly basic and increasing the current to 15 A/M^2 shifts the profiles toward the anode.

The steady state gradients formed by a three component system are presented in Fig. 3. This system was selected to approximately reproduce the pH gradient formed by the acidic system presented in Fig. 1. This pH gradient is more nearly linear than that in the two component system. Thus, the usefulness of acidic and basic pH gradients can be improved by employing additional components.

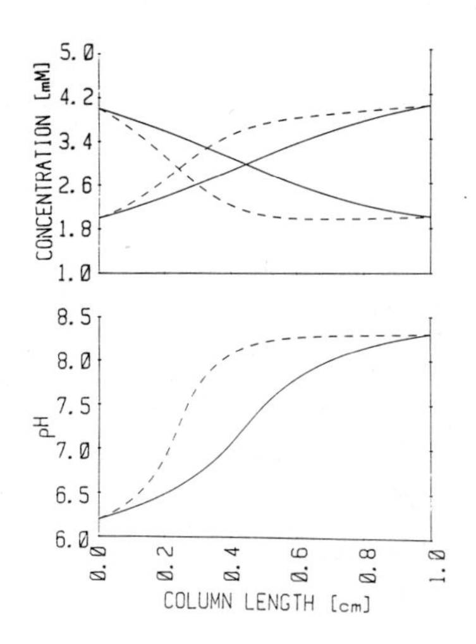

Fig. 2 Computer predicted effect of current on the steady state profiles of TRIS base (pKa = 8.3) and cacodylic acid (pKa = 6.2). Anolyte composition: 4 mM acid, 2 mM base. Catholyte composition: 4 mM base, 2 mM acid. Solid profiles generated with a current of 5 A/M^2, dashed profiles, current = 15 A/M^2. TRIS mobility = 2.41×10^{-8}, cacodylate mobility = 2.31×10^{-8} M^2/V sec.

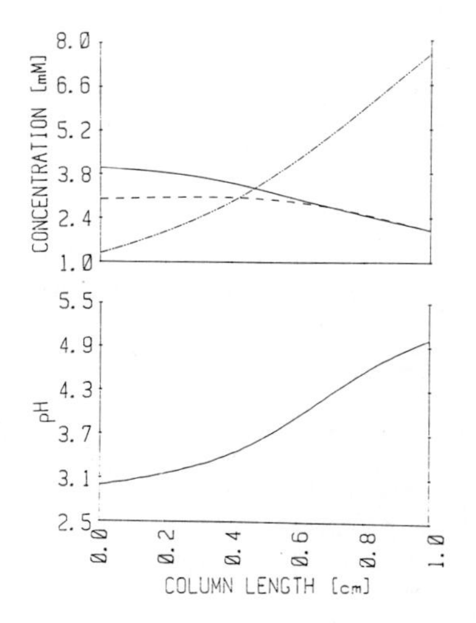

Fig. 3 Computer predicted steady state profiles formed by a 3 component system. Anolyte composition: 4 mM acid A (solid line, pKa = 3), 3 mM acid B (dashed line, pKa = 4), 1.29 mM base (broken line, pKa = 5). Catholyte composition: 2 mM acid A, 2 mM acid B, 7.58 mM base. Current = 0.1 A/M^2. All mobilities = 3.0×10^{-8} M^2/V-sec.

4 DISCUSSION

When neutral membranes are used to isolate electrolyte reservoirs of constant composition from an electrophoresis column, a constant current will produce steady state concentration profiles regardless of the number of components present or the pH range covered. The utility of this method in laboratory experiments is limited by the lack of truly neutral membranes (2). Any charge which is present will have two deleterious effects. The first is selective transport of the ion of opposite charge and retardation of the ion of like charge. This will create local pH variations, initially at the membrane surface (2) which propagate into the column. The second problem is electroosmotic flow. Rilbe has calculated the effects of electroosmosis upon the gradients formed in his rheoelectrolysis device (5) in an attempt to explain the discrepancies between his theoretical predictions and experimental data. He has shown that such flows will severely skew the gradients formed. It is also true however, that the current has an effect on the gradients formed (Fig. 2). The theory of rheoelectrolysis does not predict this, in part because the effect of the solvent ions is neglected.

We have used a pH gradient formed with one weak acid and one weak base to separate 2 human hemoglobins in density stabilized free solution (6). It has been suggested that such a viscosity gradient would prove unworkable because of the effect on transport numbers and diffusion coefficients (2), however our gradients were stable for at least 22 hours. There has also been a report of this concept having been used successfully in gels (7). The technique in free solution is limited to 2 components and therefore must be employed in the neutral pH region.

5 REFERENCES

(1) H. Rilbe, Electrophoresis 2 (1981) 261-272.

(2) M. Jonsson, S. Fredriksson, Electrophoresis 2 (1981) 193-202.

(3) A. J. P. Martin, F. Hampson, J. Chromatogr. 159 (1978) 101-110.

(4) M. Bier, O. Palusinski, R. A. Mosher and D. A. Saville, Science 219 (1983) 1281-1287.

(5) H. Rilbe, Electrophoresis 3 (1982) 332-336.

(6) M. Bier, R. A. Mosher, W. Thormann and A. Graham, Electrophoresis '83 H. Hirai, Ed., de Gruyter, Berlin 1984, pp. 99-107.

(7) K. Shimao, Electrophoresis '83 Tokyo, Japan May 1983 (in press).

INVESTIGATION OF ALTERNATIVE GEL MEDIA AND DENATURANTS AND A COMPARISON OF BUFFER FOCUSING WITH CARRIER AMPHOLYTES FOR USE IN THE FIRST DIMENSION OF 2D-PAGE

Arthur H.M. Burghes, Ketan Patel and Michael J. Dunn

Jerry Lewis Muscle Research Centre, Department of Paediatrics and Neonatal Medicine, Royal Postgraduate Medical School, DuCane Road, London W12 OHS, U.K.

1 INTRODUCTION

There are certain technical limitations inherent in the technique of two-dimensional gel electrophoresis (2D-PAGE). This is particularly true of the first, isoelectric focusing (IEF) dimension, where, for example, the solubility of the sample is of great importance. Also the breakdown of urea with the production of cyanate is a great inconvenience as it precludes storage of gels except at very low temperatures. Acrylamide can hydrolyse at high alkaline pH resulting in the formation of carboxyl groups and electroendosmosis. Acrylamide is also not compatible with a wide range of hydrophobic, organic environments which may be more powerful solubilising agents and be more convenient to use than urea. Lastly, it is possible that carrier ampholytes interact with proteins even in the presence of 8M urea (1), causing separation artefacts and, perhaps more importantly, they suffer from batch variability. We have, therefore, investigated some alternative denaturants and detergents for incorporation into IEF gels, and also a modified electrophoresis medium that is compatible with hydrophobic, organic environments. In addition we have compared a buffer focusing technique and focusing using conventional carrier ampholytes.

2 ALTERNATIVE GEL MEDIUM

Polyacrylamide is an excellent anticonvective medium, however two disadvantages that it has are its incompatibility with organic environments and its susceptibility of the amide to alkaline hydrolysis (2). While this work was in progress, a report appeared describing an alternative gel medium which could be mixed with acrylamide (3). Modified acrylamides have been used in industrial applications and we have used N'-methylacrylamide (MA), N',N'-dimethylacrylamide (DMA), dihydroxyacetone-acrylamide (DHA) in our tests. Both MA and DMA gave acceptable gels after purification of the monomer, but DHA gels were opaque and cloudy. Good focusing patterns were obtained when DMA was substituted for acrylamide on a molar basis in gels containing 8M urea and the zwitterionic detergent CHAPS (3-[(3-cholamidopropyl)-dimethylammonio]-1-propane sulphonate). It was thought that DMA might be more stable to alkaline hydrolysis. Indeed, unlike polyacrylamide gels, DMA gels do not appear to swell when placed in NaOH. However, in IEF using DMA gels, the pH gradient was appreciably expanded at the acidic end. The reason for this is not clear. We found that MA gels can also be used as a medium for IEF in the presence of 8M urea. In addition, a 7.5% DMA gel was found to be compatible with 7M dimethylurea and 50% dimethylformamide.

3 ALTERNATIVE SOLVENTS

There are a wide variety of denaturants potentially available, but only a limited number of these have been found to be effective. We have investigated some alternative compounds. Dimethyl formamide (DMF), tetramethylene sulphone, N,N-dimethylethyleneurea (DMEU) and tetramethylurea (TMU) were found to precipitate at least some proteins. All of these compounds have a lower dielectric constant than water. N-methyl-formamide (MF), dimethylurea (DMU) and ethyleneurea (EU) were not found to result in such precipitation. DMU could be incorporated into a DMA gel, whereas polyacrylamide gels were cloudy, but such gels did not polymerise at a DMA concentration below 7.5%. MF or EU could be incorporated into either polyacrylamide or DMA gels, but using conventional bis-acrylamide concentrations gels containing EU did not polymerise unless the gel concentration was greater than 12%. By increasing the bis-acrylamide concentration, weaker gels could be successfully cast. A 5% gel with 50% MF was transparent but very soft and spongy. More extensive studies of these reagents are required, but it appears that a high dielectric constant is required to maintain some proteins in solution. In addition, it appears difficult to cast weak gels in some of the potentially useful reagents with a high dielectric constant and in the presence of high concentrations of organic components.

4 AMPHOLYTES AND BUFFER FOCUSING

We have examined the recently reported (4) 47-component buffer mixture (a 2x concentrated sample of this buffer was the generous gift of Dr. C.B. Cuono) for its suitability for IEF in the presence of 8M urea and CHAPS as the first dimension in 2D-PAGE. A pattern of spots was obtained using this buffer mixture in the first, IEF dimension. However, these spots appeared in vertical lines with large gaps between them. We therefore examined the IEF dimension in more detail.

It was found that the IEF band pattern of [^{35}S]-methionine-labelled skin fibroblast proteins using buffer focusing was not as complex as that obtained using carrier ampholytes. Rather than being distributed across the whole gel, the protein bands appeared to be clustered into three main regions. A buffer focusing IEF gel containing 8M urea, CHAPS and a low concentration of ampholyte was run. When the gel was placed in TCA, the resulting precipitates of ampholyte-detergent complexes were only observed in the three regions where the proteins were located. Increased separation of the proteins in these regions was noted when ampholyte was included in the buffer focusing gels. A "diagonal" gel technique was performed using Pharmalyte pH 5-8 in the first dimension followed by a second dimension buffer focusing gel. The expected diagonal distribution of protein was not observed.

Instead, the proteins were found to lie on a horizontal line at the same position at which ampholyte-detergent complexes were precipitated by TCA.

5 CONCLUSIONS

An alternative gel medium would be very useful for 2D-PAGE, provided it showed low restrictivity, resistance to alkaline hydrolysis, and compatibility with a variety of solvents. Some of the solvents that are most suitable have a higher dielectric constant which appears to make them compatible with acrylamide. However, difficulties still remain with their polymerization into the gel, so that their full potential for increasing solubility cannot be adequately tested. Although it may be useful in certain circumstances, the 47-component buffer mixture which we have tested does not appear to be useful for the first IEF dimension in 2D-PAGE.

6 ACKNOWLEDGEMENTS

We are grateful to Dr. C.B. Cuono for the generous gift of the sample of twice-concentrated 47-component buffer mixture. We thank Mrs. C. Trand for skillfully typing the manuscript. Financial support from the Medical Research Council and the Muscular Dystrophy Group of Great Britain is acknowledged.

7 REFERENCES

(1) G.P. Vlasuk, F.G. Wolz, Anal. Biochem. 105 (1980) 112-120.

(2) P.G. Righetti, G.J. Macelloni, J. Biochem. Biophys. Methods 5 (1982) 1-15.

(3) G. Artoni, E. Gianazza, M. Zanoni, C. Gelfi, M.C. Tazi, C. Barazzi, P. Ferroti, P.G. Righetti, Anal. Biochem. 137 (1984) 420-428.

(4) C.B. Cuono, G.A. Chapo, Electrophoresis 3 (1982) 65-75.

PREPARATIVE ASPECTS OF IMMOBILIZED pH GRADIENTS

Cecilia Gelfi, Patrizia Casero and Pier Giorgio Righetti

Chair of Biochemistry, Faculty of Pharmacy and Department of Biomedical Sciences and Technology, University of Milano, Via Celoria 2, Milano 20133, Italy

The physico-chemical parameters of preparative runs in immobilized pH gradients (IPG) have been optimized. The load ability a) increases with ionic strength to level off between 20 to 30 mM buffering Immobiline; b) increases linearly with gel thickness with no apparent limit (due to joule effects, a practical 5 mm limit is suggested); c) increases with decreasing pH gradient width (J. Biochem. Biophys. Methods 8 (1983) 157-172). An equation has been derived linking the maximum load in a single zone to the pI distance (ΔpI) with the nearest contaminant, to the gel cross-sectional area and to the slope of the pH gradient. It is seen that very shallow pH gradients (e.g. 0.02 pH units/cm) allow extremely high protein loads (up to 80 mg/cm^2) while still retaining a resolution better than ΔpI = 0.01. Conversely, broad pH gradients (e.g. 0.2 pH units/cm) allow a resolution of only ΔpI=0.1 with a protein load of less than 40 mg/cm^2 (J. Biochem. Biophys. Methods 8 (1983) 135-155).

Conventional Immobiline gels are run in 5%T polyacrylamide matrices, containing an average of 10 mM buffering group: in this system, it is impossible to load more than 40 mg protein/ml gel volume. We have discovered that this "solubility limit" is function of %T: the load ability increases linearly by lowering the matrix content from 5% to 3%T; below 3%T, in very soft gels, it increases exponentially up to 90 mg protein/ml gel volume in 2.7%T gels (J. Biochem. Biophys. Methods 9 (1984) in press). This phenomenon has been interpreted as a competition for the available water between the two hydrophilic polymers, the polyacrylamide matrix and the protein "invading" it.

An electrophoretic system has been described for retrieval of purified protein bands from Immobiline matrices. The gel strip with the focused protein zone is embedded in low-gelling agarose and electrophoretically collected into a 2 cm wide layer of hydroxyapatite (HA-Ultrogel, crystals of calcium phosphate coated with a skin of agarose). The HA beads are then scooped up in the barrel of a syringe and the protein eluted with 6x7 ml washings of 0.2 M phosphate buffer, pH 6.8. However, the HA beads system is not satisfactory with uncolored proteins, as they could travel the entire length of the Ultrogel layer and be lost in the surrounding agarose bed. A new system will be described, based on the absorption of anionic proteins into DEAE-Trisacryl and of cationic species into CM-Trisacryl.
Supported by CNR, progetto Finalizzato "Chimica Fine e Secondaria".

TWO-DIMENSIONAL ANALYSIS OF HUMAN SERUM WITH IMMOBILIZED pH GRADIENTS

Elisabetta Gianazza and Pier Giorgio Righetti

Faculty of Pharmacy and Department of Biomedical Sciences and Technologies
University of Milano - via Giovanni Celoria 2 - I-20133 Milano - Italy

Reproducibility is the major concern when the results of a large number of experiments are to be compared - mainly so if several parameters are to be evaluated by automatic procedures. This is for instance the case with the two dimensional (2-D) electrophoretic analysis of biological fluids by isoelectric focusing (IEF) followed by sodium dodecyl sulfate polyacrylamide gel electrophoresis (SDS-PAGE) at right angle (a comprehensive review in 1). This technique has been proposed as the most direct approach for all situations where an overall view on the protein composition of a complex sample is required (2). It enables one to survey variability of genetic constitution and expression, in such fields as genetics, mutagenesis, embriology, endocrinology, pathology and clinical chemistry.

Thus far, a serious inconvenience encountered when utilizing these methodologies has been the instability of the pH gradient established during the IEF step by electric trasport of carrier ampholytes (3). It is then hardly feasible to drive to their equilibrium position slow-migrating, high Mr proteins, and alkaline species are often insufficiently resolved as a consequence of the cathodic drift of the gradient as a whole. This problem is caused by the incorporation of fixed negative charges into the gel matrix during the polymerization step and by the higher cationic as compared to the anionic mobility of isoprotic carrier ampholytes.

Immobilized pH gradients (IPGs) (4) offer definite advantages in this respect. They allow to prepare gels for IEF whose pH intervals are known with certainty. Their courses are linear between the stated extremes, with deviations not exceeding 2% of the pH gradient span (5). Additional parameters of the gradient - buffering power and ionic strength - can be computed (6) and their average values and deviations may be altered to fit specific requirements. The grafted pH gradients are indefinitely stable with time, to the passage of the current (even at very high field strengths, e.g.1000 V/cm) and to the presence of (non-buffering) salts in the sample solution (4). Any pH interval in the 4-10 range (spanning between 0.1 (4) and 6 pH units (5)) may be covered with IPGs. Extended gradients are of more general interest if they are to be used as first step of 2-D separations. These require the use of several buffering species, which may be mixed according to one of three alternative protocols, as described in (5-7), and summarized in the review by Righetti et al. in this book.

'In order to polymerize IPGs with the highest reproducibility, the accurate mixing of the various Immobiline buffers is of the utmost importance. The experimental approach we have described in (7) requires the preparation of a single mixture containing all the buffering species. This is then subdivided into two aliquots, that are titrated to the limiting pHs of the desired interval with non-buffering (strongly acidic and strongly basic) Immobilines and linearly combined with a two-chamber gradient mixer. This approach allows to reduce to a minimum the number of volumetric measurements and to have a single reference for both limiting solutions. Moreover, such buffer mixtures may be mixed in large batches and aliquots stored for use in several independent experiments. The precision of each buffer addition may be checked step by step through the correctness of the pH in the solution (5). A stack of gel slabs may then be polymerized at once, to allow for both, a sample to sample and a run to run reproducibility. The evenness of the gradient formation may be checked photometrically (4) if a dye, like bromophenol blue, is added to one of the mixing chambers. When running IPG slabs, any irregularity in the sample migration would become immediately evident, as the bands of the most abundant proteins appear as refractile ridges across the gel (4).

For 2-D analysis, it is customary to perform the first step in presence of denaturing/dissociating concentrations of urea. This allows to maximize the number of detectable spots. In the case of serum, it also clears from the overwhelming presence of albumin the pI region around 5, where the majority of serum proteins are isoelectric. Albumin pI, in fact, shifts, under denaturing conditions, by more than 1 pH unit toward alkaline values. The addition of urea to the IEF medium also improves the protein transfer from the first- to the second-dimension gel and abolishes protein trailing. The length of the IPG strip needs to fit the width of the SDS-slab, to avoid slanted migration; its width, not to exceed 5 mm, to allow band stacking. The IEF strip is equilibrated for 20 minutes in 25 mM Tris/Glycine buffer, pH 8.6, containing 3% SDS and 2% 2-mercaptoethanol. It is then embedded onto the SDS slab with 1% agarose in the same buffer at 60*C. The two gels have to stay in close contact, and any excess agarose should be squeezed from the gap between them, to avoid severe lateral diffusion and spot merging.

Figure 1 shows the results of 2-D serum fractionation, using, for the first dimension, a 4-7 IPG. Except for albumin, no major streaking or trailing of the protein spots is evident. No background staining

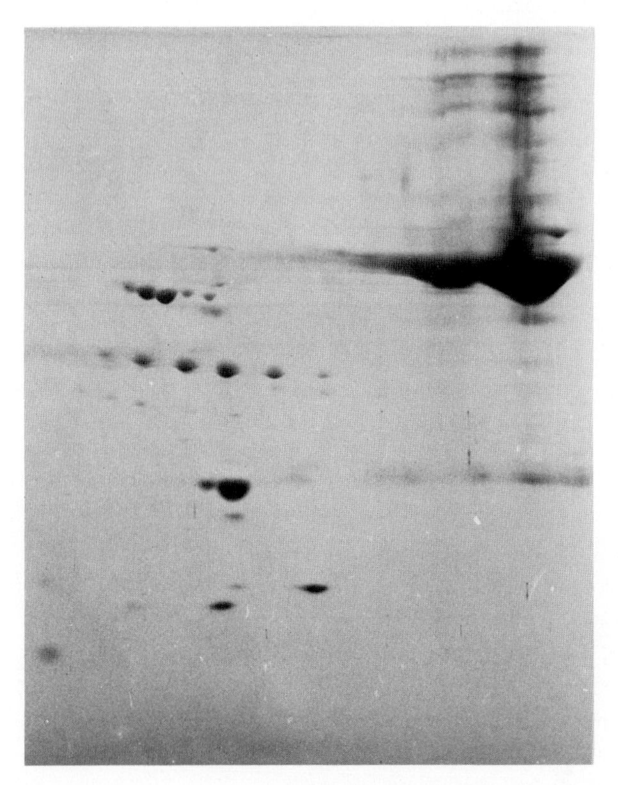

Figure 1 - Serum fractionation by IEF on immobilized pH gradients-SDS electrophoresis. Experimental: an IPG covering, in presence of urea, the pH range 4-7 was polymerized according to the formulation in (8). The gel size was 10x15x0.1 cm; the slab was supported on reactive polyester foils (GelBond PAG). After 2x1 hr washing in distilled water, the gels were dried, then reswollen in presence of urea. 7.5 uL of human serum, made 8 M in urea and 2% in 2-mercaptoethanol, were applied near the cathode without prerunning. The sample was run overnigth at 2000 V. The gel was equilibrated for 20 min in electrode buffer added with 3% SDS and 2% 2-mercaptoethanol. Strips 5 mm wide were then embedded on the SDS-slab with 1% agarose in electrode buffer. For the SDS-gel, a discontinuous buffer system, from Laemli, U.K., Nature 277 (1970) 680-682, was used. The stacking gel was 5% T, the running gel a linear polyacrylamide concentration gradient 5-15% T. The run lasted 5 hrs at 30 mA / gel. The protein pattern after SDS-PAGE was directly stained in 0.2% Coomassie Blue in 30% ethanol-10% acetic acid.

occurs in the high pI-low Mr region, in absence of interfering carrier ampholytes. The relative migration of components of different molecular mass is the same as if they were loaded in solution. Notwithstanding the presence of a charged matrix, no distortion appears to be caused by electroendoosmotic flow or by ionic interaction between protein and supporting IPG gel.

Acknowledgements

Supported by Consiglio Nazionale delle Ricerche, Progetto Finalizzato "Salute dell'uomo" Sottoprogetto Meccanismi di invecchiamento.

References

(1) Dunn,M. and Burghes,A.H.M., Electrophoresis 4 (1983) 97-116 and 173-189

(2) Clinical Chemistry 28 (1982) 737-1092

(3) Rilbe,H., in: "Electrofocusing and isotachophoresis" (Radola B.J. and Graesslin,D. eds.) W.deGruyter, Berlin 1977, pp.35-50

(4) Bjellqvist,B., Ek,K., Righetti,P.G., Gianazza,E., Görg,A., Westermeier,R. and Postel,W., J.Biochem.Biophys.Methods 6 (1982) 317-339

(5) Gianazza,E., Celentano,F., Bjellqvist,B. and Righetti,P.G., Electrophoresis 5 (1984) 88-97

(6) Dossi,G., Celentano,F., Gianazza,E. and Righetti,P.G., J.Biochem.Biophys. Methods 7 (1983) 123-142

(7) Gianazza,E., Dossi,G., Celentano,F. and Righetti,P.G., J.Biochem.Biophys. Methods 8 (1983) 109-133

(8) Gianazza,E., Frigerio,A., Tagliabue,A. and Righetti,P.G., Electrophoresis, in press

ELECTROFOCUSSING WITH IMMOBILINES OF PHOSPHORYLATED FORMS OF RIBOSOMAL PROTEIN S6

Keith L. Manchester, Joy E. Manchester

Department of Biochemistry, University of the Witwatersrand, Johannesburg 2001, South Africa

1 INTRODUCTION

The eukaryotic ribosomal protein S6 undergoes reversible phosphorylation in vivo in response to a variety of stimuli (1). There appear to be multiple sites of phosphorylation and up to 5 phosphorylated derivatives can be observed on two dimensional electrophoresis on acrylamide gels (2,3). It is also possible to separate the phosphorylated S6 from the unphosphorylated form on one dimensional gels, identifying the S6 after transfer to nitrocellulose with a monoclonal antibody and peroxidase staining (4,5). This procedure has the advantage over the two dimensional method that many samples can be analysed on one gel and that much less protein, and in a much less pure state, is required for each sample. However by this procedure we have never observed more than two clear phosphorylated bands, though sometimes there is a general "fuzz" that could be indicative of multiple forms. Since it must be presumed that the different phosphorylated species have differing pI's - hence their different relative retardations in the two dimensional gels, it should be possible to separate the different forms from each other by electrofocussing. Because of the high resolution claimed for immobiline pH gradients (6), their use for this purpose has been investigated.

2 METHODS

Immobiline-containing acrylamide gels covering the pH range 9-10 were cast following the procedures described in the maker's instructions (7). Gradient gels of a thickness of 0.4 mm and 11 x 11 cm were poured between two glass plates, one washed with Repel-Silane and the other with Bind-Silane. After polymerisation the plates were prized apart leaving the gel on one surface. The plate bearing the gel was laid horizontal and the samples applied to the gel with a Pipetman and allowed to soak in for 10 or so minutes. Cytochrome c, pI $\approx$ 10, was used as a visual indicator. Electrophoresis limited to 2 watts was applied for a number of hours, the voltage rising to ≈ 2 000 volts. Staining with Coomassie blue indicated the ultimate position of the ribosomal proteins. In order to detect S6 specifically proteins in the gel were transferred to nitrocellulose by laying a sheet on the gel, covering it with a quantity of tissue paper and a 3 kg weight. After an hour or so the nitrocellulose was removed and developed for visualisation of S6 as described previously (4,5).

3 RESULTS

There do not appear to be published values for the pI's of ribosomal proteins. Their basicity, pI ≈ 9.5-10.5, renders them at the extreme limit of potential electrofocussing with Immobilines and it was necessary to modify the pH range used by about 0.5 units by decreasing the amount of 3.6 immobiline according to the Henderson-Hasselbalch equation. Ribosomal proteins easily precipitate and whilst some successful runs were achieved with the proteins dissolved in water, ultimately proteins and gels containing 8 M urea were used. Unexpectedly sucrose contained in the ribosomal protein preparations proved to cause serious disturbance in the gels. To date it has not proved possible to improve on the separation of the phospho forms over what can be achieved with the existing antibody method, but it is possible that a narrower pH range could produce more resolution.

4 REFERENCES

(1) J. Gordon, P. Nielsen, K.L. Manchester, H. Towbin, L. Jimenez de Asua, G. Thomas, Current Topics in Cellular Regulation 21 (1982) 88-89.

(2) A.M. Gressner, I.G. Wool, J. Biol. Chem. 249 (1974) 6917-6925.

(3) G. Thomas, M. Siegmann, A-M. Kubler, J. Gordon, L. Jimenez de Asua, Cell 19 (1980) 1015-1023.

(4) P.J. Nielsen, K.L. Manchester, H. Towbin, J. Gordon, G. Thomas, In Electrophoresis '82 (1983) 453-460.

(5) P.J. Nielsen, K.L. Manchester, H. Towbin, J. Gordon, G. Thomas, J. Biol. Chem. 257 (1982) 12316-12321.

(6) B. Bjellqvist, K. Ek, P.G. Righetti, E. Gianazza, A. Görg, R. Westermeier, W. Postel, J. Biochem. Biophys. Methods 6 (1982) 317-339.

(7) B. Bjellqvist, K. Ek, LKB Application Note 321 (1982) 1-13.

HETEROGENEITY OF MURINE MONOCLONAL ANTIBODIES AS EXAMINED BY ISOELECTRIC FOCUSSING ON IMMOBILISED pH GRADIENTS

E.S. Bos, A.A. van der Doelen, E. van der Struik, E.W. Bergink, A.H.W.M. Schuurs, Organon Scientific Development Group, P.O.Box 20, Oss, The Netherlands

As was found by Williamson and collaborators IgG produced by myeloma cell lines showed a microheterogeneity in IEF (1). A similar heterogeneity thought to be due to a differential loss of labile amido groups and to a variable carbohydrate composition was observed with monoclonal antibodies (MCAs) produced by hybridoma technology (2).
The studies summarised below were performed in order to gain a more precise insight into the origin of this phenomenon.

MCAs directed against various antigens viz. human chorionic gonadotrophin (hCG), human prolactin, Hepatitis B surface antigen and Rubella antigen were isolated from ascitic fluid or cell culture supernatant by salt fractionation and gel filtration. They were over 95% pure as shown by high performance size exclusion chromatography and SDS-polyacrylamide gel electrophoresis. When examined by IEF on immobilised pH gradients the MCAs showed a more extensive heterogeneity than was expected from classical IEF experiments: usually 10-25 bands distributed over a range of 0,5-1,0 pH unit could be detected. One of the (anti-hCG) MCAs was investigated in more detail. Western blotting of the polyacrylamide gel, which had been peeled from the polyester support after focussing, and a subsequent immunochemical analysis with peroxidase-labelled antigen revealed immunoreactivity in each Coomassie-stained band. Quantitation of the antigen-binding capacity in enzyme-immunoassay or receptor-binding inhibition assay suggested differences in specific activity between the individual components.

REFERENCES

1. A.R. Williamson in D.M. Weir (Ed), Handbook of Experimental Immunology, Vol. I, Blackwell, Oxford, 1974, 9.1.-9.31 .
2. M. Suzan et al. Molec. Immunol. 19 (1982) 1051-1062.

SEPARATION OF SOME POLYMORPHIC PROTEIN SYSTEMS OF FORENSIC SIGNIFICANCE BY: I ISOELECTRIC FOCUSING WITH SEPARATORS

Peter Gill, Sara A Westwood, J. G. Sutton

Central Research Establishment, Home Office Forensic Science Service, Aldermaston, Reading, Berkshire, RG7 4PN, U.K.

1 INTRODUCTION

The use of zwitterionic buffers or separators mixed with carrier ampholytes in isoelectric focusing gels (separator-IEF) provides a simple method of producing narrow pH gradients for the separation of proteins. Separator-IEF has been used for the analysis of alpha-1 antitrypsin phenotypes (1) and group-specific component (Gc) (2). We report here the use of separators to identify phenotypes of phosphoglucomutase (PGM1), including some rare variants; the separation of seminal acid phosphatase (SAP) from vaginal acid phosphatase (VAP); the separation of esterase D (EsD) phenotypes and transferrin (Tf) phenotypes. Each enzyme system is separated on a gradient incorporating different buffer/carrier ampholyte mixtures.

2 MATERIALS AND METHODS

2.1 Carrier Ampholytes and Separators.

LKB Ampholines were used and the following separators were evaluated:

(1) N-(2-Hydroxyethyl)piperazine-N'2-ethanesulphonic acid (HEPES) pKa = 7.5

(2) N-(2-Hydroxyethyl)piperazine-N'3-propanesulphonic acid (EPPS) pKa = 8.0

2.2 Preparation of polyacrylamide gels and isoelectric focusing

Both ultra-thin and 1 mm thick gels were used. The basic procedure is described by Gill and Sutton (3). The following mixture was prepared:

7 ml acrylamide (29.1% w/v); 7 ml bis-acrylamide (0.9% w/v); either 5 ml glycerol (87% w/v) or 5 g sucrose; 2 ml Ampholine; 1 g separator; made up to 40 ml with distilled water.

The total run-time was 3 hours at 10 W for 1 mm thick gels whereas ultra-thin gels were run at 1.0 W for 30 minutes and 4 W for 2.5 hours.

Improved resolution has been obtained for the following enzymes:

1) PGM1: 1 g EPPS + 2 ml pH 5-7 LKB Ampholine.
2) SAP/VAP: 0.5g ACES + 0.5 g HEPES + 2 ml pH 4-6 LKB Ampholine.
3) EsD: 1 g HEPES + 1 ml pH 5-7 + 1 ml pH 4-6 LKB Ampholine.
4) Tf: 0.7 g HEPES + 0.3 g EPPS + 2 ml pH 5-7 LKB Ampholine.

3 pH GRADIENT CHARACTERISTICS

pH gradients generated by separator-IEF are given in Fig. 1. Considerable flattening of pH gradients was achieved compared with control pH 5-7 or pH 4-6 Ampholine gradients. Gradients characteristically showed greatest flattening in the cathodal two thirds of the gel (Fig. 1). Specific gradients could be constructed by mixing different separators and ampholytes producing narrow pH gradients with a flexibility which may approach that of using LKB Immobilines.

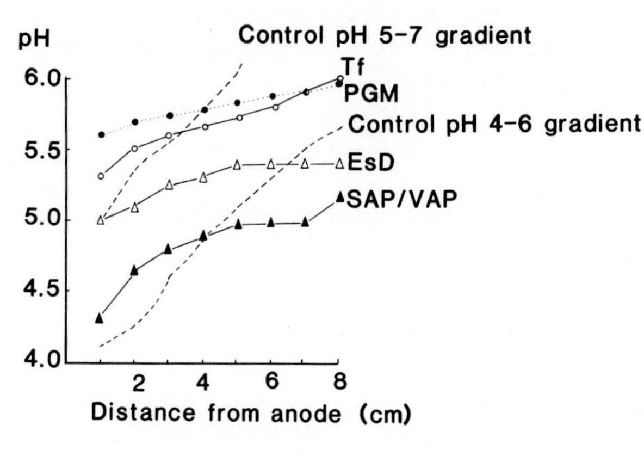

Fig. 1. pH gradients generated to separate variants in 4 protein systems - Tf, PGM_1, EsD and SAP/VAP.

4 PGM1 PHENOTYPING

The pH gradient range for PGM typing extends from pH 5-6 to pH 5.9. If the system was used on ultra-thin gels, it was observed that sensitivity to low enzyme activity was increased. This system was preferable to an Immobiline gel since enzyme activity tended to be much lower in the latter, while the separation obtained was just as good. This was an important consideration for forensic science because it is often necessary to analyse blood stains having low enzyme activity.

The system efficiently separated the common 1+ (Bark's notation (4)) or a1 (Dykes notation (5)) variant (pI 5.98) from the rare a8 (pI 5.9) and a9 (pI 5.89) variants. In fact it was found that when conventional ultra-thin gels were used, the separation between a1, a8 and a9 variants was not sufficient for confident identification. Other rare variants separated by the system included the rare anodal 7+ phenotype (pI 5.67). The rare cathodal variants a10 (pI 6.22); 8 (pI 6.36); 6 (pI 6.14) and a6 (pI 6.17) focused at the same position approximately 1 cm from the cathodal wick because their pI's were too high for this particular gel. It was observed that if gels were run at temperatures of 5°C then the migration rate was reduced compared with that observed at 10°C (Fig. 2). This resulted in a reduced spread of isoenzyme bands. Gels were always removed before full focusing had been achieved as this practice resulted in the visualisation of sharper enzyme bands (6).

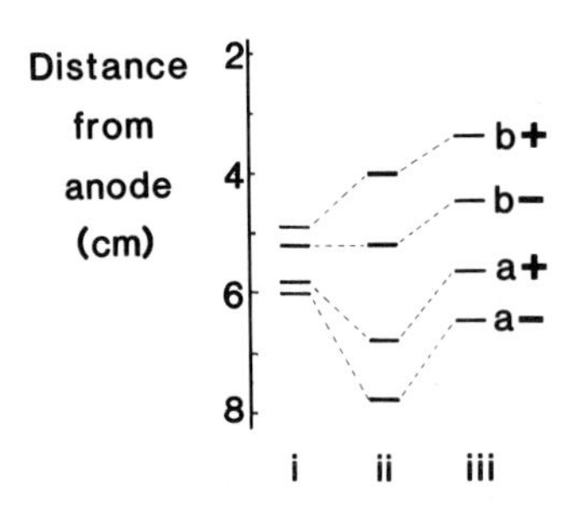

Fig. 2. Separation of PGM_1 on ultra-thin gels.
i) Conventional gel with no separators added at 10°C.
ii) Gel with 0.1M EPPS added and run at 10°C.
iii) Gel with 0.1M EPPS added and run at 5°C.

5 SEPARATION OF VAGINAL (VAP) FROM SEMINAL ACID PHOSPHATASE (SAP)

The identification of SAP is an extremely important step in establishing a charge of rape. SAP and VAP are immunologically indistinguishable but can be separated by electrophoresis (7) provided concentrations of each type are not too great. SAP is present in high concentrations in semen so the determination can carried out quantitatively using a Laurell rocket technique (8). Reliance on a quantitative technique has the disadvantage that levels of SAP could fall to within those normally recorded in VAP hence positive identification of SAP in a SAP/VAP mixture is impossible. The application of an electrofocusing technique in which SAP can be separated from VAP is described.

Both SAP and VAP produce multiple banding patterns on IEF with pI's ranging between pI 4.5-6.0. However, in the range pI 4.5-4.8, VAP is either absent or very faint. The use of separator-IEF, generating a pH gradient between pH 4.3-5.2 (Fig. 1), was used to separate the two acid phosphatase forms.

6 THE USE OF SEPARATORS FOR OTHER POLYMORPHIC PROTEINS OF FORENSIC SIGNIFICANCE

Mixtures of HEPES with pH 4-6 and pH 5-7 Ampholines produced a pH gradient of pH 5.0-5.4 which markedly improved separation of common EsD phenotypes. A HEPES/EPPS mixture produced a pH 5.3-6.0 gradient which was used for the identification of Tf C phenotypes. Reliable separation of Tf C phenotypes in blood stains was not possible because of the presence of extra sub-bands. Both systems were run using ultra-thin gels which increased sensitivity to low quantities of protein.

7 CONCLUSION

The use of ultra-narrow pH gradients for the separation of polymorphic proteins represents a significant advance for forensic science purposes. The use of separator-IEF can combine the advantages of ultra-narrow pH gradients with the increased sensitivity of the ultra-thin gel to low quantities of protein. The disadvantage is that at present precise gradients cannot be formulated by prediction. All the gradients described in this paper were discovered by trial and error.

8 REFERENCES

(1) R. R. Frants, A. W. Erikson. Hum. Heredity 28 (1978) 201-209.

(2) M. Baxter, I. White, J. Forens. Sci. Soc. 24 (1984) In press.

(3) P. Gill, J. G. Sutton. XXXII Colloquium, Protides of the Biological Fluids (1984) In press.

(4) J. E. Bark, M. J. Harris, M. Firth. J. Forens. Sci. Soc. 16 (1976) 115-120.

(5) D. D. Dykes, B.A. Copouls, H. F. Polesky. Electrophoresis 3 (1982) 165-168.

(6) G. B. Divall, M. Ismail. Forens. Sci. Int. 22 (1983) 253-263.

(7) B. G. Wraxall, E. G. Adams. Forens. Sci. 3 (1974) 57-62

(8) S. J. Baxter. Med. Sci. Law 13 (1973) 155-165.

SEPARATION OF SOME POLYMORPHIC PROTEIN SYSTEMS OF FORENSIC SIGNIFICANCE BY: II ELECTROFOCUSING IN IMMOBILIZED pH GRADIENTS.

Sara A Westwood, J.G. Sutton and Peter Gill.

Central Research Establishment, Home Office Forensic Science Service, Aldermaston, Reading, Berkshire. RG7 4PN. U.K.

1 INTRODUCTION

Electrofocusing is being used in the U.K. Forensic Science Service for typing phosphoglucomutase (PGM1) (1), erythrocyte acid phosphatase (ACP1) (2), esterase D (EsD) (3) and group-specific component (Gc) (4) from bloodstains. In an attempt to improve the resolution of these systems their behaviour in immobilized pH gradients (containing Immobilines) was evaluated. Gradients of this type have properties which suit their application to forensic science. It is possible to prepare very narrow pH gradients structured to obtain the optimal separation of isoproteins with similar pIs. The pH gradients are very stable and can tolerate variable concentrations of proteins and salts without undue disturbance. In this study we report our findings on using immobilized pH gradients for the separation of some polymorphic plasma proteins [Gc, transferrin (Tf) and alpha-1-antitrypsin (Pi)] from plasma and bloodstain extracts and some polymorphic erythrocyte enzymes (PGM1, ACP1 and EsD) from bloodstain extracts and lysates of erythrocytes.

2 MATERIALS AND METHODS

Immobilized pH gradients were prepared as described by Bjellqvist and Ek (5) and by Westwood and co-workers (6,7). Gradients used in this study are given in Table 1. The pH end-points for the quoted gradients were measured at room temperature (18-20°C) before making the gels and any adjustments in the end-points were made with the appropriate stock Immobiline solutions.

It was found that in order to preserve enzyme activity the gels had to be thoroughly washed and dried before use. Also low voltages were initially applied to the gels followed by higher voltages in order to separate the isoenzymes in as short a time as possible (ideally within 4 hours). Samples had to be applied anodally to preformed slots for PGM1 and ACP1 isoenzymes, while EsD isoenzymes could be separated after sample application on the surface or in slots at the anode.

Electrofocusing conditions for separating the isoenzymes are given in Table 2.

Table 1. Summary of pH gradients used in this study

Protein System	pH Gradient	Basic Solution (ml)		Acidic Solution (ml)	
PGM 1	5.8-6.8	pK6.2	0.350	pK6.2	0.350
		pK3.6	0.080	pK3.6	0.275
ACP 1	5.5-7.6	pK7.0	0.350	pK6.2	0.350
		pK3.6	0.080	pK3.6	0.300
EsD	4.9-5.85	pK4.6	0.380	pK4.6	0.560
		pK6.2	0.500	pK6.2	0.360
Gc	4.8-5.3	pK4.6	0.590	pK4.6	0.440
		pK6.2	0.500	pK6.2	0.260
Tf	5.1-5.85	pK4.6	0.380	pK4.6	0.500
		pK6.2	0.500	pK6.2	0.410
Pi (M subtypes)	4.5-4.7	pK4.6	0.750	pK4.6	0.750
		pK6.2	0.440	pK6.2	0.310
(M,S & Z sub-types)	4.5-5.05	pK4.6	0.750	pK4.6	0.750
		pk6.2	add to make pH5.05	pK6.2	0.310

Table 2. Electrofocusing conditions for separating erythrocyte enzymes.

Enzyme	Electrical Conditions (Maximum settings)			Time (min)	Total Time (hrs)
PGM 1	1000V	5mA	5W	10	
	2000V	5mA	5W	30	2.16
	3500V	5mA	5W	90	
ACP 1	800V	25mA	5W	30	
	1500V	25mA	5W	180	3.5
EsD	500V	20mA	5W	30	
	3000V	20mA	7W	150	3.0

Separation of the common phenotypes of Gc, Tf and Pi was achieved without washing or pre-running the Immobiline gels. Gc and PiM, S and Z subtypes could be resolved after 4 hours focusing at 2000V, 20mA, 5W maximum settings. The TfC subtypes were separated after overnight focusing at 1000V, 20mA, 5W maximum settings. Samples were applied to preformed cathodal slots when plasma proteins were analysed.

3 RESULTS AND DISCUSSION

3.1 Red Blood Cell Enzymes

The primary typing bands, a+, a-, b+ and b-, produced by the 4 common alleles of the PGM1 locus were separated on immobilized pH gradients (8). Typing of bloodstains greater than 2 months old was only moderately successful. In all instances a decrease in PGM1 activity was observed compared with the activity recorded after electrofocusing in ampholyte pH gradients. At present an explanation cannot be provided for this, although it is possible that once the isoenzymes have reached their pIs, in such a narrow and stable pH gradient, they become unstable and lose activity as a result of enzyme precipitation in conditions of low conductivity.

The six common ACP1 isoenzymes could be separated on immobilized pH gradients provided that electrofocusing times were kept to a minimum (6). ACP1 activities could be detected in bloodstains up to 7 weeks old. The profile of the isoenzymes was different from that seen after electrofocusing in ampholyte pH gradients (2). Only one band of activity was seen in the a1, a2 region of the gel for the A isoenzyme and a CB phenotype did not express more activity in the c1+b1 region than in the c2+b2 region of the gel.

The 2-1 and 1 phenotypes of EsD from red blood cell lysates were widely separated on immobilized pH gradients. The degree of separation was greater than that achieved with ampholyte gels containing separators (see first communication).

3.2 Plasma Proteins

The results that were obtained from Gc, TfC, and Pi M,S and Z subtypes in human plasma were similar to those reported by Cleve et al (9) and Gorg et al (10,11) for human sera. The Gc 2, 1S and 1F protein bands could be clearly resolved in bloodstains up to 7 months old after their identification by immunofixation (7). Their resolution was much greater than that achieved by focusing methods employing ampholytes (4) or ampholytes with separators (12), and represents a considerable advance in the potential use of Gc as a marker in forensic science.

TfC subtypes do not appear to be stable in bloodstains and this could limit the usefulness of Tf, as a polymorphic marker, to criminal cases where sera or plasma are available for testing.

Whole blood and bloodstains stored at -20°C had Pi protein bands which were detectable on immobilized pH gradients but reliable typing of Pi in bloodstains stored at room temperature could not be made. Like Tf, Pi appears to have a role in forensic science casework where sera or plasma are available. For general screening of the protein products of the Pi M,S and Z alleles the pH gradient of pH4.5-5.05 is recommended.

4 REFERENCES

(1) J. E. Bark, M. J. Harris and M. Firth, J. Forensic Sci. Soc. 16 (1976) 115-120.

(2) T. Randall, W. A. Harland and J. W. Thorpe, Med. Sci. Law 20 (1980) 43-47.

(3) G. Horscroft and J. G. Sutton, J. Forensic Sci. Soc. 23 (1983) 139-142.

(4) M. Baxter, T. W. Randall and J. W. Thorpe, J. Forensic Sci. Soc. 22 (1982) 367-371.

(5) B. Bjellqvist and K. Ek, LKB Application Note No 321 (1982).

(6) S. A. Westwood and J. G. Sutton, Electrophoresis (1984) in press.

(7) S. A. Westwood and J. G. Sutton and D. J. Werrett, J. Forensic Sci. Soc. (1984) in press.

(8) J. G. Sutton and S. A. Westwood, Electrophoresis (1984) in press.

(9) H. Cleve, W Patutschnick, W. Postel, J. Weser and A. Gorg, Electrophoresis 3 (1982) 342-345.

(10) A. Gorg, W. Postel, J. Weser, S. Weidinger, W. Patutschnick and H. Cleve, Electrophoresis 4 (1983) 153-157.

(11) A. Gorg, J. Weser, R. Westermeier, W. Postel, S Weidinger, W. Patutschnick and H. Cleve, Hum. Genet. 64 (1983) 222-226.

(12) M. Baxter, I. White, J. Forensic Sci. Soc. (1984) in press.

PURIFICATION OF CHARGED ISOMERS OF HUMAN GROWTH HORMONE BY ELECTROFOCUSING IN IMMOBILIZED pH GRADIENTS

B. Skoog (1), B. Sahlin (2) and C. Blanche (2)

(1) KabiVitrum AB, S-112 87 Stockholm, Sweden
(2) LKB-Produkter AB, S-161 26 Bromma, Sweden

Pituitary human growth hormone (hGH) preparations for clinical use are all heterogeneous with respect to charge, mainly due to contamination by deamidated forms. Isohormones of hGH can also be found in biosynthetic hGh preparations. The preparation and purification of hGH isohormones is of great importance in studies of hormone action. Results from such studies can be used as a guideline for biosynthetic hHG production. In this preliminary study we have evaluated the use of preparative isoelectric focusing in immobilized pH gradients for isolation of the isohormones in hGH. Besides the fractionation of the hormone into carrier - ampholyte - free b- and c-forms, several subforms were discovered due to the high resolving power of the system.

IMMOBILINE® CANAL - ISOELECTRIC FOCUSING; A SIMPLE PREPARATIVE METHOD FOR PROTEIN RECOVERY FROM NARROW pH GRADIENT GELS

Rainer Bartels and Lothar Bock

Borstel Research Institute, D-2061 Borstel, FRG

1 INTRODUCTION

Carrier-ampholyte-based focusing in granulated gels is a well established method to purify proteins efficiently in a preparative scale (1). Advantages and disadvantages of this technique have been discussed in many papers.

Most of the disadvantages of the carrier-ampholyte IEF can be avoided by the introduction of the polyacrylamide-based IMMOBILINE®-technique which is especially useful for electrofocusing in narrow pH gradients (2,3).

However, for preparative application the recovery of the focused proteins from the compact polyacrylamide gel is a rather laborious procedure (4).

Here we present a new convenient and simple method to avoid this complication.

IMMOBILINE Canal-Isoelectric Focusing (IC-IEF) is a technique combining the high resolution power of IMMOBILINE pH gradients and the convenient recovery of proteins from a granulated gel. This is performed by collecting the protein of choice in a specially inserted canal of IEF-SEPHADEX® by the electrofocusing procedure.

2 GENERAL

An appropriate IMMOBILINE pH gradient slab gel is cast and processed according to (2) with the following modifications:

1.) The cuvette for casting the gel is from DESAGA Corp., Germany, consisting of a glass-plate support, 19 x 14 cm and a PVC-cover supplied with a rubber sealing providing a gel thickness of 0.5 mm.
2.) Before mounting at each side in the direction of the gradient from the rear of the glass-plate a zone of about 20 mm width is scratched with the aid of a glass cutter.
3.) A preliminary focusing run is performed to select a suitable pH range within the IMMOBILINE gradient where later on the canal for protein collection has to be engraved. Aliquots of the sample are supplied at the narrow two edges of the glass-plate separated by

the scratched lines.

4.) After electrofocusing each edge of the gel supporting glass-plate is carefully broken along the scratched lines and stained for protein detection (2).

5.) By putting the developed analytical stripes back into their original positions, in the middle preparative area a pH range of interest is selected and a canal is cut out with the aid of a scalpel and a spatula.

6.) The remaining trough is filled with an IEF-SEPHADEX slurry equilibrated solely by bidest. water.

7.) The preparative sample is applied at the same position and run under identical conditions as have been used in the analytical prerun.

8.) During this focusing procedure the desired protein is collected in the IEF-SEPHADEX canal.

9.) Subsequently the SEPHADEX matrix is removed by a spatula and transferred into a suitable micro-column to elute the protein.

10.) Finally, to control the efficiency of the trial the preparative IMMOBILINE gel can be fixed and stained for the remaining protein pattern.

3 RESULTS

In Fig.1 isoelectric focusing of an ovalbumin sample is shown using an IMMOBILINE pH gradient from 4.3 to 5.3. Six canals have been prepared as indicated corresponding to pH ranges of distinct protein double bands the positions of which have been evaluated in a prerun. After focusing of the sample and removal of the SEPHADEX charges the preparative gel has been fixed and stained for a check. As can be seen the development of the protein pattern has not been disturbed by the different canals.

Fig. 2 shows the refocusing of the distinct protein zones eluted solely by water from the corresponding SEPHADEX charges. The high efficiency of the previous procedure is clearly demonstrated.

Fig.3 shows that no band distortions do occur at a ΔpH of the canal width up to 30 % of the total pH range. This is valid even if the pH gradient is interrupted by the SEPHADEX canal within the whole latitude (not shown).

Recovery of the proteins from the SEPHADEX gel has not yet been attempted, however, it should be in the same range as has been reported for conventional gel chromatography.

Finally, it should be noted that precipitations of proteins at the starting point may occur and prevent the remaining proteins to enter the gel. This may be the result of a drastically reduced ionic strength in the application trough caused by the analytical prerun.

Regardless of these difficulties it should be possible to scale-up the IC-IEF procedure from 0.5 to 5 mm thick preparative IMMOBILINE gels.

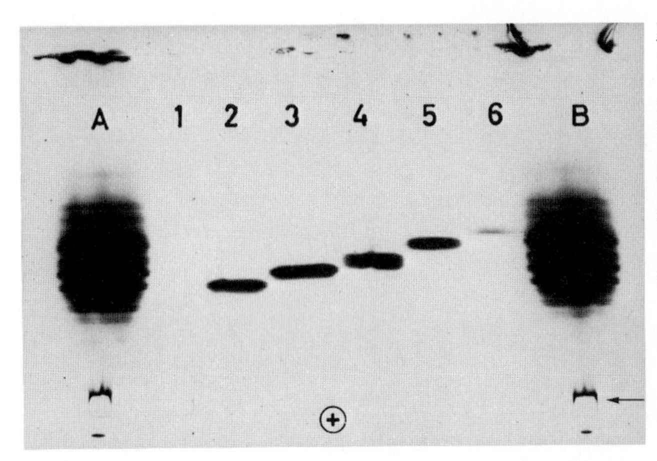

Fig.1a:

IC-IEF of ovalbumin (SERVA 11840) dissolved in water. IMMOBILINE gel: 185 x 125 x 0.5 mm, pH gradient 4.3 to 5.3; +4°C; 80 kVh, max. 5 W and 5 kV; fixing and staining, see (2).

A,B: edges for the analytical prerun

1-6: canals for the collection of proteins, filled with an aqueous slurry of IEF-SEPHADEX

←: sample application in a trough

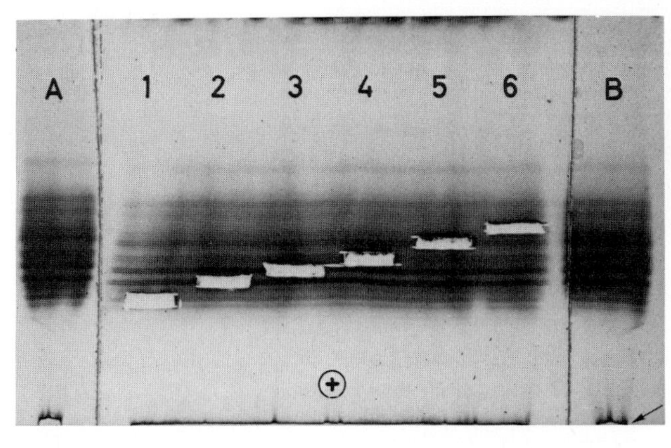

Fig.1b:

Refocusing of the six protein samples collected in the canals 1-6; the IEF-SEPHADEX from the canals was directly inserted in the troughs (←). lane A,B: control (ovalbumin); IMMOBILINE gel conditions see Fig.1a

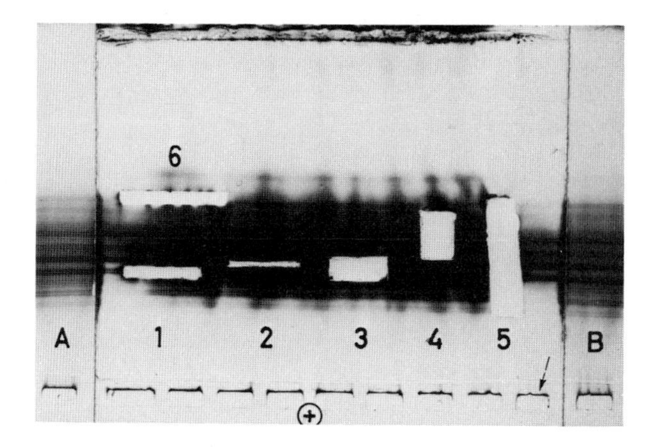

Fig.2a:

IC-IEF of ovalbumin (SERVA) in a 0.5 mm thick IMMOBILINE gel; pH gradient 4.3-5.3; lane 1-6: different canals (widths 1 - 30 mm); conditions see Fig.1a.

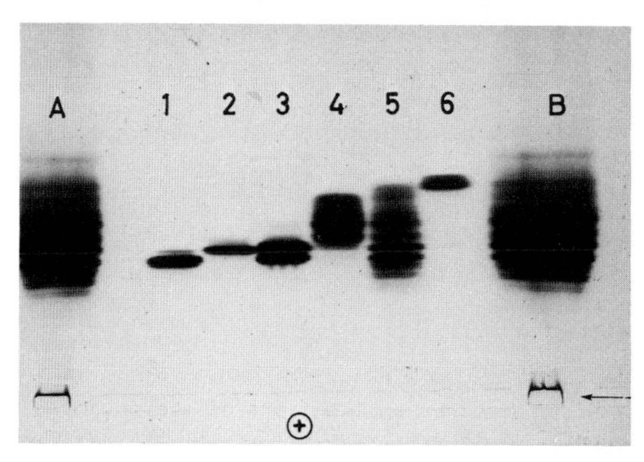

Fig.2b:

Refocusing of the six samples collected in the different canals 1-6 and ovalbumin as a control (A,B).
IMMOBILINE gel conditions see Fig.1b.

4. REFERENCES

(1) Radola, B.J., Isoelectric focusing in granulated gels. Isoelectric Focusing (Catsimpolas, N. ed.) Academic Press, New York 1976, pp. 119-171.

(2) Bjellqvist, B., Ek, K., (1982) LKB Application Note No. 321.

(3) Bjellqvist, B., Ek, K., Righetti, P.G., Gianazza, E., Görg,A., Westermeier, R. and Postel, W., J.Biochem.Biophys.Methods 6 (1982) 317-339.

(4) Preparative Electrofocusing in Immobiline pH Gradients. LKB Application Note No. 323.

ULTRATHIN ISOELECTRIC FOCUSING IN POLYACRYLAMIDE SLAB GELS AT LOW pH GRADIENTS.

Giovanni Candiano, Gian Marco Ghiggeri, Gerolamo Delfino, Giosuè Pallavicini*, Carlo Queirolo.

Hemodialysis Service, Hospital of Lavagna, Genova. *Department of Biochemistry, University of Pavia, Italy.

1 INTRODUCTION

Gradients for isoelectric focusing (IEF) in the 1 - 3 pH range, originally reported by Peterson (1), have been obtained by adding a mixture of strong acids to commercially available carrier ampholytes (2). This method has been widely used to create a gradient of pH in column apparatus, its major drawback with the slab gel technique being a quite complete inhibition of gel polymerization due to the low pH of the mixture. Such a hindrance is of no small import, since after the introduction of the highly sensitive silver staining methods (3), IEF in slab gels constitutes an invaluable technique of investigation of all highly diluted solutions of proteins. A simple method, mainly based on the addition to the polymerized gel, through a slit on his surface, of a strong acid mixture is described herein. This technique, which allows the formation of a 1.5 - 3 pH gradient has been applied to the study of pepsin isoenzymes. Other applications of the method include the study of acidic red blood cells membrane's glycoproteins.

2 OPERATIONS AND RESULTS

2.1 Preparation of the gel

Ultrathin (240 µm) slab gels containing polyacrylamide (T = 5.5%, C = 3.5%) were precoated on silanized glass plates (12.5 x 12.5 cm), gaskets being formed of Parafilm. The polymerization solution (1.9 ml) contained 12% glycerol (or alternatively 12% sorbitol, 2M urea), 1% Triton, ammonium persulfate, TEMED and 1.6% (v/v) Servalyt polyampholytes pH 2 - 3. The electrode solutions were Servalyt polyampholytes 2 - 3 (dil. 1:10) for the cathode and 0.4 M HCl for the anode.

2.2 Formation of a low pH gradient

A mixture of strong acids (Dichloracetic pK 1.48, Phosphoric pK 2.12, Monochloracetic pK 2.84) was added simultaneously by means of a slit obtained on the gel surface and prefocusing was carried out for 6 hours by increasing the voltage from 200 to 400 V. Optimal concentrations for acids, studied for a wide range (from 0.01 M to 0.4 M), were found to be 0.2 M for Dichloracetic, 0.4 M for Phosphoric and 0.1 M for Monochloracetic. The addition of other acids such as ossalic and citric gave no improvement of the separation system. In this condition the pH gradient was stable from 6 to 50 hours. Fig. 1 shows the pH gradient (obtained as here described) measured by cutting little slices of gel (0.5 cm) and placing them in 10 mM KCl (300 µl of KCl) at room temperature, without correction for carbon dioxide and ionic strength. In this system pepsin from hog stomach focuses with four bands as detected by silver stain (Fig.1) after four hours of electrophoresis at 1200 V.

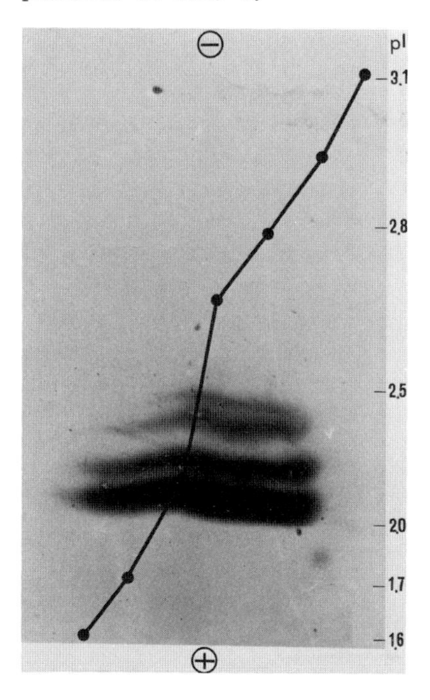

Fig.1. Ultrathin IEF of pepsin from hog stomach. The sample was run for 4 hours at 1200 V. Silver stain.

3 CONCLUSIONS

A stable gradient of pH can be formed in polyacrylamide slab gels by mixing various amounts of strong acids. Main advantages of the system compared to the column apparatus are its speed and ease of execution and the possibility of detection of low concentrated proteins by silver stains. Eventually, many samples may be run simultaneously.

4 REFERENCES

(1) E. Pettersson, Acta Chem. Scand. 23 (1969) 2631-2635.

(2) V.H. Stenman, R. Gräsbec, Biochim. Biophys. Acta 286 (1972) 243-251.

(3) C.R. Merril, D. Goldman, M.L. Van Keuren, Electrophoresis 3 (1982) 17-23.

HIGH PERFORMANCE ELECTROPHORESIS. AN ALTERNATIVE DETECTION TECHNIQUE

Ming-de Zhu and Stellan Hjertén*

Institute of Biochemistry, University of Uppsala, Biomedical Center, P.O. Box 576, S-751 23 Uppsala, Sweden

*To whom correspondence should be addressed.

1 INTRODUCTION

High performance electrophoresis (HPE) is the electrophoretic counterpart of high performance liquid chromatography (HPLC) (1,2). Characteristic of HPE is the small diameter (0.05-0.3 mm) and the wall thickness (0.1-0.2 mm) of the electrophoresis tube which afford efficient dissipation of the Joule heat. For high resolution, particularly of macromolecules, it is often an advantage to perform the experiments in a gel of polyacrylamide. In the previously described equipment for HPE we used an on-column detection system: the solutes were recorded as they migrated electrophoretically past a stationary UV-detector (1,2). On-column UV-monitoring has previously been used, for instance by Hjertén (3), Arlinger and Routs (4) and by Jorgensen and DeArman Lukacs (5). In this communication we will report on an alternative detection method.

2 THE PRINCIPLE OF THE DETECTION TECHNIQUE

The solutes migrate electrophoretically down the column and into an elution chamber. A continuous buffer flow, created with the aid of an HPLC pump, transfers the solutes from the elution chamber to a UV-detector connected to a recorder. This detection system differs from that previously used for preparative polyacrylamide gel electrophoresis (3,4,5) in that the volume of the cuvette is large enough to accomodate all or most of the solute molecules corresponding to a peak (and not only a small fraction of them), which means that the peak height recorded by a given detector for a certain sensitivity range is higher in this detection method than in the conventional one where the cuvette volume is only a small fraction of the volume of a solute zone (advantages and disadvantages of the two detection methods will be discussed in more detail elsewhere).

An advantage of the detection technique outlined herein in comparison with the previously described on-column detection method (1,2) is that it permits recovery of the solutes. High performance electrophoresis can therefore now be employed not only for analytical but also for preparative runs on a microscale. The migration-elution technique described is very versatile in the sense that it permits the use of any detector employed in HPLC, for instance those based on fluorescence.

3 EXPERIMENTS AND RESULTS

3.1 HPE of low molecular weight compounds (nucleosides)

The run was performed at a voltage of 2000 volts (0.25 mA) in a polyacrylamide gel of the composition T=6%, C=3% (for definition of these parameters, see ref. 6), cast in a glass tube with a length of 100 mm and an inner diameter of 0.2 mm. A 0.05 M sodium formate solution, pH 2.85, was used as buffer. The sample consisted of cytidine (C), adenosine (A), guanosine (G) and uridine. Since uridine is uncharged at the pH used, only three peaks were obtained (Fig. 1). The

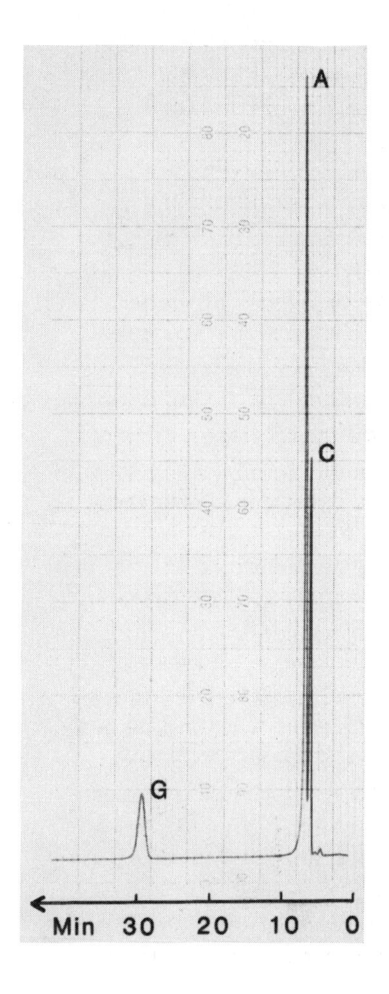

Fig. 1.

High performance electrophoresis of nucleosides. Following electrophoretic migration out of the polyacrylamide gel, the nucleoside zones were transfered continuously to the cuvette of a UV-monitor by a stream of diluent and were detected by the absorbance at 260 nm. Observe the sharpness of the symmetrical peaks and the stability of the baseline.

electropherogram (based on absorption measurements at 260 nm) illustrates the advantages of HPE and the detection technique described: short run times; symmetrical, narrow peaks; stable base line permitting detection of minor peaks (see those in front of the cytidine zone); resolution also of very adjacent zones (C and A).

3.2 HPE of macromolecules (proteins)

An example showing the separation of monomer, dimer, and trimer of albumin is given in Fig. 2. The capillary tube contained a polyacrylamide gel of the composition T=6%; C=3%. Detection was made at 230 nm.

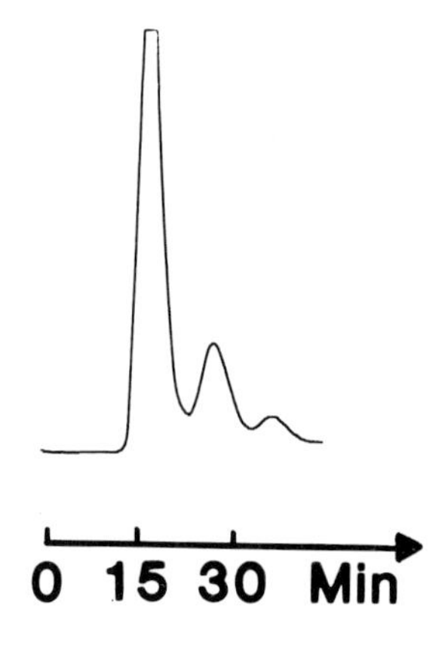

Fig. 2.

High performance electrophoresis of monomer (the first peak), dimer and trimer of albumin. The detection method was the same as that described in the legend to Fig. 1. The absorbance measurements were made at 230 nm.

4 ACKNOWLEDGEMENTS

The work has been financially supported by the Swedish Natural Science Research Council and the Wallenberg Foundation.

5 REFERENCES

(1) S. Hjertén, J. Chromatogr. 270 (1983) 1-6.

(2) S. Hjertén, in H. Hirai (Ed.) Electrophoresis '83, Walter de Gruyter & Co., Berlin, 1984, pp. 71-79.

(3) S. Hjertén, Chromatogr. Rev. 9 (1967) 122-219.

(4) L. Arlinger and R. Routs, Sci. Tools 17 (1970) 21-23.

(5) J.W. Jorgensen and K. DeArman Lukacs, J. Chromatogr. 218 (1981) 209-216.

(6) S. Hjertén, J. Chromatogr. 11 (1963) 66-70.

(7) S. Hjertén, S. Jerstedt, A. Tiselius, Anal. Biochem. 11 (1965) 211-218.

(8) S. Hjertén, S. Jerstedt, A. Tiselius, Anal. Biochem. 27 (1969) 108-129.

(9) S. Hjertén, Arch. Biochem. Biophys., Suppl. 1 (1962) 147-151.

AN APPARATUS FOR THE DETERMINATION OF THE ELECTRIC FIELD DISTRIBUTION IN ISOELECTRIC FOCUSING

Wolfgang Thormann*, Garland Twitty, Amos Tsai & Milan Bier

Biophysics Technology Laboratory, University of Arizona, Tucson, AZ 85721, USA
*Present address: Chemical and Physical Sciences, Deakin University, Victoria, 3217, Australia

1 INTRODUCTION

The knowledge of the electric field distribution along an electrofocusing column before and after the attainment of steady state is important for both theoretical and practical purposes. It is certainly a prerequisite for the understanding and characterization of analytical isoelectric focusing (IEF). Without accurate measurement of the local potential gradient it is particularly difficult to give a physicochemical description of a focused protein zone. The local electric field strength further determines the migration rate of components and the heat generation. In IEF conductance gaps are often established during the course of an experiment. In general, these gaps are undesirable since they prolong the focusing time, can form a barrier for reaching the isoelectric position of an ampholyte or may cause protein denaturation due to large Joule heat.

Jackiw et al (1) constructed a device for measuring the segmental voltages along focusing tube gels. Their detector consists of 11 platinum sensors sealed into the wall of a pyrex tube (6mm ID) at 1 cm intervals. This apparatus is a significant improvement over the utilization of sliding contacts across a gel surface (2) but provides only a rough estimate of the field profile. We designed an apparatus enabling us to monitor the potential gradient at 99 or 255 equidistant positions along a 10 cm column. The instrument is based on the principle described by Thormann et al (3) for the detection of transient and steady state zone structures in electrophoresis. Monitoring the electric field with this array detector allows the following of its dynamics in a continuous fashion, fully controllable by a computer.

2 APPARATUS DESCRIPTION

Fig. 1 depicts a schematic of the separation cell. The separation trough (2) consists of a rectangular main part between points (1) and (3) which is 10 cm long and two small cylindrical sections with a diameter of 1 mm (between points (1) and (3) respectively and the membranes (7)). The dimension of the rectangular part is defined by the silicone gasket (D). Typically we use a height of 0.4 mm and a channel width of 0.7 mm. The initial conditions for an experiment require a uniform distribution of all components throughout the separation trough. The solution with carrier and test components is filled in excess through ports (6). The first silicone gasket (18), the membrane (7) and the second gasket (19) are then carefully inserted, followed by the membrane holder (4), which keeps everything in proper place. The remaining liquid in the electrode compartments (8) has to be replaced by a small amount of electrode solution before the application of the electrical current. The ion permeabilities at the ends of an IEF separation column are important for the formation of stationary pH gradients. An electrode assembly is needed which will function as a current induced H^+ donor on the anodic side and one for OH^- on the cathodic side. We have investigated dialysis, ion exchange and palladium membranes.

A new 100 element sensor array was designed as shown in Fig. 2. Its measuring electrodes are spread over the whole column length, are perpendicular to the current flow, have a width of approximately 0.025 cm and are about 0.076 cm apart. They are deposited on a pyrex glass plate and are produced from formulated metallo-organics (Engelhard Corp., East Newark, NJ, USA). These 'inks' are metallic solutions with no discrete particles in suspension. The major fraction consists of organics which must be thermally decomposed by air firing. In addition, base metals are incorporated which oxidize during the heat treatment to form an oxide layer necessary for the bonding between the metal film and the substrate. We investigated the application of gold and platinum ink by silk screening, followed by a 20 min air firing at 650°C. Film thicknesses from 0.05 to 0.2 μm can be obtained. The apparatus can also be equipped with the 256 semiconductor sensor array described in ref. (3).

The potential gradient between adjacent electrodes is recorded by means of a high impedance detection electronics with voltage divider, low pass filter and isolation amplifier. The remaining dc signal is fed into the data acquisition system described in ref. (4). The electrode array is scanned mechanically at its outer edge. The scanner consists of two graphite brushes which are moved by an HP plotter device, controlled by the HP 9825A computer. Its small step size permits incremental scanning of sequential electrode pairs. This procedure allows us to obtain data points from at least 10 different readings, thus ensuring a reliable result. The data are processed and stored in the computer.

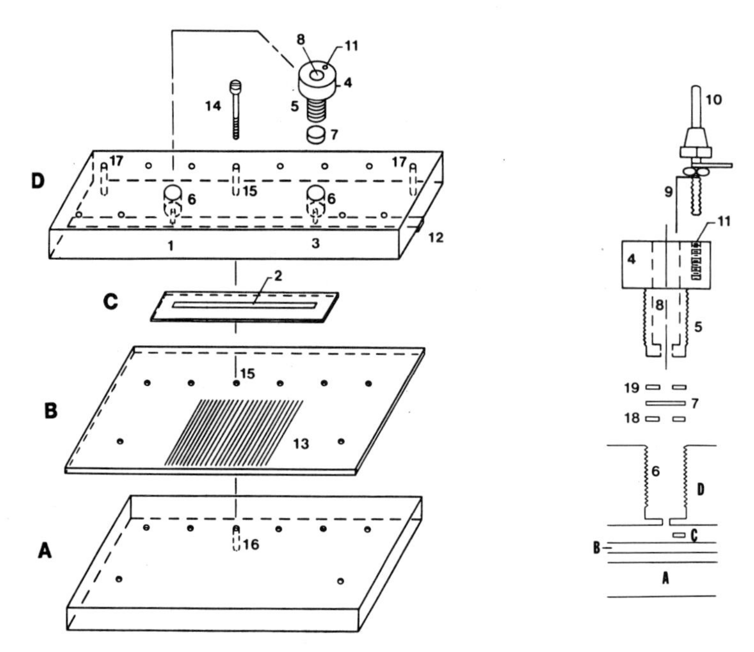

Fig. 1. Assembly of the separation cell, consisting of a block of plexglass (D) with fittings, a silicone rubber gasket (C), a sensor bearing glass plate (B) and a cooled aluminum plate (A).

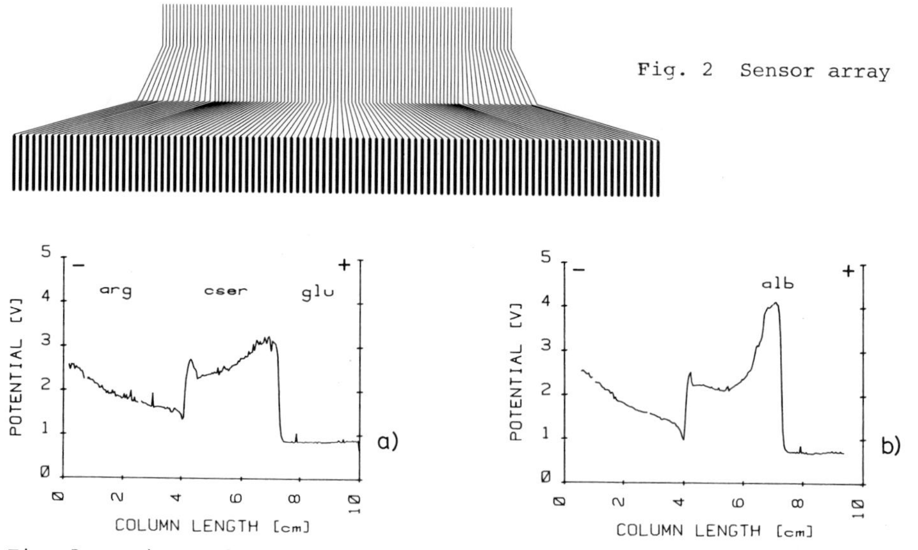

Fig. 2 Sensor array

Fig. 3 a) Steady state electric field distribution of an electrolyzed mixture of glutamic acid, cycloserine and arginine. b) Profile obtained with the addition of 10 µg of human serum albumin, which focuses between glutamic acid and cycloserine.

3 RESULTS AND DISCUSSION

Fig. 3 displays uncorrected scans of the electric field distribution along both a steady state three component buffer system without protein (a) and with about 10 μg of focused albumin (b). The initial buffer solution consists of three amino acids, glutamic acid, cycloserine and arginine respectively, 10 mM each. A constant voltage of 400 V was applied. The currents decreased within about an hour from 180 μA to 37 μA(a) and 33 μA(b), the steady state values under which the scans were taken. The two detected field profiles are very comparable, except at the location of the protein spot. The stationary boundaries between each pair of amino acids are marked by a sudden change of the electric field. Albumin focuses nicely in the pH gradient established between glutamic acid and cycloserine. The protein at this concentration is interactive with the buffer components. This results in a substantially higher electric field within the focused protein than in the adjacent zones of carrier amino acids.

The apparatus described provides a methodology to gain insight into the features of various IEF systems. In its present design, separation occurs in free solution. This permits the performance of validation studies of computer predictions (5) and the investigation of various electrode assemblies for focusing. The device will also be useful for the evaluation of conductivity profiles across IEF gels, in particular Immobiline gels (2).

This work was supported in part by NASA Grant NSG-7333 and a grant from the Swiss National Science Foundation. The artwork for the sensor array was generously contributed by G. Watkins, IBM, Tucson.

4 REFERENCES

(1) B. A. Jackiw, B. E. Chidakel, A. Chrambach, R. K. Brown, Electrophoresis 1 (1980) 102-106.

(2) G. Dossi, F. Celentano, E. Gianazza, P. G. Righetti, J. Biochem. Biophys. Methods 7 (1983) 123-142.

(3) W. Thormann, D. Arn, E. Schumacher in H. Hirai (Ed.), Electrophoresis '83, Walter de Gruyter, Berlin 1984, in press.

(4) N. B. Egen, G. E. Twitty, M. Bier in 17th Aerospace Sciences Mtg., New Orleans, Jan. 15, 1979, paper No. 79-0405.

(5) M. Bier, O. A. Palusinski, R. A. Mosher, D. A. Saville, Science 219 (1983) 1281-1287.

EXPERIMENTAL AND THEORETICAL DYNAMICS OF ISOELECTRIC FOCUSING

Wolfgang Thormann*, Richard A. Mosher & Milan Bier

Biophysics Technology Laboratory, University of Arizona, Tucson, AZ, 85721, USA
*Present address: Chemical and Physical Sciences, Deakin University, Victoria, 3217, Australia

1 INTRODUCTION

A knowledge of the dynamics in isoelectric focusing (IEF) is essential for the characterization of this electrophoretic mode (1-3). The electric field is the most general physical property in electrophoresis. We designed an apparatus enabling us to monitor the field distribution along an electrofocusing column before and after the attainment of steady state (4). It comprises an array detector with 100 (or 256) equidistant sensing electrodes along a 10 cm column. The potential difference between adjacent electrodes is measured by repetitive scanning, fully automated and controlled by a computer. The apparatus allows focusing in free solution or gels.

Computer modeling is the only methodology at hand for the prediction of concentration, potential and conductivity profiles as functions of time. The general mathematical model of Bier et al (5) predicts the salient features of all the classically recognized methods in electrophoresis, including IEF. This model produced results consistent with the experimentally monitored dynamics of the electric field.

2 RESULTS AND DISCUSSION

All experiments were performed in free solution using gold electrodes for detection (4). The cross sectional area of the rectangular separation trough was about 5×10^{-3} cm^2. The electrode assemblies included dialysis membranes for the isolation of the separation column from the electrode compartments. Small amounts of 0.1 M H_3PO_4 as anolyte and 0.1 M NaOH as catholyte were used. The solution with carrier components was uniformly distributed throughout the column before application of a constant current of 10 μA. The total voltage drop after attaining steady state was between 100 and 200V. Consecutive scans were taken with an interval of 21 minutes. The registration of a full scan required 14 $\pm$ 0.5 minutes. Data points of each scan were stored on tape by the computer.

Fig. 1 shows the dynamics of the electric field during the focusing of a mixture of glutamic acid, cycloserine and arginine, 10 mM each. Each scan, corrected for variations in the trough profile (6), is plotted with an offset of 0.5 V (in y-axis) from the preceding profile. The experiment clearly illustrates the formation of two transient moving boundaries originating from both electrodes and migrating toward the center. The faster boundaries (trailing boundary of arginine on the right and of glutamic acid on the left side) represent a small field gradient only, whereas the slower ones are characterized by a substantial change of the potential gradient. The latter two define trailing boundaries of the cycloserine on both sides and the fronts of the evolving zones with glutamic acid on the anodic and arginine on the cathodic side.

As soon as the two faster boundaries meet, the pure zone of the ampholyte with the intermediate pI value (cycloserine) starts to evolve. This is clearly shown by the establishment of a sudden voltage jump in the middle section of the column as documented with the profile of scan 8. From this time on, two new moving boundaries are present which migrate in opposite direction. They define the fronts of the evolution of the pure cycloserine zone. Each of them meet the corresponding boundary approaching from its column end and produces a stationary boundary at this location. After about 200 minutes of current flow the steady state pattern is fully established (scan 11). The field profile of this state is characterized by two stationary boundaries with steady state shape. Both of them represent substantial field changes. It is interesting to note that all migrating boundaries have a steady state shape due to the field increase opposite to their moving direction. They also represent pH gradients.

Fig. 2 depicts the computer simulated field profiles for the same system. A current density of 0.001 A/cm^2 was applied. The assumed pK and mobility values of the three amino acids are summarized in Table I. A column of 1 cm length was overlaid by 101 grid points. For each of those points concentration, conductivity and pH values were calculated for various times of current flow.

Table I pK and mobility values for computer simulation

component	pK_1	pK_2	mobility [cm^2/Vsec]*
glutamic acid	2.16	4.29	$2.97\cdot10^{-4}$
cycloserine	4.40	7.40	$3.42\cdot10^{-4}$
arginine	9.04	12.48	$2.26\cdot10^{-4}$

*It was assumed that all species of a component have equal mobilities.

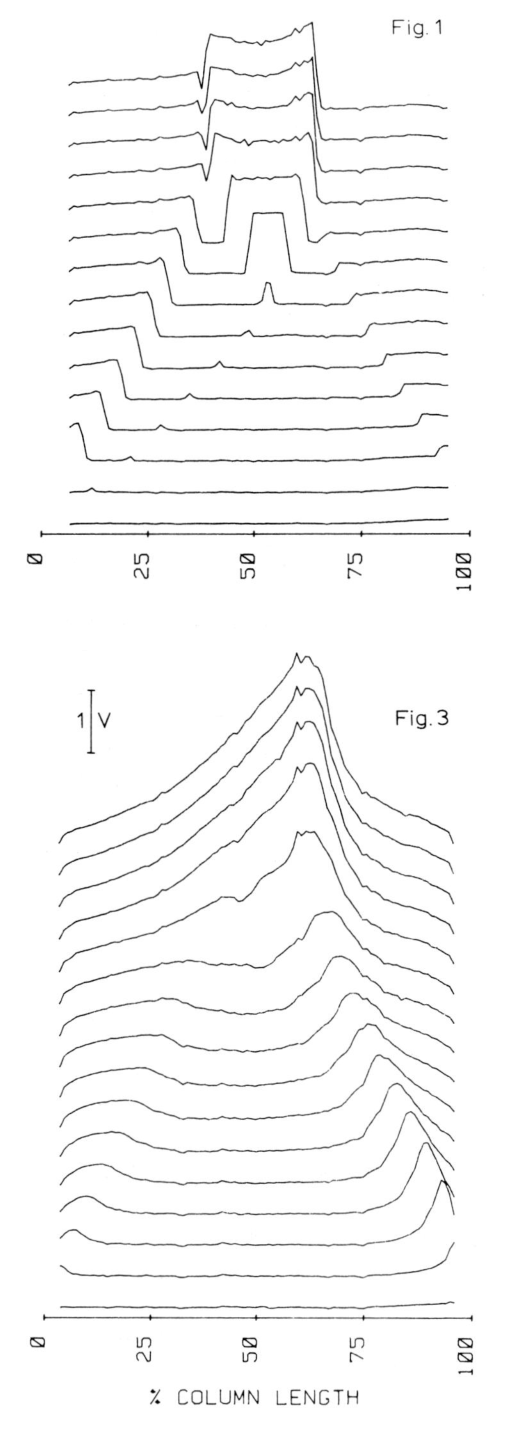

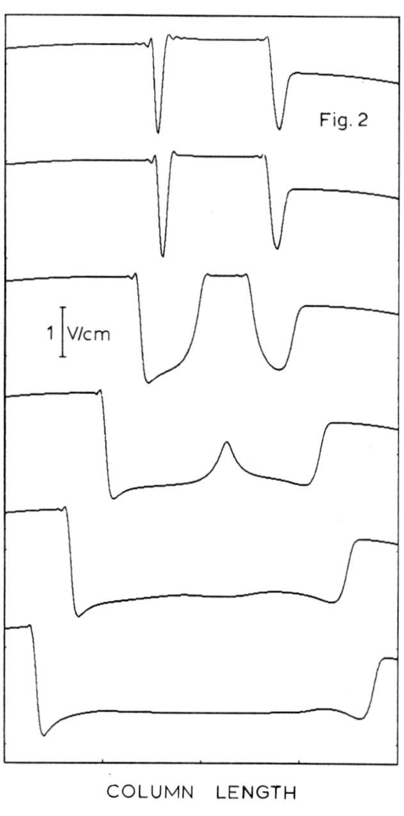

Fig. 1 Detected dynamics of the potential gradient with arginine, cycloserine and glutamic acid. The anode is to the right.

Fig. 2 Computer simulated electric field profiles for the system of Fig. 1. The time points plotted, from bottom to top, are 5,10,15, 20,25 and 30 minutes.

Fig. 3 Characterization of a synthetic ampholyte mixture.

The computer predicted profiles are consistent with the detected evolution of the electric field. All transient moving boundaries are present in both set of graphs which validates the model prediction of the separation scheme in isoelectric focusing. The detailed shape of the gradients, as predicted by the model, is not detected with our sensor array. Under the experimental conditions, the current density is about twice the value used for the computer simulation. This results in boundaries which are much sharper than the resolution of the detector. Another reason is the ever present convective mixing within boundary regions which is neglected in our computer model. However, the small field decrease present in the steady state arginine/cycloserine boundary is detected.

From the information gained with systems consisting of three buffer components one can deduce that the number of established, transient moving boundaries on either side is equal to the number of constituents. This is difficult to monitor in the presence of a large number of such components. Fig. 3 displays the evolution of the field distribution with 1% Ampholine (pH 3.5 - 10), containing hundreds of different constituents. The scans visualize the formation of a conductance gap, which remains stationary after about 4 hours (scan 13) of current flow.

These few data illustrate the usefulness and versatility of the apparatus which permits, for the first time, detailed monitoring of the focusing process. The device is computer controlled and has a resolution which is far better than that obtained by Jackiw et al (3).

This work was supported in part by NASA Grant NSG-7333 and a grant from the Swiss National Science Foundation.

3 REFERENCES

(1) G. H. Weiss, N. Catsimpoolas, D. Rodbard, Arch. Biochem. Biophys. 163 (1974) 106-112.

(2) N. Catsimpoolas in P. G. Righetti (Ed.), Progress in Isoelectric Focusing and Isotachophoresis, North Holland, Amsterdam 1974, pp. 77-92.

(3) B. A. Jackiw, B. E. Chidakel, A. Chrambach, R. K. Brown, Electrophoresis 1 (1980) 102-106.

(4) W. Thormann, G. Twitty, A. Tsai, M. Bier, this symposium.

(5) M. Bier, O. A. Palusinski, R. A. Mosher, D. A. Saville, Science 219 (1983) 1281-1287.

(6) E. Schumacher, D. Arn, W. Thormann, Electrophoresis 4 (1983) 390-392.

PREPARATION OF REHYDRATABLE POLYACRYLAMIDE GELS AND THEIR APPLICATION IN ULTRATHIN-LAYER ISOELECTRIC FOCUSING

Manuela D. Frey, M. Bassim Atta, Bertold J. Radola

Institute of Food Technology and Analytical Chemistry, Technical University Munich, D- 8050 Freising-Weihenstephan, FRG

1 INTRODUCTION

In the current practice of polyacrylamide gel isoelectric focusing wet gels are used. There are several drawbacks to this practice. (i) Gel polymerization is poorly defined in presence of carrier ampholytes (1). (ii) Variable amounts of unpolymerized monomers, linear polymers, ammonium persulfate and other reagents necessary for free radical generation persist in the gel (2). (iii) Some additives, at high concentration, interfere with gel polymerization (3). (iv) Incorporation of all components already into the polymerization mixture is an intricate procedure because for any change in composition, separate gels must be cast. Some of these disadvantages have been early recognized (4) but the procedures described for overcoming them were not practical. In this report we describe the preparation of rehydratable ultrathin gels which in dry form may be stored for extended periods and which prior to use are rehydrated with solutions of carrier ampholytes of any desirable composition.

2 PREPARATION OF REHYDRATABLE POLYACRYLAMIDE GELS

Polyacrylamide gels of different %T and %C content were prepared using several crosslinkers (Bis, DHEBA, AcrylAide). Most experiments were carried out with the popular 5 %T , 3 $\%C_{Bis}$ gel. The polymerization mixture did not contain carrier ampholytes but was supplemented for better pH control during the polymerization reaction with 0.05 M Tris buffer, pH 8.0. Ammonium persulfate and TEMED were used at concentrations ensuring at room temperature gel polymerization within 10-15 min. Gels with 50, 100 and 200 µm thickness were prepared on silanized polyester films or commercially available supports (GelBond, Gel-Fix) using the flap technique (5). The gels were washed in distilled water, e.g. the 50-100 µm gels

20–30 min, to remove soluble contaminants. The efficiency of washing was monitored using Ponceau S (M_r 480) and sperm whale myoglobin (M_r 17800) as indicators. Prior to drying the gels were usually placed in 10 % v/v glycerol for 10 min but a variety of other low and high molecular weight additives was also tested. The gels were dried overnight at room temperature; in a few experiments drying was accelerated by using an infrared lamp, an oven at 40–50 °C or a fan. The dry gels were stored at room temperature, covered with a plastic foil with repellent properties. Forced aging was simulated by incubating the dry gels in an oven at 80–100 °C for 1, 3, 5, 8 and 20 h.

3 REHYDRATION

3.1 Techniques

Two techniques were developed for the rehydration of dry gels. (i) "Rolling technique": A calculated amount of a 3% solution of carrier ampholytes is placed on a glass plate. The film with the dry gel is rolled onto the liquid care being taken to uniformly spread the solution over the entire gel surface. After contact for 10–15 s the gel is lifted, turned by 90° and rolled again over the residual solution. This technique is economical because the solution is quantitatively soaked up by the gel layer. (ii) "Floating technique": The dry gel is equilibrated with a 3% solution of carrier ampholytes by placing the film with the gel on the surface of the solution.

3.2 Rehydration kinetics

Experiments on rehydration kinetics, based on weight determination relative to the weight of the wet gels after polymerization (100%), have shown that the 50–100 µm gels are rehydrated in 1–3 min. In only a few seconds ($\leq$5s) these gels regain their original weight, followed by a slower process of swelling which is virtually complete in a few minutes. In the 200 µm gels both processes require $\geq$5–10 min. The rehydration kinetics of gels dried with 10% glycerol are similar to those of gels without glycerol, however, both types of gel differ with respect to the relative amounts of water taken up during rehydration. Heating at elevated temperatures progressively decreases the extent of rehydration without qualitatively changing the course of kinetics.

4 ULTRATHIN-LAYER ISOELECTRIC FOCUSING

Dry gels of various formats were rehydrated with Servalyt carrier ampholytes of different pH ranges and used for isoelectric focusing of a variety of marker proteins and crude fungal enzymes (5). Excellent results were obtained with all glycerol-containing gels, even after severe heat treatment whereas gels dried without glycerol gave inconsistent results (Fig.1).

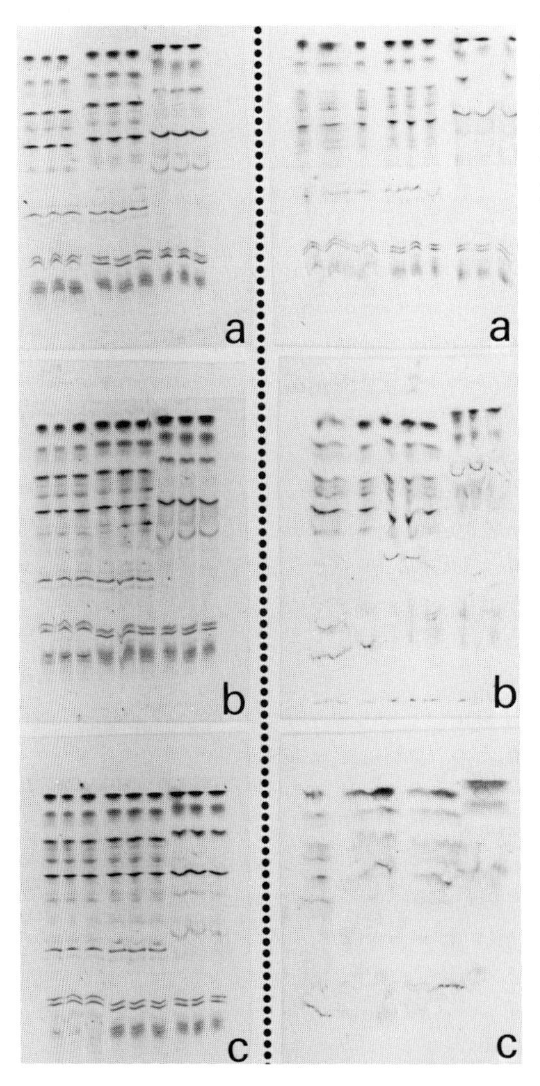

Fig.1 Ultrathin-layer isoelectric focusing of marker proteins in rehydrated polyacrylamide gels (5%T,3%C_{Bis}). Separation distance 5 cm, pH 4-9 Servalyt T carrier ampholytes, 650 Vh, 500 V/cm. On the left gels containing 10% glycerol, on the right gels dried without glycerol.

(a) Gels dried overnight at room temperature,
(b) gels dried at 100 °C, 1 h,
(c) gels dried at 100 °C, 3 h.

Depending on gel thickness and extent of heating the focusing patterns in gels without glycerol, deteriorated indicating irreversible damage of the gels, the 200 µm layers being the most resistant. The initial current, at the same concentration of carrier ampholytes, is much lower in rehydrated gels than in wet gels, obviously a result of washing out contaminating electrolytes during gel preparation. Higher field strengths, e.g. 500-700 V/cm, were tolerated when applied over 5-10 cm separation distances, with resultant improved zone sharpness and resolution. In the rehydrated gels containing glycerol isoelectric focusing could be conducted to equilibrium, by the criterion of anodically and cathodically migrating samples. By contrast, 50–100 µm gels dried without glycerol could not be focused to equilibrium. An easily recognizable change of gels dried without glycerol, aggravated by heating, was that the rehydrated gel surface has acquired strongly hydrophilic properties. The samples could not be deposited as droplets with defined geometry resulting in irregular patterns.

5 PROSPECT

Rehydratable gels offer a new approach to polyacrylamide gel isoelectric focusing. The gels can now be prepared under well standardized conditions, any undesirable contaminants, which are known to disturb pH gradient formation, are removed by washing, and the dry gels are storable for extended periods. The major advantages of rehydratable gels are the easy handling and unsurpassed flexibility. The gels may be rehydrated with solutions of carrier ampholytes of any pH range, different blends, with additives, e.g. urea, detergents or separators. Rehydratable gels seem to be an ideal tool for research but owing to their operational simplicity they may also prove useful in routine applications.

6 REFERENCES

(1) A. Chrambach, T.M. Jovin, P.J. Svendsen, D. Rodbard, in: N. Catsimpoolas (Ed.), Methods of Protein Separation, Plenum Press, New York 1976, Vol. 2, pp. 27–144.
(2) C. Gelfi, P.G. Righetti, Electrophoresis 2 (1981), 213–219.
(3) H.H. Althaus, S. Klöppner, H.M. Poehling, V. Neuhoff, Electrophoresis 4, (1983), 347–353.
(4) D.M. Leaback, H.C. Rutter, Biochem. Biophys. Res. Commun. 32, (1968), 447–453.
(5) B.J. Radola, Electrophoresis 1 (1980), 43–56.

ENZYME VISUALIZATION WITH REHYDRATABLE POLYACRYLAMIDE GELS

Manuela D. Frey, Angelika Kinzkofer, Friedrich Kögel, Bertold J. Radola

Institute of Food Technology and Analytical Chemistry, Technical University Munich, D- 8050 Freising-Weihenstephan, FRG

1 INTRODUCTION

In a recent publication we have shown that traditional techniques of enzyme visualization, requiring extended incubation periods, cannot be applied to ultrathin gels (1). A strategy for high resolution enzyme visualization was developed, based on three principles. (i) Acceleration of the enzyme reaction by using high concentrations of substrate and visualization reagents , (ii) incubation at elevated temperatures , and (iii) controlling diffusion by replacing incubation in solution by contact prints with either dimensionally stable membranes or ultrathin agarose replicas. Particularly the ultrathin agarose replica technique proved versatile and superior to the traditional agarose overlay technique. An advantage of the ultrathin agarose replicas is that "empty" gels are prepared which may be equilibrated with a solution of any desired substrate composition prior to visualization. In later experiments we have found that gel equilibration is difficult with some macromolecular substrates, e.g. pectins of different degrees of esterification (2) or carboxymethylcellulose (3). Therefore, these substrates had to be incorporated into the agarose on casting the gels thus limiting the flexibility of the technique. In an attempt to overcome the drawbacks of ultrathin agarose replicas we have applied rehydratable polyacrylamide gels to enzyme visualization.

2 PREPARATION OF SUBSTRATE GELS

Rehydratable polyacrylamide gels were prepared as described in an accompanying contribution (4). Standard 5%T , 3%C_{Bis} gels (the same type of gel was employed as matrix for isoelectric focusing) as well as gels crosslinked with AcrylAide or with different %T, %C content were used as substrate gels. The dry gels, trimmed to the same size as the running gels, were rehydrated with the rolling technique by placing a calculated amount of substrate solution on a glass plate. For some enzymes it may be necessary to wash out the glycerol, prior to use, and redry the gel. Depending on reagent stability, some substrate gels can be prepared in advance and stored in wet form. Substrate gels of different thickness (50,100 and 200 μm) were employed. The gels were rehydrated in 1-2 min, longer rehydration times offered no advantage. Even in the case of viscous solution of macromolecular substrates (pectins, carboxymethylcellulose) incorporation of the substrate into the gel was rapid and uniform.

3 ENZYME VISUALIZATION

After isoelectric focusing the substrate gel was rolled onto the surface of the running gel, care being taken not to entrap air bubbles. The gel sandwich was incubated under conditions ensuring optimum visualization for the enzyme. For many enzyme reactions, the incubation times were in the order of a few minutes, but at low enzyme levels incubation for up to 30 min was necessary. Rehydration of dry polyacrylamide gels with substrate solutions presents a simple and versatile technique for enzyme visualization. The technique was used for the location of (i) enzymes acting on high molecular weight substrates, e.g. amylases, cellulases, pectinases and proteases and (ii) enzymes acting on low molecular weight substrates, e.g. esterases, phosphoglucomutase. Rehydratable polyacrylamide substrate gels overcome the drawbacks of ultrathin agarose gels. Their preparation is simpler and their handling more convenient. Rehydratable substrate gels possess all attributes necessary for fast and high resolution enzyme visualization following ultrathin-layer isoelectric focusing (1). However, their application is not limited to ultrathin gels and encouraging results were obtained also with 0.5-1 mm gel layers.

4 REFERENCES

(1) A. Kinzkofer, B.J. Radola, Electrophoresis 4, (1983), 408-417.

(2) M.D. Frey, B.J. Radola, in: B.J. Radola (Ed.), Elektrophorese-Forum '83, Technische Universität München 1983, pp. 252-257.

(3) H.K. Sreenath, B.J. Radola, in: B.J. Radola (Ed.), Elektrophorese-Forum'83 Technische Universität München 1983, pp. 258-262.

(4) M.D. Frey, B.J. Radola, these Proceedings.

ISOELECTRIC FOCUSING OF CATALASE AND PEROXIDASE FROM SERRATIA MARCESCENS

O.E. Santana, R.H. Lopez-Orge, Z. Gonzalez-Lama

Department of Microbiology, Colegio Universitario de Medicina, Apartado 550, Las Palmas de Gran Canaria, Spain

1 INTRODUCTION

Adequate defense against oxygen toxicity requires efficient scavering of both O_2^- and of H_2O_2. Superoxide dismutases, which scavenge O_2^- and catalases and peroxidases, which scavenge H_2O_2, provide the necessary defenses. Catalases and peroxidases have been studied in bacteria Gram positives (1,2), Mycobacteria (3,4,5), Enterobacteriaceae (6,7,8), Pseudomonas (9,10) and other bacteria (11,12,13), but their isoelectric points are not so well known. We wish to report here the application of isoelectric focusing in polyacrylamide gel to the study of isoelectric points from catalases and peroxidases in Serratia marcescens.

2 MATERIALS AND METHODS

Serratia marcescens was isolated from a clinical specimen and grown in Brain-Heart Infusion (Difco lab. Detroit, Michigan, USA) at 37°C, 24 h, under aeration. Cells of Serratia marcescens were harvested and cell-free extracts were prepared as described elsewhere (14). Isoelectric focusing was carried out in a thin layer polyacrylamide gel, with an ampholine gradient pH: 3.5-9.5., using the multiphor apparatus (LKB Produkter, Bromma, Sweden).Peroxidase activity was detected in the gel as already described (15). Catalase activity in the gel was located as earlier described (10) modified by us by soaking the slabs of gel in a solution of 1% hydrolysed starch. The bands are seen as white zones, due to catalase activity, appering on a dark blue background.

3 RESULTS AND DISCUSSION

Figure 1, are a photographs demostrating peroxidase and catalase activities in the cell-free crude extracts of Serratia marcescens by isoelectric focusing in polyacrylamide thin layer gel. We found only one band with peroxidase activity (I) with pI: 3.9, and three distinct catalases (II) with pI's: 4.2, 4.5 and 4.8. One problem encountered is that focused bands of catalase diffuse rapidly in the gel after development. This precludes satisfactory recording of results, since serial photographs are usually necessary to show the weaker bands which develop more slowly.

Other catalases from bacteria sources have been studied, and the electrophoretic mobility of catalases were used as taxonomic criterion of Mycobacteria (3). Two different catalases were identified in Escherichia coli (6) and only one in Proteus mirabilis (7)(pI:4.8) this one is similar to the band less acidic found by us in Serratia marcescens. In Pseudomonas aeruginosa in earlier studies (10) we found four catalase activities. Serratia marcescens shows one band similar to the more acidic isoelectric pH (pI: 4.2) band of catalase activity in Pseudomonas aeruginosa.

The relations between catalase, peroxidase and the activities of other components of the hydrogen peroxidase metabolism, such as superoxide dismutase are presently under investigation.

Figure 1. Isoelectric focusing of catalase and peroxidase from Serratia marcescens.

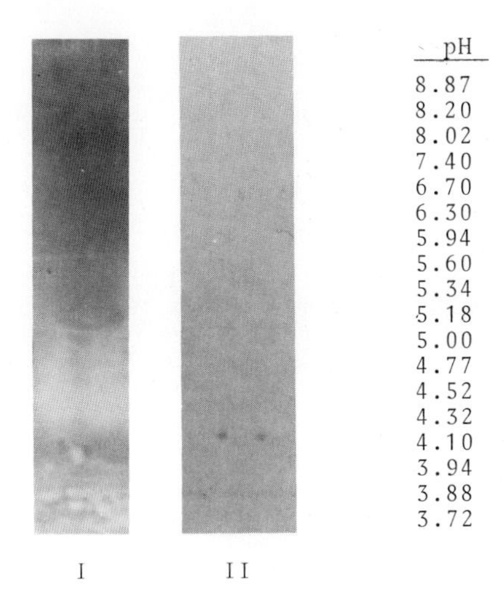

4 REFERENCES

(1) A.L. Marie,H.Priess,F. Parak, Hoppe-Seyler's Physiol.Chem.359, 857-862 (1978)

(2) Y. Yoko, I. Fridovich, J.Bacteriol. 155, 742-746 (1983)

(3) H. Stavri, D. Stavri, Arch. Roum. Path. Exp. Microbiol.34, 85-89 (1975).

(4) P.M. Tierno,Jr., M. Milstoc, J.Clin.Microbiol. 13, 998-999 (1981)

(5) L.G. Wayne, G.A. Diaz, Int.J.Syst.Bacteriol. 32, 296-304 (1982)

(6) H.M. Hassan, I. Fridovich, J.Biol.Chem. 253, 6445-6450 (1978)

(7) H.M. Jouve, S. Tessier, J. Pelmont, Can.J.Biochem.Cell Biol. 61, 8-14 (1983)

(8) P.C. Loewen, J.Bacteriol. 157, 622-626 (1984)

(9) S. Rodriguez-Bravo, J.M. Pionetti, Biochimie 63, 535-540 (1981)

(10) Z. Gonzalez-Lama, M.J. Cutillas, A.M. Lamas, E. Melendez-Hevia, Electrophoresis'82, Walter de Gruyter &Co, Berlin-New York 1983 pp. 481-484

(11) D. Nies, H.G. Schlegel, J.Gen.Appl. Microbiol. 28, 311-319 (1982)

(12) E.T. Akporiaye, O.G. Baca, J.Bacteriol. 154, 520-523 (1983)

(13) E.M. Gregory, D.D. Fanning, J.Bacteriol. 156, 1012-1018 (1983)

(14) Z. Gonzalez-Lama, O.E. Santana, P. Betancor, Electrophoresis'81, Walter de Gruyter & Co, Berlin-New York 1981, pp. 699-702

(15) Z. Gonzalez-Lama, R.N. Feinstein, Proc.Soc.Exp.Biol.Med.154,322-324 (1977)

LACTATE DEHYDROGENASE POLYMORPHISM IN KRILL (EUPHAUSIA SUPERBA) DETECTED BY IEF IN AGAROSE GELS AND CELLOGEL^R ELECTROPHORESIS.

Reinhard Schneppenheim, Silke Kühl, Gisela Janssen

Institut für Polarökologie, Universität Kiel, Olshausenstrasse 40-60, 2300 Kiel, FRG

1 INTRODUCTION

Enzyme electrophoresis, a combination of electrophoretic techniques and histochemical staining methods (1) has become a very useful tool in population genetics. Its application in fishery biology, e.g. the identification of populations, provides essential data for soundly based fisheries management programs. In our study on the population genetics of the Antarctic krill (Euphausia superba) we analyzed samples routinely by means of Cellogel^R electrophoresis. In the case of lactate dehydrogenase we could score two loci, a polymorphic "fast" LDH_{II} and a monomorphic "slow" LDH_I. However the corresponding bands of LDH_I were in some cases blurred which is indicative of heterozygous phenotypes, although none of the conventional electrophoretic systems used could really demonstrate this polymorphism. Since enzyme polymorphism in krill is not very high, we were satisfied with any additional scorable polymorphic locus. We subsequently tried to obtain a better separation of this locus by means of IEF in agarose gels.

2 MATERIALS AND METHODS

Krill were obtained from five geographically and oceanographically different locations in the Antarctic waters, the two main sampling areas being the Weddell Sea sector and the Pacific ocean off the Antarctic Peninsula. 50 specimens per sample were homogenized individually in distilled water and centrifuged for 10 min at 4,000 RPM. The supernatant was taken for Cellogel^R electrophoresis (2) and for IEF in agarose gels using a pH gradient from pH 5-8 (Pharmalyte^R pH 5-8) according to the instructions given by Pharmacia (3). 10 µl from each specimen were applied near the cathodic end of the gel by means of filter papers. The run was started without prefocusing and finished after attaining 2,000 VH. Staining of Cellogel^R sheets was done according to an earlier study (2); for the staining of the agarose gels the following agar overlay method was applied:

0.3 g Agar Noble (Difco), 70 mg lactate (hemi-calcium salt, Sigma), 30 mg NAD, 3 mg PMS, 5 mg MTT (Serva) in 30 ml 0.5 M Tris/HCl buffer pH 8. Bands appeared immediately; the gels were fixed in a solution of ethanol, glacial acetic acid and distilled water (2:1:7) and photographed.

3 RESULTS

E. superba which were homozygous at both L D H loci showed the typical five banded pattern of L D H isozymes after electrophoresis on Cellogel^R. Following IEF however, this pattern was confused by the appearence of additional bands which we considered to be secondary isozymes. Despite these additional bands a separation into five zones could still be demonstrated. Furthermore the secondary isozymes did not interfere substantially with our interpretation of the electrophoretic pattern. At both loci a number of different allelic variants could be identified.

LDH_{II} : The locus exhibited polymorphism, using either method. Electrophoretic patterns were very similar, but were easier to score in the case of the Cellogel^R run (fig.1a&b).

LDH_{I} : This locus could be reliably scored only by means of IEF. 4 alleles were identified. Two homozygous phenotypes could be observed, being the product of the two most common alleles "100" and "125" respectively. The corresponding bands of these alleles were sharp and clearly distinct from each other. Heterozygotes "100/125" in only a few cases showed a sharp five banded pattern in the first zone of L D H activity, however in most other cases at least an expected four banded pattern in the second zone could be recognized, verifying our scoring of a heterozygote (fig.1b).

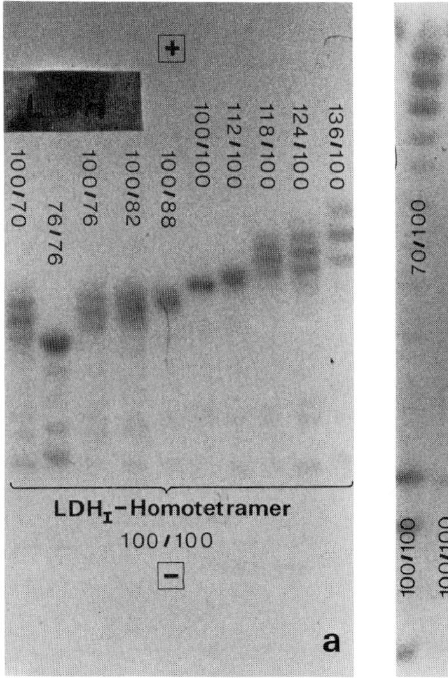

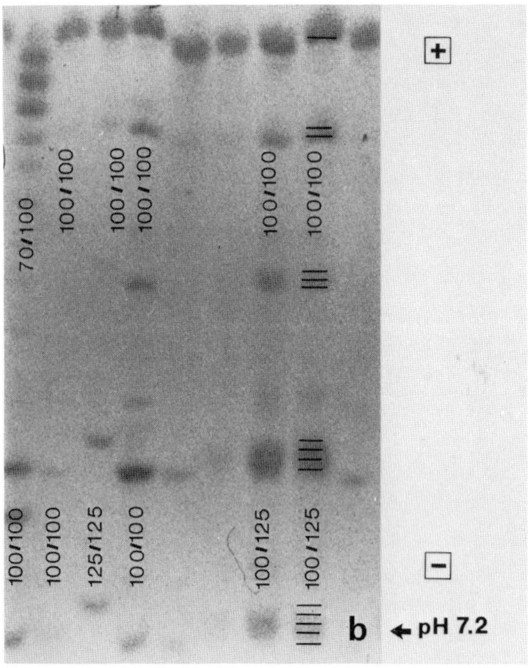

Figure 1 a&b. LDH phenotypes in E. superba detected by Cellogel^R electrophoresis (a) and IEF in agarose gels (pH gradient 5-8) (b).

Allelic frequencies for both loci from all five samples are almost identical. The frequency of the most common allele "100" in LDH_I was 0.718, the mean frequency of allele "100" in LDH_{II} was 0.970, the mean frequency of heterozygotes 0.372 and 0.058 respectively. Deviations from random mating expectations according to the Hardy-Weinberg principle (4) were non significant at the P = 0.05 level.

4 CONCLUSIONS

These data agree with our former findings from Cellogel^R electrophoresis for 15 further loci from similar sampling sites (2), which infer the existence of only one genetically homogenous krill population in the investigated area. Since our results are at odds with those of other authors (5), the analysis of LDH_I -another "good" polymorphism -, by means of agarose IEF offers a further possibility to verify our single population hypothesis.

5 REFERENCES

(1) R.L. Hunter, C.L. Markert, Science 125 (1957) 1294-1295

(2) R. Schneppenheim, C.M. MacDonald, Polar Biol. 3 (1984) 19-28

(3) Pharmacia Fine Chemicals, Isoelectric Focusing - Principles and Methods, Uppsala 1982

(4) G.H. Hardy, Science 28 (1908) 49-50

(5) S.E. Fevolden, F.J. Ayala, Sarsia 66 (1981) 167-181

ISOENZYME SCREENING WITH ISOELECTRIC FOCUSSING FOR AN EARLY IDENTIFICATION OF SOMATIC HYBRIDS OF TOMATO AND POTATO

Walter Gekeler

Institut für Chemische Pflanzenphysiologie der Universität
Correnssstraße 41 D-7400 Tübingen

1 INTRODUCTION

Parental plants and fusion products of somatic hybridisations performed by G. Melchers (1,2) between various strains of Solanum tuberosum and Lycopersicon esculentum were analyzed for isoenzyme patterns. After regeneration to plants (1 year after the fusion) the hybrids have been characterized morphologically and cytologically, and some of them with respect to chloroplast origin (3,4). From calli, the GLC-pattern of volatiles has been analyzed (5).

2 METHODS

Crude extracts were desalted and 10 µl were applied, without prefocussing, directly onto the surface of the ultrathin (240 µm) gels (consisting of 4% T; 3% C; 2,3% (w/v) Servalyte pH 2-11; 10% (w/v) Sorbitol and 10^{-4}M DTT) on GelBond-PAG^{TM} films (FMC corp.), prepared and run (on LKB equipment) according to(6)(modified). Immobilized pH-gradients were prepared and run according to (7) and (8)(modified); For extremely acidic Peroxidase (E.C.1.11.1.7) isoenzymes a gradient pH 3,1-4,1 was prepared using Immobiline^{TM} pK 3,6 as buffering Immobiline, omitting the washings and applying samples after 30 min. of prefocussing.

The gels were stained, by incubation for no more than 10 min., for enzymatic activities of peroxidases with the benzidine - blue method according to (9) and superoxide dismutase according to (10).

3 RESULTS

For rapid isoenzyme - screening of calli, Peroxidases proved to be most versatile. A complex pattern of some 30 bands was resolved on pH 2-11 gradients, with differences between the parents and between various tissues of the parents. High variability of isoenzymes pI 5-9 was observed, depending on growth conditions. Therefore, these isoenzymes could not be used for hybrid identification. In contrast, the patterns of extremely alkaline (pI 9-10,5) and extremely acidic (pI 3,3 - 4) isoenzymes were constant in various differentiated tissues of either parent, but both, tomato and potato, showed characteristic individual patterns. From callus tissue, only the extremely acidic (pI 3,3-4) isoenzymes could be resolved. For reliable hybrid identification, however, the resolution on pH 2-11 gradients was not high enough. On immobilized pH gradients pH 3,1-4,1, the acidic isoenzymes could be further resolved. In some cases (plants from (2)) differences occurred between patterns of unorganized and organized tissues in the parents and their hybrids, in other cases (plants from (1)), all differentiation states showed the same pattern. The patterns were constant in all growth conditions of the same tissue and different between each parent and their hybrids. Thus, comparison of peroxidase - isoenzyme patterns with pI 3,3 - 4 from both, callus and differentiated, tissues permitted reliable hybrid identification.

The patterns of superoxide dismutase were identical in both parents. Similar isoelectric focussing and staining gels for activities of amylases, ATPases, Cyt.c oxidase, dehydrogenases and esterases did reveal activity of reference standard enzymes, but failed with plant extracts.

4 ABBREVIATIONS

DTT, Dithiothreitol; GLC,gas - liquid chromatography

5 REFERENCES

(1) Melchers, G.(1978) in: Alfermann,H.W., Reinhard,E. eds.: Proceedings of an Intl. Symposium on Plant Cell Culture. Ges.f.Strahlen-und Umweltforschung mbH, München 1978, 306-311.

(2) Melchers, G. (1983): Topatoes and Pomatoes, Somatic Hybrids between Tomatoes and Potatoes. Plenary Lecture on the Joint Cong. of the Eur. Tissue Cult. Soc. and the Eur. Reticulo-Endothelial Society, Budapest 9.-13.5. 1983.

(3) Melchers,G., Sacristán,M.D. and Holder,A.A. (1978): Carlsberg Res. Commun. Vol.43, 203-218

(4) Schiller,B., Herrmann,R.G. and Melchers,G.(1982): Mol.Gen.Genet.186,453-459.

(5) Ninnemann,H. and Jüttner,F. (1981): Z. Pflanzenphysiol. 103, 95 - 107

(6) Radola, B.J. (1980): Electrophoresis 1 , 43 - 56

(7) Bjellqvist, B. and Ek, K.(1982): LKB-Application Note 321

(8) Ek, K., Bjellqvist, B. and Bishop, R. (1983): LKB-Application Note 322

(9) van Dujin,P. (1955): Rec.Trav.Chim.74, 771-778

(10) Beauchamp,C. and Fridovich,I. (1971): Anal.Biochem.44 276-287.

THREE-DIMENSIONAL CROSSED IMMUNOELECTROPHORESIS FOR TWO-DIMENSIONAL LECTIN AFFINITY ELECTROPHORESIS OF HUMAN α-FETOPROTEIN

Kazuhisa Taketa, Eriko Ichikawa, Masaki Izumi

Health Research Center, Kagawa University, Takamatsu 760, Japan

Hiroko Taga, Hidematsu Hirai

Tumour Laboratory, Kokubunji 185, Japan

1 INTRODUCTION

Human α-fetoprotein (AFP) has been separated into lectin-reactive and nonreactive molecular species by affinity electrophoresis under a defined condition (1,2). The reactivity of AFP with concanavalin A (Con-A) is independent of its reactivity with *Lens culinaris* agglutinin A (LCA-A) or erythroagglutinating phytohemagglutinin (E-PHA). Thus, the following eight molecular species of AFP have been separated by combination of Con-A and LCA-A (or E-PHA): AFP-00 (or AFP-0X0), neither reactive with Con-A or LCA-A (or E-PHA); AFP-10 (or AFP-1X0), reactive with only Con-A; AFP-11 (or AFP-1X1), reactive with both Con-A and LCA-A (or E-PHA); and AFP-01 (or AFP-0X1), reactive with only LCA-A (or E-PHA) (see Fig. 1 and Reference 3).

In the present study, those molecular species of AFP were separated by two-dimensional lectin affinity electrophoresis and detected by a newly developed crossed immunoelectrophoresis, which is referred to as electro-affinity transfer (4), as the third dimension electrophoresis. By this technique, AFP was specifically transferred to nitrocellulose membrane, which had been initially treated with affinity purified polyclonal horse anti-AFP and amplified by an enzyme-labeled antibody method. The term 'electro-affinity transfer' was derived from 'electroblotting' (5) and 'filter affinity transfer' (6).

2 MATERIALS AND METHODS

The first-dimension affinity electrophoresis was carried out at 5°C with a barbital/barbital-Na system, pH 8.6, on 1.0% and 1.5 mm-thick agarose (Litex, LSB, Litex, Glostrup) gels containing 0.5 mg/ml LCA-A

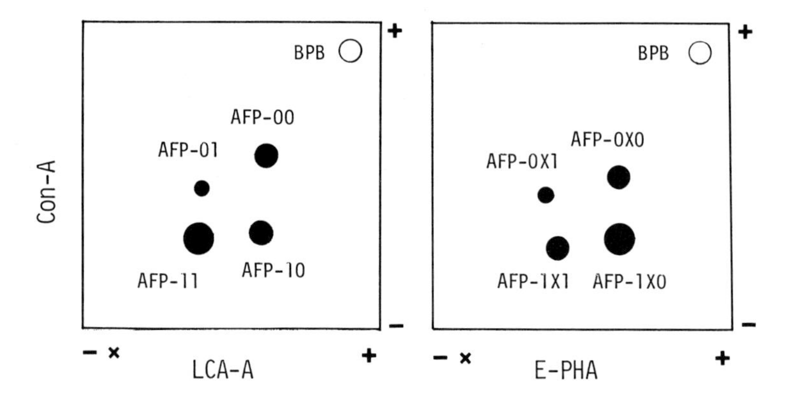

Fig. 1. Schematic illustration of different molecular species of human AFP separated by two-dimensional affinity electrophoreses with LCA-A and Con-A and with E-PHA and Con-A. x denotes the origin.

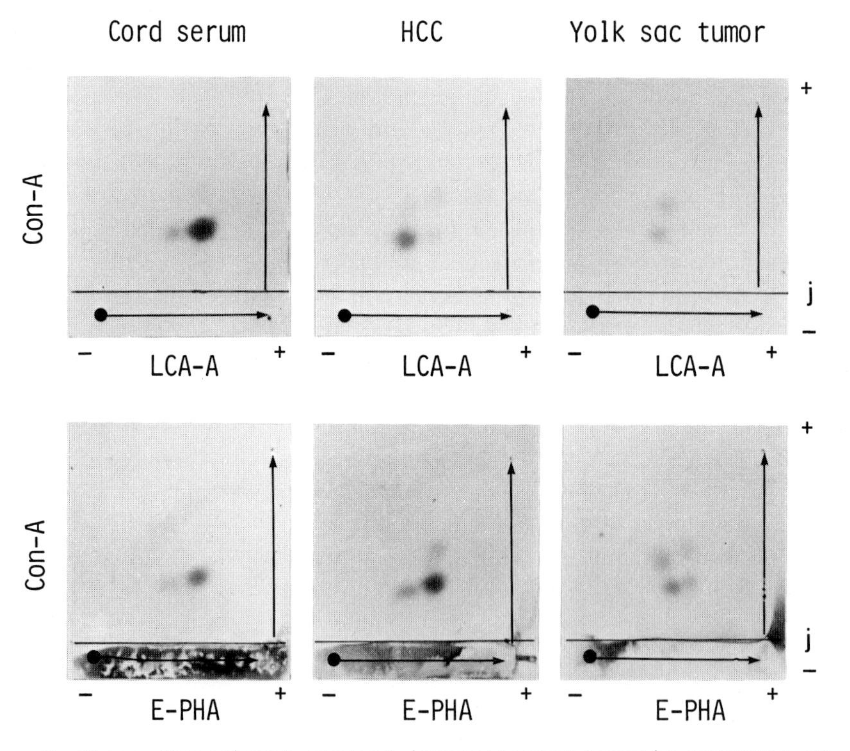

Fig. 2. Three-dimensional crossed immunoelectrophoretic patterns of human AFP separated by two-dimensional affinity electrophoreses with LCA-A and Con-A and with E-PHA and Con-A.

(E-Y Lab., San Mateo) or 1.0 mg/ml E-PHA (E-Y Lab.) by apllying 4 µl of samples with 4,000 ng/ml AFP. As sources of AFP, cord serum (AFP standard, DAKO immunoglobulins Lab., Copenhagen), ascites fluid from a case of hepatocellular carcinoma (HCC), cultured media of cell lines derived from human HCC (HuH-7 and PLC/PRF/5, from Dr. J. Sato, Division of Pathology, Cancer Institute, Okayama University Medical School), and serum from a patient with yolk sac tumor were used. After a marker spot of bromophenol blue (BPB) migrated 3.5 cm from the origin at 15 V/cm, the second-dimension affinity electrophoresis was started at 25°C and 10 V/cm with a similar agarose gel containing 2.0 mg/ml Con-A (Pharmacia Fine Chem., Uppsala). Other details appear in our previous paper (1). After BPB moved 3.5 cm from the junction (j) of the first and second lectin gels, separated AFP spots were transferred to horse anti-human AFP-coated nitrocellulose membranes by electrophoresis (40 V-200 mM, 1 hr at room temperature) with a Marysol Gel-Membrane-Transfer apparatus (Marysol Industry Co., Tokyo) and a buffer system of Tris (41 mM)-boric acid (40 mM), pH 8.3. The transferred AFP was reacted with rabbit anti-AFP (DAKO Immunoglobulins Lab.), followed by affinity-purified goat anti-rabbit IgG-horseradish peroxidase conjugate (Bio-Rad Lab., Richmond) for color development with diaminobenzidine. The intensities of AFP spots were determined by densitometry using similarly prepared calibration curves. Other conditions of the electro-affinity transfer are given elsewhere (4).

3 RESULTS AND DISCUSSION

Representative patterns of AFP species separated by two-dimensional affinity electrophoreses with LCA-A and Con-A and with E-PHA and Con-A are shown in Fig. 2. A maximum of four spots were revealed (lower detection level, 1 ng of AFP) and their patterns differed depending on the source of AFP used or as the combination of the lectins used was altered. Separated spots of AFP were identified from the known properties of AFP-lectin interaction as illustrated in Fig. 1 and quantitated by densitometry with simultaneously prepared calibration curves (not completely linear and slightly hyperbolic) to calculate their per cent distribution. The results obtained by this method were compared with those obtained by combination of affinity chromatography and affinity electrophoresis (1,2) and given in Fig. 3. The agreement between the two methods was satisfactory, indicating the usefulness of the present method for quantitative evaluation of AFP species separable by differential affinities for lectins.

4 REFERENCES

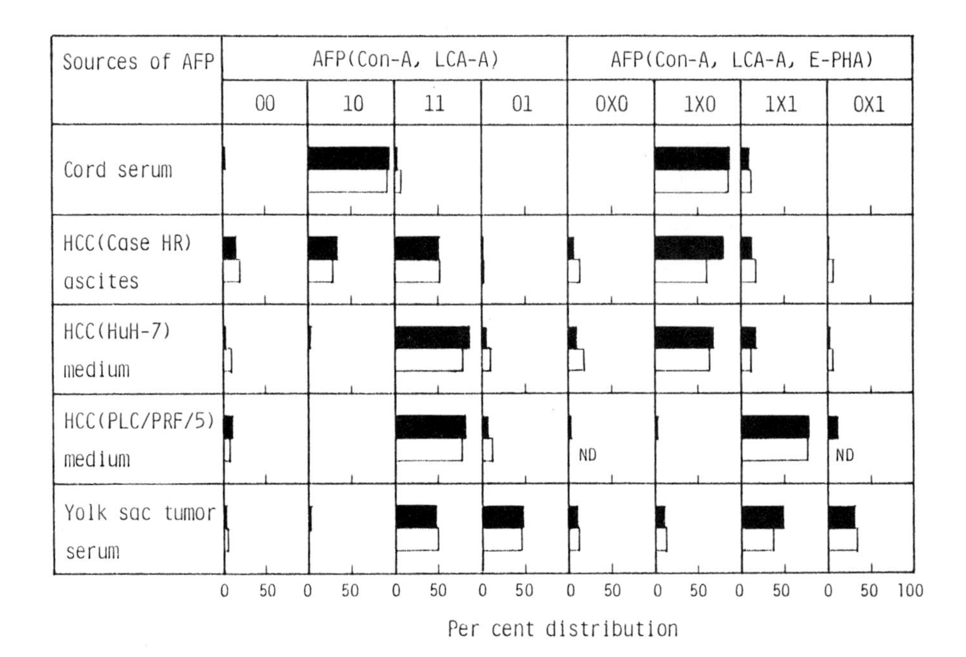

Fig. 3. Comparison of per cent distributions of eight molecular species of human AFP determined by the present method (closed column) with those quantitated by a combination of affinity chromatography and affinity electrophoresis (open column). ND, not determined.

(1) K. Taketa, M. Izumi, E. Ichikawa, Ann. N.Y. Acad. Sci. 417 (1983) 61-68.

(2) K. Taketa, Proceeding the APASL Scientific Meeting, Bangkok 1984, in press.

(3) K. Taketa, M. Izumi, H. Nakabayashi, J. Sato in H. Hirai (Ed.), Electrophoresis'83, Walter de Gruyter, Berlin, 1984, pp. 611-618.

(4) K. Taketa, H. Taga, H. Hirai, Acta Med. Okayama (1984) in press.

(5) J. M. Gershoni, G. Palade, Anal. Biochem. 124 (1982) 396-405.

(6) H. A. Erlich, J. R. Levinson, S. N. Cohen, H. O. McDevitt, J. Biol. Chem. 254 (1979) 12240-12247.

AFFINITY ELECTROPHORESIS: THE EFFECTS OF INCREASED PROTEIN CONCENTRATION. DETERMINATION OF EFFECTIVE CONCENTRATION OF THE IMMOBILIZED LIGAND.

Václav Hořejší[1], Marie Tichá[2]

[1]Institute of Molecular Genetics, Czechoslovak Academy of Sciences, Vídeňská 1083, 142 20 Prague 4, Czechoslovakia

[2]Department of Biochemistry, Charles University, Albertov 2030, Prague 2, Czechoslovakia

1 INTRODUCTION

Affinity electrophoresis can be used for quantitative evaluation of the strength of interaction between immobilized ligand molecules and proteins capable of specific binding of these ligands in terms of dissociation constants K_i (1). One of the prerequisites for this quantitative use of the method is that the concentration of the electrophoresed protein is much lower than that of the immobilized ligand. In this study we examine further the effects of increased concentration of the ligand-binding protein in the sample (A) on the value of apparent dissociation constant (K_i) obtained. It is shown that under the conditions of continuous gel electrophoresis using large volume of the sample (i.e. the conditions minimizing the concentration changes during electrophoresis), the value of ($A+K_i$) is determined by the usual procedure instead of K_i. On the other hand, from a series of measurements at various A's the value of effective concentration $\underline{c}_i$ of the immobilized ligand can be determined. This provides an information about the fraction of ligand molecules accessible for interaction with the electromigrating protein.

2 THEORY

If the effects of diffusion and stacking are negligible, the results of our previous paper (2) lead directly to the equation

$$\frac{d}{d_o - d} = \frac{1}{c_i} \cdot \frac{d \cdot a}{d_o} + \frac{K_i}{n \cdot c_i} \qquad (1)$$

where $\underline{d}$ is the distance migrated by the protein (possessing $\underline{n}$ ligand binding sites) in an affinity gel at given $\underline{c}_i$ (effective concentration of the immobilized ligand) and $\underline{a}$ (concentration of the protein in the migrating zone); $\underline{d}_o$ is the distance migrated by the protein in a control (noninteracting) gel under the same conditions. The width of the sample layer originally applied at the top of the affinity gel will decrease by the factor $f = d/d_o$ after entering the gel as a result of the interaction with the immobilized ligand (2) and therefore Eqn. 1 can be rewritten as

$$\frac{d}{d_o - d} = \left(A + \frac{K_i}{n}\right) \cdot \frac{1}{c_i} \qquad (2)$$

where A is the protein concentration in the original sample. Eqn. 2 can be used for evaluation of the effective $\underline{c}_i$ and "true" K_i by plotting $d/(d_o - d)$ vs. A at constant total $\underline{c}_i$.

3 EXPERIMENTAL RESULTS AND DISCUSSION

Eqn. 2 was tested in two experimental systems: a) Electrophoresis of pea seed lectin in polyacrylamide gels with incorporated 0.05% α-D-mannosyl polyacrylamide copolymer containing 14% D-mannose (3) in 50 mM sodium bicarbonate buffer pH 9.5 and b) Electrophoresis of lentil seed lectin in polyacrylamide gels containing 0.1% of the same α-D-mannosyl polyacrylamide copolymer, in 50 mM ammonium acetate buffer pH 5.2. In both cases 15 mm high sample layers were used containing 0.1 - 5 mg/ml of the protein (i.e. 2 - 100 μM). In control gels the mannosyl-polyacrylamide copolymer was omitted.

In both cases the dependence of $\underline{d}$ on A as predicted by Eqn. 2 was observed and effective $\underline{c}_i$ values were estimated. In both cases the values of effective $\underline{c}_i$ obtained were approximately 17% of the total analytical concentration of immobilized mannose. "True" K_i for the pea or lentil lectin was 1.8×10^{-4} M or 3.6×10^{-4} M, respectively.

These results indicate that

(a) Only a small fraction of the immobilized ligand molecules may be really capable of interaction with the migrating protein, presumably due to sterical restrictions imposed by the structure of the glycosylpolyacrylamide copolymer used for immobilization of the sugar residues.

(b) The K_i values as determined by affinity electrophoresis should be corrected for effective $\underline{c}_i$ and protein concentration.

(c) The effects of increased protein concentration may be especially marked in discontinuous buffer systems, where the protein zones are very concentrated due to stacking. This high protein concentration is predicted to lead to underestimation of the strength of the interaction observed. Therefore, it is necessary to use protein concentrations as low as possible and to avoid discontinuous buffer systems for determination of K_i. Correct K_i values and effective $\underline{c}_i$ should be determined as described here, i.e. from the dependence of mobility on the concentration of protein in the sample. Of course, for qualitative or semiquantitative purposes, (demonstration of an interaction between the protein and an immobilized ligand), discontinuous buffer systems with higher resolving power can be used. Analogous results were described also in an affinity chromatography system (4).

4 REFERENCES

(1) V. Hořejší, Anal. Biochem. 112 (1981) 1-12.

(2) V. Hořejší, M. Tichá, J. Chromatogr. 216 (1981) 43-62.

(3) V. Hořejší, M. Tichá, J. Kocourek, Biochim. Biophys. Acta 499 (1977) 290-300.

(4) K. Kasai, S. Ishii, J. Biochem. (Tokyo) 84 (1978) 1051-1060.

THERMODYNAMIC ANALYSIS OF MOUSE DNP SPECIFIC MYELOMA PROTEIN, MOPC-315 BY AFFINITY ELECTROPHORESIS

Kazusuke Takeo, Tatehiko Tanaka, Ryosuke Suzuno, Kazuyuki Nakamura
Akira, Kuwahara, Masanori Fujimoto

Department of Biochemistry, Yamaguchi University School of Medicine,
Kogushi-1144, J-755 Ube, Japan

1 INTRODUCTION

Dissociation constants for myeloma proteins for their haptens have been studied mainly by equilibrium dialysis (1,2). Since myeloma proteins are consisted, in general, of the mixture of monomer, dimer, and higher polymerized forms of immunoglobulin, the obtained results gave only an average value. Dextran-specific myeloma proteins in mouse ascitic fluid contain monomer and dimer of IgA type. Affinity electrophoresis have enabled to calculate dissociation constants of the IgA monomer in the ascitic fluid (3).

We have reported thermodynamic parameters for the interaction between concanavalin A and various carbohydrates using affinity electrophoresis (4). We present here thermodynamic studies on the interaction between a Dnp-specific myeloma protein and its haptens by means of the affinity electrophoresis.

2 MATERIALS AND METHODS

MOPC 315 myeloma protens and affinity ligands

The myeloma protein has beeb separated from ascitic fluid of mice bearing MOPC 315 using Dnp-lysine-Sepharose column chromatography(5). It contains other than IgA monomer (IgA_1) a small portion of IgA dimer (IgA_2) and a minor fraction of polymers as seen in Fig. 1.

The water soluble Dnp-polyacrylamide conjugate (Dnp-PA) and Tnp-polyacrylamide conjugate (Tnp-PA) have been prepared by coupling dinitrofluorobenzene or trinitrobenzene sulfonate with a non-cross-linked acrylamide-allylamine (5:1 w/w) copolymer (6).

Affinity electrophoresis

Electrophoresis was carried out with the buffer system according to Davis (7) using thermostatic PAGDE apparatus (4). The affinity ligand was added to the separating gel. One set of the electrophoresis was run with 12 tubes, duplicated gels of 6 different concentrations of the affinity ligand. The relative migration distance of the protein band was expressed as the ratio of the migrating distance of protein to that

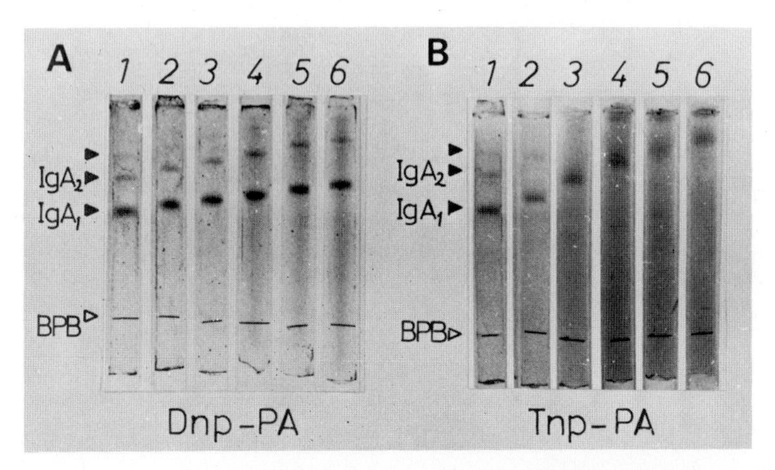

Fig. 1. Affinity patterns for the interactions between MOPC-315 myeloma protein and Dnp-PA (A) and Tnp-PA (B). Gels A-1, 2 3, 4, 5, and 6 contain Dnp-PA in the separating gels at 0, 0.21, 0.43, 0.64, 0.85, and 1.06 mM, respectively. Gels B-1, 2, 3, 4, 5, and 6 contain Tnp-PA in the separating gels at 0, 0.075, 0.15, 0.225, 0.30 and 0.375 mM, respectively. IgA_1, IgA_2 and BPB represent the fractions of the monomer and the dimer of the myeloma protein and the position BPB band. Electrophoresis was carried out at 20°c.

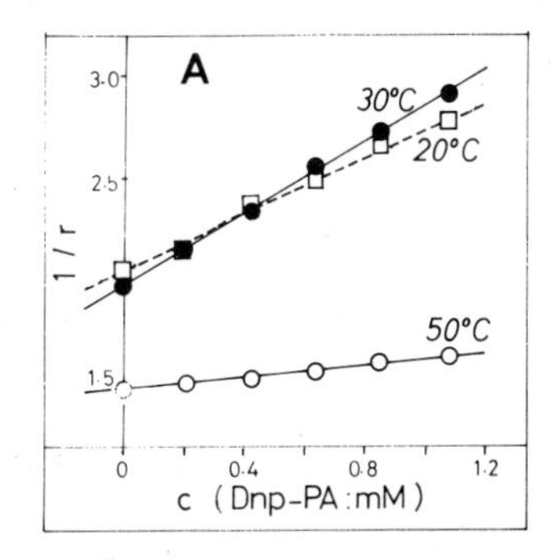

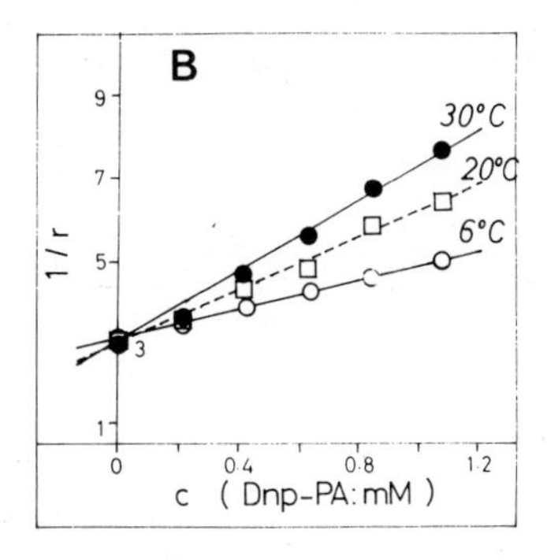

Fig. 2. Affinity plots for the interactions between the monomer (A) and the dimer (B) of MOPC 315 myeloma protein and Dnp-PA at various temperatures. The working temperatures are indicated on the plots.

of the BPB band. Dissociation constants (K) were calculated using the affinity equation (8,9):

$$1/r = (1/R_o)[1 + (c/K)] \qquad (1),$$

where r and R_o are the relative migration distances of the protein band in the presence and the absence of affinity ligand and c is the concentration of the affinity ligand. A straight line can be obtained, when 1/r is plotted as the ordinate and c as the abscissa. Its intercept on the c-axis gives a negative value of K. ΔH° is calculated from van't Hoff plot obtained from K values at varying temperatures. ΔG° and ΔS° at 20°C are calculated from K values at 20°C and ΔH°.

3 RESULTS AND DISCUSSION

Fig 1A shows an affinity pattern for Dnp-PA at 20°C. The relative migration distance in the absence of Dnp-PA (R_0) is estimated to be 0.49 for IgA_1 and 0.33 for IgA_2. The mobility of IgA fractions decreases when the concentration of Dnp-PA in the separating gel in-

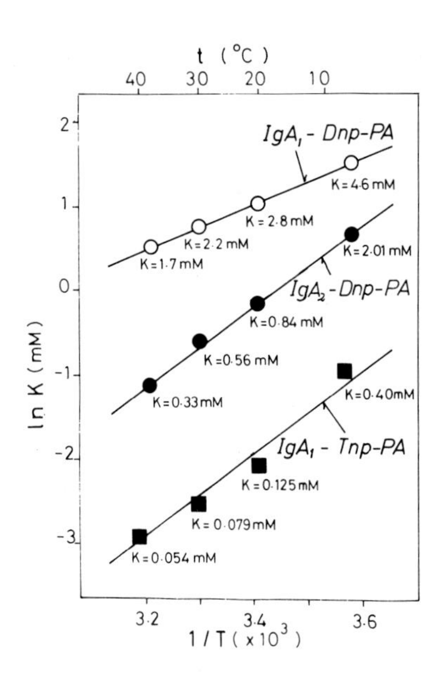

Fig. 3. Van't Hoff plots for the interactions between MOPC 315 myeloma protein and Dnp- and Tnp-PA. K values for IgA_1-Dnp-PA interaction were estimated to be 4.6, 2.8, 2.2, and 1.7 mM at 6, 20, 30, and 39°C, respectively, for IgA_2-Dnp-PA 2.01, 0.84, 0.56, and 0.33 mM at 6, 20, 30, and 39°C, respectively, and for IgA_1-Tnp-PA interaction 0.40, 0.125, 0.079, and 0.054 mM at 7, 20, 30, and 40°C, respectively.

creases. The rate of decrease of the mobility of IgA_2 is higher than that of IgA_1. Fig 1B shows the affinity pattern for Tnp-PA. The decrease of the mobility is much stronger in the presence of Tnp-PA than Dnp-PA. Fig 2A shows the affinity plots obtained from the equation (1) using the results in Fig 1A. The affinity plots at various temperatures are also shown. From the plot, K value of IgA_1 for Dnp-PA is estimated to be 2.8 mM at 20°C. At 50°C, the affinity plot is nearly parallel to the abscissa showing a very low affinity of the myeloma protein to Dnp-PA. Fig 2B shows the same affinity plot for the interaction of IgA_2 to Dnp-PA. The K value of IgA_2 for Dnp-PA at 20°C is estimated to be 0.84 mM. Hence IgA_2 has a 3.5-times stronger affinity to Dnp-hapten than IgA_1 has. In the legend of Fig 3, the K values at varying temperatures are listed.

Fig 3 shows the van't Hoff plots for the interactions between IgA_1 and Dnp-PA, IgA_2 and Dnp-PA, and IgA_1 and Tnp-PA. All three plots give straight lines in the temerature range between 6 and 40°C. In Table I, ΔH° and other thermodynamic parameters were summerized.

The positive values of ΔS° reveal that the interactions should be of hydrophobic character as reported by Mukkur (10). Below 40°C, MOPC 315 myeloma protein is separated into 3 to 4 bands as shown in Fig 1 and the R_o value for IgA_1 is estimated to be about 0.50 regardless of temperature difference. On the other hand, at 50°C, it shows very low affinity to the ligands and migrates as a single band having much faster mobility. Its R_o value is estimated to be 0.69. Those results indicate that MOPC 315 myloma protein changes the molecular structure accompaning depolymerization above 50°C. The structral change results in the loss of affinity to the hapten.

Table I. Thermaodynamic parameters of MOPC 315 myeloma protein

Interactions	K at 20°C (mM)	ΔG° (kcal/mol)	ΔH° (kcal/mol)	ΔS° (cal/mol/deg)
IgA_1-Dnp-PA	2.8	-2.99	5.16	29.2
IgA_2-Dnp-PA	0.84	-4.09	9.24	45.5
IgA_1-Tnp-PA	0.125	-4.43	10.52	53.4

4 REFERENCES

(1) H. N. Eisen, Methods in Med. Res. 10 (1964) 106-114.

(2) J. Cisar, E. A. Kabat, M. M. Dorner, J. Liao, J. Exp. Med. 142 (1975) 435-459.

(3) K. Takeo, E. A. Kabat, J. Immunol. 121 (1978) 2305-2310.

(4) K. Takeo, Lectins, Biol., Biochem., Clin. Biochem. 2 (1982) 583-594.

(5) D. Inbar, M. Rotman, D. Givol, J. Biol. Chem. 246 (1971) 6272-6275

(6) K. Takeo, R. Suzuno, M. Fujimoto, T. Tanaka, A. Kuwahara, Proceedings of Electrophoresis '82, Walter de Gruyter, Berlin 1982, p.277

(7) B. J. Davis, Ann. N. Y. Acd. Sci. 121 (1964) 404-427.

(8) K. Takeo, S. Nakamura, Arch. Biochem. Biophys. 153 (1972) 1-7.

(9) K. Takeo, Electrophoresis 4 (1984) in press.

(10) T. K. S. Mukkur, Biochem. J. 173 (1978) 39-44.

UNIFORMLY SPACED BANDING PATTERNS IN DNA SEQUENCING GELS USING FIELD STRENGTH GRADIENTS

Anders Olsson[1], Tomas Moks[1], Mathias Uhlén[1], Keith Gooderham[2] and Andras Gaal[2].

[1]Department of Biochemistry and Biotechnology, Royal Institute of Technology, S-100 44 Stockholm, Sweden.
[2]LKB-Produkter AB, Box 305, S-161 26 Bromma, Sweden.

1 INTRODUCTION

Polyacrylamide gel electrophoresis performs a central role in the rapid and high resolution separation of oligonucleotides produced by DNA sequencing reactions (1,2). During the last three to four years a number of important refinements have been made to these gels; including the use of ultrathin gels, the covalent binding and drying of the gel toone plate, temperature control to ensure even heating of the gel during the course of the run (3), the use of 35 S labelled nucleotides and the use of buffer gradient gels (4). All of these modifications have combined, not only to make the reading of the gel easier but also to extend the area of the gel from which useful sequence information can be obtained.

The introduction of buffer gradient gels has been a particularly valuable innovation. Using this system only a single gel needs to be run, whereas previously two gels were frequently required in order to read the complete DNA sequence in a single sample. However, buffer gradient gels are difficult to prepare; to pour even and reproducible gradients requires considerable skill and practice. In addition, this method cannot be used for the 0.2 mm ultrathin gels. In order to overcome these problems we have devised an alternative gradient gel system which is both simple and highly reproducible.

2 PREPARATION OF GRADIENT GELS

Gradient gels were prepared by the sliding plate method, essentially as described by Garoff and Ansorge (3), using a LKB 2010 series Macrophor electrophoresis unit and a Macromould gel casting table. The gradient was formed by making a wedge shaped gel with the aid of two sets of side spacers. The first set of "standard" (0.2 mm thick) spacers running the full length of the gel (550 mm), while the second set of short spacers were placed on top of these at the very bottom of the gel. The secondary spacers were 0.35 mm thick and of varying lengths depending on the type of gradient required (see Table 1). The length and thickness of the resulting gradient was determined not only by the length of these secondary spacers but also by the position of the lowest pair of clamps holding the two plates together once the gel had been cast (see Table 1).

Table 1. Preparation of wedge-shaped gels with different characteristics[a].

Gradient type[b]	Length of secondary (0.35 mm thick) spacers	Distance of lowest pair of clamps from bottom of gel (mm)	Approximate thickness of gel at bottom of gradient (mm)
1	60	200	0.7
2	60	150	0.7
3	60	50	0.7
4	80	150	0.8
5	100	150	0.9

(a) 4% acrylamide gels containing 7 M urea and x1 TBE buffer were used throughout. The thermostatic plate was allowed to come to temperature (55 °C) before loading the samples. x1 TBE electrode buffer was used in both the upper and lower chambers and the samples were loaded in formamide dye mix. The samples were run at 1.5 kV for 5´ and then at 2.5 kV until the bronophenol marker dye had migrated to the bottom of the gel (approx 115 min.).
(b) The wedge shaped thickness gradient results in a field strength gradient. The exact shape of this field strength gradient is unknown as it is difficult to calculate with any accuracy and all of these gradients have been derived empirically.

3 RESULTS AND DISCUSSION

All of the gradient gels described in Table 1 produced good, even separations of oligonucleotides in the size range of 60 to 300 basis. The separation of oligonucleotides using the first gradient (type 1) shown in Table 1 was particularly effective, producing an extremely uniform spacing of oligonucleotides within this size range. These separations are in marked contrast to those obtained with standard gels of uniform thickness. In these gels the oligonucleotides are not uniformly separated down the gel. Instead the smallest molecules are widely separated in the lower half of the gel while the larger ones remain poorly resolved in the upper portion of the gel. This failure to separate the high molecular weight oligonucleotides means that much of the potential sequence information is lost. With this type of gel the only way that this information can be obtained is by running a second duplicate gel but for a longer time so as to permit the separation of the larger oligonucleotides.

The gradient gel systems described here, therefore represent a significant improvement in oligonucleotide separations. The ease of preparation and the reproducibility of this system, combined with the other refinements in DNA sequencing gel technology mentioned previously, ensure that DNA sequencing samples can be analysed rapidly and with confidence.

4 REFERENCES

(1) F. Sanger, S. Nicklen, A.R. Coulson, Proc. Natl. Acad. Sci. USA 74 (1977) 5463-5467.

(2) A.M. Maxam, W. Gilbert, Proc. Natl. Acad. Sci. USA 74 (1977) 560-564.

(3) H. Garoff, W. Ansorge. Anal. Biochem. 115 (1981) 450-457.

(4) M.D. Biggin, T.J. Gibson, G.F. Hong, Proc. Natl. Acad. Sci. USA 80 (1983) 3963-3965.

TITRATION CURVES OF SERUM ALBUMIN: THE EFFECT OF LIGANDS

Michael F. Vickers, András L. Tárnoky

Clinical Biochemistry Department, Royal Berkshire Hospital,
Reading RG1 5AN, England

Righetti et al. (1) described acrylamide gel electrophoresis across an ampholine gradient for the production of protein titration curves. Our preliminary report (2) showed a modified procedure using cellulose acetate (3) being applied to albumin and its variants. The technique, using both media, is now being applied to test the effect of ligands on wild-type and hereditary variant serum albumins. This has involved studying ligand behaviour in the course of the two phases of the procedure, taking the HSA - salicylate system as a model.

Titration curves, obtained with different proportions of protein and ligand, have been evaluated. Preparation of the acrylamide gel followed Righetti's original procedure but omitted the addition of the aminoacid mixture. Cellulose acetate membranes were prepared by the method of Ambler and Walker (4). Ampholyte treatment, IEF and electrophoresis was as previously described (3, 2), except that all experiments were carried out with and without incorporating the ligand molecule in the ampholyte mixture in order to compare conditions akin to affinity electrophoresis as applied by Ek and Righetti (5) with the survival of a preformed protein - ligand complex. The model forms an approach to pharmacological applications.

REFERENCES

(1) P.G. Righetti, R. Krishnamoorthy, E. Gianazza, D. Labie, J.Chromatogr. 166 (1978) 455-460.

(2) A.L. Tárnoky, M.F. Vickers, Abstr. 5th European Congr. Clin. Chem. (1983) p.520.

(3) M.F. Vickers, P.A. Robinson, J.Chromatogr. 275 (1983) 428-431.

(4) J. Ambler, G. Walker, Clin.Chem. 25 (1979) 1320-1322.

(5) K. Ek, P.G. Righetti, Electrophoresis 1 (1980) 137-140.

ELECTROPHORETIC SEPARATION OF MOLECULAR SUBFORMS OF ASPARTATE AMINOTRANSFERASE FROM CARP LIVER

Zsuzsanna Buzás[+], László Orbán[+], Andreas Chrambach[++]

[+]Biochemical Department, József Attila University, Szeged, Hungary,
[++]Endocrinology and Reproduction Research Branch, National Institute of Child Health and Human Development, National Institutes of Health, Bethesda MD, USA

1 INTRODUCTION

The monitoring of serum aspartate aminotransferase (ASAT, EC 2.6.1.1.) activity in human and animal serum is a reliable tool for determining tissue and organ injury. In most species ASAT exists in two isoenzyme forms, both containing molecular subforms differing in electrophoretic mobility. The determination of quantitative distribution of these isoenzymes and subforms in organs of a given species is a preliminary condition of studying organ injury caused by various reasons.

2 METHOD

Polyacrylamide gel electrophoresis (PAGE) in multiphasic buffer systems has one major advantage over PAGE in a single, continuous buffer of being able to concentrate the sample into the narrow starting zone prior to resolution (1). The automatic concentration of the sample is achieved most conveniently by use of the "stacking" procedure introduced originally by Ornstein (2) and Davis (3) and defined further physicochemically by Jovin (4). In our experiments we used multiphasic buffer systems with positive and negative polarity (5) and an all-Pyrex gel tube apparatus.

3 APPLICABILITY

This method suitable for

a/ the quantitative differentiation of two ASAT isoenzymes from carp liver

b/ the separation of the subforms of one isoenzyme

This electrophoretic separation gives useful information, which could contribute to the understanding of fish aspartate aminotransferase and to the importance of in vivo and in vitro approaches in assesing chemical effects, and their potential hazards in aquatic environment.

4 REFERENCES

(1) A. Chrambach and D. Rodbard in B. D. Hames and D. Rickwood (Eds), Gel Electrophoresis of Proteins: A Practical Approach, Information Retvieval Ltd. Press, Oxford 1980, pp. 98

(2) L. L. Ornstein, Ann. N. Y. Acad. Sci 121 (1964) 321

(3) B. J. Davis, Ann. N. Y. Acad. Sci. 121 (1964) 404

(4) T. M. Jovin, Biochemistry, 12 (1973) 871, 879, 890

(5) Zs. Buzás and A. Chrambach, Electrophoresis, 3 (1982) 121

A DEVICE TO ELUTE BIOMOLECULES OUT OF GELS

Stephan Diekmann

Max-Planck-Institut fuer biophysikalische Chemie, Am Fassberg
3400 Goettingen - Nikolausberg, West-Germany

Many biochemical procedures require the elution of biomolecules (for example proteins or nucleic acids) from gels before proceeding to subsequent steps. Techniques which are commonly used for this purpose are usually elaborate, time consuming, or have a low yield. The device presented here (see figures A,B,C) is easy to handle, rapid, has a high yield, and requires no maintenance.

Agarose or acrylamide gel slices containing the macromolecules are placed in small cups of convenient size (see figure B). Several samples can be processed at the same time. The slices are covered with a buffer of low salt molarity. For nucleic acids 10 mM Tris (pH 8.0) with 1 mM EDTA was convenient, for proteins a buffer containing SDS has been used. Finally, a small volume (50 ul) of high molarity salt solution is layered underneath the buffer within the V-boring (see figure B). The volume of the high-salt solution must be large enough so that the macromolecules cannot bypass the high-salt solution.

After applying an electric field the macromolecules migrate out of the gel slice into the V-boring. In the low-salt buffer they contribute considerably to the charge transport. Once the macromolecules reach the high-salt region they are effectively immobilized since the major charge transport is due to the ions in the high-salt solution. Thus, the macromolecules concentrate in the V-boring where they meet the high-salt solution. Co-migrating drugs also display this effect. Under normal conditions the concentrated sample remains within the V-boring for several hours.

The salt of high molarity can be chosen conveniently for further preparating steps. 3 M Na-acetate allows precipitation of nucleic acids by simply adding ethanol. For proteins, the high-salt solution might contain SDS to avoid precipitation in the V-boring.

As soon as all macromlecules reach the high-salt region the electric field is turned off. The buffer level is lowered under the cup level to separate the high-salt solution in the V-boring from the low-salt buffer. The high-salt solution containing the macromolecules (total 50 to 200 ul) is pipeted out of the V-boring.

An extremely high yield is expected in general. Greater than 95% yields are routinely obtained working with nucleic acids. The device has already functioned reliably for many months.

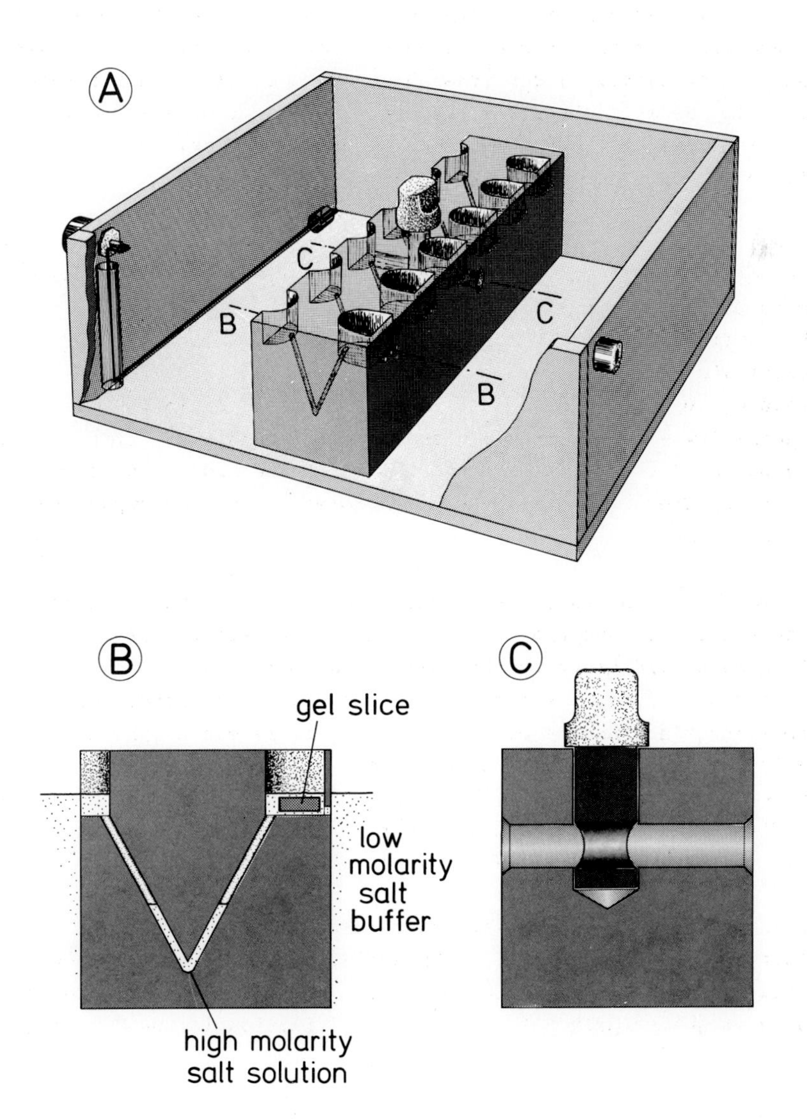

DOUBLE ANTIBODY AVIDIN-BIOTIN PEROXIDASE LABELING FOR DETECTION OF OLIGOCLONAL IgG IN UNCONCENTRATED CSF SEPARATED BY AGAROSE ISOELECTRIC FOCUSING

Vasilios Kostulas, Hans Link

Department of Neurology, Karolinska Institutet, Huddinge University Hospital, S-141 86 Huddinge, Stockholm, Sweden

1 INTRODUCTION

Several methods have been proposed for demonstration of oligoclonal bands in cerebrospinal fluid (CSF) without previous concentration of the fluid, such as separation of CSF by isoelectric focusing (IF) and silver staining (1), immunoperoxidase staining (2) or radioimmunofixation (3). Using the latter technique more extensively, we have experienced that it is less reproducible. The sensitivity of the other methods used till now is not high enough to enable the safe demonstration of oligoclonal bands in CSF specimens with normal IgG concentrations, and none of them has found its way to the routine clinical laboratory.

The avidin-biotin system is based on the high affinity between avidin, a glycoprotein with a molecular weight of 68,000, and the low molecular weight vitamin biotin which has four binding sites for avidin and may be coupled to proteins such as enzymes or antibodies. We have recently adopted this amplification system after separation of CSF and serum proteins by agarose IF (avidin-biotin AIF) (4). Here we report our results from use of this method in our routine CSF laboratory on paired samples of CSF and serum from 1,114 unselected, consecutive patients with various neurological disorders.

2 MATERIALS AND METHODS

The major diagnostic groups are summarized in Table 1. 5 µL of CSF containing 125 ng of IgG (25 mg/L) and 5 µL of the patient's serum diluted to the same IgG concentration were applied to troughs measuring 4.5 x 0.6 mm in agarose gel and submitted to AIF (5). Proteins were then transferred to a cellulose nitrate membrane and immunolabeled by incubation of the membrane with rabbit antiserum to human IgG Fc, biotinylated goat antiserum to rabbit IgG and, finally, avidin-biotin peroxidase complex followed by peroxidase staining (4). The membrane was then dried and inspected for IgG patterns. The occurrence of two or more homogeneous bands in addition to those in pooled control serum run on each plate was considered to present oligoclonal IgG.

Table 1. Frequencies of oligoclonal IgG bands on agarose isoelectric focusing (AIF) of unconcentrated CSF and avidin-biotin amplification, and of above-normal CSF IgG index in 1,114 consecutive neurological patients.

Diagnosis	No. patients	No. (and %) of patients with Oligoclonal bands on AIF	CSF IgG index >0.7
Multiple sclerosis	65	58 (89%)	44 (68%)
Optic neuritis	13	6 (46%)	4 (31%)
Nervous system infection	29	8 (28%)	4 (14%)
Other neurological diseases	1007	95 (9%)	63 (6%)
Paraesthesia	106	19 (18%)	11 (10%)
Myelopathy	20	6 (30%)	5 (25%)
Cerebrovascular diseases	186	20 (11%)	5 (3%)
Epilepsy	34	1 (3%)	1 (3%)
Dementia	28	2 (7%)	1 (3%)
Parkinson's disease	14	2 (14%)	1 (7%)
Nervous system tumor	14	1 (7%)	2 (14%)
Radicular syndrome	99	4 (4%)	8 (8%)
Polyneuropathy	45	6 (13%)	4 (9%)
Mononeuropathy	29	2 (7%)	2 (7%)
Bell's palsy	12	0	1
Trigeminal neuralgia	9	0	1
Headache	208	13 (6%)	9 (4%)
Vertigo	59	5 (9%)	3 (5%)
Psychoneurosis	31	3 (10%)	2 (7%)

CSF IgG index equal to (CSF IgG/serum IgG):(CSF albumin/serum albumin) (6).

3 RESULTS AND DISCUSSION

With this method, oligoclonal IgG bands (Fig. 1) were found in 58 of 65 (89%) patients with clinically definite multiple sclerosis, in 8 (28%) of 29 with infectious diseases of the nervous system, and in 95 (9%) of 1,007 patients with a variety of other neurological disorders (Table 1). These frequencies are in good agreement with those previously presented when CSF was separated by AIF after concentration and stained with Coomassie Blue (5). Of the 95 patients with other neurological diseases who were positive for oligoclonal IgG bands, 32 displayed bands of identical number and migration properties in the corresponding serum. It is most probable that the oligoclonal IgG in these instances derived from plasma cell clones outside the nervous system. None of the patients with multiple sclerosis or optic

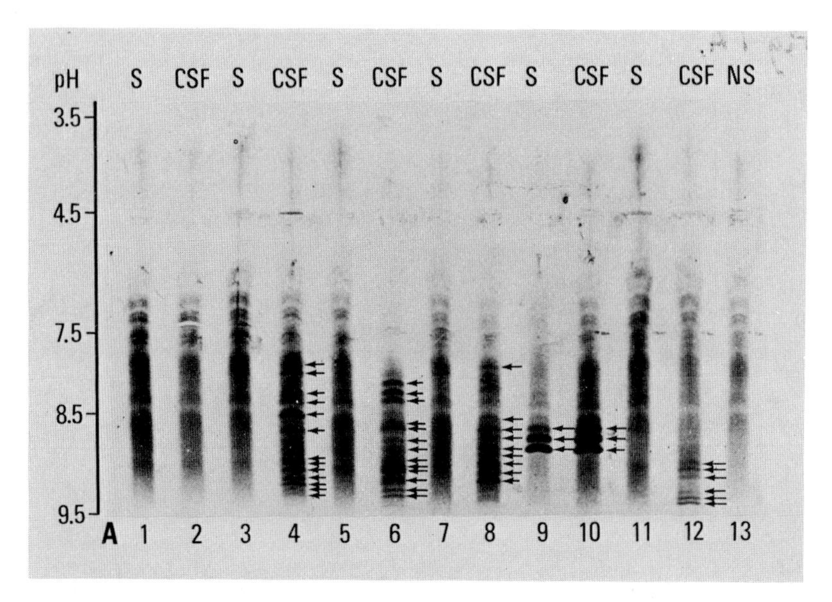

Fig. 1. Patterns from avidin-biotin amplified IF of diluted serum (S) and unconcentrated cerebrospinal fluid (CSF). 1 and 2, patient with tension headache; 3 and 4, patient with aseptic meningitis; 5 and 6, multiple sclerosis; 7 and 8, paraesthesia; 9 and 10, benign monoclonal gammopathy; 11 and 12, Guillain-Barré syndrome; 13, pooled normal serum. Arrows denote oligoclonal bands.

neuritis, and only one of those with a nervous system infection displayed such a pattern. Like other CSF separation procedures previously used for demonstration of oligoclonal bands (5), avidin-biotin AIF for demonstration of oligoclonal IgG bands was more sensitive as indicator of intrathecal IgG production than determination of CSF IgG index equal to (CSF IgG/serum IgG):(CSF albumin/serum albumin) (Table 1) (6). The avidin-biotin AIF method is also highly specific because only the protein of interest (i.e., IgG) is immunolabeled. For optimal information about the occurrence of oligoclonal IgG,one should investigate controlled amounts of CSF IgG and serum IgG. The use of concentrated CSF necessitates the determination of the concentration of IgG in the specimen before and after the concentration procedure, whereas only one IgG determination is required in the avidin-biotin amplified procedure.

In summary, obviating CSF sample concentration, the high specificity and sensitivity make avidin-biotin AIF a useful alternative for demontration of oligoclonal IgG bands in routine clinical work.

4 REFERENCES

(1) U. Wurster, In Electrophoresis '82, Walter de Gruyter & Co., Berlin, 1983.

(2) M. V. Iivanainen, W. Wallen, M. E. Leon et al, Arch. Neurol. 38 (1981) 427-430.

(3) V. K. Kostulas, H. Link, J. Neurol. Sci. 54 (1982) 117-127.

(4) T. Olsson, V. Kostulas, H. Link, Clin. Chem. (1984) In press.

(5) H. Link, V. Kostulas, Clin. Chem. 29 (1983) 810-815.

(6) G. Tibbling, H. Link, S. Öhman, Scand. J. Clin. Lab. Invest. 37 (1977) 385-390.

5 ACKNOWLEDGEMENTS

This study was supported by grants from the Swedish Medical Research Council (grant No. 3381).

LIMITATIONS OF AVIDIN-BIOTIN SYSTEM IN DETECTION OF CEREBROSPINAL FLUID IgM SEPARATED BY AGAROSE ISOELECTRIC FOCUSING

Francesca Chiodi, Hans Link

Department of Neurology, Karolinska Institutet, Huddinge University Hospital, S-141 86 Huddinge, Stockholm, Sweden

1 INTRODUCTION

The avidin-biotin complex, based on the extraordinarily high affinity of the glycoprotein avidin to the vitamin biotin has, since the first application reported in 1976 (1), been used to a large extent in immunological studies (2). Transfer of proteins to cellulose nitrate membrane after agarose isoelectric focusing (AIF), followed by double-antibody peroxidase labeling and avidin-biotin amplification (avidin-biotin AIF) has also been used to demonstrate oligoclonal IgG bands in unconcentrated cerebrospinal fluid (CSF) (3). Based on recent evidence for local production of IgM within the central nervous system in patients with multiple sclerosis and other inflammatory neurological diseases (4), our interest has focused on possible occurrence of oligoclonal IgM bands in CSF. We have applied avidin-biotin AIF for this purpose, and describe now our finding that it is not possible to define the IgM pattern on AIF, nor the patterns of other proteins present in low concentrations in CSF, when using avidin-biotin amplification.

2 MATERIALS AND METHODS

CSF and serum were obtained from patients with clinically definite multiple sclerosis selected on the basis of presence of elevated CSF IgM index (4). γ, α, and μ chain myeloma sera were obtained from Dr. A. Sidén.

15 µL of CSF and serum adjusted to IgM concentrations of 15 mg/L as measured by ELISA (4) were applied into preformed slits on agarose gel. After AIF and protein transfer to cellulose nitrate membrane, this was soaked with bovine serum albumin to block still free protein binding sites. Thereafter, the membrane was incubated with monospecific rabbit antiserum against human μ chain (primary antiserum) and then with biotinylated goat antiserum against rabbit IgG (second antiserum) and avidin-biotin peroxidase complex, and finally stained for peroxidase (3). For identification of IgG or IgA patterns, identical amounts of protein were run.

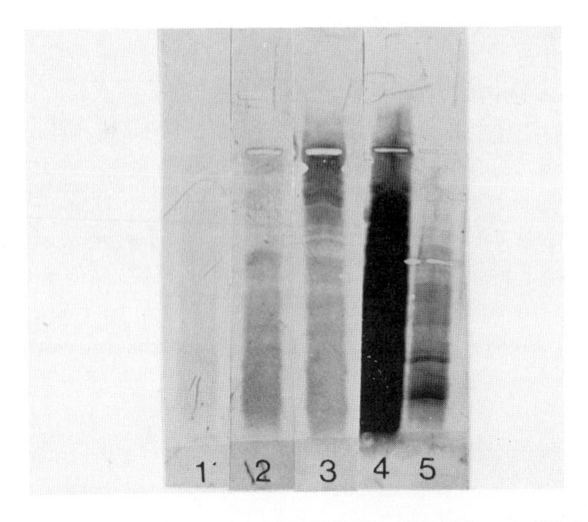

Fig. 1. Avidin-biotin AIF of CSF from one patient with MS and oligoclonal IgG bands. 15 μL of CSF concentrated to 1 g/L of IgG were applied at (1-4), 15 μL of native CSF diluted to 15 mg/L at (5). Primary antiserum used was anti-μ (2), anti-α (3), and anti-γ (4 and 5), while no primary antiserum was included at (1).

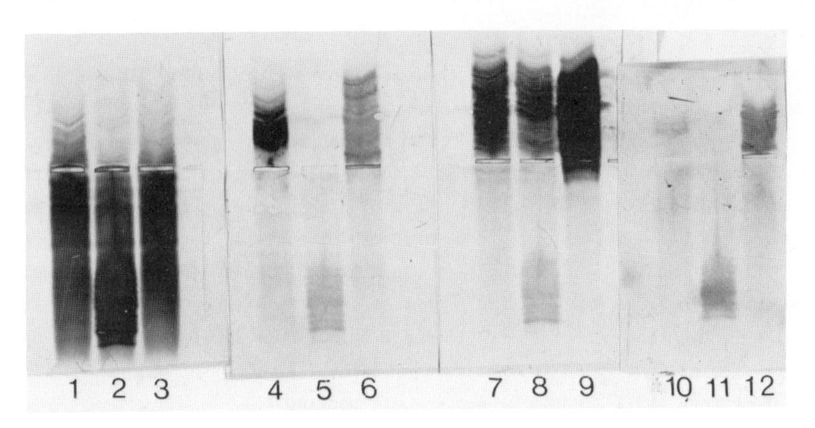

Fig 2 Avidin-biotin AIF of serumfrom a patient with μ chain myeloma (1, 4, 7, 10), γ chain myeloma (2, 5, 8, 11), and α chain myeloma (3, 6, 9, 12). Primary antisera used were directed against γ chains (1-3), μ chains (4-6), and α chains (7-9). No primary antiserum was used for (10-12).

3 RESULTS AND DISCUSSION

Normal human serum IgM migrates on AIF over the pH range 4-6. When examining such serum by avidin-biotin AIF, we found protein regularly to be stained also in the alkaline region, that is where IgG is migrating. Examination of MS CSF by avidin-biotin AIF for IgM revealed a pattern similar to that of oligoclonal IgG, although fainter (Fig. 1). These data led us to control our system of avidin-biotin amplification, subtracting the primary antiserum (Fig. 1, run 1), and primary as well as secondary antiserum. In both instances, patterns similar to those of oligoclonal IgG bands were still detectable, indicating reactivity of the reagents present in the avidin-biotin system used.

These results were further corroborated by experiments performed on serum specimens from myeloma of G, A, and M classes. Anti-μ used as primary antiserum revealed, in addition to IgM paraprotein in IgM myeloma, paraproteins of G and A classes in the corresponding myelomas as well. Corresponding results were obtained with anti-γ and anti-α (Fig. 2). This non-specificity observed with avidin-biotin amplification was not a consequence of crossreactivity with the primary antiserum but, as again shown from experiments when the primary antiserum was omitted (Fig. 2, run 10-12), due to non-specific binding both to the biotinylated antiserum (secondary antiserum) and to avidin-biotin complex.

Summarizing these data, it has become clear that avidin-biotin AIF, because of unspecific binding between immunoglobulins and biotinylated antiserum as well as avidin-biotin complex, is not suitable for the analysis of oligoclonal IgM which might be present in MS CSF, nor is this method applicable for the characterization of migration properties on AIF of other proteins which are present in e.g. CSF at low concentrations. Limitations of the avidin-biotin system for ultrastructural localization of antigens have also been described (5), being due to the capacity of the positively charged protein avidin to bind proteins with negative charge at physiological pH and unknown carriers of vitamin biotin. These limitations of the avidin-biotin system are not valid for analysis of CSF for presence of oligoclonal IgG bands since very small amounts of protein are applied (3).

4 REFERENCES

(1) E. A. Bayer, M. Wilchek, S. Skutelsky, FEBS Lett. 68 (1976) 240-244.

(2) M. Wilchek, E. A. Bayer, Immunology Today 5 (1984) 39-43.

(3) T. Olsson, V. Kostulas, H. Link, Clin. Chem. (1984) In press.

(4) P. Forsberg, A. Henriksson, H. Link, S. Öhman, Scand. J. clin. Labl Invest. 44 (1984) 7-12.

(5) R. E. Morris, C. B. Saelinger, Immunology Today 5 (1984) 127.

APPLICATION OF 2D IEF/PA AND PROTEIN BLOTTING TO THE ANALYSIS OF VARIANT FORMS OF ALPHA 1-ANTICHYMOTRYPSIN

Martina Daly* and Frank Hallinan*+

*Children's Research Centre, Our Lady's Hospital for Sick Children, Crumlin, Dublin 12, Ireland.
+Department of Biology, College of Technology, Kevin Street, Dublin 8, Ireland.

1 INTRODUCTION

Plasma protein microheterogeneity may be readily analysed by polyacrylamide gel isoelectric focusing (IEF/PA) and simple capillary blotting techniques (1,2). These methods enable highly sensitive immunological detection of variant forms (isoforms) of specific proteins in multi-protein mixtures such as serum (2,3).

The molecular basis and functional properties of these different isoforms has been investigated in a few cases by incubation of serum with appropriate enzymes and subsequent electrophoretic separation (e.g. 4,5). However, the possibility that a particular altered banding pattern is a secondary effect of the enzyme and the inability to precisely determine the shift of any one isoform is a major limitation of this approach. We have developed a technique of 2 dimensional (2D) IEF/PA and immunoblotting which avoids these short-comings firstly, by the partial purification inherent in the first dimension IEF/PA and secondly by enabling precise determination of the alterations induced in any one isoform after enzyme treatment. We here present our results of the application of this technique to the analysis of isoforms of alpha 1-antichymotrypsin (ACT).

2 MATERIALS AND METHODS

Serum was collected from 6 healthy donors, pooled, aliquoted and stored at -20°C until needed. Sheep antiserum to human ACT was from Serotec. Horseradish peroxidase (HRP) conjugated rabbit immuno-globulins to sheep immunoglobulins (RaS) was from Dako. Bovine pancreatic alpha-chymotrypsin (Type II) and *C. perfringens* neuraminidase (Type X) were from Sigma.

Isoelectric focusing in the first dimension was carried out in (T = 6%; C = 3%) polyacrylamide slab gels (250 x 113 x 0.8) mm containing 2% (w/v) ampholytes (LKB Ampholines). Pooled serum (approximately 460 µl/gel) was applied on a continuous strip (1x23) cm of 3MM paper at the cathode and focused for 2 hours at 4°C to a maximum power of 10 W and a maximum voltage of 2000V. The portion of the gel containing focused ACT was then removed and cut into (2.5 x 0.5) cm segments at right angles to the direction of the focused proteins and stored at -20°C until required.

The effects of neuraminidase and alpha-chymotrypsin on ACT were examined by incubating segments of the first dimension gel with these enzymes for (10-30) min at 37°C before the second focusing step. (2.5 x 0.5) cm segments of the first gel were laid lengthwise at the cathode of the second dimension gel and focused identically to the first dimension gel.

The gel was capillary blotted (1) to nitrocellulose and ACT was detected immunochemically (6).

3 RESULTS AND DISCUSSION

7 isoforms of ACT can be immunodetected on nitrocellulose blots of one dimensional IEF/PA gels ranging in pI from 4.5 to 5.1 (Fig. 1A). Similar results have been reported using immunofixation (5). Thus, in a second dimension gel a diagonal pattern of spots with pI values corresponding to those of the first dimension was observed (Fig. 1B).

Incubation of the first dimension gel segment with water had no effect on the final pattern while incubation with neuraminidase for 10 minutes caused a cathodal shift of approximately 1.8 pH unit and a reduction to 4 isoforms (Fig. 1C). The microheterogeneity of ACT is, therefore, partially attributable to variable amounts of sialic acid. Further investigation will be required to correlate the different isoform patterns before and after neuraminidase treatment. These results are in agreement with those previously reported (5).

The effect of chymotrypsin on the ACT isoform was examined (Fig. 1D) at varying ratios of enzyme to inhibitor. Two effects were observed: firstly, the appearance of a cathodally shifted (by 0.6 pH unit) parallel series of isoforms first evident at a chymotrypsin concentration of 4 µg/ml and forming an increasingly more diffuse pattern at higher chymotrypsin concentrations. Secondly, the appearance of an anodally shifted (by 0.05 pH unit) parallel series of isoforms also first evident at a chymotrypsin concentration of 4 μg/ml. The majority of the original ACT is shifted at the higher chymotrypsin concentrations.

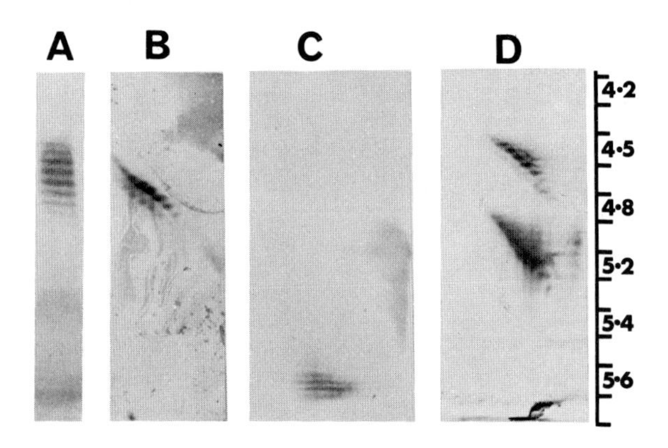

Figure 1: 1D and 2D IEF/PA of ACT
(a) 1D IEF/PA of ACT; 2D IEF/PA of ACT (b) directly (c) following incubation of first dimension gel segment with 1.25 units neuraminidase for 30 min. at 37°C (d) following incubation of the first dimension gel segment with 8.5 μg alpha chymotrypsin for 10 min. at 37°C. The pH scale on the right refers only to panel D. The ACT immunoreactive material was detected using sheep anti-human ACT followed by HRP conjugated RaS immunoglobulins.

This reaction appears to represent specific chymotrypsin-ACT complexes since incubation with pepsin (data not shown) causes a general blurring of the pattern with no evidence of specific shifts.

ACKNOWLEDGEMENT

We are grateful to the Medical Research Council of Ireland for supporting this work.

4 REFERENCES

1. M.P. Reinhart, D. Malamud. Anal. Biochem. 123 (1982), 229-235.

2. M. Daly, F. Hallinan. Biochem. Soc. Trans. (in press)

3. D.B. Whitehouse, W. Putt. Ann. Hum. Genet. 47, (1983), 1-8.

4. S.P. Daiger, R.S. Wildin, Biochem. Genet. 19, (1981) 673-685.

5. E. Gianazza, P. Arnaud, Electrophoresis, 2, (1981) 247-250.

6. H. Towbin, T. Staehelin, J. Gordon, Proc. Nat. Acad. Sci. U.S.A. 76 (1979) 4350-4354.

HOW EFFICIENT IS THE ELECTROPHORETIC REMOVAL OF PROTEINS FROM POLYACRYLAMIDE GELS AND THEIR RETENTION ON NITROCELLULOSE PAPER IN THE PRESENCE OF SDS ?

C. Kiecke, V. Neuhoff and T.V. Waehneldt

Max-Planck-Institut für experimentelle Medizin, Forschungsstelle Neurochemie, D-3400 Göttingen

The electrophoretic transfer of a number of soluble proteins (bovine serum albumin, ovalbumin, carbonic anhydrase, trypsin inhibitor, lactalbumin) and a membrane protein (PNS myelin P_0 glycoprotein) was examined using the commercially available Transblot Cell (Biorad Laboratories). The Laemmli-type SDS gels were 13 % in acrylamide (140 x 100 mm, 1.5 mm thick, 20 slots of 4 mm each), the transfer buffer was 25 mM Tris, 192 mM Gly, pH 8.3, 0.04 % SDS, 20 % methanol, the nitrocellulose sheets were BA 85, 0.45 µm from Schleicher und Schüll, D-3354 Dassel. Prior to blotting, the buffer was cooled for half an hour to 14-16° C with tap water of 8-10° C. During the 3 h transfer at 500 mA the buffer temperature rose to 24-26° C with a concomitant voltage decline from 120 V to about 95 V.

The presence of SDS in the transfer buffer led to the complete removal of all protein bands from the gel after 3 h (the hydrophobic P_0 glycoprotein included), irrespective of the load initially applied (ranging from 1-30 µg per slot).

The nitrocellulose paper was then stained for 3 min with 0.1 % amidoblack in methanol-acetic acid-water (45:10:45) and the excess stain removed with five washes of 3 min each with water. The bands were cut out and extracted with 500 µl methanol-acetic acid (7:3) and the O.D. at 600 nm determined. A linear relationship between original protein loads, up to 6 µg, and staining intensities were obtained in the case of the soluble proteins, while at 30 µg the staining intensities were reduced by 20-50 %, depending on the protein species. By contrast, the hydrophobic myelin P_0 protein showed linearity throughout the whole concentration range.

In another series, controlled amounts (1-30 µg) of each protein were directly placed onto nitrocellulose paper covering an area equivalent to that of the transferred proteins, stained with amidoblack and destained with water. The dots were cut out, extracted and analyzed at 600 nm, resulting in linear relationships between loads and staining intensities up to 30 µg.

In a third series, controlled amounts (1-30 µg) of each protein were also directly placed onto nitrocellulose sheets, but then subjected to the 3 h electrophoretic transfer conditions by suspending the protein-loaded nitrocellulose paper between the electrodes. Thereafter, the paper was stained and destained as above, the dots were cut out, extracted and analyzed at 600 nm. As in the case of the gel-transferred proteins, only up to 6 µg protein was a linear relationship of loads and staining intensities noted, with reductions at higher loads quite similar to those of the gel-transferred proteins. Here again, the P_0 glycoprotein was completely retained on the paper throughout the whole loading range.

Although only a limited number of proteins have been subjected to this initial study, the following trends appear: (1) Owing to the presence of SDS in the transfer buffer proteins in the range of 14-68 KDalton could be fully transferred from the gel to the paper. This was also valid for the hydrophobic protein examined and of great general importance when membrane proteins are analyzed by immunoblotting. (2) Only a limited amount of soluble proteins could be retained per area of the nitrocellulose paper, still exhibiting a linear relationship. With the nitrocellulose paper mentioned above, the limiting capacity was around 0.4 $\mu g/mm^2$. At higher concentrations the proteins "bled" away from the anodal side of the sheet. By contrast, the hydrophobic protein examined here could be fully retained up to approximately 2 $\mu g/mm^2$.

CELL ATTACHMENT-PROMOTING FACTORS FROM PARTIALLY HEPATECTOMIZED RAT PLASMA. A COMBINED IMMUNOBLOTTING BIODETECTION STUDY

Jose V. Castell, M. Isabel Guillen, M. Jose Gomez-Lechon

Centro de Investigacion. Hospital La Fe. Avda. Campanar 21, Valencia-9. Spain.

1 INTRODUCTION

Fetal calf serum is generally considered an essential component of culture media for the survival of mammalian cells in culture. With regard to hepatocytes, serum is needed to facilitate attachment and spreading of cells to plastic dishes. Fibronectin is the serum protein which is basically responsible for this activity (1). As we previously reported, rat serum, like other animal sera, can promote hepatocyte attachment with the same efficiency as fetal calf serum (2). In the course of our studies on the mechanisms that initiate liver regeneration after partial hepatectomy (PH), we found that plasma of partially hepatectomized rats promoted the adhesion of hepatocytes to plastic culture dishes with greater efficiency than normal rat serum or fetal calf serum. This activity increased after a partial hepatectomy and remained at high levels during the hyperplasic phase of liver regeneration (3), that is, during the initial restorative period. In order to investigate the nature of this activity, we developed a combined technique which essentially is based on the separation by electrophoresis in polyacrylamide gels of active fractions of plasma, followed by an electrophoretical blotting on nitrocellulose paper, and identification of the active protein/s by incubating the nitrocellulose paper with a suspension of freshly isolated hepatocytes. After staining for cells, a hepatocyte band superimposed on a protein band could be detected, thus allowing the identification of the active protein. The technique and the results are summarized in this paper.

2 MATERIAL AND METHODS

Hepatectomies were performed in S&D rats weighing 100 ± 5 g, as described (4). Hepatocytes were obtained by liver perfusion with collagenase and maintained in Ham's F-12 medium in a CO_2/O_2 atmosphere. Nitrocellulose was HAWP 304F0 from Millipore. Pure rat serum fibronectin was obtained by affinity chromatography on gelatin-sepharose (5) and further purified by preparative gel electrophoresis. The purity of the sample was assesed by SDS-PAGE in mercaptoethanol. Pure fibronectin gave two bands (215-220 kd), and a minor proteolitic fragment (205 kd). Rabbit antisera against rat fibronectin was obtained after injecting 250 µg in complete adjuvant, followed by a 250 µg dosis in uncomplete adjuvant every three weeks. High titer bleedings were obtained after three months.

2.1 Cellulose acetate electrophoresis.- This was carried out with serum samples in the usual way, using veronal buffer pH 8.9 and 200 V for 2 h. To transfer proteins into the nitrocellulose paper, the strip was then laid over the dull surface of a wet millipore sheet, with a dry filter paper placed under it. Several strips of Whatmann paper soaked in buffer veronal were laid over the cellulose acetate strip. The sandwich was placed between two sheets of glass and pressed slightly. The samples were allowed to diffuse into the nitrocellulose sheet for 30 min.

2.2 Gel electrophoresis.- Samples were run in polyacrylamide gel, 4% T, 2% C 0.75 mm thickness. Buffer was the conventional Tris-Glycine pH 8.3, 0.1% SDS, (0.1% mercaptoethanol in reducing gels) Samples were run at 180 V in the cold, until the bromphenol front left the gel (3-4 hours).

2.3 Electrophoretic blotting into nitrocellulose sheets.- The sandwich was disposed in a sequential order: anode (+), aluminium plate; sponge; Whatman 3MM; Nitrocellulose sheet, the dull side up; polyacrylamide gel; Whatman 3MM; sponge; catode (-), stainless steel. The electrophoretic blotting was carried out using buffer Tris/Veronal/Glycine (0.75/3.7/7.5 mM) pH 8.8, voltage 3-4 V/cm for 4 h. To check optimal transfer of proteins, either a part of the nitrocellulose or the polyacrylamide gel was stained with Coomassie.

2.4 Visualization of the cell attachment promoting factor.- To detect the active protein in the electrophoretic transfers, the nitrocellulose sheet was first washed with PBS and then soaked with 0.5% BSA in PBS (30 min). A cell suspension of hepatocytes (5×10^5 cell/ml) was poured on the nitrocellulose paper to cover it and gently shaken for 10-30 min in a CO_2/O_2 incubator. The paper was then washed with warm PBS to remove unspecifically attached cells, drained, and immediately fixed for 10 min with absolute ethanol. Following this step, the paper was stained 2 min with 2% eosine in 50% ethanol, then gently washed several times with tap water and finally soaked in methanol/acetic/water (5:7:88). This allowed a rapid de-staining of the paper, but not of the stained cells. Cells remained attached to a protein band in the paper, and appeared as a deep red zone.

2.5 Immunological detection of fibronectin.- The nitrocellulose blotting was also stained with antibodies against rat fibronectin. The millipore was first soaked in PBS-Tween 0.05% for 10 min. Then it was incubated for 2 hour at 37°C with the first antibody, rabbit anti rat fibronectin 1/200 in PBS-Tween. The second antibody was peroxidase labelled goat anti rabbit IgG's, 1/100, and was incubated for 1 hour. Between steps, the paper was thoroughly washed with PBS-Tween. Finally the paper was soaked in a solution containing 0.05% 3-amino 9 ethyl carbazole, 0.001% H_2O_2 in buffer acetate 50mM, pH= 5. The reaction was allowed to proceed for about 5-10 min. Brick coloured bands were clearly visible for positive bands after staining.

3 RESULTS AND DISCUSSION

When PH rat serum was electrophoresed in cellulose acetate and the proteins were transferred to nitrocellulose and incubated with hepatocytes, cells attached to a defined zone of the paper. It became evident that a α_2-β protein was responsible for this biological activity. It could also be clearly observed that attachment was greater in samples of PH rat serum. Fig. 1.

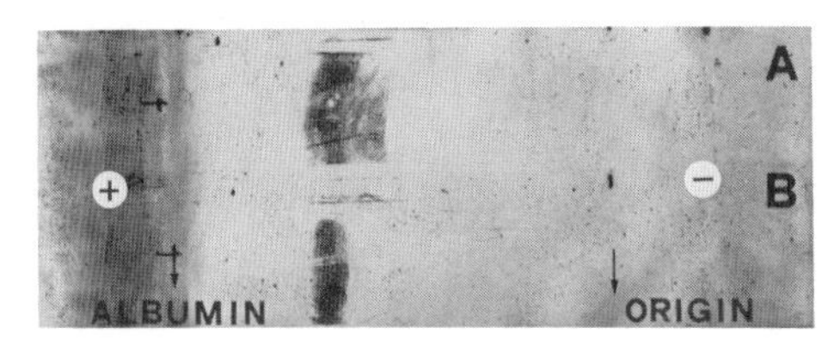

Fig 1 Cell atachment activity of rat serum.

A. 70% PH rat serum
B. Normal rat serum

Electrophoresis in cellulose acetate, and transference to nitrocellulose paper.

Serum from PH rats is very efficient in promotting cell attachment to plastic culture dishes. To quantify this biological activity we coated plastic dishes with seriated dilutions of serum. Then we added an excess of cells ($85x10^3$ cell/cm^2), incubated for 1 h and calculated the number of attached cells (1 OD, 66O nm = $4.2x10^5$ cell/ml). Due to steric reasons maximal cell density was $65x10^3$ cell/cm^2. We expressed the adhesion index as percentage of this value. 1 Unit is defined as the amount adsorbed per cm^2 that allowed an adhesion index of 50%. PH rat serum is very efficient in facilitating hepatocytes attachment in comparison to fetal serum. Table 1.

TABLE I

Sample	Cell attachment activity	Fibronectin (ELISA)
Fetal Calf Serum	60 U/ul	40.6 ug/ml
Control Rat Plasma	200 "	252 "
70% PH Rat Plasma *	460 "	320 "

* Samples were obtained 18 hours after partial hepatectomy.

To characterize this factor, active samples were electrophoresed and transferred to nitrocellulose paper. Part of the paper was immunologically stained an the rest, biologically stained. As Fig 2 shows, the biological activity of PH rat plasma was associated to a protein duplet which immunologically was identified as fibronectin. Fig 2, B and C. To futher asses if only fibronectin was responsible for the cell-attachment activity of PH serum, the blottings were incubated first with IgG anti rat fibronectin, followed by incubation with cells. Cell attachment could not be observed. It therefore suggests that fibronectin accounts for the activity found in regenerating serum.

As Table 1 points out, there was a discrepancy between the biological activity (attachment index) and ELISA measurable fibronectin. In order to find an explanation for this discrepancy, we turned our attention to studying, both by immunoblotting and biodetection, the nature of circulating fibronectin in plasma of PH rats during the regenerative process. It was found that, fibronectin was present in several molecular aggregates in plasma. Following a PH, there was a clear alteration in the distribution of fibronectin that changed along the course of regeneration. The molecular species were similar when studied under dissociating conditions (Fig 3 C), as revealed by immunodetection. However, they did not show equivalence in promoting cell attachment of hepatocytes. Cells basically attached to one of the bands.

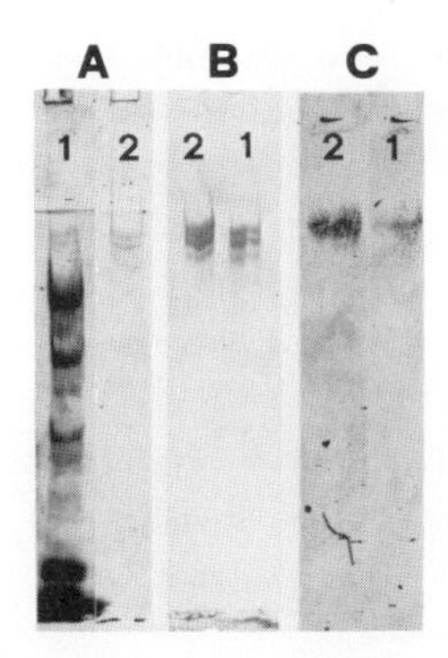

Fig 2 Identification of the active protein. 1: PH rat serum. 2: pure fibronectin. A: PAGE 7.5%T,2.5%C B: Immunoblotting; C: Biodetection.

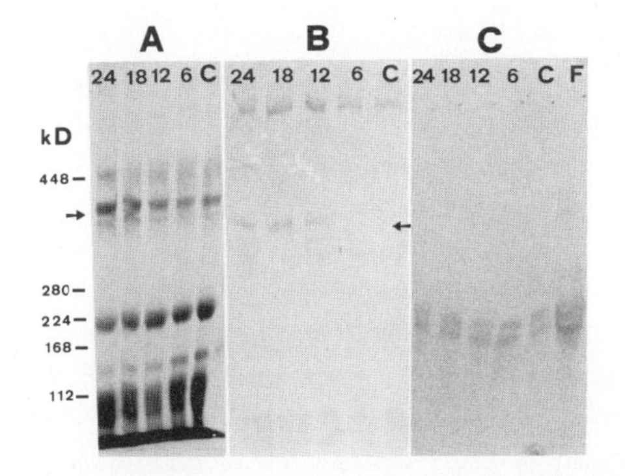

Fig 3 Fibronectin aggregates in PH rat plasma. A: PAGE. B: Immunoblotting. C: Immunoblotting after SDS-PAGE-ME. C denotes control. Numbers indicate time after PH. Arrow denotes cell attachment. F denote pure fibronectin sample.

In conclusion, the increased activity found in PH rat plasma was due to the relative increase of one of the circulating fibronectin species that proved to be biologically active. The technique described here provided a simple and efficient way of examining cell attachment promoting factors in plasma of PH rats, and the nature of circulating fibronectin complexes and it is being used at present in our laboratory to study the fibronectin present in sera.

REFERENCES

(1) Gomez-L. M.J., Castell J.V. in "Hormonally Defined Media" Ed. G. Fischer and R. Wieser. Springer Verlag 1983. pg 340-343.

(2) Gomez-L. M.J., Castell J.V., Cienc. Biol.(1983) 8, 49-56

(3) Castell J.V., Gomez-L. M.J. 17th. Meeting European Asociation for the Study of Liver. Goteborg 1982. Abstract 123.

(4) Higgins G.M., Andersen R.M., Arch. Pathol. (1931) 12, 186-202

(5) Ruoslahti E., Hayman E.G., Piersbacher M., Methods in Enzymology, 82 803-831.

ANALYSIS OF THE SPECIFICITY AND SELECTION OF THE ANTIGENIC T.GONDII COMPONENTS RECOGNISED BY IgG, IgM, IgA or IgE SPECIFIC HUMAN ANTIBODIES : VALUE OF ENZYME-LINKED-IMMUNO-FILTRATION-ASSAY WITH COMPARED IMMUNOLOGICAL PROFILES (E.L.I.F.A.-C.I.P. - METHOD) IN THE STUDY OF THE COMPONENTS-ISOTYPES RELATIONSHIP.

J.M. Pinon, C. Trichet and H. Thoannes

Laboratory of Parasitology and Mycology, Hôpital Maison Blanche - C.H.U. - 51092 REIMS CEDEX - FRANCE

The soluble antigenic components of *T.gondii* recognised by IgG, IgM, IgA or IgE specific antibodies during acquired or congenital toxoplasmosis have been studied using the ELIFA-CIP method (1). This doubly analytical technique, carried out on a microporous membrane, enables in 3 hours the simultaneous study of antibody specificity by Immunoprecipitation (2) and the characterisation of antibody isotypes by Immuno-Filtration using enzyme-labelled antibodies. The reactive fractions were selected from the examination of 6.000 samples (sera, cord blood, CSF) from acquired toxoplasmosis adults or children with suspected congenital infections. At least 22 fractions of different specificities were reactive and revealed by the specific antibodies. A small number (5 to 7) of antigenic components are dominant by the frequency and isotypic diversity with which the antibodies induced during a natural infestation recognise their epitopes. This may concern not only IgG or IgM isotypes in a system, but also associations of classes forming couplets (IgG-IgM ; IgG-IgA ; IgG-IgE ; IgM-IgA) or triplets (IgG-IgM-IgA ; IgG-IgA-IgE). Detection of specific IgM (without the IgG-IgM couplet) is always transitory. In contrast, couplets (IgG-IgM ; IgG-IgA) or triplets (IgG-IgM-IgA) often persist for 9 months after infestation. Specificity analysis by ELIFA-CIP seems to us constitute an important stage in the selection of the functional (3, 4) antigenic components of *T.gondii*.

REFERENCES

(1) J.M. Pinon, N. Gruson, Symp. Internat. Toxo., Lyon Méd. 248 (1982) 27-30

(2) J.M. Pinon, G. Dropsy, J. Immunol. Methods, 16 (1977) 15-22

(3) S.D. Sharma, J. Mullenax, F.G. Araujo, H.A. Erlich, J.S. Remington, J. of Immunol., 131 (1983) 977

(4) P. Partanen, Fl.J. Turunen, R.Paasivuo, E. Forsbolm, J. Suni, P.O. Leinikki, FEBS Letters, 158 (1983) 252

DETECTION OF OLIGOCLONAL IgG BANDS IN UNCONCENTRATED MULTIPLE SCLEROSIS (MS) CSF: ISOELECTRIC FOCUSING IN AGAROSE GEL

P. D. Mehta, B. A. Patrick and J. Black*

New York State Office of Mental Retardation and Developmental Disabilities, Institute for Basic Research in Developmental Disabilities, Staten Island, NY 10314, and Isolab Inc.*, Akron, OH. 44321

We analyzed cerebrospinal fluid (CSF) from 30 MS and 20 other neurologic disease (OND) patients in agarose gel isoelectric focusing (IEF) (RESOLVE Kit, Isolab Inc., Akron, OH.). Ten to 12 ul of unconcentrated CSF from MS patients containing 0.4 to 0.8 ug of IgG was found to be optimum for detection of oligoclonal IgG bands. IEF followed by silver staining was completed in about 4 hours. Twenty eight of 30 MS CSF showed distinct oligoclonal bands in pH region 8.0 to 9.3 whereas, 18 of 20 CSF from OND patients had diffuse pattern. The oligoclonal bands were identified as IgG in immunofixation using rabbit anti human IgG serum. The method is simple, sensitive and rapid. Employing the premade IEF agarose gel plates, the clinical laboratory will be able to analyze unconcentrated CSF for presence or absence of oligoclonal bands.

Symposium

Two-dimensional Electrophoresis – Methods and Applications

Chairmen:
J. Klose and R. P. Tracy

SYSTEMATIC ANALYSIS OF TOTAL CELL PROTEINS

Joachim Klose

Institut für Humangenetik, Institut für Toxikologie und Embryonalpharmakologie,
Freie Universität Berlin, Garystraße 5, D-1000 Berlin 33, FRG

1 ONE-DIMENSIONAL AND TWO-DIMENSIONAL ELECTROPHORESIS. TWO CONCEPTS IN USING ELECTROPHORESIS OF PROTEINS

The electrophoretic separation of proteins is a method which is used in many different fields of basic research as well as in a number of fields which have an immediate practical relevance. Two concepts can be distinguished according to which electrophoresis is employed: one of these may be considered as the conventional concept, the other has become available more recently. According to the conventional concept, a single (or a few) well-known and electrophoretically demonstrable protein is selected from the presently known proteins and used as a model protein to study the problem in question. Often, this model protein dictates the object of the investigation. This concept was necessarily the only one available as long as proteins were separated by one-dimensional electrophoresis (1DE). The 1DE reveals, in principle, only one out of the large number of proteins, which may be present in a protein sample, namely that which is made visible by a specific detection method (specific staining, specific antibody). Since the number of specific detection methods available for proteins is limited, the number of proteins which can be taken into account for a particular investigation is also limited. This situation restricted the spectrum of problems which could be investigated by electrophoretic protein analysis.

According to the concept which became available later on (1, 2, 3, 4, 5), the object best suitable to study the problem of interest is selected first, and all the proteins offered by this object will then be analysed. Usually these are all unknown proteins. This concept became feasible when the two-dimensional electrophoresis (2DE) of proteins had been developed to a technique of high resolution power (1, 2, 3, 4, 5).

To illustrate the two different concepts, four areas in which electrophoresis of proteins plays an important role, will be considered: 1. The study of gene activity during cell differentiation (or following cell transformation, or gene transfer); 2. the genetic variability of proteins; 3. mutagenicity testing (or testing for cancerogenic or teratogenic effects of environmental agents); 4. clinical diagnostics. Hemoglobin is one of the best analysed proteins and most easily demonstrable by 1DE. Consequently, the changes of gene activity during differentiation have been studied particularly intensively in the various globin genes using a suitable object, e.g. the mouse embryo. The genetic variability of proteins was also studied most intensively in hemoglobin, especially human hemoglobin. Furthermore, an attempt to perform mutagenicity testing on 1DE patterns was made with hemoglobin (6). Blood samples from 8621 mice treated via the parental generation were tested. Finally, the first genetic diseases of man which could be diagnosed on the protein level was the sickle cell anemia, recognizable on the 1DE pattern of hemoglobin. Enzymes such as G-6-PD, LDH or esterase represent other examples for model proteins often used in one or the other field mentioned here.

In the following, the use of the 2DE in the four different fields, selected here as examples, will be considered. The gene expression on the protein level taking place during cell differentiation and embryonic development can be studied in any cell type or any organism when the 2DE is used, and when the interest is concentrated on a broad spectrum of proteins. In other words: instead of one or a few proteins which may be available "by chance" for a particular biological system to be investigated, a large number of proteins representative for this system can be studied by this experimental approach. Such studies have been performed, for example, on embryos of the mouse (7), sea urchin (8), frog (9), pig (10), rabbit (11), Drosophila (12), and, furthermore, on different cell types such as erythroblastic cells (13), myoblasts (14), ovarian granulosa cells (15), spermatogenic cells (16, 17).

The genetic variability of proteins has been studied extensively in the past according to the conventional concept. Enzymes which can be stained specifically on the basis of their substrate specificity were the preferential proteins analysed by 1DE. Recently, the 2DE has been used to investigate the genetic variability of proteins on a broad spectrum of proteins, as offered by complex protein extracts from whole cells. Natural populations of man, mouse and Drosophila and also inbred strains of the mouse were investigated in this respect (18, 19, 20, 21, 22, 23, 24, 25, 26, 27). The results showed a considerably lower degree of genetic variability among the proteins revealed by 2DE than found previously in 1DE patterns of enzymes. Two-dimensional patterns from proteins of different cell fractions or different organs showed that the frequency of genetic protein variants varies between different protein classes (24, 27, 28). Therefore, the results obtained by 2DE suggested that the genetic variability ascertained for enzymes (i.e., for a group of solubilized enzymes), by 1DE is not representative for the total cell proteins. The question, however, whether the 2DE is as sensitive in detecting small electrophoretic changes of qualitative protein variants as the 1DE is still under discussion. Another genetic finding was obtained when the genetic variability of proteins was studied with the 2DE. The frequency of genetic changes in the amount of proteins (cellular protein concentration) was found to exceed by far the frequency of qualitative protein variants (24, 27, 28). Quantitative changes cannot be recognized directly on 1DE patterns of enzymes. Assuming that genetically determined quantitative changes in proteins result, at least partially, from other DNA sequences than electrophoretic mobility changes (indicating alterations in the structural genes), 2DE offers the possibility to study the genetic variability in various gene classes. Therefore, results can be obtained in this way which may be representative for the whole active genome of the cell.

A field of greatest practical significance is the testing of pharmaca and other environmental agents for deleterious effects on human health. Considering the mutagenic effect, an urgent need exists for a practicable test system that allows the detection of point mutations induced in vivo in the germ cells of a mammal. Electrophoretic analysis of proteins in mice treated in the parental generation with a substance to be tested, represents such a system. Point mutations become expressed (in a certain percentage of cases) in the electrophoretic protein pattern by changes in the electrophoretic mobility of those proteins the genes of which are affected by the substance. Since the frequency of point mutations per gene locus is extremely low (approximately 1 spontaneous mutation per 10^6 gene loci per generation) - even after mutagen treatment - electrophoretic test systems using a single protein (e.g. hemoglobin) or a relatively small number of proteins (enzymes) (29, 30) require an enormous number of experimental animals to observe a significant increase in the mutation rate. Moreover, testing one or a few genes may not yield representative results, since the mutation rate can differ considerably between different gene loci (31). Mutagenicity testing by 2DE (1, 32, 33, 34) overcomes these disadvantages. With this test system, the Protein-Mapping Test, a large number of proteins (gene loci) can be tested in a single experimental animal. It has been shown recently (33, 35) that this method is apparently much more effective and therefore more useful in practice when the two-dimensional protein patterns are analysed with regard to quantitative protein changes.

Proteins exist as components of all morphological structures of a mammalian organism, and they are involved in all physiological processes. Thus, it is reasonable to assume that most human diseases are accompanied by abnormal proteins, abnormal with regard to their synthesis or structure or both. This is certainly true for genetic diseases, since any abnormality in the genome has consequences for the protein encoded or regulated by the affected gene. The detection of disease-specific protein variants has a great significance for clinical diagnostics. Moreover, a protein known to play a specific role in a certain disease offers a basis for the elucidation of the etiology of this disease. In case of hereditable diseases a genetically variant protein may be the starting point for a molecular genetic analysis of the mutated gene.

The 2DE, i.e., the possibility to analyse an enormous number of proteins in man opened up a new perspective for clinical diagnostics (36). This approach may be of particular interest for the many different inborn diseases which are often difficult to diagnose and, furthermore, for the early recognition of diseases (e.g. cancer) and for prenatal diagnostics. Some protein changes, characteristic for certain diseases, have already been detected by 2DE (37, 38, 39, 40, 41).

The examples outlined above for the application of electrophoresis of proteins may indicate that the development from the 1DE to the 2DE was not only important because of the increased electrophoretic resolution power reached in this way. The 2DE offered the possibility to apply electrophoresis according to a new concept. The advanatage of this concept opposed to the conventional strategy can be summarized as follows: 1. Proteins can be studied for each cell type, tissue or organism relevant for the problem in question. 2. A large number and a broad spectrum of different proteins can be analysed in each biological system. Therefore, results can be obtained which are representative for the proteins and genes of the biological system investigated. 3. Two-dimensional protein patterns reveal both qualitative and quantitative protein changes. - An inherent problem in the use of 2DE is that each investigation results in a large number of unknown proteins. However, there is principally no reason not to analyse subsequently in all details those proteins of the 2DE pattern which were found to be of particular interest.

2 LIMITATIONS IN ANALYSING PROTEINS BY TWO-DIMENSIONAL ELECTROPHORESIS

In the preceding chapter it was pointed out that the 2DE opened a new way in which electrophoretic protein analysis can be employed in research and other fields. However, investigations performed so far with the 2DE show that this concept cannot be realized in its full extent. This has several reasons: 1. A two-dimensional protein pattern, even one of high quality, does not reveal all proteins of a certain cell type or tissue. At present it is quite unclear how many different proteins a single cell type contains. This number may range between 2,000 (42) and 10,000 primary gene products and may lie at 50,000 or even higher for whole organisms. Therefore, 2DE patterns from protein extracts of whole cells certainly display only a portion, probably only a small portion of all proteins of an organism. 2. The proteins of a complex cell extract detected by a 2DE pattern may not represent all the different protein classes (enzymes, transport proteins, hormones, antibodies, receptors; glycoproteins, lipoproteins, phosphoproteins; mitochondral, ribosomal, lysosomal, chromosomal proteins, etc.) of a cell type, at least not in the natural proportion. The 2DE, in the first place, reveals from the mass of proteins the most abundant proteins. It is, however, unlikely that all the different protein classes of a cell type have, on the average, the same concentration in the cell. Therefore, the possibility is given that the protein class which might be the most relevant for a certain investigation is not represented by the

2DE pattern investigated. 3. As shown by the examples outlined in the first chapter the fact that the structure and function of the proteins revealed by the 2DE are usually all unknown did not prevent the drawing of important conclusions from the results. Furthermore, as already mentioned, proteins showing an interesting abnormality can be isolated from the 2DE pattern and analysed in more details by using other biochemical methods. On the other hand, there is no doubt that the number of information obtained by investigating 2D-protein patterns would be drastically increased if all protein spots of a 2DE pattern were known. However, an enormous expenditure of work and time would be required to investigate the structure and function of all proteins, spot by spot. A more feasible way may be to collect information for each polypeptide spot by classifying systematically the mass of cell proteins as far as possible.

Problems which may arise from the situation that protein patterns, as usually obtained by 2DE, do not yield a complete analysis of cell proteins, will be illustrated in some examples. Supposing that fibroblasts of a number of patients who carry the same genetic disease are investigated by 2DE, and that one and the same protein spot out of 500 spots (assuming primary gene products) per pattern is abnormal in each case. Since the 500 proteins represent a randomly selected portion of the total number of proteins of a human individual, it is reasonable to assume that 4 abnormal proteins would be found if 2000 proteins per pattern were analysed. Concequently, approximately 40 abnormal proteins may exist, if the human organism contains 20,000 different proteins and 100 may exist among 50,000 proteins. If the abnormal protein actually found in the fibroblasts is the only abnormal protein in these cells and in the whole organism (most likely, if the total number of proteins per cell and organism is low), this finding might be of great significance. This protein probably represents the primary product of the mutated gene which is responsible for the genetic disease. If, however, about 100 other abnormal proteins are associated with this particular disease, the variant protein found most likely is one of the secondarily arisen protein variants and possibly plays an unimportant role in the development of this disease. Moreover, this abnormal protein may not even be obligatory for this disease and may therefore represent an uncertain candidate for clinical diagnostics.

Other examples may show the necessity to detect and characterize all protein classes of the cell. Assuming induced mutations occur in some protein classes more frequently than in the others, mutagenicity testing on the protein level would then be considerably more effective and more practicable if the electrophoretic test system included only these classes of proteins. The observation mentioned above, that chemical mutagens induced more quantitative than qualitative protein changes, is one step in this direction although it rather reflects the reaction of different gene classes.

The low genetic variability in natural populations found by analysing 2DE patterns of total cell proteins could be explained by certain highly variable protein classes (i.e. certain groups of enzymes) which are underrepresented in the 2DE patterns (27). Finally, it has been suggested (7) that characteristic protein populations rather than single more or less unrelated proteins occur in different embryonic stages. The recognition and characterization of such protein classes may be an important contribution to the understanding of the differentiation process during embryonic development.

3 THE SYSTEMATIC ANALYSIS OF TOTAL CELL PROTEINS

Considering the mass of different proteins which a single cell, tissue or organism may contain, an enormous lack of knowledge becomes apparent. The total number of different protein species per cell, the frequency of primary proteins in relation to the frequency of secondarily modified proteins, the degree of genetic variability of proteins and the characteristics of each single protein species, each group and class of proteins - all of these are largely unsolved problems. For example, the genetic variability of human proteins has been studied on enzymes of approximately 100 gene loci (43), and on a much smaller number of non-enzymatic proteins. The amino acid sequence is known for 149 human proteins (in 1978).

The preceding chapter may have shown that this lack of information limits the interpretation of the results which can be obtained in many important fields by 2DE. Generally, there is a great discrepancy between the central role the proteins play in all biochemical processes and cellular structures of a living organism and the poor knowledge of these proteins. A systematic study of all cell proteins of the human organism and other relevant species may yield a substantial contribution to many unsolved problems in biology and medicine. The first attempt to analyse the mass of unknown cell proteins was made on E. coli by O'Farrell (3) and on mouse tissue by Klose (1, 2) using 2DE.

A systematic study of total cell proteins should start with the more unrelated cell types (liver, brain, muscle cells) of an organism and then proceed with the more similar cell types. The analysis of the proteins of the various cell types may be performed according to the following programm: 1. Determination of the total number of different proteins of a single cell type. Discrimination between primary proteins and secondarily modified proteins, i.e. determination of the number of single genes from which the total number of polypeptides results. 2. Classification of proteins: a) Biochemical characterisation: investigation of the cell type (organ) specificity, cell organelle specificity, and the cell subfraction (solubilized and structure-bound proteins) specificity of proteins; characterization of proteins with respect to special chemical groups, assumed to have special biological functions, e.g. glycoproteins, lipoproteins, phosphoproteins; determination of structural characteristics of proteins, e.g. molecular weight, isoelectric point, peptide and amino acid composition; measurement of the relative concentration of cell proteins. b) Genetic characteristics: genetic analysis of the qualitative and quantitative variability of proteins among individuals; discrimination between genetic and non-genetic variability of proteins.

The most attractive object for such a systematic study of cell proteins is doubtless the human organism. However, a number of difficulties have to be taken into account in this case: most of the human tissues (liver, brain, muscle) are not easily obtained, at least not in quantities necessary for the study of certain cell fractions and biochemical characteristics. The investigation of proteins from various embryonic stages would be a particular problem. For the study of protein concentrations and their variability between individuals a large number of normal persons must be available, ideally, all of the same age, sex, health condition, tribe etc. The genetic analysis of human proteins is restricted to family studies with all the difficulties and limitations inherent in such studies. Problems like these do not exist when an appropriate animal is used. The mouse, one of the best investigated mammals (particularly with regard to its genetic nature) would be most suitable for a systematic protein analysis. The availability of inbred strains of this species is of special advantage for the genetic analysis of proteins.

The systematic analysis of cell proteins on the mouse can be considered as a model study for man. Because of the high structural and functional conservatism of many or most of the proteins the results obtained from the mouse may be valid in many cases for man as well. For example, the finding made in the mouse that membrane proteins reveal far less genetic variants than proteins solubilized in the cell does not need to be confirmed by studies in the human population. On the other hand, for a correct assessment of the data available for man comparable data of another species are desirable. Needless to mention that the mouse is the most important mammal in research and routine testing.

Anderson and Anderson (36; Science 211, 33-35, 1981) put forward the idea to analyse and list all proteins of man using 2DE. The practical approach is to start with cell types (e.g. lymphocytes, erthrocytes, fibroblasts) and body fluids (e.g. serum, urine) most easily obtainable from man, and to identify or characterize first those proteins which are readily revealed by 2DE, i.e. the abundant proteins. The data are to be collected together with adequate data from other laboratories. The aim is to build up a complete catalogue of human proteins, the "human protein index". A particular aspect of this project is to collect clinically relevant data to make this comprehensive body of information useful for clinical diagnostics. The concept includes the establishment of a data bank.

4 MOLECULAR GENETIC ANALYIS ON THE DNA LEVEL NEEDS THE ANALYSIS ON THE PROTEIN LEVEL

Modern technical developments and results in molecular genetics attract great interest because of the scientific as well as economic (biotechnological) significance of this field of research. It became possible to study the genetic material of the cell, the DNA, on the molecular level. Single genes can be isolated, sequenced and localized in the genome. A single eucaryotic gene can be transfered into a bacterial cell and integrated into its genome with the effect that the gene product, the protein, can be produced in large amounts. Modern gene technology has led to substantially new knowledge about the genetic organisation and function of the DNA. The practical significance lies, for example, in the molecular genetic analysis of genetic diseases, in more detailed genetic diagnostics, and possibly in the finding of new ways for the therapy of genetic defects. A biotechnological field of application is, for example, the industrial production of human proteins such as insulin, interferon, blood clotting factors or growth hormones.

Molecular genetics is concerned with the genetic analysis of the DNA. The analysis of all genes (at least the structural genes) of an eucaryotic genome seems to be a realistic aim in the future. This development, however, may be hindered or blocked later on if the analysis of total cell proteins does not run in parallel. The molecular analysis of a gene has usually to start with a known protein since the protein (its amino acid sequence or its mRNA) is often needed for the elucidation of the DNA sequence. Moreover, the interest in a particular gene usually bases on the interest on a known protein. In view of the fact that only a small percentage of all proteins is known, the extension of the molecular genetic analysis towards the whole genome depends on the extension of the analysis of the cell proteins. It is, however, possible to sequence a DNA section without any information on corresponding proteins. Furthermore, the interest in a particular gene may not be caused in each case by its protein. The interest in a certain DNA sequence may arise, for example, from its ability to induce cell transformation. However, even if a piece of DNA has been analysed without any reference to a protein, the question whether the analysed DNA is responsible for the synthesis or regulation of a certain protein has to be answered to characterize the isolated DNA sequence completely. If the sequence encodes a protein this protein can be synthesized, as already mentioned, with the help of gene technological methods. However, a protein obtained in this way has to be identified with a known protein to confirm the experimental results and to obtain additional informations (the functions) concerning this protein. Therefore, the analysis of the naturally occuring cell proteins is necessary even for those proteins which were detected in the molecular genetic way. To summarize: the molecular genetic analysis of the DNA is closely linked with the protein analysis. The proteins are involved in the molecular genetic methods. They are necessary to elucidate the function of the DNA sequences (coding sequences, regulating sequences, none of these) as well as the function of the genes in the cell. The molecular genetic analysis of the cell should include the analysis of the cell proteins.

5 REMARKS TO THE METHODICAL CONDITIONS OF A SYSTEMATIC ANALYSIS OF CELL PROTEINS

Considering the methodical conditions of such a comprehensive project of protein analysis as the one outlined above, it may be trivial to mention that besides the 2DE and the techniques directly involved, e.g. fluorography, silver staining, blotting, computer analysis, a number of other biochemical techniques is required. Methods for cell fractionation and protein extractions and preparative methods for subfractionation of complex protein extracts are needed before the 2DE can be set about. Following the separation of proteins by 2DE, further characterization of the proteins obtained is necessary with methods like e.g. immunological techniques, methods for peptide and amino acid sequence analysis.

A complete analysis of total cell proteins requires, however, also the technical explanation of new problems. A significant portion of cell proteins cannot be recovered in two-dimensional polyacrylamide gels for several reasons. Other proteins may be difficult to recognize because of their low cellular concentration, or because a small and weak spot is overlapped by a large and dark spot. Another problem is to recognize the "spot families" in a 2DE pattern, i.e. those spots which are modifications of one and the same protein. However, regardless of the possible difficulties there is no doubt that biochemical and genetic research will proceed toward a complete analysis of cell proteins of man and other relevant organisms.

6 REFERENCES

(1) J. Klose, Humangenetik 26 (1975a) 231-243.

(2) J. Klose in D. Neubert, H.-J. Merker (Eds.) New approaches to the evaluation of abnormal embryonic development, Thieme, Stuttgart 1975 (b), pp. 375-387.

(3) P.H. O'Farrell, J. Biol. Chem. 250 (1975) 4007-4021.

(4) G.A. Scheele, J. Biol. Chem. 250 (1975) 5375-5385.

(5) G. Iborra, J.M. Buhler, Anal. Biochem. 74 (1976) 503-511.

(6) L.B. Russell, W.L. Russell, R.A. Popp, C. Vaughan, K.B. Jacobson, Proc. Natl. Acad. Sci. USA 73 (1976) 2843-2846.

(7) J. Klose, H. von Wallenberg-Pachaly, Dev. Biol. 51 (1976) 324-331.

(8) B.P. Brandhorst, Develop. Biol. 52 (1976) 310-317.

(9) E.M. de Robertis, J.B. Gurdon, Proc. Natl. Acad. Sci. USA 74 (1977) 2470-2474.

(10) R.W. McGaughey, J. van Blerkom, Develop. Biol. 56 (1977) 241-254.

(11) E.B. Tucker, G.A. Schultz, Exp. Cell Res. 114 (1978) 438-443.

(12) Y. Sakoyama, S. Okubo, Develop. Biol. 81 (1981) 361-365.

(13) J.L. Peterson, E.H. McConkey, J. Biol. Chem. 251 (1976) 555-558.

(14) J.I. Garrels, Develop. Biol. 73 (1979) 134-152.

(15) T.D. Landefeld, K.L. Campbell, A.R. Midgley, Proc. Natl. Acad. Sci. USA 76 (1979) 5153-5157.

(16) C. Boitani, R. Geremia, R. Rossi, V. Monesi, Cell Differentiation 9 (1980) 41-49.

(17) C.F. Millette, C.T. Moulding, J. Cell Sci. 48 (1981) 367-382.

(18) A.J.L. Brown, C.H. Langley, Proc. Natl. Acad. Sci. USA 76 (1979) 2381-2384.

(19) K.E. Walton, D. Styer, E.I. Gruenstein, J. Biol. Chem. 254 (1979) 7951-7960.

(20) E.H. McConkey, B.J. Taylor, D. Phan, Proc. Natl. Acad. Sci. USA 76 (1979) 6500-6504.

(21) R.R. Racine, C.H. Langley, Nature 283 (1980) 855-857.

(22) S. Singh, I. Willers, J. Klose, H.W. Goedde, Fresenius Z. Anal. Chem. 301 (1980) 193-194.

(23) C.S. Giometti, N.L. Anderson, J. Biol. Chem. 256 (1981) 11840-11846.

(24) J. Klose, M. Feller, Biochem. Genet. 19 (1981)859-870.

(25) H. Hamaguchi, A. Ohta, R. Mukai, T. Yabe, M. Yamada, Hum. Genet. 59 (1981) 215-220.

(26) D.E. Comings, Clin. Chem. 28 (1982) 798-804.

(27) J. Klose, J. Mol. Evol. 18 (1982) 315-328.

(28) J. Klose, I. Willers, S. Singh, H.W. Goedde, Hum. Genet. 63 (1983) 262-267.

(29) H.V. Malling, L.R. Valcovic in W.G. Flamm, M.A. Mehlman (Eds.), Advances in Modern Toxicology, Hemisphere Publishing Corp., Washington, London 1978, pp. 149-171.

(30) F.M. Johnson, G.T. Roberts, B.K. Sharma, F. Chasalow, R. Zweidinger, A. Morgan, R. W. Hendren, S.E. Lewis, Genetics 97 (1981) 113-124.

(31) U.H. Ehling, A. Neuhäuser, Mut. Res. 59 (1979) 245-256.

(32) J. Klose, Arch. Toxicol. 38 (1977) 53-60.

(33) E. Zeindl, K. Sperling, J. Klose, Mut. Res. 97 (1982) 67-78.

(34) R.R. Marshall, A.S. Raj, F.J. Grant, J.A. Heddle, Can. J. Genet. Cytol. 25 (1983) 457-466.

(35) J. Klose in R. Bass, D. Neubert (Eds.), Critical evaluation of mutagenicity tests, W. de Gruyter, Berlin, New York 1984, in press.

(36) N.G. Anderson, L. Anderson, Clin. Chem. 28 (1982) 739-748.

(37) D.E. Comings, Nature 277 (1979) 28-32.

(38) C.R. Merril, D. Goldman, M. Ebert, Proc. Natl. Acad. Sci. USA 78 (1981) 6471-6475.

(39) J. Klose, E. Zeindl, K. Sperling, Clin. Chem. 28 (1982) 987-992.

(40) E. Rosenmann, C. Kreis, R.G. Thompson, M. Dobbs, J.L. Hamerton, K. Wrogemann, Nature 298 (1982) 563-565.

(41) J. Klose, B. Putz, Proc. Natl. Acad. Sci. USA 80 (1983) 3753-3757.

(42) R. Duncan, E.H. McConkey, Clin. Chem. 28 (1982) 749-755.

(43) H. Harris, D.A. Hopkinson, Y.H. Edwards, Proc. Natl. Acad. Sci. 74 USA (1977) 698-701.

THE DEVELOPMENT OF NEW CLINICAL ASSAYS THROUGH THE USE OF TWO-DIMENSIONAL GEL ELECTROPHORESIS AND HYBRIDOMA TECHNOLOGIES

Russell P. Tracy [1], Jerry A. Katzmann[2] and Donald S. Young[3]

[1]Department of Pathology, University of Rochester Medical Center, Rochester, NY 14642 and [2]Department of Laboratory Medicine, Mayo Clinic, Rochester, MN 55905

SUMMARY

Two-dimensional gel electrophoresis may be used as a "front-end" analytical tool to identify a potential disease related marker. The individual spot of interest may then be used to immunize mice, and prepare monoclonal antibodies. These reagents may then be used to isolate the protein by affinity chromatography and establish quantitative immunological assays. In this manner potential new disease markers may be detected, and evaluated rapidly and efficiently, without the need for their isolation by traditional biochemical methods.

1 INTRODUCTION

The search for new, more sensitive, more specific markers for the diagnosis of various diseases has proven to be a difficult and laborious process. While several proteins have been shown to be useful in monitoring disease (e.g., carcino-embryonic antigen in colon cancer), there have been few successes in the area of diagnosis, especially diagnosis of cancer (1). Both two-dimensional gel electrophoresis (2DGEL) and hybridoma are techniques of high resolution, i.e., they both can discern characteristics specific to an individual protein, while that protein exists amid a large number of other proteins. 2DGEL recognizes characteristics of size and change, while hybridoma techniques recognize specific antigenic qualities. The use of either of these techniques as the sole investiga-

Table I. Combining 2DGEL and Hybridoma to Evauate Protein Markers of Disease

1. Disadvantages of 2DGEL Alone
   - 1.1 Quantitation, especially with silver stain
   - 1.2 Through-Put even with special equipment
   - 1.3 Only small amounts of protein can be isolated from gels, and this is denatured
   - 1.4 Sensitivity
2. Disadvantages of Hybridoma Alone
   - 2.1 Immunodominance of certain antigens
   - 2.2 Restricted to cell-surface antigens, as it is usually done
3. Combination has potential to overcome these disadvantages, plus:
   - 3.1 High resolution (2DGEL)
   - 3.2 Can utilize any specimen: serum, urine, tissue (2DGEL)
   - 3.3 Small specimen requirement (2DGEL, Hybridoma)
   - 3.4 Yields an immunological reagent (hybridoma)
     - 3.4.1 Protein isolation
     - 3.4.2 Structure/Function Probe
     - 3.4.3 Clinical uses; e.g., assay development

tive tool in the search for a protein marker of disease, however, is restrictive. Over the last several years, we have been involved in developing techniques to combine these two methods to aid in the search. The objectives of this paper are: a) to describe our rationale for the combination of 2DGEL and hybridoma; b) to describe the methods by which this may be accomplished; and c) to mention briefly the areas we are currently investigating. Some discussion of these topics has already taken place (2).

2 RATIONALE

The reasons for combining 2DGEL and hybridoma are outlined in Table I. While 2DGEL is unrivaled in resolution as a protein separation technique, at the present time there are some problems with using this technique as the sole investigative tool in the evaluation of potential disease markers.

2.1 Quantitation of 2DGEL Spots

Foremost among these problems is the question of quantitation. We have done extensive work concerning quality assurance of the quantitative aspects of 2DGEL (3) using radioactively labelled marker proteins (α_2-macroglobulin, albumin and β_2-microglobulin). Under the best of conditions the with-in run CV (i.e., SD/$\bar{x}$) is on the order of 10-12%. This does not include error accompanying the staining and visualization processes (or the error associated with autoradiography) and the densitometric error. For example, looking at staining error alone, while quantitation of individual spots on silver stained gels maybe done (4,5), clearly it is difficult to envision this technique being used routinely to measure an hypothetical potential marker of leukemia in an evaluation phase where several hundred specimens may need to be examined. Also, the necessary through-put would be unobtainable by most laboratories, with a few exceptions. An immunologic method would be preferred, such as ELISA or RIA.

2.2 Protein Isolation from 2DGEL

Another disadvantage with 2DGEL alone, is that very little actual protein may be isolated from the gel itself. This would make characterization difficult, especially since the protein that can be isolated is substantially denatured by the 2DGEL process.

2.3 Sensitivity of 2DGEL

Also, there is the question of sensitivity, especially as it relates to the analysis of serum. 2DGEL is an excellent tool for analyzing cells and tissues for changes in protein content, especially since it can detect protein species representing as little as 0.0001% of the total cellular protein when metabolic labelling with $[^{35}S]$ -methionine and fluorographic technique are used (6). Extrapolating to staining techniques, this corresponds to detecting a spot containing 0.5 ng of protein assuming a protein load of 500 ug. Silver stain is generally considered to be somewhat less sensitive than this technique, with lower limits for most proteins in the range of 0.02-0.05 ng/mm^2 or approximately 5 ng (5). For silver stained two-dimensional gels of serum, we routinely apply a maximum of 1 ul of serum potein, or approximately 70 ug, of which 50% is available for staining due to losses during the 2DGEL process (7). This represents a maximum application load due to spreading of the spots representing the major serum proteins such as albumin, IgG, etc. A spot containing 5 ng represents 0.014% of the total, corresponding to an apprximate serum concentration of 1 mg/dl. This is born out by the fact that retinol binding protein (4 mg/dl; reference 8) is clearly seen on 2DGEL analysis of serum, but β_2-microglobulin (0.1-0.2 mg/dl; reference 8) is not. For comparison, the upper limit of normal for the tumor marker CEA is 0.5 ug/dl. The silver stain 2DGEL technique would lack the sensitivity to measure this marker by approximately three orders of magnitude.

2.4 Immunodominance

In any mix of immunogens, such as the structures present on a cell surface, or the proteins present in urine, there is a strong likelihood that a few of these will be immunodominant, i.e., strongly immunogenic. This does not mean that antibodies to minor immunogens are not made, but rather that they may be very low in relative abundance and therefore hard to uncover by standard hybridoma techniques (9). We have seen this problem with urinary proteins (10). When a mix of normal human urine proteins was used as immunogen, analysis of antibody-producing hybrids revealed specificity for human albumin in almost 100% of the cases. Although many other proteins were present, albumin seemed to be immunodominant in this mixture.

Complicated, labor-intensive "cascade" schemes have been devised to overcome this problem, based on standard hybridoma techniques (9), but clearly if a method were available to know before-hand which protein was of interest, this could prove to be of great importance in certain situations.

2.5 Cell Surface vs. Total Gene Expression

Hybridoma techniques have been used extensively to search for markers of malignancy (11). As these techniques are usually peformed, this search is restricted to cell surface antigens, partly due to the usefulness of such a marker were one to be found, and partly due to the ease of screening for such a marker, using fixed

Table II. Partial List of Input Specimens

Specimen	Disease	Reference
1. Serum	Monoclonal gammopathies	16
	Serum Lipid Disorders	17
2. Urine	Various Renal Diseases	18
	Muscular Dystrophy	19
	Prostatic Cancer	20
3. CSF	Demyelinating Disease	21
4. Erythrocytes	Sickle Cell Disease	22
5. Leukocytes	Leukemia	23,24,25
	Mononucleosis	26
6. Bone	Osteoporosis	27
7. Colon	Colon Cancer	28
8. Brain	Various Neuropathies	29,30
9. Muscle	Dermatomyositis	31
	Idiopathic Scoliosis	32

cells. While there are good reasons to believe that cell surface alterations accompany malignant transformation (12), several clinically useful tumor markers are not located on the cell surface (e.g., prostatic acid phosphatase (13), prostate specific antigen (14)), and many other disease markers are also essentially cytoplasmic in origin (e.g., creatine kinase-MB in myocardial infarct). There is no reason to believe that cellular alterations associated with specific disease states are necessarily restricted to the cell surface. In fact, recent evidence concerning the molecular biology of malignant transformation indicates that at least one oncogene apparently directs the synthesis of a transforming factor which is bound on the inside of the plasma membrane (15). A technique that limits the search to cell surface changes, therefore, may be unnecessarily restrictive.

2.6 Advantages of Combining 2DGEL and Hybridoma

By using 2DGEL as the "front-end" analytical tool and then combining it with hybridoma, one may reap several benefits. 2DGEL offers high resolution and small sample requirement. Also, it is virtually universal in its application. Table II lists several systems that have been examined with 2DGEL, all of which are suitable for further study using the special hybridoma methods outlined in this paper.

If one were able, then, to use the 2DGEL information to generate a monoclonal antibody (MoAb), ideally using the spots themselves as immunogens, this MoAb could then be used as an investigative tool: to isolate the protein, probe its structure and function, and develop quantitative assays for both research and clinical use. Hybridoma techniques are preferable to raising a rabbit or goat antiserum because the amount of immunogen is minimal, the amount of antibody is virtually limitless, and defined reagents such as MoAbs are usually superior for biochemical procedures such as affinity chromatography.

3 METHODS

This now bring us to a discussion of the methods involved in combining 2DGEL and hybridoma. These methods are simple in design and are summarized in Figure I. A normal specimen and a disease specimen are prepared for 2DGEL and the results analyzed. If a potential disease-related marker protein is identified, gel spots are cut out and used to immunize mice. Also, screening antigen is prepared from protein eluted from gel spots. Secondary screens are done to assure reactivity of positive clones with the native antigen, and then large quantities of MoAb are produced in mouse ascites. This MoAb can then be used to isolate the protein, probe structure/function, study tissue distribution and develop quantitative assays. This process has been discussed in two recent publicatins (2,10). There are several discrete functions which can be defined as necessary to the combined 2DGEL/MoAb process (Table III).

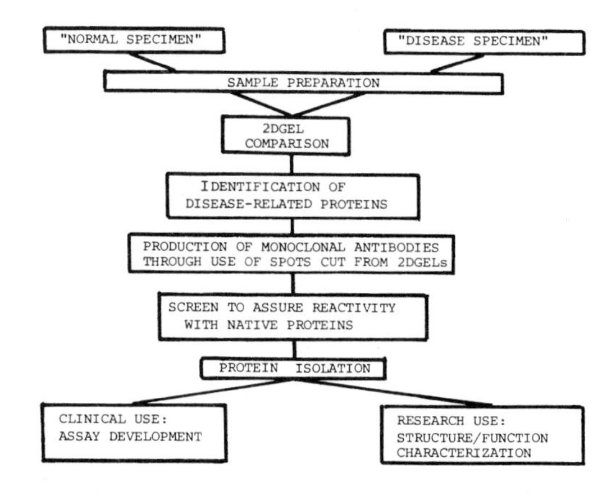

Figure 1. General scheme for combining 2DGEL and MoAb production. This figure is discussed in the text.

3.1 2DGEL

The 2DGEL methods we use have been described extensively , and summarized recently (7). They are described here briefly.

3.1.1 Specimen Procurement

This is an extremely crucial step, as we have previously emphasized (7,28), especially if whole cells or tissue specimens are involved. Histological examination of these specimens is necessary to assure the relative proportions of various cell types, the viability of the cells, the absence of necrosis, fat, etc.

3.1.2 Sample Preparation

Various sample dissociation schemes have been described (7, the entire book; 4, the entire issue). In certain cases a pre-fractionation step (or steps) is required to prepare the sample for dissociation. For example, urine proteins must be separated from non-protein urine compounds (21) and the non-collagenous proteins of bone must be extracted from the mineral phase and separated from collagen (27). Concentration may also be necessary, usually done by lyophilization or ultrafiltration. In the case of cultured cells, metabolic labelling with $[^{35}S]$ - methionine is usually done, and the spot pattern visualized by fluorography.

In all cases, if spots are to be cut from gels for injection into mice, there must be enough protein present to illicit an immune response. We have found 5 ug per injection to be more than adequate in the cases we have tried but the minimum requirement is not known (10). We have injected homogenized Coomassie blue gel

Table III. List of Functions and Procedures for 2DGEL/Hybridoma

Function	Procedure
1. Specimen procurement	Histological analysis
2. Sample preparation	Dissociation/solubilization
	pre-separation step
	concentration
	[^{35}S] - met labelling
3. 2DGEL	Isoelectric focusing
	SDS Electrophoresis
4. Visualization	Silver, Coomassie blue, fluorography
5. Immunogen	Homogenization/injection of gel spots
6. Hybridoma	Cell fusion, tissue culture
7. 1° screen	[^{125}I]-labelled protein binding assay
8. 2° screen	Native protein - protein A-affinity column
9. Protein isolation	MoAb-affinity column
10. Tissue specificity	Immunohistological analysis
11. Protein assay	RIA, ELISA

spots, acrylamide included. Rather than hindering the immunization, acrylamide apparently has an adjuvant effect (10).

3.1.3 Isoelectric Focusing - SDS Electrophoresis

We use the method of Anderson and Anderson (33) with some modifications (7). The isoelectric focusing is done in 9M urea, 2% NP40, pH 4-9 gradient, under reducing conditions. Our SDS slab gel gradient is exponential, 10-20% acrylamide.

3.1.4 Visualization

The majority of our work is done with silver stain, which yields higher resolution than Coomassie blue in our laboratory, probably due to the smaller total amount of sample required with silver stain. When a spot is identified as a potential marker, the process is scaled-up, so that Coomassie blue stain may be used, and a larger amount of protein extracted from a spot.

3.2 MoAb Production

The methods used to produce MoAbs from 2DGEL spots have been described in detail (10) and are discussed here only briefly.

3.2.1 Immunogen Preparation and Injection

Our general method has been to homogenize 5-10 gel spots containing 5-25 ug of protein, total, in a ground glass homogenizer, along with several ml of water, essentially to remove the acetic acid that is present. The sample is centrifuged and the blue pellet collected, which contains virtually all the protein. This is emulsified with saline and Freund's adjuvant (complete for the primary injection, and incomplete for all boosts) and injected at several spots along the flanks of the mouse.

3.2.2 Hybridoma

Standard cell fusion techniques (using the "NS-1" mouse myoloma cell line) and tissue culture methods are used (10).

3.2.3 Primary Screening of Hybrids

Since very little protein can be obtained from gel spots, a primary screen for specific antibody production, which would use solid-phase absorbed antigen, would be impractical. Instead, we use a solid-phase absorbed anti-mouse reagent to bind any

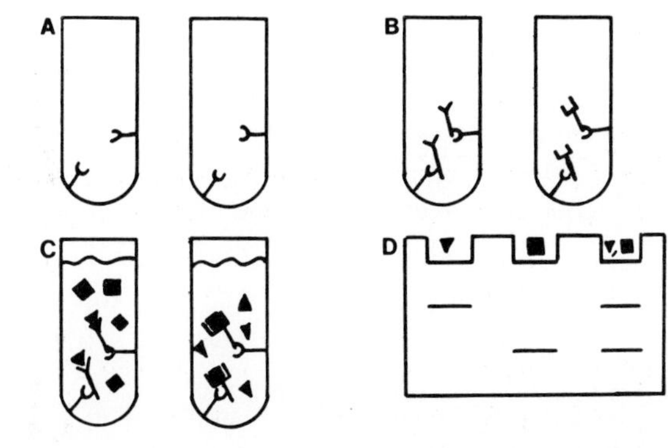

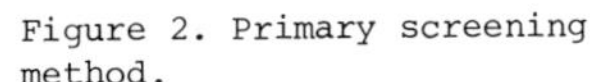

Figure 2. Primary screening method.
(A) illustrates the coating of plastic tubes with an anti-mouse immunoglobulin reagent.
(B) shows that two MoAbs from two different hybrid wells with two different specificities would both bind to the solid-phase reagent.
In the best case, a pure screening antigen would be labelled with ^{125}I and incubated with the bound immunoglobulin. In (C) we show the addition of a labelled mixture of two antigens, each specific for one of the MoAbs. This can be sorted out by washing the bound material with SDS buffer, running SDS slab gels and doing autoradiography. Part (D) illustrates the autoradiograph, which shows the specificities of the MoAbs (first two lanes) when compared to the labelled mix (last lane on left).

mouse immunoglobulin being produced by a hybrid clone and then add $[^{125}I]$ -labelled antigen to determine the specificity of the binding. This $[^{125}I]$ - labelled antigen is made by extracting protein from gel spots, though homogenization in guanidine - HCl, and labelling this protein with $[^{125}I]$ by the chloramine T method. The primary screening method we use is shown in Figure 2.

3.2.4 Secondary Screen

Hybrid wells shown to be positive in the primary screen are cloned by limiting dilution and expanded. At this stage, or if there are only a few positive clones, after ascites tumors are produced, the specificity of the MoAb for the native protein is assessed by a secondary screen. The general form of this screen (Figure 3) which is based upon the method of Pearson and Anderson (31) is as follows: a) small columns of Protein A-Sepharose (40 ul) are made in pipettor tips (yellow); the washing of these columns and subsequent washings are facilitated by a vaccum attachment; b) 50 ul of supernatant or ascitic fluid is applied to the column, washed in, and incubated for a few minutes; c) 50 ul (or more) of starting material (containing "native" protein) is then washed into the column and incubated; d) finally, after extensive washing, 50 ul of SDS dissociation buffer is added, incubated and eluted by centrifugation; the pipettor tip is wedged into a 1.5 ml microcentrifuge tube which has the bottom cut off; this in turn rests on the top of

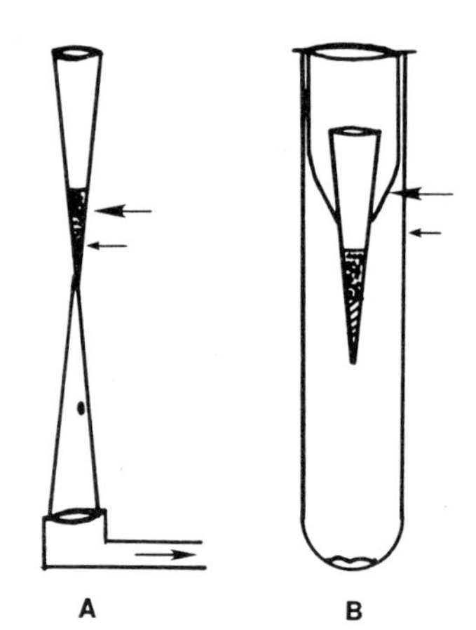

Figure 3. Secondary screen to assure reactivity with the native protein. The methodology is described in the text. This figure illustrates the device used to do the screen. In (A) the small arrow indicates a glass wool plug and the large arrow points to a 40 ul protein A-sepharose column. The running of this column is facilitated by a vacumn system (the lower part of (A)) which can be regulated by finger pressure on the hole drilled into the side. (B) illustrates the method for eluting the SDS solubilized protein from the column. The small arrow points to a 13 x 100 mm test tube, which supports a 1.5 ml microfuge tube, in turn supporting the column (large arrow). After centrifugation, the eluted protein is found in the bottom of the test tube.

a 13 x 100 test tube, which is centrifuged at 500 x g x 10 min. The effluent is collected from the bottom of the test tube, and analyzed by 2DGEL. If the MoAb has specificity for the native potein, the gel should show the protein of interest, and the monoclonal heavy and light chain (10).

3.2.5 Protein Isolation

We have used MoAbs produced in this manner (as well as conventionally prepared MoAbs) to isolate trace serum proteins by MoAb-Sepharose affinity chromatographly. MoAbs are covalently linked to CNBr-activated Sepharose by standard techniques. Figure 4 illustrates this method for the one-step isolation of α_1-microglobulin (2) and β_2-microglobulin (35) from serum.

3.2.6 Tissue Specificity

MoAbs may then be used immunohistochemically to localize the protein to specific tissues. The most popular methods are the peroxidase sandwich techniques and the fluorescine conjugation methods.

3.2.7 Protein Assay

We have had some experience establishing both solid-phase (2) and liquid-

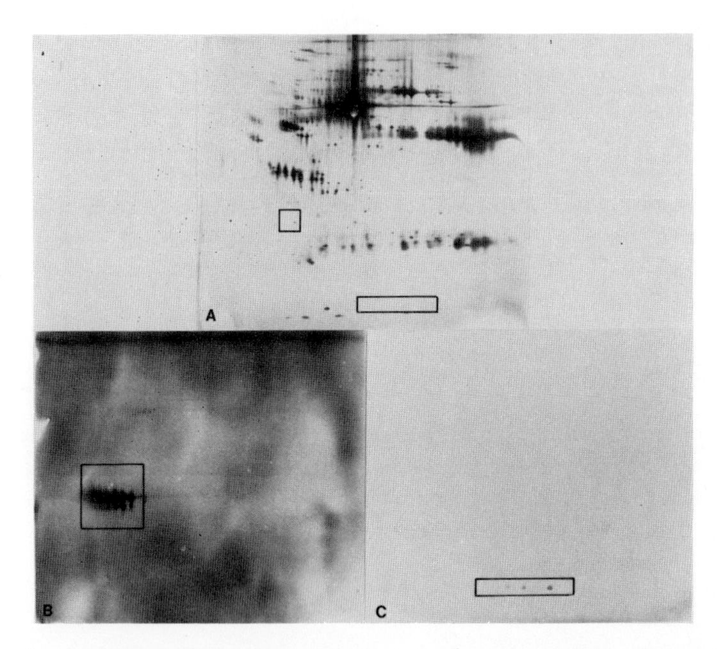

Figure 4. Isolation of α_1-microglobulin and β_2-microglobulin from serum by MoAb affinity chromatography. (A) Is a silver stain 2DGEL of serum. The square box indicates α_1-microglobulin while the rectangular box depicts the area of the gel where β_2-microglobulin is found. As can be seen, only trace amounts of these proteins are normally present. (B), (C) illustrate affinity purified proteins.

phase (35) serum assays using MoAbs. We have previously prepared standard curves for α_1-microglobulin, using MoAb (made from 2DGEL spots) absorbed to plastic as the binding reagent, and $[^{125}I]$-labelled α_1-microglobulin competing with the unlabelled protein (both made through the use of MoAb-affinity chromatography) to make the standard curve.

4 CURRENT RESEARCH

Our current research encompasses two main areas. The first concerns the development of assays related to renal disease. We have recently summarized our findings related to urine protein pattern changes in various renal disorders (18). We have already produced MoAbs to one of the proteins shown to be altered in relative abundance (2) and are actively investigating several others.

The second project we are pursuing is the comparison of normal renal cortex and renal cell carcinoma in an effort to identify a marker for this neoplasm. Preliminary data has been presented (17,36) and a complete analysis is in preparation.

Our research aim is to pursue both projects with the methods presented in this paper, in the hopes of producing new, more sensitive and more specific clinical assays.

ACKNOWLEDGEMENTS

The authors would like to thank Ms. Gwyn Hurst, Ms. Teri Kimlinger and Dr. Les Wold for help with developing several of the methods described and Electro-Nucleonics for use of the 2DGEL equipment. Part of this work was supported by NIH Grant CA-16835 and by grants from the Mayo Clinic/Foundation. Ms. Cathy Collins is thanked for preparing the manuscript as camera-ready.

REFERENCES

1. D.S. Young, R.P. Tracy, Electrophoresis 4 (1983) 117-121.

2. R.P. Tracy, D.S. Young, J.A. Katzmann, R. Jenny, Ann. NY Acad. Sci., in press.

3. R.P. Tracy, R.M. Currie, D.S. Young, Clin. Chem. 28 (1982) 908-914.

4. R.P. Tracy, R.M. Currie, D.S. Young, Clin. Chem. 28 (1982) 890-899.

5. C.R. Merrill, D. Goldman, in J.E. Celis, R. Bravo (Eds.), Two-Dimensional Gel Electrophoresis of Proteins, Academic Press, N.Y. 1984, pp. 93-111.

6. R. Duncan, E.H. McConkey, Clin. Chem. 28 (1982) 749-755.

7. R.P. Tracy, D.S. Young in (5), pp. 194-240.

8. S.E. Ritzmann, J.C. Daniels (Eds.), Serum Protein Abnormalities, Little, Brown and Co., Boston 1975, p. 529 (Appendix).

9. T.A. Springer, J. Biol. Chem. 256 (1981) 3833-3839.

10. R.P. Tracy, J.A. Katzmann, T.K. Kimlinger, G.A. Hurst, D.S. Young, J. Immunol. Meth. 65 (1983) 97-107.

11. E.S. Lennox, K. Sikora in A.J. McMichal, J.W. Fabre (Eds.), Monoclonal Antibodies in Clinical Medicine, Academic Press, London 1982, p. 111

12. R.H. Kennett, Z.L. Jonak, R. Byrd, Meth. Can. Res. 20 (1982) 355-370.

13. B.E. Statland, Diagnostic Med. 4 (1981) 21.

14. M.C. Wang, L.A. Valenzuela, G.P. Murphy, T.M. Chu, Invest. Urol. 17 (1979) 159-163.

15. C.J. Tobin et al. Nature 30 (1982) 143-149.

16. R.P. Tracy, R.M. Currie, R.A. Kyle, D.S. Young, Clin. Chem. 28 (1982) 900-907.

17. V.I. Zannis, P.W. Just, J.L. Breslow, Am J. Hum. Genet. 33 (1981) 11-24.

18. R.P. Tracy, D.M. Wilson, D.S. Young, submitted.

19. N. Frearson, R.D. Taylor, S.V. Perry, Br. Med. J. 282 (1981) 2002-2003.

20. J.J. Edwards, N.G. Anderson, S.L. Tollaksen, A.C. von Eschenbach, J. Guerara, Clin. Chem. 28 (1982) 160-163.

21. R.P. Tracy, R.M. Currie, H.D. Hill, D.S. Young, Prot. Biol. Fluids 30 (1983) 581-586.

22. R.W. Rubin, C.Milikowski, G.E. Wise, Biochim. Biophys. Acta 595 (1980) 1-8.

23. N.L. Anderson, et al., Clin. Chem. 29 (1983) 762-767.

24. S.M. HAnash, et al., Clin. Chem. 28 (1982) 1026-1030.

25. R.L. Felsted, S.K. Gupta, J. Biol. Chem. 257 (1982) 13211-13217.

26. K.E. Willard, Clin. Chem. 28 (1982) 1031-1035.

27. P.D. Delmas, R.P. Tracy, B.L. Riggs, K.G. Mann, Calc. Tiss. International, in press.

28. R.P. Tracy, L.E. Wold, R.M. Currie, D.S. Young, Clin. Chem. 28 (1982) 815-919.

29. D.E. Comings, Clin. Chem. 28 (1982) 782-789.

30. P. Jackson, R.J. Thompson, J. Neurol. Sci. 49 (1981) 429-438.

31. M.J. Danon et al., Arch. Neurol. (Chicago) 38 (1981) 761-766.

32. R.G. Whalen, M.S. Ecob, Clin. Chem. 28 (1982) 1036-1040.

33. N.L. Anderson and N.G. Anderson, Proc. Natl. Acad. Sci. (USA) 74 (1977) 5421-5425

34. T. Pearson, N.L. Anderson, Anal. Biochem. 101 (1980) 101.

35. R.A. Swanson, R.P. Tracy, J.A. Katzmann, D.M. Wilson, D.S. Young, Clin. Chem. 28 (1982) 2033-2040.

36. R.P. Tracy, L.E. Wold, R.M. Currie, D.S. Young, presented to Acad. Clin. Lab. Physicians and Scientists, National Meeting, 1982.

SOME APPLICATIONS OF TWO DIMENSIONAL GEL ELECTROPHORESIS IN CELL BIOLOGY

Julio E. Celis, *Rodrigo Bravo

Division of Biostructural Chemistry, Department of Chemistry, University of Aarhus, Langelandsgade 140, DK-8000 Aarhus C, Denmark

*European Molecular Biology Laboratory, Postfach 10.2209, Meyerhofstrasse, Heidelberg 6900, Germany

1 INTRODUCTION

High resolution two dimensional gel electrophoresis (1,2) has allowed the separation of thousands of proteins from a given cell type with a degree of resolution not previously achieved. The unique properties of this technique has encouraged researchers to apply this technology to the study of various problems in cell biology such as transformation and cancer (3-20), detection of mutational events (21-23), differentiation (24-33), embryonic development (34-39), polymorphism (40-51), the cell cycle (52-54) and translational errors (55-62). Furthermore, this technique has been used to prepare protein catalogs (63-71) and to determine the polypeptide composition of cellular organelles and cytoskeletal systems (68,72-83).

Given space limitations, this article briefly reviews only some applications of two dimensional gel electrophoresis. These include the identification of the growth rate sensitive protein cyclin in cultured cells and tissues (5,8,10,14-16,54,84-91), and the separation, identification and cataloguing of human keratins (cytokeratins) (68,75,77,79,81,83,92-98). Both examples clearly emphasize the value of this technique as a high resolution research tool in cell biology.

Abbreviations: IEF: Isoelectric focussing; NEPHGE: Non-equilibrium pH gradient electrophoresis; PCNA: Proliferating cell nuclear antigen.

Fig. 1. Two dimensional gel electrophoresis (IEF, NEPHGE)of [^{35}S]-methionine labelled proteins from asynchronous HeLa cells labelled for 24 hr. In IEF the pH ranges from 7.5 (left) to 4.5 (right). In NEPHGE the pH varies from 7.5 (right) to 10.5 (left). 1357 proteins (946 acidic and 411 basic) are indicated in this Figure. From Bravo et al. (65).

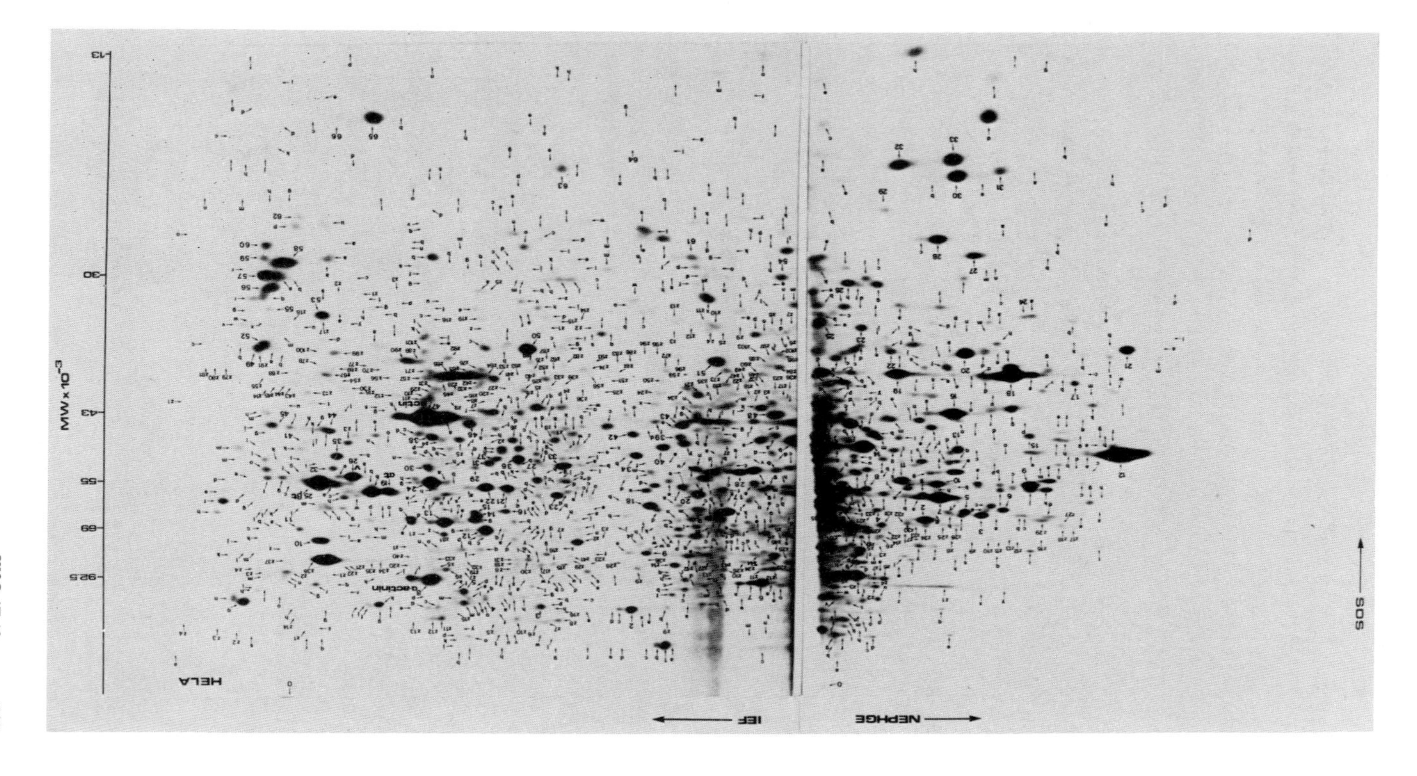

2 IDENTIFICATION OF THE GROWTH RATE SENSITIVE PROTEIN CYCLIN IN CULTURED CELLS

Understanding of the molecular mechanisms underlying malignant transformation and cancer will require first to unravel the pathway(s) that control cell proliferation in normal cells (16 and references therein). A first step towards this goal would be to identify some of the proteins that may be component of this pathway(s) amongst the thousands of polypeptides thought to be present in a somatic cell (99).

Encouraged by the high resolving power of two dimensional gel electrophoresis it seemed feasible to us to search for such proteins provided one could devise a simple screening procedure. One assay that came to our mind was to screen for proteins whose rate of synthesis increased preferentially in proliferating cells (normal as well as transformed) as compared to non dividing cells,as elevated levels of some of these proteins may be necessary in order to cope with an increased growth rate. With this in mind, we set up to compare the two dimensional protein patterns of normal somatic cells under various growth conditions (dividing vs non dividing) and between normal and transformed cells. Several proteins have been revealed using this approach (for reviews see references 14 and 16), but of these, "Cyclin" (M_r=36,000; protein IEF 49 in the HeLa protein catalogue (65,67,71);Figure 1) is the most striking as the levels of this protein correlate directly with the proliferative state of the cells (5,8,10, 14-16,54,84-91). Cyclin has so far been detected in proliferating cultured cells from the following vertebrate species: aves (100,101), bat (100), dog (100), dolphin (100), goat (100), hamster (8,17,84), human (8,17,84,89), mink (100), monkey (100), mouse (8,17,84), pisces (100), potoroo (17,102), rabbit (100) and rat (8,17,84,89).

2.1 Cyclin is a nuclear protein

The cellular location of cyclin was determined by Bravo et al. (84) using [^{35}S]-methionine labelled HeLa cells treated with Cytochalasin B and enucleated by centrifugal force. The purity of the cytoplasts (enucleated cells) was higher than 90% but the karyoplasts (nucleus containing fraction) were slightly contaminated with small cytoplasmic vesicles. Figure 2 shows enlargements of the appropiate region of two dimensional IEF gels of whole HeLa cells (Figure 2a), cytoplasts (Figure 2b) and karyoplasts (Figure 2c). Clearly, cyclin is found mainly in the karyoplast (nucleus) and it is barely detected in cytoplasts. Confirmation of these results have been obtained by Mathews et al. (89) using conventional nuclei preparation procedures.

2.2 Increased synthesis of cyclin during the S-phase of the cell cycle

A detailed study of the polypeptides synthesized during the cell cycle in HeLa cells was described by us in 1980 (54). Synchronized HeLa cells in different stages of the cell cycle were labelled with [^{35}S]-methionine for 30 min pulses starting at the beginning of each phase or after collection, in the case of mitosis. Quantitative two dimensional gel electrophoretic analysis of the amount of [^{35}S]-methionine

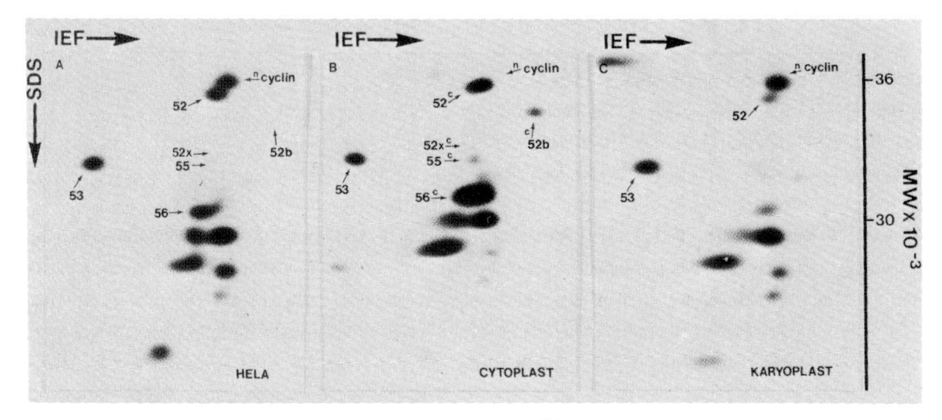

Fig. 2. Two dimensional gel separation (IEF) of [^{35}S]-methionine labelled proteins from (a) whole HeLa cells, (b) cytoplasts and (c) karyoplasts. Cells were prelabelled with [^{35}S]-methionine previous to enucleation with Cytochalasin B and centrifugal force (84). Only the relevant region of the gels are shown. From Bravo et al. (84).

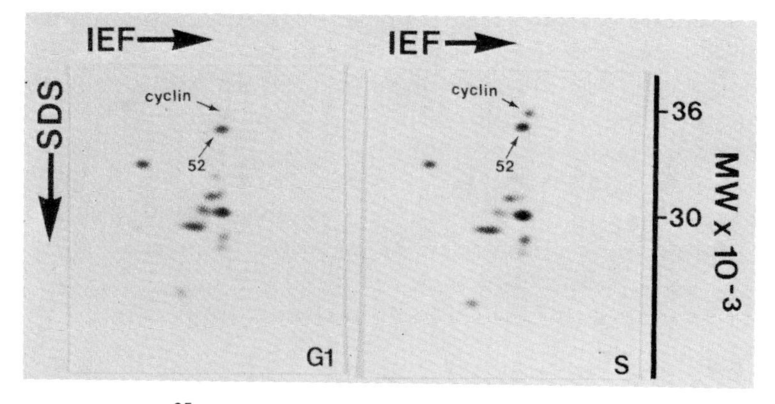

Fig. 3. Synthesis of [^{35}S]-methionine labelled cyclin in synchronized HeLa cells. Synchronized cells were obtained by mechanical detachtment of mitotic cells. (a) G1, (b) S-phase. The position of the tropomyosin related polypeptide IEF 52 is indicated for reference. From Bravo and Celis (54).

labelled cyclin in the various stages of the cell cycle showed an important increase in the level of cyclin during S-phase (54). Figures 3a and b show the appropiate regions of IEF gels from G1 (a) and S-phase cells (b). The relative proportion of cyclin in G1 is 0.012 as compared to 0.024 in S-phase (54).

2.3 Levels of cyclin in normal and transformed cells

There are at least three states of cell proliferation in which there is variation in the synthesis of cyclin.

1. *Normal cycling cultured cells* (primary and secondary cultures) synthesize cyclin at low passages but its synthesis declines or ceases as cell division and DNA synthesis stop (87). Normal cycling cells so far studied include human skin fibroblasts (87) and various human epithelial amnion cells (10,103). Figure 4 shows examples of IEF gels (only the pertinent region is shown) of [^{35}S]-methionine labelled proteins from cultured human skin fibroblast labelled at passage 8 (split ratio 1:3, thymidine labelling index=20%; relative proportion of cyclin=0.084) (Figure 4a) and 11 (split ratio 1:3; thymidine labelling index=4%; relative proportion of cyclin=0.048) (Figure 4b) (87). Similar analysis of human fibroblasts throughout their life span have shown that a decrease in the synthesis of cyclin parallels a decrease in the number of cells that label with [^{3}H]-thymidine (thymidine labelling index) (87).

Further evidence demonstrating a direct correlation between cell proliferation and cyclin synthesis has been obtained from studies of morphologically transformed skin fibroblasts that arose spontaneously in a senescent culture that reached p23 (split ratio 1:3; thymidine labelling index=<0.1%) (87). The morphologically transformed cells were passed 8 times (split ratio 1:2) before they ceased to proliferate and died. Figures 4c and d show IEF gels of [^{35}S]-methionine proteins from the morphologically transformed cells labelled at p28 (thymidine labelling index=6%) and 31 (thymidine labelling index=<0.5%), respectively. The relative proportion of cyclin at both passages is 0.086 and 0.030, respectively. The increase in cyclin was observed at p24 (not shown), and its level remained more or less constant until p29.

2. *Noncycling cells* (mortal and immortal) as well as most tissues so far studied synthesize very low levels of cyclin (18,84,87,88,90,102). Noncycling cells so far studied include lymphocytes (102), monocytes (102) and epidermal cells (18,90). Various tissues of mouse (brain, dermis, epidermis, heart, liver, lung, etc.) (102,104) and human origin (dermis, epidermis) (18,90) have also been studied and with few exceptions (84,102,104) these synthesize very little cyclin. In the latter case the cells synthesizing cyclin are thought to represent the proliferating cell population of this tissue.

Recent studies of quiescent 3T3 cells induced to proliferate by means of serum stimulation have further shown a direct correlation between cyclin and DNA synthesis (88). Some of these results are shown in Figures 5 and 6. An increase in cyclin synthesis following serum stimulation was observed only after 8-10 hr (Figures 5c and 6)

Fig. 4. Synthesis of cyclin in growing, senescent and morphologically transformed fibroblasts. Human skin fibroblasts at various passages were labelled with [^{35}S]-methionine. (a) p8, (b) p11, (c) p28, (d) p31. The position of the tropomyosin related polypeptide IEF 52 is indicated for reference. From Celis and Bravo (87).

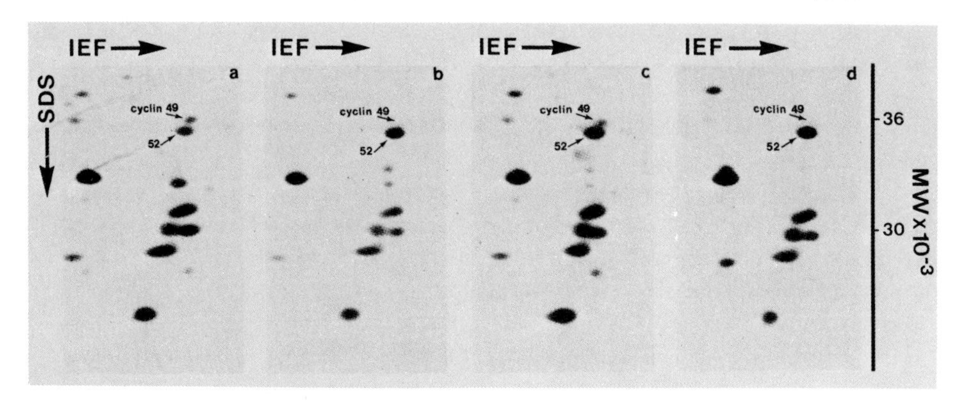

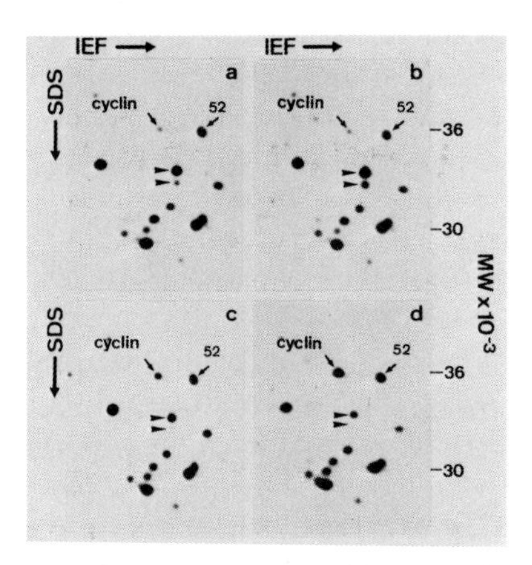

Fig. 5. Two dimensional gel electrophoresis (IEF) of [^{35}S]-methionine labelled polypeptides from serum-stimulated quiescent 3T3 cells. (a) quiescent non-stimulated cells; (b) cells after 6 hr stimulation; (c) cells after 10 hr stimulation; (d) cells after 14 hr stimulation. Only the appropiate area of the fluorograph is shown. From Bravo (88).

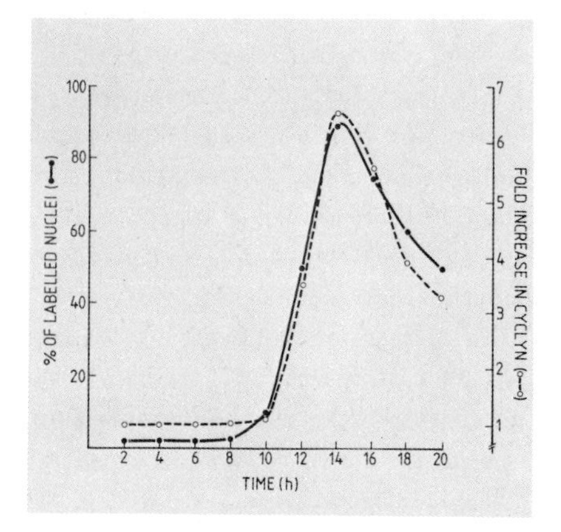

Fig. 6. Synthesis of cyclin and DNA following serum stimulation of quiescent 3T3 cells. The data is given as fold increase in cyclin compared with non-stimulated quiescent 3T3 (o-o). Cells labelled with [^{3}H]-thymidine were processed for autoradiography according to standard procedures (2 weeks exposure). About 500 nuclei were counted in each case (•-•). From Bravo (88).

reaching a maximum at 14-16 hr (Figures 5d and 6). Interestingly, DNA synthesis (as determined by [^{3}H]-thymidine incorporation and autoradiography) (Figure 6) follows very closely the levels of cyclin, suggesting that the activity of this protein is closely related to events associated or related to DNA replication.

3. *Transformed cells* (immortal, or immortal and tumorigenic). Two dimensional gel electrophoretic analysis of established cell lines from human (HeLa, EJ19, SVK14, AMA, Wish, Fl-amnion, Detroit 98, Raji, Chang liver, Molt-4, Kb, W1-38 SV40, A431), hamster (CHO, RJK39, BHK21, BHK21 Py Y, BHK21 SV40), mouse (Sarcoma 180, X63, CLID, 3T3B, 3T3B SV40, IEF 3) and rat (Rat-1, NRK, HTC, TCA-A1, BRL62, L6J and SV40 REF52) have shown that cyclin is present in all these cell lines and that it is synthesized in elevated but variable amounts (5,10,14,16-20,89-91,102,105). In some cases cyclin is synthesized constitutively.

Only a few tumours have been studied so far and these include two basaliomas (18, 90), a melanoma (106), four lymphomas (107), mesenchymomas (15), fibrous histiocytomas (15) and mesenchymal chondrosarcomas (15). In all cases, an increased synthesis of cyclin has been detected as compared to control normal tissue.

2.4 Distribution of cyclin during the cell cycle as determined by immunofluorescence using PCNA antibodies

Tan's group was the first to demonstrate that a few percentages of the sera of patients with systemic lupus erythematosus (SLE) contain autoantibodies that react preferentially with dividing cells (108-110). The antigen, termed proliferating cell nuclear antigen (PCNA), cannot be detected in resting cells and normal tissues but is present in established cell lines and some tumours so far analysed. Furthermore, it has been shown that the distribution of PCNA fluctuates during the cell cycle of Wil-2 cells with a striking accumulation in the nucleolus during late G1 and early S-phase (109). Mathews et al. (89) have recently presented evidence showing that PCNA and cyclin are identical.

Figure 7 shows immunofluorescence staining of an asynchronous population of transformed human amnion cells (AMA) fixed with methanol and reacted with PCNA antibodies. About 42% of the total cell population stain with the antibody and these correspond to S-phase cells as determined by [^{3}H]-thymidine incorporation (see Figures 8a and b) (100). G1 cells show a weak but distinct staining, while G2 and mitotic cells exhibit very little staining (arrows in Figure 7; in this picture G1 cells cannot be distinguished from G2 cells) (100).

Cells in S-phase show variable patterns both in terms of intensity and distribution of the antigen. At the beginning of DNA synthesis (1 in Figure 8b) cyclin is found throughout the nucleus with the exception of the nucleolus. A similar,but more intense pattern is observed as the cells progress in S-phase (2 in Figure 8b). At a stage close to maximum DNA synthesis cyclin staining redistributes to reveal a punctated pattern with foci of staining throughout the nucleus (3 in Figure 8b). This pattern preceeds a major change in the distribution of cyclin which is then detected

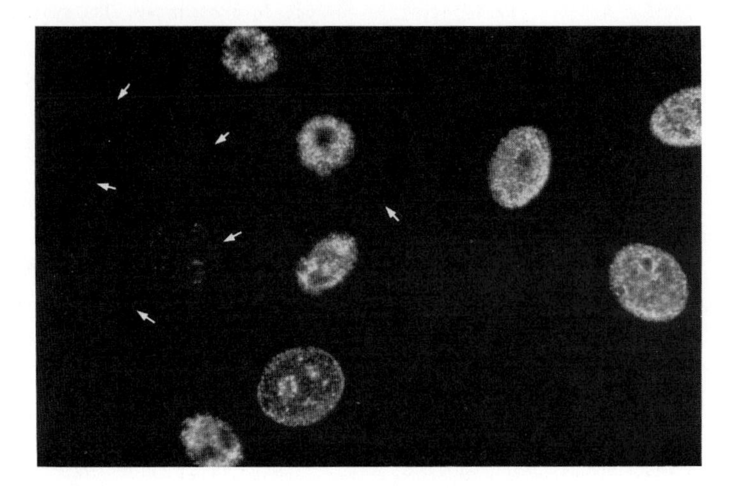

Fig. 7. Immunofluorescence staining of transformed human amnion cells (AMA) with PCNA antibodies. The antibodies were a gift of M. Mathews and R.M. Bernstein from Cold Spring Harbor Laboratory, New York. Cells that stain weakly with the antibody are indicated with arrows.

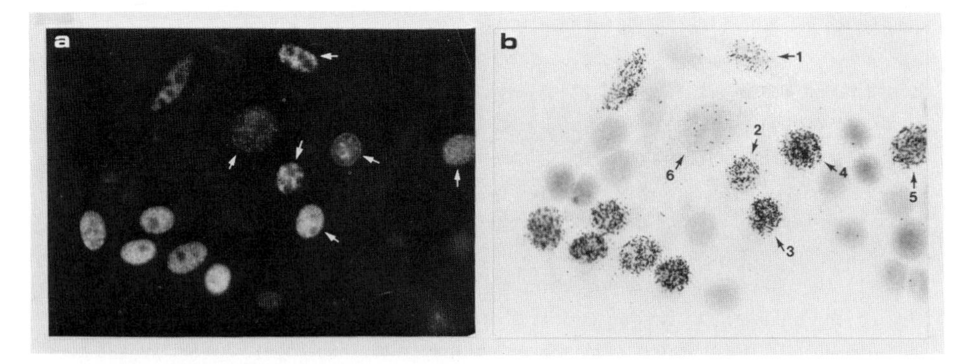

Fig. 8. Immunofluorescence (PCNA antibodies) and autoradiographic analysis ([^{3}H]-thymidine incorporation) of asynchronous AMA cells. AMA cells were labelled with [^{3}H]-thymidine (30 min; 2 μCi/ml), fixed with methanol and reacted with PCNA antibodies. Immunofluorescence pictures (a) were taken prior to autoradiography (b).

into large globular structures that correspond to the nucleolus (4 in Figure 8b; note that nucleolar staining is observed at the beginning of S-phase in Wil-2 cells (109)). At this stage DNA synthesis seemed to have reached a maximum. Thereafter, there are further changes in the pattern of cyclin staining which became punctated (5 in Figure 8b) and of decreasing intensity (6 in Figure 8b).

At present we do not know whether the different staining patterns reflects movements of cyclin or of structures to which it is attached. Nevertheless, it seems likely that these changes in distribution may reflect important changes in the functional state of this protein (100).

2.5 Conclusion

Given the enhanced synthesis of cyclin (PCNA) in growing cultured cells and tumours as compared to noncycling or slowly cycling cells this polypeptide may be considered as a marker for proliferating cells. At present, little is known concerning the function of this protein, although, from all the available information, it would seem that cyclin is a central component of the pathway(s) that control cell proliferation in most if not all cells,and that its activity may be linked with events associated or related to DNA replication. Further elucidation of the function of cyclin as well as of the proteins coded by the oncogenes should eventually lead us to a better understanding of the mechanisms underlying normal control of cell proliferation and hence neoplastic transformation and cancer.

3 SEPARATION, IDENTIFICATION AND CATALOGUING OF HUMAN KERATINS (CYTOKERATINS)

An important area in cell biology in which high resolution two dimensional gel electrophoresis has greatly contributed to our advance in knowledge is the elucidation of the various polypeptide components of the keratin-type intermediate-sized filaments present in cultured epithelial cells and tissues (68,75,77,79,81,83,92-98).

Intermediate-sized filaments (7-11 nm in diameter) are a major component of the cytoskeleton and are found in most vertebrate cells. The polypeptide subunits that compose these filaments have been classified in five groups: 1) keratins (also termed cytokeratins), present in epithelial cells; 2) vimentin, present in mesenchymal derived cells, astrocytes, Sertoli cells, vascular smooth muscle cells and some cultured epithelial cells; 3) desmin, present in myogenic cells; 4) glial filament proteins, present in glial cells and 5) neurofilament proteins, present in neuronal cells (for reviews see references 77,83,111).

The presence of intermediate-sized filaments of the keratin type in epithelial cells of non-epidermal origin was first assessed by indirect immunofluorescence using polyclonal antibodies raised against authentic epidermal α-keratins (95,112-116). These antibodies show a wide cross-reactivity among species suggesting that keratins are immunologically related (111 and references therein). An important step forward in the elucidation of the various keratins present in cultured epithelial cells and tissues was provided by the observation that the cytoskeleton of cells extracted with low concentrations of non ionic detergents and high salt buffers were highly enriched in intermediate-sized filaments (75,79,117-123). Accordingly, several laboratories began to analyse the polypeptide composition of these cytoskeletons using one and two dimensional gel electrophoresis. To date, high resolution two dimensional gel electrophoresis has become the technique of choice and W. Franke's laboratory in Heidelberg has made important contributions to the standardization of conditions for resolving both basic and acid keratins. A total of 19 keratins (cytokerations; number 1-19) (68) that are themselves differentially expressed in different epithelial tissues and cultured epithelial cells have been resolved, identified and catalogued by Franke's group (68 and references therein). A schematic representation of this data (taken from the work of Moll et al. (68)) is shown in Figure 9 and a few examples of two dimensional gel electrophoretic patterns (NEPHGE) of human cytoskeletal proteins from epithelia and epithelia derived cell lines are shown in Figure 10 (kindly provided by Drs R.A. Quinlan and W. Franke). Keratin polypeptides show various isoelectric variants (Figures 9,10; legend of Figure 9) and these usually correspond to phosphorylated modifications (68,75,78,111,124-128). The authenticity of these keratins has been demonstrated by immunoblotting using keratin antibodies (68 and references therein) and more recently by reconstitution experiments (129). Furthermore, in a few cases, it has been possible to raise polyclonal keratin antibodies by immunizing mice with single keratins eluted from two dimensional gels (81). The procedure for preparing such antibodies is given in the legend of Figure 11,which show indirect immunofluorescence staining of various cell types reacted with polyclonal antibodies raised against keratin 7 (68) or protein IEF 31 in the HeLa protein catalogue (65,67,71).

A great deal of research is now being directed towards an understanding of the biological significance of keratin heterogeneity.

3.1 Conclusions

Keratins constitute the most heterogenous group of proteins amongst the intermediate-sized filament proteins. These proteins are component of a large multigene family whose expression is regulated as a function of epithelial differentiation, cellular growth environment and disease (83 and references therein). Keratins are excellent markers for distinguishing and classifying epithelial cells (83 and references therein). Furthermore, monoclonal antibodies specific for individual keratin polypeptides may be valuable new tools in surgical pathology.

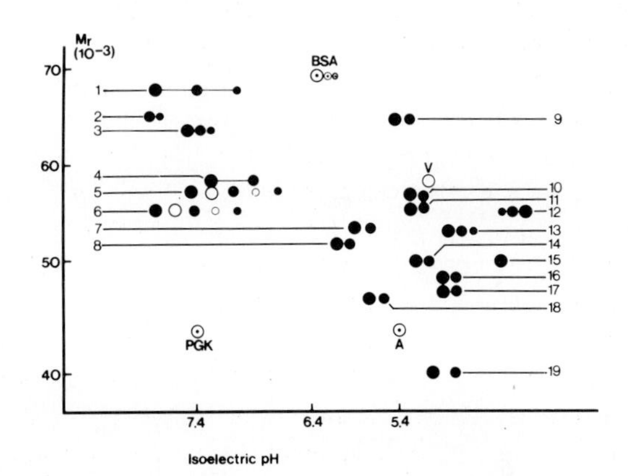

Fig. 9. Schematic chart of human cytokeratin polypeptides. Cytoskeletal proteins from various human epithelia, carcinomas and cultured epithelial cells were separated by two-dimensional gel electrophoresis. Cytokeratin polypeptides detected and identified by antibody binding in immunoblot experiments, and in most cases also by peptide mapping, are arranged according to their mobilities in these gel electrophoretic systems. Abscissa: isoelectric pH values for molecules denatured in 9.5 M urea (data combined from IEF and NEPHGE).Ordinate: relative molecular weight (M_r) as determined by SDS-polyacrylamide gel electrophoresis. Cytokeratin polypeptides are designated by Arabic numerals. Horizontal series of spots: different isoelectric variants of the same polypeptide. Large dots: the specific major variant, usually the most basic, non-phosphorylated one. Small dots: minor variants. Open circles: variants of the specific polypeptide not always found in analyses from various cell types: PGK: 3-phosphoglycero-kinase. BSA: bovine serum albumin. A: rabbit α-actin. V: human vimentin. Two dimensional gel electrophoresis was performed with non-equilibrium pH gradient electrophoresis (2) (ampholine range, pH 2-11; lysis buffer containing 0.25% SDS) or isoelectric focusing (1) (ampholine range, pH 4-7) in the first dimension. For second dimension electrophoresis on 12% SDS-polyacrylamide gels, a modified electrode buffer and an acrylamide to N,N'-methylene bisacrylamide ratio of 30:0.15 was used (130). Gels were stained with Coomassie brilliant blue or, mostly for analysis of protein present in micro-dissected samples, by a silver staining method (131). Gels containing [^{35}S]-methionine-labelled proteins were processed for autoradiofluorography. Usually cytoskeletal material was dissolved directly in lysis buffer (2). Cytoskeletons of cultured cells and, for control experiments, total epithelial tissue were lysed in boiling SDS-containing sample buffer (132), and the solubilized protein was acetone-precipitated, dried and taken up in lysis buffer (2), as described by Franke et al. (96). From Moll et al. (68).

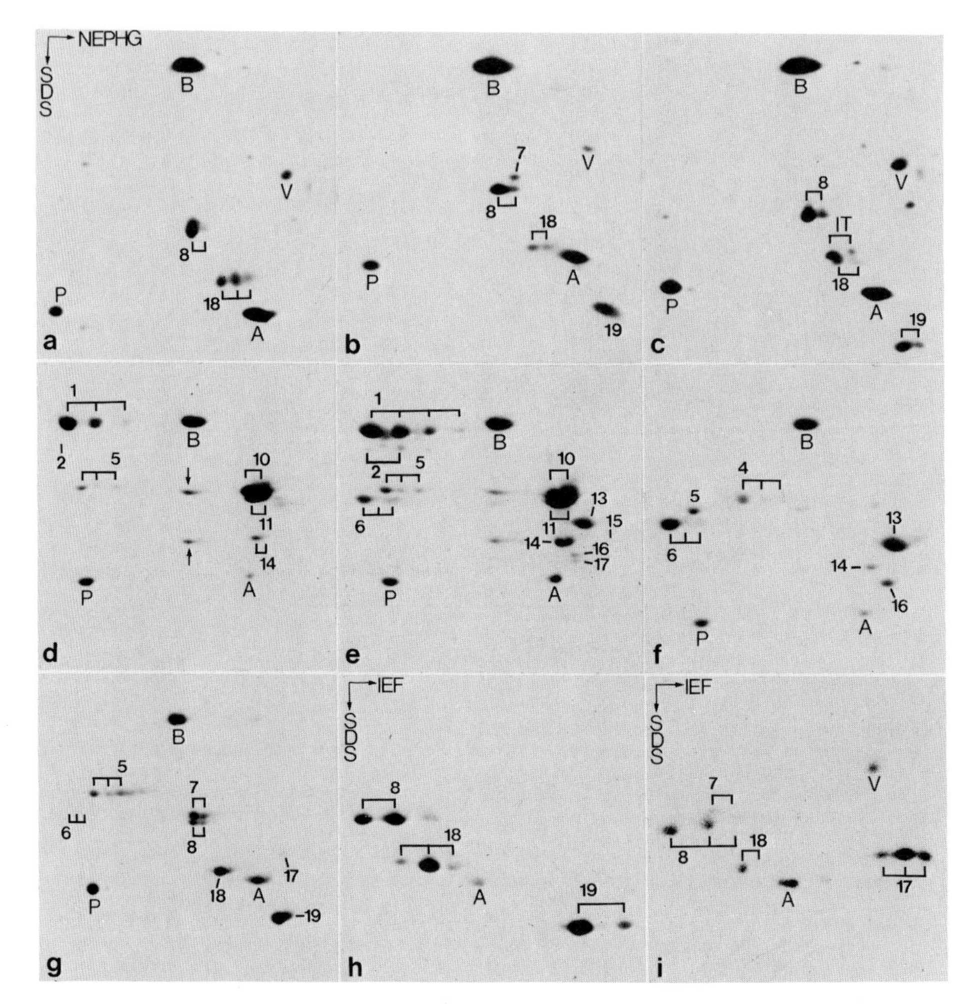

Fig. 10. Two dimensional gel electrophoretic patterns of human cytoskeletal proteins from epithelia (a-f) and epithelia derived cell lines (g-i). NEPHGE, first dimension using non-equilibrium pH gradient electrophoresis; IEF, first dimension using isoelectric focusing; SDS, direction of second dimension electrophoresis in the presence of SDS. The anode is on the right hand side for the first dimension. For the designation of cytokeratin polypeptides (number 1-19) see Moll et al. (68)). Brakets indicate the major isoelectric variants of the same polypeptide. V, vimentin resulting from contaminating connective tissue, stromal cells and blood vessels in samples prepared by microdissection from frozen sections (a-d). In some epithelial derived cell lines such as HeLa (i), vimentin is also co-expressed with cytokeratins. Marker polypeptides included are: P, 3-phosphoglycerokinase, pI 7.4, M_r=43,000; B, Bovine serum albumin, pI 6.35, M_r=68,000; A, skeletal α-actin, pI 5.4, M_r=42,000. (a) Hepatocytes (microdissected lower lobules devoid of portal fields), (b) Gall bladder epithelium. (c) Colon mucosa (microdissected basal regions from crysts). It is a component observed in variable amounts which may represent a degradation product (96), (d) Interfollicular epidermis microdissected from frozen sections of arm skin. Arrows mark cytokeratins 5 and 14 which are still present as a complex in 9.5 M urea.

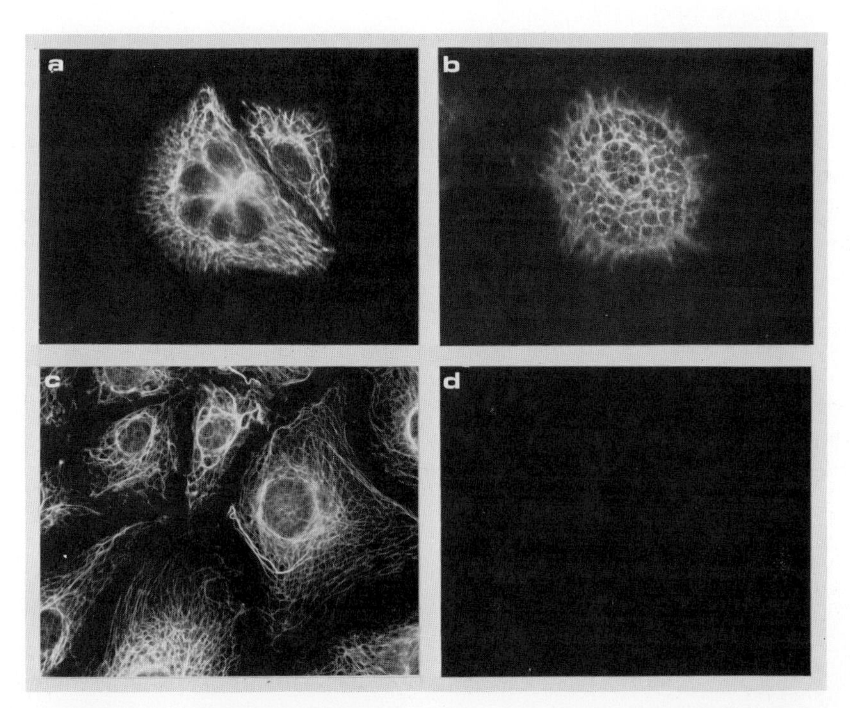

Fig. 11. Indirect immunofluorescence of various cultured cells reacted with a mouse polyclonal antibody raised against keratin IEF 31 (keratin 7 in the catalogue of human keratins (68)). (a,b) AMA, (c) PTK2 and (d) human skin fibroblasts. For antibody production the cell content of approximately 30 confluent Nunc flasks (250 ml) seeded with transformed human amnion cells (AMA) was used to prepare proteins for immunization. The cell monolayers were washed four times with sterile Hanks' and scraped off with a rubber policeman in a final volume of 10 ml of Hanks'. After centrifugation, the pelleted cells were treated with DNAse and RNAse, lyophilised, and dissolved in IEF lysis buffer. The procedure for two dimensional gel electrophoresis (IEF) has been described in detail elsewhere. Following electrophoresis of samples (mixed with tracer radioactive proteins), IEF 31 was located using the autoradiograms and cut from the unfixed dried gels. The protein was eluted from the gels by shaking overnight at room temperature in 1 ml of 0.1% SDS, lyophilized, and redissolved in 1 ml of sterile Hanks'. An equal volume of complete Freund's adjuvant was added to this solution. Two BALB/c mice were immunized intraperitoneally each with 0.3 ml of this suspension (containing ~ 20 μg of proteins) and the injections were repeated at 15 days intervals until a positive test was obtained as judged by immunofluorescence of methanol:acetone-fixed AMA cells. After a booster injection, the animals were bled from the heart. About 0.4 ml of sera was obtained in each case. The animals also produced ~ 1 ml of ascites fluid as a result of the repeated intraperitoneal injections. Both the sera and the ascites fluid yielded the same immunofluorescent patterns. From Bravo et al. (81).

Fig. 10. cont.

A similar complex can be seen in (e) and (f). For more information on the dissociation of cytokeratin complexes with increasing urea concentrations see Franke et al. (133). (e) Total anal canal epithelium. (f) Tongue mucosa, (g) 'Detroit 562 cells' derived from pleural effusion of a pharynx carcinoma, (h) MCF-7 cells, (i) HeLa cells, normal subline monolayer culture. For details of the sample reparation in (a), (b), (e), (f-i), see Moll et al. (68). Courtesy of R.A. Quinlan and W. Franke.

3 CONCLUDING REMARKS

From the foregoing it is clear that applications of high resolution two dimensional gel electrophoresis to studies of various problems in cell biology will result in important advances in the separation and identification of proteins not previously detected by other conventional techniques. Indeed, this technique in conjunction with the recombinant DNA and hybridoma technologies will provide a unique opportunity for the analysis and understanding of the function of many cell molecules in the near future.

4 ACKNOWLEDGEMENTS

We would like to thank our colleages A. Celis, S.J. Fey and P. Mose Larsen for discussions. This work has been supported by grants from the Danish Medical and Natural Science Research Councils, the Danish Cancer Society, Euratom and Novo.

5 REFERENCES

(1) P.H. O'Farrell, J. Biol. Chem. 250 (1975) 4007-4021.

(2) P.Z. O'Farrell, H.M. Goodman, P.H. O'Farrell, Cell 12 (1977) 1133-1142.

(3) J. Leavitt, B. Moyzig, J. Biol. Chem. 253 (1978) 2497-2500.

(4) K. Radke, T. Ege, Cell 22 (1980) 513-522.

(5) R. Bravo, J.E. Celis, Exp. Cell Res. 127 (1980) 249-260.

(6) J. Brzeski, T. Ege, Cell 22 (1980) 513-522.

(7) J. Leavitt, T. Kakunaga, J. Biol. Chem. 255 (1980) 1650-1661.

(8) R. Bravo, S.J. Fey, J.E. Celis, Carcinogenesis 2 (1981) 769-782.

(9) J.A. Cooper, T. Hunter, Mol. Cell. Biol. 1 (1981) 165-178.

(10) R. Bravo, J.E. Celis, Clin. Chem. 28 (1982) 949-954.

(11) J. Leavitt, D. Goldman, C. Merril, T. Kakunaga, Clin. Chem. 28 (1982) 850-860.

(12) R.P. Tracy, L.E. Wold, R.M. Curie, S. Young, Clin. Chem. 28 (1982) 915-919.

(13) A.K. Thorsrud, M.H. Vatu, E. Jellum, Clin. Chem. 28 (1982) 884-889.

(14) R. Bravo, J. Bellatin, S.J. Fey, P. Mose Larsen, J.E. Celis in Gene Expression in Normal and Transformed Cells (J.E. Celis and R. Bravo eds) Plenum Press (1983) 263-290.

(15) J. Forchhammer, H. Macdonald-Bravo in Gene Expression in Normal and Transformed Cells (J.E. Celis and R. Bravo eds) Plenum Press (1983) 291-314.

(16) J.E. Celis, R. Bravo, P. Mose Larsen, J. Bellatin, A. Celis in Two-Dimensional Gel Electrophoresis of Proteins: Methods and Applications (J.E. Celis and R. Bravo eds) (1984) 307-362.

(17) J.E. Celis, R. Bravo, P. Mose Larsen, S.J. Fey, Leukemia Research 8 (1984) 143-157.

(18) J.E. Celis, S.J. Fey, P. Mose Larsen, A. Celis in The Cancer Cell (A. Levine, W. Topp, G. van de Woude, J.D. Watson eds) Cold Spring Harbor Laboratory (in press).

(19) R. Bravo in The Cancer Cell (A. Levine, W. Topp, G. van de Woude, J.D. Watson eds) Cold Spring Harbor Laboratory (in press).

(20) J.I. Garrels, R. Franza in The Cancer Cell (A. Levine, W. Topp, G. van de Woude, J.D. Watson eds) Cold Spring Harbor Laboratory (in press).

(21) R.A. Steinberg, P.H. O'Farrell, U. Friedrich, P. Coffino, Cell 10 (1977) 381-391.

(22) D. Goldman, C.R. Merril in Two-Dimensional Gel Electrophoresis of Proteins: Methods and Applications (J.E. Celis and R. Bravo eds) Academic Press (1984) 241-268.

(23) J.V. Neel, B.B. Rosenblum, C.F. Sing, M.M. Skolnick, S.M. Hanash, S. Sternberg in Two-Dimensional Gel Electrophoresis of Proteins: Methods and Applications (J.E. Celis and R. Bravo eds) Academic Press (1984) 259-306.

(24) J.L. Peterson, E.H. McConkey, J. Biol. Chem. 251 (1976) 555-558.

(25) B. Hoffman-Liebermann, L. Sachs, Cell 14 (1978) 825-834.

(26) J.I. Garrels, Dev. Biol. 73 (1979) 134-152.

(27) R. Reeves, P. Cseryesi, J. Biol. Chem. 254 (1979) 4283-4290.

(28) R.H. Lovell-Badge, M.J. Evans, J. Embryol. Exp. Morph. 59 (1980) 187-206.

(29) D. Liebermann, B. Hoffman-Liebermann, L. Sachs, Dev. Biol. 79 (1980) 46-63.

(30) D. Paulin, Biochimie 63 (1981) 347-363.

(31) E.P. Lester, P. Lemkin, L. Lipkin, Clin. Chem. 28 (1982) 828-839.

(32) L.M. Marshall, R.C. Hunt, J. Cell Sci. 54 (1982) 97-113.

(33) D. Montarras, M.Y. Frozman, F. Gros, J. Biol. Chem. 257 (1982) 545-548.

(34) B.P. Brandhorst, Dev. Biol. 52 (1976) 310-317.

(35) J. van Blerkom, S.C. Barton, M.H Johnson, Nature 259 (1976) 319-321.

(36) S.L. Abreu, R.L. Brinster, Exp. Cell Res. 114 (1978) 135-141.

(37) J. van Blerkom, R.W. McGanghey, Dev. Biol. 63 (1978) 151-164.

(38) R. Bravo, J. Knowland, Differentiation 13 (1979) 101-108.

(39) E.A. Sturgess, J.E.M. Ballantine, H.R. Woodland, P.R. Mohin, C.D. Iane, G.J. Dimitriadis, J. Embryol. Exp. Morph. 58 (1980) 303-320.

(40) D.E. Comings, Nature 277 (1977) 28-32.

(41) N.L. Anderson, N.G. Anderson, Proc. Natl. Acad. Sci. USA 74 (1977) 5421-5425.

(42) R.W. Elliot, Genetics 91 (1979) 295-308.

(43) E.H. McConkey, B.J. Taylor, D. Phan, Proc. Natl. Acad. Sci. USA 76 (1979) 6500-6504.

(44) H. Hamaguchi, A. Otha, R. Mukai, T. Yabe, M. Yamada, Human Genet. 59 (1981) 215-220.

(45) C.S. Giometti, N.L. Anderson, J. Biol. Chem. 26 (1981) 11840-11846.

(46) L.A. Wanner, J.V. Neel, M.H. Meisler, Ann. J. Hum. Genet. 34 (1982) 209-215.

(47) D.E. Comings, Clin. Chem. 28 (1982) 805-812.

(48) D. Goldman, C.R. Merril, R.J. Polinsky, M.H. Ebert, Clin. Chem. 28 (1982) 1021-1025.

(49) D.E. Comings, Clin. Chem. 28 (1982) 813-818.

(50) D. Goldman, C.R. Meriil, Am. J. Hum. Genet. 35 (1983) 827-837.

(51) C.S. Giometti, N.L. Anderson, J. Mol. Biol. 173 (1984) 109-123.

(52) C. Milcarek, K. Zahn, J. Cell Biol. 79 (1978) 833-838.

(53) S.G. Elliot, C.S. McLaughlin, Proc. Natl. Acad. Sci. USA 75 (1978) 4384-4388.

(54) R. Bravo, J.E. Celis, J. Cell Biol. 84 (1980) 795-802.

(55) P.H. O'Farrell, Cell 14 (1978) 545-557.

(56) J. Parker, J.W. Pollard, J.D. Friesen, C.P. Stanners, Proc. Natl. Acad. Sci. USA 75 (1978) 1091-1095.

(57) D.L. Wilson, M.E. Hall, G.C. Stone, Gerontology 24 (1978) 426-433.

(58) J. Parker, J.D. Friesen, Mol. Gen. Genet. 177 (1980) 439-446.

(59) C.B. Harley, J.W. Pollard, J.W. Chamberlain, C.P. Stanners, S. Goldstein, Proc. Natl. Acad. Sci. USA 77 (1980) 1885-1889.

(60) J. Parker, J. Flanagan, J. Murphy, J. Gallant, Mech. Ageing Dev. 16 (1981) 127-139.

(61) J.W. Pollard, C.B. Harley, J.W. Chamberlain, S. Goldstein, C.P. Stanners, J. Biol. Chem. 257 (1982) 5977-5979.

(62) J.W. Pollard in Two-Dimensional Gel Electrophoresis of Proteins: Methods and Applications (J.E. Celis and R. Bravo eds) Academic Press (1984) 363-395.

(63) S. Pedersen, P.L. Bloch, S. Reek, F.C. Neidhardt, Cell 14 (1978) 179-180.

(64) T.A. Phillips, P.L. Bloch, F.C. Neidhardt, J. Bacteriol. 144 (1980) 1024-1033.

(65) R. Bravo, J. Bellatin, J.E. Celis, Cell Biol. Int. Rep. 5 (1981) 93-96.

(66) S.J. Fey, R. Bravo, P. Mose Larsen, J. Bellatin, J.E. Celis, Cell Biol. Int. Rep. 5 (1981) 491-500.

(67) R. Bravo, J.E. Celis, Clin. Chem. 28 (1982) 766-781.

(68) R. Moll, W.W. Franke, D.L. Schiller, B. Geiger, R. Krepler, Cell 31 (1982) 11-24.

(69) S.J. Fey, R. Bravo, P. Mose Larsen, J.E. Celis in Two-Dimensional Gel Electrophoresis of Proteins: Methods and Applications (J.E. Celis and R. Bravo eds) Academic Press (1984) 169-189.

(70) F.C. Neidhardt, T.A. Philips in Two-Dimensional Gel Electrophoresis of Proteins: Methods and Applications (J.E. Celis and R. Bravo eds) Academic Press (1984) 169-189.

(71) R. Bravo, J.E. Celis in Two-Dimensional Gel Electrophoresis of Proteins: Methods and Applications (J.E. Celis and R. Bravo eds) Academic Press (1984) 445-476.

(72) J.G. Hensler, A. Srere, J. Biol. Chem. 254 (1979) 5488-5497.

(73) B.W. Jackson, C. Grund, E. Schmid, K. Bürki, W.W. Franke, K. Illmensee, Differentiation 17 (1980) 161-179.

(74) N.L. Anderson, Proc. Natl. Acad. Sci. USA 78 (1981) 2407-2411.

(75) W.W. Franke, D.L. Schiller, R. Moll, S. Winter, E. Schmid, I. Engelbrecht, H. Denk, R. Krepler, B. Platzer, J. Mol. Biol. 13 (1981) 933-959.

(76) D.E. Comings, K.E. Peters in The Cell Nucleus (H. Busch ed) Academic Press (1981) 9-118.

(77) G. Albrecht-Buehler (J.D. Watson ed.) Cold Spring Harbor Symp. Quant. Biol. 46 (1982).

(78) P. Mose Larsen, R. Bravo, S.J. Fey, J.V. Small, J.E. Celis, Cell 31 (1982) 681-692.

(79) R. Bravo, J.V. Small, S.J. Fey, P. Mose Larsen, J.E. Celis, J. Mol. Biol. 154 (1982) 121-143.

(80) C.S. Giometti, K.E. Willard, N.L. Anderson, Clin. Chem. 28 (1982) 955-961.

(81) R. Bravo, S.J. Fey, P. Mose Larsen, N. Coppard, J.E. Celis, J. Cell Biol. 96 (1983) 416-423.

(82) F. Matsumara, S. Yamashiro-Matsumara, J-C.J. Lin, J. Cell Biol. 258 (1983) 6636-6644.

(83) E. Wang, D. Fishman, R.K.H. Liem, T-T. Sun, Proc. New York Acad. Sci. (in press).

(84) R. Bravo, S.J. Fey, J. Bellatin, P. Mose Larsen, J. Arevalo, J.E. Celis, Exp. Cell Res. 136 (1981) 311-319.

(85) J. Bellatin, R. Bravo, J.E. Celis, Proc. Natl. Acad. Sci. USA 79 (1982) 4367-4370.

(86) R. Bravo, S.J. Fey, J. Bellatin, P. Mose Larsen, J.E. Celis in Embryonic Development. Part A (M. Burger ed.) Alan R. Liss, New York (1982) 235-248.

(87) J.E. Celis, R. Bravo, FEBS Lett. 165 (1984) 21-25.

(88) R. Bravo, FEBS Lett. 169 (1984) 185-188.

(89) M.B. Mathews, R.M. Bernstein, R. Franza, J.I. Garrels, Nature 309 (1984) 374-376.

(90) J.E. Celis, S.J. Fey, P. Mose Larsen, A. Celis, Proc. Natl. Acad. Sci. USA (in press).

(91) R. Bravo, Proc. Natl. Acad. Sci. USA (in press).

(92) T.I. Doran, A. Vidrich, T.-T. Sun, Cell 22 (1980) 17-25.

(93) E. Fuchs, H. Green, Cell 19 (1980) 1033-1042.

(94) E. Fuchs, H. Green, Cell 25 (1981) 617-625.

(95) W.W. Franke, H. Denk, R. Kalt, E. Schmid, Exp. Cell Res. 131 (1981) 299-318.

(96) W.W. Franke, S. Winter, C. Grund, E. Schmid, D.L. Schiller, E.-D. Jarasch, J. Cell Biol. 90 (1981) 116-127.

(97) L.M. Milstone, J. McGuire, J. Cell Biol. 88 (1981) 312-316.

(98) Y.-J. Wu, J.G. Rheinwald, Cell 25 (1981) 627-635.

(99) Clin. Chem. 28, No. 4 (1982) Special Issue on Two-Dimensional Gel Electrophoresis.

(100) J.E. Celis, P. Mose Larsen, A. Celis (in preparation).

(101) R. Bravo, unpublished observations.

(102) R. Bravo, J.E. Celis, unpublished observations.

(103) P. Mose Larsen, A. Therkelsen, S.J. Fey, J.E. Celis, unpublished observations.

(104) P. Mose Larsen, cand. sci. dissertation (1981).

(105) P. Mose Larsen, S.J. Fey, J.E. Celis, unpublished observations.

(106) S.J. Fey, P. Mose Larsen, H. Søgaard, J.E. Celis, unpublished observations.

(107) P. Mose Larsen, S.J. Fey, M. Vetner, unpublished observations.

(108) K. Miyachi, M.J. Fritzler, E.M. Tan, J. Immunol. 121 (1978) 2228-2234.

(109) Y. Takasaki, J.S. Deng, E.M. Tan, J. Exp. Med. 154 (1981) 1899-1909.

(110) E.M. Tan, Adv. Immun. 33 (1982) 167-240.

(111) E. Lazarides, Nature 283 (1980) 249-256.

(112) T.-T. Sun, H. Green, Nature 269 (1977) 489-493.

(113) E. Fuchs, H. Green, Cell 15 (1978) 887-897.

(114) W.W. Franke, E. Schmid, M. Osborn, K. Weber, Proc. Natl. Acad. Sci. USA 75 (1978) 5034-5038.

(115) E. Fuchs, H. Green, Cell 19 (1980) 1033-1042.

(116) W.W. Franke, E. Schmid, C. Freudenstein, B. Appelhans, M. Osborn, K. Weber, T.W. Keenan, J. Cell. Biol. 84 (1980) 633-654.

(117) P. Cooke, J. Cell Biol. 68 (1976) 539-556.

(118) J.V. Small, A. Sobieszek, J. Cell Sci. 23 (1977) 234-268.

(119) J.M. Starger, R.D. Goldman, Proc. Natl. Acad. Sci. USA 74 (1977) 2422-2426.

(120) J.V. Small, J.E. Celis, J. Cell. Sci. 31 (1978) 393-409.

(121) W.W. Franke, E. Schmid, M. Osborn, K. Weber, Cytobiologie 17 (1978) 392-411.

(122) P. Drochmans, C. Freudenstein, J.C. Wanson, L. Laurent, T.W. Keenan, J. Stadler, R. Leloup, W.W. Franke, J. Cell Biol. 79 (1978) 427-443.

(123) D.L. Gard, P.B. Bell, E. Lazarides, Proc. Natl. Acad. Sci. USA 73 (1979) 4344-4348.

(124) T-T. Sun, H. Green, J. Biol. Chem. 253 (1978) 2053-2060.

(125) M.E. Gilmartin, V.B. Culbertson, I.M. Freedberg, J. Invest. Dermatol. 75 (1980) 211-216.

(126) P.M. Steinert, M.L. Wantz, W.W. Idler, Biochemistry 21 (1982) 177-183.

(127) S.J. Fey, P. Mose Larsen, J.E. Celis, FEBS Lett. 157 (1983) 165-169.

(128) J.E. Celis, P. Mose Larsen, S.J. Fey, A. Celis, J. Cell Biol. 97 (1983) 1429-1434.

(129) W.W. Franke, J.L. Jorcano, M. Rieger, J.K. Franz, T.M. Magin, D.L. Schiller, R. Moll, R.A. Quinlan, Proc. New York Acad. Sci. (in press).

(130) J.O. Thomas, R.D. Kornberg, Proc. Natl. Acad. Sci. USA 72 (1975) 2626-2630.

(131) W. Ansorge in Proc. of the 3rd International Conference on Electrophoresis (D. Stathakos ed.) (1982) Berlin: de Gryter.

(132) U.K. Laemmli, Nature 227 (1970) 680-685.

(133) W.W. Franke, D.L. Schiller, M. Hatzfeld, S. Winter, Proc. Natl. Acad. Sci. USA 80 (1983) 7113-7117.

AUTOMATIC ANALYSIS OF TWO-DIMENSIONAL GEL ELECTROPHORETOGRAMS: THE PROCESSING OF MULTIPLE GELS

Mark J. Miller and Arthur David Olson

Laboratory of Experimental Carcinogenesis,
Division of Cancer Etiology,
National Cancer Institute, National Institutes of Health,
Bethesda, MD. 20205. U.S.A

1. SUMMARY

The organization of data for the computerized analysis of two-dimensional gel electrophoretograms is described. Individual gels are scanned and their images analyzed. Polypeptide spots in the gels are found and their locations, shapes, and intensities measured. The results are stored in directories of a hierarchal file system. Groups of gels can be manipulated within this system to allow the comparison of multiple gels. Programs are written to be usable by people with varying computer knowledge and skills. We also describe an interactive program, PROCESS, designed to aid both new and experienced users in the analysis of multiple gels.

2. INTRODUCTION

The development of two-dimensional gel electrophoresis (1, 2) has made it possible to examine the synthesis of thousands of cellular polypeptides under a variety of environmental and experimental conditions. It has long been recognized that, because of the vast amount of data generated by this technique, the computational and organizational power of a computer is useful both in analyzing the raw data and in organizing and cross referencing the results of experiments that use these gels. To this end, several computerized systems have been developed (3 - 5). The analysis system originally developed at the University of California by Xuong, Geiduschek, and their co-workers (3, 6, 7) has been reproduced at the National Cancer Institute in the Laboratory of Experimental Carcinogenesis and extensively revised. This modified system is referred to here as LECtro. A detailed description of the system is to be presented elsewhere.

Besides the detection and quantitation of polypeptide spots, LECtro is designed for the analysis of multiple gels. Many of the investigators who use LECtro are new to computers, or use the system infrequently. LECtro is designed to let them analyze electrophoretograms with a minimum of supervision by more experienced users. This paper describes the way LECtro organizes and accesses the data of a single, multi-gel experiment, our philosophy of program design, and a program, PROCESS[1], that is designed to help users monitor and control the analysis of experiments.

The LECtro system is written in the "C" programming language and operates under the UNIX[2] operating system. The system runs on a VAX 11/750[3] computer. Most of the programs are in the public domain and are available to laboratories with compatible hardware and software.

3. ORGANIZATION OF DATA

The analysis of individual electrophoretograms is seldom of interest in and of itself. Generally, experimenters are interested in the relative rates of synthesis of a set of polypeptides or in the presence or absence of polypeptide spots in a set of related gels. In our laboratory, for example, we are often interested in the comparison of multiple gels to find spots that are significantly stimulated or suppressed during chemically induced neoplasia. To organize the data associated with multiple gels, we make use of UNIX's hierarchical file system (8). This system provides a powerful and flexible way of organizing data. UNIX also includes a number of programs and utilities that can be used to create, maintain, and manipulate data derived from individual gels.

---

[1]Program names are set in UPPER CASE letters to set them apart from the rest of the text.

[2]UNIX is a trademark of AT&T's Bell Laboratories.

[3]VAX is a trademark of Digital Equipment Corporation

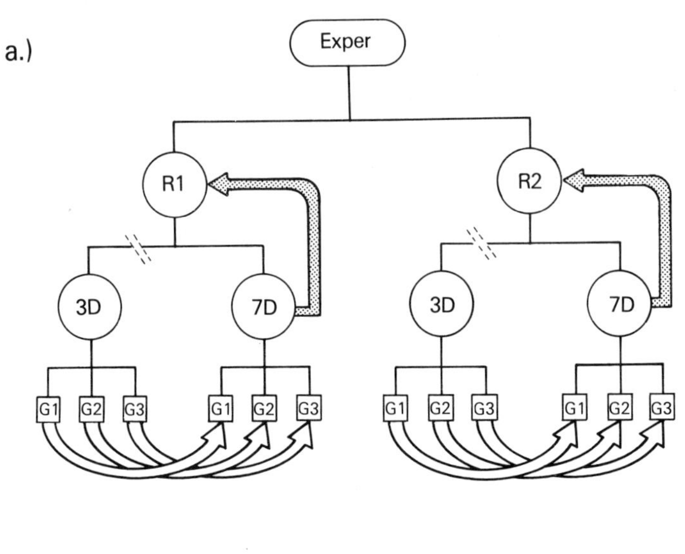

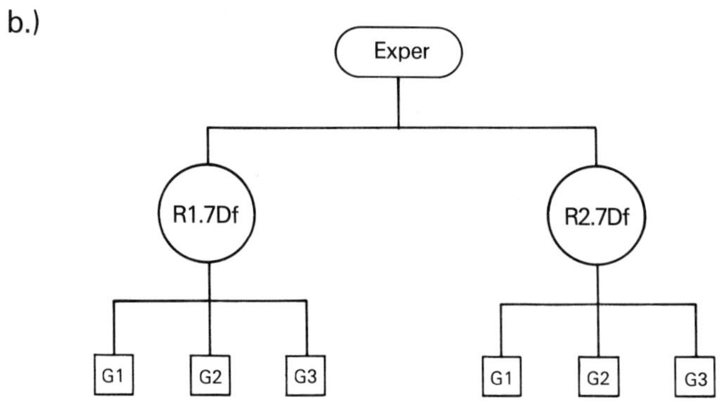

Fig. 1.) Organization of data for experiments. (a) An experiment, Exper, has been repeated twice, R1 and R2, and two exposures, three-day (3D) and seven-day (7D) of the resulting gels (G1, G2 and G3) have been developed and analyzed. Spots which are saturated in the seven-day exposures are replaced by data from corresponding spots in the three-day exposures (clear arrows). The subdirectories are later reorganized as indicated by the shaded arrows. (b) Final organization to the two data sets.

The data consists of individual files, each of which contains analysis information such as spot shapes or spot intensities. The files for each experiment are stored in single directories as illustrated in Fig. 1. If the data is to be further organized into subgroups, the appropriate subdirectories may be created and the data files moved. For example, in Fig. 1, an experiment has been repeated twice and the relevant data files are kept in subdirectories R1 and R2. If the experiment involves the analysis of autoradiograms, and multiple exposures are being used to analyze the full dynamic range of gels, the data from different exposures are kept in additional subdirectories. In Fig. 1a, three-day and seven-day exposure data are stored in subdirectories 3D and 7D. When the saturated data in the seven-day exposures have been replaced by unsaturated data from the three-day exposures, and the gels are ready to be compared, the 7D subdirectories replace the R subdirectories and are renamed R1.7Df and R2.7Df to indicate they contain fused data. The 3D subdirectories, with their data files, are removed (Fig. 1b). The data can readily be regrouped to add or remove gel sets. This organization scheme allows investigators to group and process data in any way which is useful in a given experiment.

The gel information is accessed by referring to the directory's name, the names of the individual files are known by the programs. Thus, the user need not be concerned with the names or formats of the files produced by programs in the LECtro system. The system is still under development, new programs and capabilities are constantly being added, some of which require modification of the resulting data files. This organizational scheme lets us modify the output of programs in a way that is invisible to the user. For example, the program AUTOMATCH is used to automatically match the resolved spots in two gels (9). To compare the polypeptide spot patterns of gels G1 and G2 in experiment R1, one needs only to change into the R1.7Df subdirectory and run the program by specifying the two subdirectories. That is:

```
AUTOMATCH G1 G2
```

4. PROGRAM INTERACTION

The LECtro system is a set of programs, each designed to perform a part of the total analysis of a two-dimensional gel. The BACKGROUND program calculates the background of a gel image: CPMCONVERT subtracts that background, smooths the data and converts the optical density readings into their counts-per-minute-per-pixel[4] equivalent; MAKESPOTS finds the spots and determines their shapes; AUGMENT determines the total area contained in the spots (3, and unpublished modifications of the analysis system). Different types of gels have different characteristics: glycoprotein gels tend to form large, diffuse spots; silver-stained gels often have heavy and uneven backgrounds. It is necessary for the programs in LECtro to be robust

---

[4]A pixel, or picture element, is a small (100 - 200 microns squared) region of a gel or autoradiogram whose optical density has been measured by some type of digitizing instrument.

enough to adequately analyze these different types of gels. For this reason, various options have been built into the system to make it as universally applicable as possible for the analysis of gels from diverse experiments. For example, some options allow one to specify different data smoothing algorithms, select different levels for background thresholding of gels, or to set minimum sizes for a spot (3).

An experienced user wants programs to be as flexible as possible, thus allowing direct use of parameters that will best satisfy the needs of a particular experiment. New users, on the other hand, are generally best served by programs where the parameters for an analysis are preset, or where the program asks the user what options and settings are to be used. Such "interactive" programs are particularly well suited for the investigator who uses the system infrequently. Programs that are executed by other programs usually need to have the appropriate options specified at the time they are called. Rather than write separate programs for different types of users or gels, we have chosen to make the programs flexible and then provide tools to aid casual users in the analysis.

Fortunately, the majority of analyses are similar. The investigator has a series of gels to be processed and compared. The samples can be analyzed by a common set of instructions. Hence, the programs are coded with default options that are satisfactory for most analytical requirements. For example, the program that finds spots in the gels, MAKESPOTS, allows the investigator to specify several parameters, such as the minimum allowable spot size or the intensity at which to start looking for spots. These parameters are mainly used to deal with gels that have high or uneven background. For most gels, however, the background is quite regular and default values used by the programs work well.

5. THE PROCESS PROGRAM

To allow the new or casual user to analyze gels with a minimum of supervision, the PROCESS program has been developed. This interactive program knows how to organize the data and run the various programs and protocols used to analyze an experiment. When the investigator runs PROCESS, a menu of options (Fig. 2) is displayed. To start the analysis of a set of gels, the experimenter must first call the initialization routines. These routines are responsible for, among other things, ensuring that there is sufficient space on disk for all the gels to be analyzed, for determining the optimal areas on disk to use for data storage, and for creating the directories where the data is stored. PROCESS also asks for and stores parameters used in the analysis of a set of gels; for example, the experiment name and the length of the exposure of an autoradiogram. PROCESS then arranges for the sequential analysis of the individual gels.

```
------------------------------------------------------------------------
SELECT THE PROCEDURE YOU WISH TO EXECUTE AND ENTER THE APPROPRIATE LETTER
CODE:

i        INITIALIZE: SET UP VARIABLES, TITLES, DIRECTORIES.
            THIS MUST BE DONE FIRST FOR EACH SET OF FILMS.

k        SCAN GELS. OUTPUT TO MAGNETIC TAPE
r        READ A FILM SCAN TAPE
d        ANALYZE A SET OF GELS
s        PREPARE A STANDARDIZATION CURVE
f        FUSE LIGHT EXPOSURES INTO A SET OF HEAVIER ONES
m        SET UP DATA SET FOR MATCHING
b        BACK UP DATA TO TAPE
q        EXIT PROGRAM

TYPE i,k,r,d,s,f,m,b or q<RETURN> WHEN READY

------------------------------------------------------------------------
```

Fig. 2.) Main menu of the PROCESS program.

Next PROCESS asks questions which set the various options available for analysis. Most of these are of the "yes"/"no" variety. If the user just types a lone RETURN, a default option is usually set. In cases where an irreversible, and potentially undesirable action would result by default (for example, if the question being asked is, "MAY ALL DATA FOR THIS EXPERIMENT BE REMOVED FROM THE DISK"), PROCESS requires a specific answer from the user.

Because of limited disk space, we normally store scans on magnetic tape. When the analysis of gels is started, PROCESS reads the gel scans off tape, one at a time, and calls the various analysis programs. When the analysis of the gel is completed, PROCESS removes the scan data from disk and reads in the next scan. This allows us to mount a tape with thirty or more scans on it and run the analysis programs at night in a batch-like mode, when the impact on interactive use of the computer system is minimal.

PROCESS itself does not know what programs should be called to analyze gels. Rather, it searches for a user-supplied file, called <u>profile</u>, that contains a list of commands used to analyze a particular set of gels. Figure 3 lists a typical command file. Each command in the file is executed in turn. If any of the programs exit abnormally, that is if an error occurs in the analysis, the error is detected and error recovery procedures in the _profile_ are executed.

A _profile_ is set up for every gel to be analyzed. Normally, PROCESS prepares a standard _profile_ and uses it for each gel. However, if special processing is desired, the investigator can prepare special _profiles_. In addition, PROCESS notes where it is in the analysis, sending a message to the investigator's terminal or to a special auditing file every time it finishes a program or procedure. Thus, even

```
background
if ($status || ! -e bkgdfn || -z bkgdfn) goto oops
echo Background done
cpmconvert -S250
if ( $status || ! -e data.cpm || -z data.cpm) goto oops
echo Data converted to cpm format
avelike
if ( $status || ! -e ave.like || -z ave.like) goto oops
echo Avelike done
makespots -S3
if ( $status || ! -e sl || -z sl) goto oops
echo Makespots done
augment
if ( $status || ! -e sl.aug || -z sl.aug) goto oops
echo Spots augmented
intgrt
if ( $status || ! -e integ || -z integ) goto oops
echo Spots integrated
rm -f data.ave data.cpm ave.like core
exit
oops:
echo ERROR IN ANALYSIS
rm -f data.ave data.cpm ave.like core
```

Fig. 3.) Typical command file. Lines that begin with "if ($status || ..." are designed to detect errors and start an error recovery mechanism. In the above example, error recovery consists simply of removing large data files, printing an error message, and exiting.

during a very long analysis, the user can learn what the program is doing, what it has done, and how well it is doing it. If the PROCESS program stops before the analysis is complete (due to a system crash, or whatever), this output is useful in determining which gel was being analyzed and how far along the analysis was. The processing of the gels can then be restarted where it was interrupted.

6. IN CONCLUSION

The purpose of LECtro is to fully automate the analysis of two-dimensional gels and to provide tools which let scientists efficiently examine and interpret their results. We have developed a set of programs designed to let investigators analyze gels without detailed knowledge of the inner workings of a computer. There are two basic types of programs: those which do the actual analysis, and a set of monitoring programs, headed by PROCESS, that control both the organization of the data and the analysis of gels. The interactive programs, such as PROCESS, assume a series of default parameters which the operator has the option of changing.

The programs controlled by PROCESS can be run directly by the user. Thus, as investigators become more experienced and sophisticated in the use of LECtro, they can analyze their gels in whatever way best answers the question poised by their experiment.

7. ACKNOWLEDGEMENTS

The authors wish to thank Dr. Snorri S. Thorgeirsson, Dr. Peter Wirth and Dr. Karl E. Krueger for their helpful comments during the preparation of this manuscript.

8. REFERENCES

(1) P. H. O'Farrell, J. Biol. Chem. 250 (1975) 4007-4021.

(2) M.J. Dunn and A.H.M. Burghes, Electrophoresis 4 (1983) 173-189.

(3) K.-P. Vo, M. J. Miller, E. P. Geiduschek, C. Nielsen, A. Olson and N.-H. Xuong, Anal. Biochem. 112 (1981) 258-271.

(4) N.L. Anderson, J. Taylor, A.E. Scandora, B.P. Coulter and N.G. Anderson, Clin, Chem. 27 (1981) 1807-1820.

(5) P.F. Lemkin and L.E. Lipkin, in Geisow and Barret (eds.), Computing in

biological science, Elsiever Biomedical Press, Amsterdam 1983, 181-231.

(6) J. Bossinger, M.J. Miller, K.-P. Vo, E.P. Geiduschek and N.-H. Xuong, J. Biol. Chem. 254 (1979) 7986-7998.

(7) M. J. Miller, P. K. Vo, C. Nielsen, E. P. Geiduschek and N.-H. Xuong, Clin. Chem. 28 (1982) 867-875.

(8) B.W. Kernighan and S.P. Morgan, Science 215 (1982) 779-783.

(9) M.J. Miller, A.D. Olson and S.S. Thorgeirsson, Electrophoresis, in press (1984).

ELECTRONIC AUTOFLUOROGRAPHY: PRINCIPLES, PROBLEMS, AND PROSPECTS*

J. B. Davidson

Oak Ridge National Laboratory
Box X, Oak Ridge, Tennessee 37831 USA

SUMMARY

Detection principles of electronic autofluorography are described. A comparison with film is presented which indicates the gain in sensitivity and linearity of response obtainable by electronic means. Analog integration is compared with counting of individual particles, and the compatibility of the secondary electron conduction (SEC) camera tube with both modes is shown. Lens coupling and fiber optic coupling of the scintillator light to the intensifier are discussed, along with the desirability of the former in order to remove the gel size limitations of the available image intensifier with fiber optic inputs. In an experimental system images from ^{3}H and ^{32}P were recorded in a digital memory by both direct contact and lens coupling. In a 2-min exposure 60 dpm/mm^2 of ^{3}H were measured using direct contact to a 150-mm-diam intensifier. The spatial resolution was 0.5 mm. Individual betas were registered using ^{32}P and an intensifying screen in direct contact. Using lens coupling to the same intensifier and a format of 200 × 250 mm an exposure of 5 min was required for visibility of 2 dpm/mm^2 of ^{32}P. A resolution of 2.0 mm was obtained. Exposures of 1 h are possible, with a proportional lowering of the minimum detected activity. It is concluded that the method is applicable to low- and high-energy betas as well as x-rays and, compared to film, can increase the speed of acquiring data from a gel by a factor of 100 to 1000. The possible application of the same camera to fluorescence from 2-D gels is briefly described. The future of the method appears promising.

*Research sponsored by the U.S. Department of Energy under Contract No. DE-AC05-84OR21400 with Martin Marietta Energy Systems, Inc.

1 INTRODUCTION

There are two main approaches to the elimination of film in autoradiography of electrophoretic gels and thin-layer chromatograms: (1) the use of one- and two-dimensional gas-filled multiwire proportional counters or spark chambers, which amplify and detect the ionization produced by the particles and register location by timing or charge division among the wires; and (2) the use of light-sensitive image intensifiers and TV camera tubes to detect light generated in a scintillant in contact with the radioactive layer (Ref. 1). This paper deals with the second approach--namely, electronic autofluorography. Several papers describing proportional counter applications are included in the proceedings of a recent wire chamber conference (Ref. 2) and in Reference 1. A commercial spark chamber device is available (Ref. 3), and the use of a microchannel plate electron detector in vacuo has been described (Ref. 4). The author of Reference 4 concludes that complications of introducing the gel into the necessary vacuum and the relatively small diameters of the detectors presently available may make light detection more attractive. For weak betas similar problems exist with the gas-filled detectors, which must be operated in the flowing mode with the gel inside. Windows can be used with higher energy betas such as ^{32}P and ^{14}C; however, the higher energy then becomes a problem because of the gas pressure and hence the thickness needed to stop the particle. Thickness is a factor limiting the spatial resolution because of particles which enter the chamber obliquely. Even inside a proportional counter many of the weak ^{3}H betas are absorbed in the gel or TLC plate. In autofluorography, on the other hand, the light from an absorbed scintillator can leave the layer and be detected. For higher energies such as those of ^{32}P betas, external intensifying phosphors can be interposed.

2 THE IDEAL DETECTOR

The ideal light detector for replacing film is one in which every light quantum produces a registerable event along with information about the location of the point of emission. If tedious scanning by a "point" or "line" detector is to be avoided, the ideal detector is also an area device which can be considered as a two-dimensional array of many small detectors operating independently for at least part of the detection-registering-storing process. The approximation of various position-sensing light detectors to the ideal is illustrated in Fig. 1 (Ref. 5). Included are several types of film and a number of television camera tubes with and without image intensifiers. The arrows, which

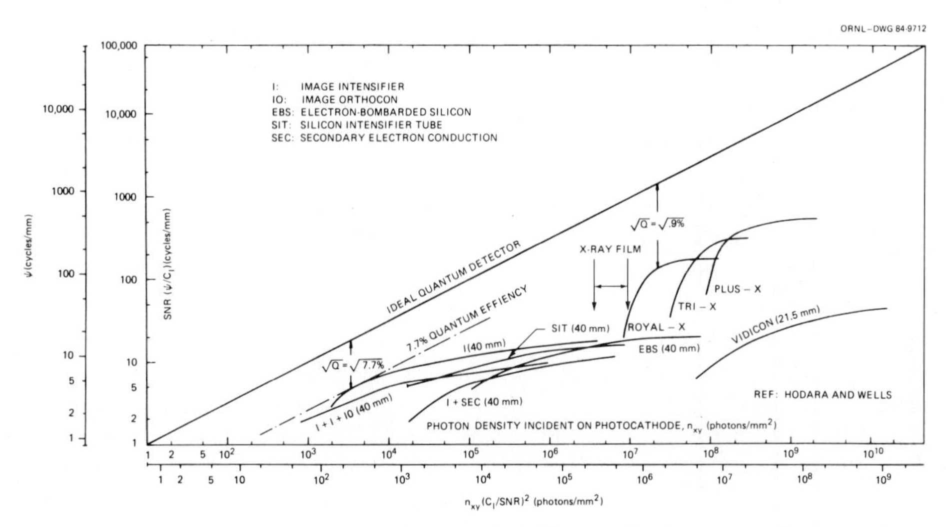

Fig. 1. Curves compiled by Hodara and Wells, Ref. 5, comparing signal-to-noise ratio, resolution of the ideal light image sensor, and film and electronic imagers. The approximate position of typical x-ray films used for autofluorgraphy have been added to the original figure. For lowest light levels the inner scales are used.

have been added to the original figure, show the general location of several x-ray films used in autofluorography. It is immediately seen that film is separated on the abcissa (photons/mm^2) by several orders of magnitude from the ideal detector and from several intensifier tube combinations. The ordinate units of cycles/mm give the resolution or fineness of detail which is discernible. A cycle/mm is an adjacent pair of resolution elements or pixels (for example, a black and a white square), each 0.5 mm wide. The performance of the ideal detector represented by the straight line is determined strictly by the counting statistics in the two adjacent pixels. If N_1 quanta (or particles) with uncertainty $\sqrt{N_1}$ fall on one element in a measurement interval t_o, and if N_2 quanta (uncertainty $\sqrt{N_2}$) fall on the adjacent pixel and the difference is not simply due to statistical fluctuations, then:

$$N_1 - N_2 = k\sqrt{N_1+N_2} \tag{1}$$

where the value of k is usually taken from 3 to 5. As the density of quanta (photons/mm^2) decreases, the pixel areas must increase in order to make the Ns large enough for the condition of Eq. 1 to be satisfied and for the areas to be resolvable. When used with a phosphor to detect

ORNL-DWG 84-9713

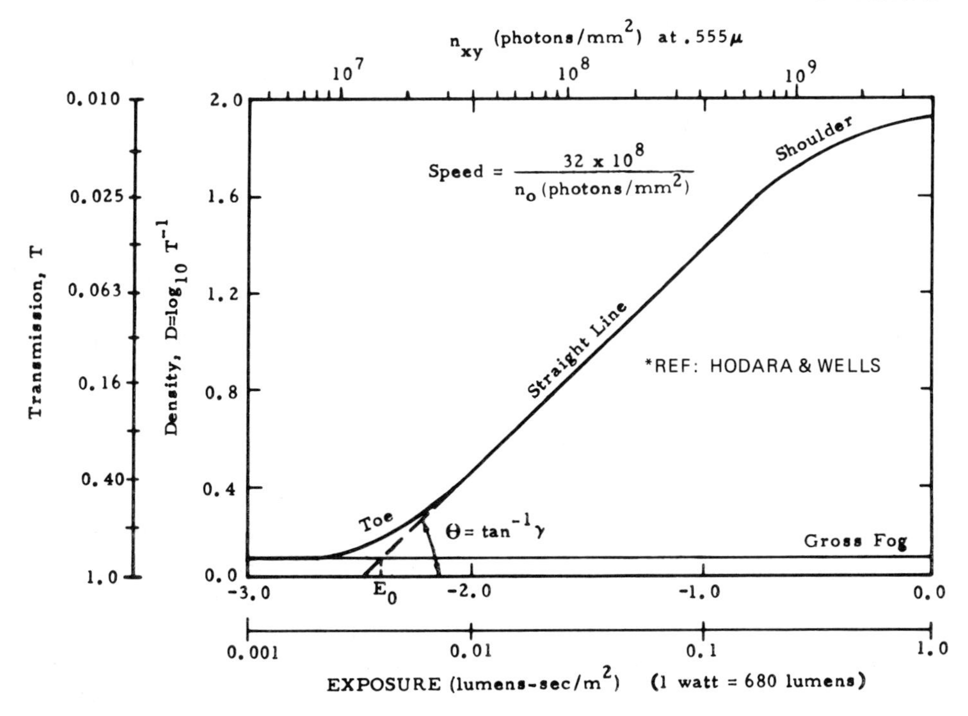

Fig. 2. Typical density versus exposure curve for film. Exposure in photons/mm^2 (top of figure) allows comparison with Fig. 1 (Ref. 5).

beta particles, the light sensors reflect the statistics of the beta emission rate. The same basic argument applies to resolving adjacent radioactive spots.

3 FILM

The superior resolution of film to light at higher photon density is clearly seen in Fig. 1. When used with phosphor layers in the typical film-screen combination, the limiting x-ray and beta resolution for the x-ray film is about 10 cycles/mm. It should be noted that the detecting areas of the camera tubes are 20 to 40 mm. This limitation will be discussed later. Film, of course, can be as large as needed.

The basic mechanisms in film exposure are also electronic, and there are rate-dependent effects which cause the well-known characteristic curve of Fig. 2 (Ref. 5). At low flux, film grains that do not get hit by three or so photons within a certain time are not developable because of an electron relaxation mechanism. This causes the "toe" of the curve. From the abscissa in Fig. 2, the "toe" corresponds to $\approx 10^7$ photons/mm^2. At higher flux many grains are already exposed and further hits on them do not increase film density. The curve then begins to saturate and produces the "shoulder." The rate-dependent effects cause the often-mentioned reciprocity failure of film, by which it is meant that the effect of intensity and time product on density is not constant.

4 ELECTRONIC SENSORS

4.1 Analog Integration versus Counting

As seen above, low activity and hence low light level indicate that an integration time is necessary. This is customary in film. In camera tubes operated at normal TV rates of 30 frames/s the integration time is 1/30 s. Some tubes such as the SEC are capable of much longer integration times and can be exposed for up to an hour before being scanned to remove the image. Figure 3 shows the response of the secondary electron conduction (SEC) camera tube (Ref. 6), which we have found very useful. It has excellent response at low levels and also saturates gracefully. The tube shows almost perfect reciprocity. As described below, the analog image can be digitized and stored in a computer memory for analysis. At extremely low light levels the ideal detector operates as a counter instead of an analog integrator. This requires high intensifier gain ahead of the camera tube if single photoelectrons are to be detectable above the system noise. A number of TV-based systems for use in astronomy and spectroscopy have been reported with this sensitivity (Refs. 7,8). Because in autofluorography each beta particle produces 10 to 1000 or more photons, counting becomes more practical. The autofluorography detector then becomes an area scintillation counter; counts are stored in the memory according to position, and the image is built up with time.

The dynamic range, which is the ratio of maximum and minimum intensities measured in a given exposure, is an important consideration both for film and for electronic detection. For analog integration of a point image the SEC tube can cover a range of more than 1000 with calibration, and for extended images the range is about 200. When the detector is used as a counter of individual events, the dynamic range is limited only by counting time and the storage capacity of the external memory.

4.2 Image Intensifiers

The increase in sensitivity necessary to count single photoelectrons, and hence the weak beta particles, must be obtained by the

ORNL-DWG. 84-10368

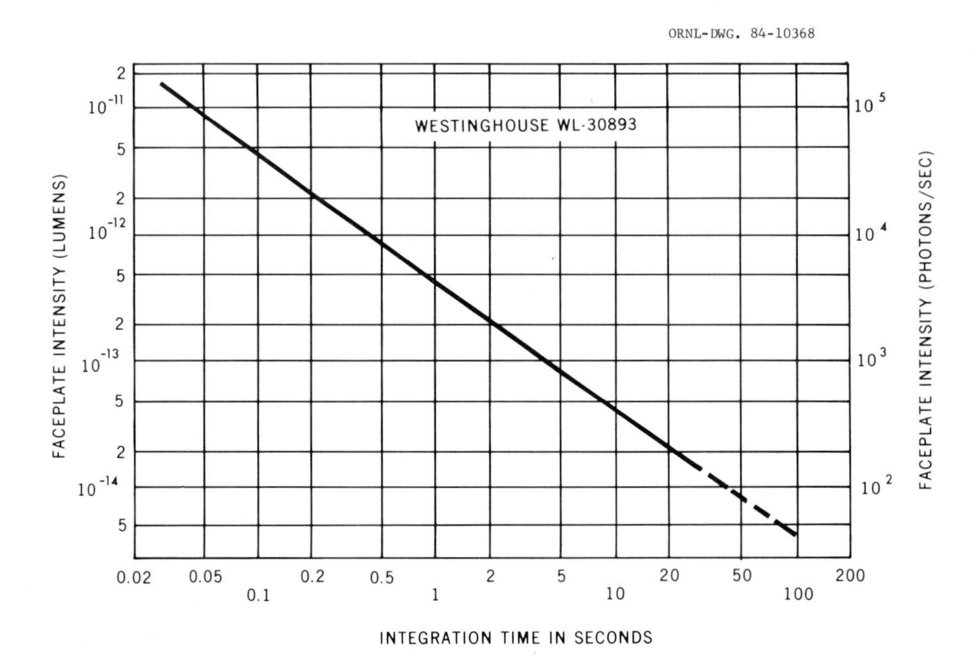

Fig. 3. Reciprocity of light intensity and exposure time for the Westinghouse WL-30893 secondary electron conduction camera tube (SEC).

use of one or more stages of image intensification. An intensifier which illustrates several principles (the so-called Gen II inverting intensifier) is shown in Fig. 4. It incorporates an input stage in which light-produced electrons from the photocathode are electrostatically focussed onto a second stage, a microchannel plate intensifier in which the input electrons are increased by secondary emission. The output electrons from the microchannels are accelerated to a third stage, a phosphor layer, and produce light. The overall light gain of such a tube can be greater than 50,000 photons/photon. The microchannel plate consists of millions of fused glass capillaries lined with an electron-emitting coating. A voltage applied across the plate causes input electrons to move through the tubes, knocking out more electrons to produce a multiplication of ≈1000 which, when combined with the gain of the output phosphor, gives the gain mentioned above. There are several types of light intensifiers, including magnetically focussed and proximity focussed ones, but detailed description would be out of place here. Two standard texts are given in References 9 and 10.

ORNL-DWG 84-9858

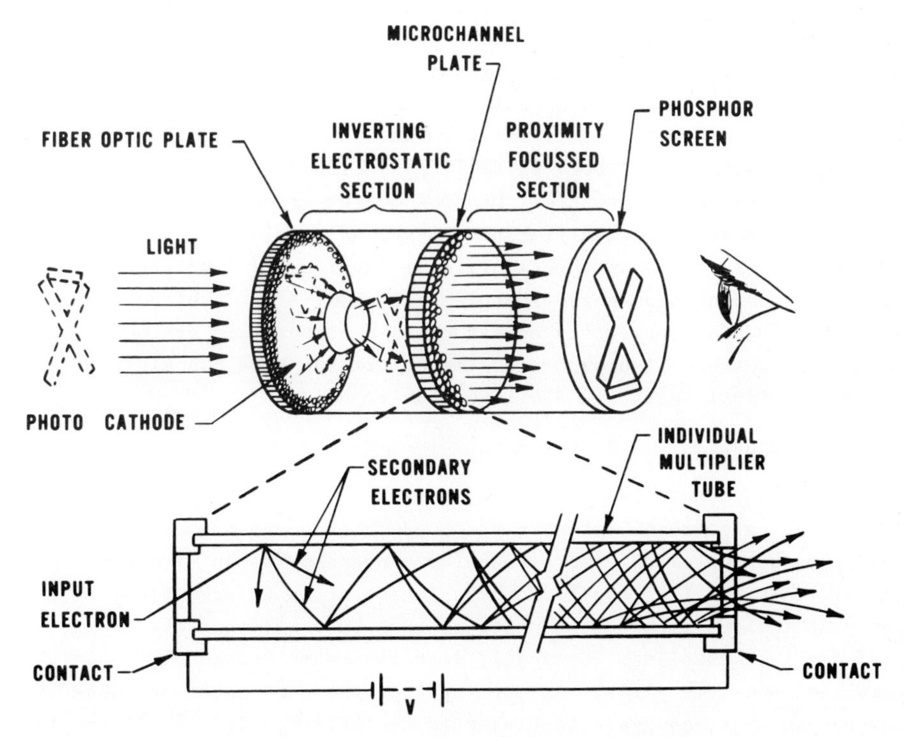

Fig. 4. Generation II (GEN-II) microchannel plate based image intensifier. Typical flux gain ≈50,000. For coupling to a TV camera tube the output is also a fiber-optic plate.

4.3 Camera Tubes

The camera tubes fall below the ideal line of Fig. 1 because of the photocathode quantum efficiency. About 10 to 20% of the incident photons give rise to detectable photoelectrons. The inner scales in Fig. 1 apply for our discussion. As the number of photons/mm^2 decreases, the product of resolution, Ψ (cycles/mm) and SNR/C_i decreases where SNR is the signal-to-noise ratio and C_i is contrast. For 100% contrast $C_i = 1$. Then if 10,000 photons/mm^2 are incident, the product $(\Psi)(\text{SNR}) = 100$. For SNR = 100 then $\Psi = 1$ cycle/mm. Note that SNR = 100 is just $\sqrt{10{,}000}$. Any finer pattern (more cycles/mm) would have a reduced visibility because the smaller areas would intercept a smaller number of photons, reducing N and thus lowering the signal-to-noise ratio.

Figure 1 shows that the three-stage intensifier, I, has a slope equal to that of the ideal detector at ~350 photons/mm^2. It also falls below the ideal curve because the actual number detected is reduced by the quantum efficiency. Depending upon the rate of photon arrival, a camera tube coupled to the intensifier could make visible and countable single photons in each resolution element. In autofluorographic terms this means that a 6-keV beta particle producing about 70 quanta (Ref. 11) should be countable. Most of our experiments have been done with a single-stage intensifier plus a secondary electron conduction camera tube (I + SEC) on the figure. We have used a time exposure rather than event counting. Approximately 100 ^{3}H/mm^2 are required for detection. We are presently constructing a higher gain system to bring us nearer to the photon and hence to the tritium beta counting limit in which individual betas are distinguishable.

5 OPTICAL COUPLING

Except where they are built into camera tubes that can respond directly to electrons, intensifiers produce at their outputs light which must be coupled to the camera tube for conversion to an electronic image. This coupling can be done by lenses or by fiber optics. The latter technique is about an order of magnitude more efficient than ordinary lens coupling. Optically flat fiber-optic face plates at the output of the intensifier and the input of the camera can be placed in contact so that the image is dissected and efficiently transferred in segments by the fibers, whose diameter is around 10 microns. This method of coupling is also much more compact than using a pair of relay lenses arranged front-to-front with the output and input images at the infinity focus.

Each fiber consists of an outer sheath and a central core. The core has an index of refraction, n_2 larger than that of the sheath, n_1. This causes light which enters one end of a fiber at less than a certain angle to be trapped by repeated total internal reflection and transmitted to the other end. Inside the fiber at the sheath the critical angle, Θ_c is given by (Ref. 12):

$$\sin\Theta_c = n_1/n_2 \ .$$

The input acceptance angle is determined by the numerical aperture, N.A., defined as

$$n \sin \Theta$$

where Θ is the entrance angle measured from the center line of the fiber and n is the index of refraction of the outside medium (usually air). Values of N.A. $\approx$ 1 are not uncommon.

In autofluorography the light-emitting gel must be coupled to the input of the intensifier. Again, this can be done by means of lenses or by direct coupling to the input fiber-optic face plate. However, in the latter method the area which can be covered is limited since most intensifiers' fiber-optic inputs are 40 mm diam or less. This size limitation is one of the "problems" referred to in the title. In our original experiments we used a single-stage intensifier tube especially made for us about ten years ago (Ref. 13) which has a 150-mm-diam fiber-optic face plate. The gel containing the fluor was pressed against the face plate for efficient coupling of the light produced by the tritium betas to the photocathode. The electron image thus produced was demagnified to 25 mm and the output intensified (flux gain ≈40X) and brightened (by a 6-to-1 area reduction ≈36X) and was fiberoptically coupled to an SEC camera tube. In order to accommodate the variety of larger gel sizes used by researchers, we have recently taken the lens-coupling approach, using the original 150-mm diam tube plus SEC camera tube. Some experiments were done with a modified Old Delft medical x-ray system designed for a 300-mm object (phosphor) coupled to an intensifier image isocon camera combination by means of a fast mirror-lens system (Ref. 14). The three methods of coupling the light from the gel are shown schematically in the left part of Fig. 5.

Efficient coupling of light from the phosphor to the input photocathode involves several factors, the magnification factor, m, the f# of the lens, and its transmission, T. These are related by the expression (for comparison with fiber optics f# = 1/2N.A. approximately)

$$E = T/4f^2(m+1)^2 \quad . \tag{2}$$

When estimating efficiency, the image-to-object ratio must be used for m in Eq. 2. If the object is distant, m can be neglected. In autofluorography m is usually 0.06 to 0.2. The transmission, T, is usually around 0.8. For an f1.0 lens and magnification of 0.1 (250-mm diam gel and 25-mm input intensifier), E = 16%.

6 SIGNAL DETECTION AND STORAGE

The light image, after being transformed to an intensified electron image, is temporarily stored on the "target" of the television camera tube. In the SEC tube the target is a layer of KCl, which emits secondary electrons when bombarded by 6-to 8-kV electrons, giving a charge gain of about 50. These secondaries are promptly collected by an anode layer, and the image is left on the target as a positive charge distribution until it is neutralized and erased by the raster-scanning beam. The video signal current is produced in this process of restoring

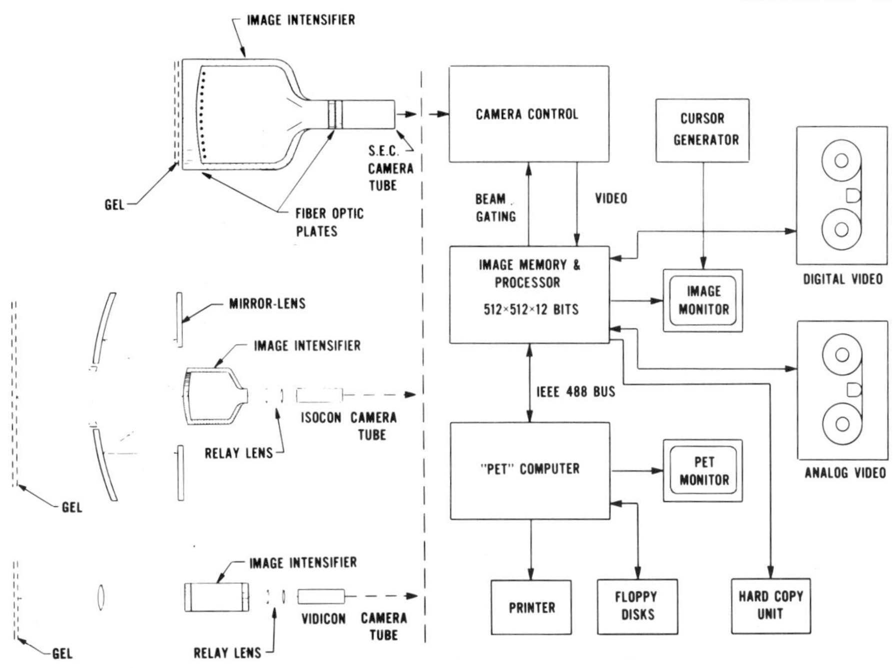

Fig. 5. Schematic of the camera system showing three ways of coupling gel to an intensifier.

electrons on the target. The video signal is amplified and sent to a digital image memory processor, to display monitors, and to recorders. Our present system is shown schematically on the right of Fig. 5. The memory processor (Ref. 15) has a 512 × 512 × 12 bit memory and is controlled by the microcomputer (Ref. 16) over the IEEE-488 instrument bus. Background subtraction, averaging, and memory quartering are useful features. As a counting memory the maximum count per pixel is 4095. An extended gray scale hard-copy unit (Ref. 17) provides a 200- × 250-mm copy of the image stored in memory in 12-26 s.

The microcomputer's floppy disc can be used to store the digital image on one side of a disc at a resolution of 256 × 256 × 8 bits. This reduced resolution is a hardware limitation and can be easily eliminated with later model floppy discs. Newer, higher density hard discs are capable of storing many images. Selected digital data in the system are read out on the printer under microcomputer program control. The system shown in Fig. 5 was intended to be used for detector development and not for detailed manipulation of the image or extraction of all of the

ORNL Photo 3123-84

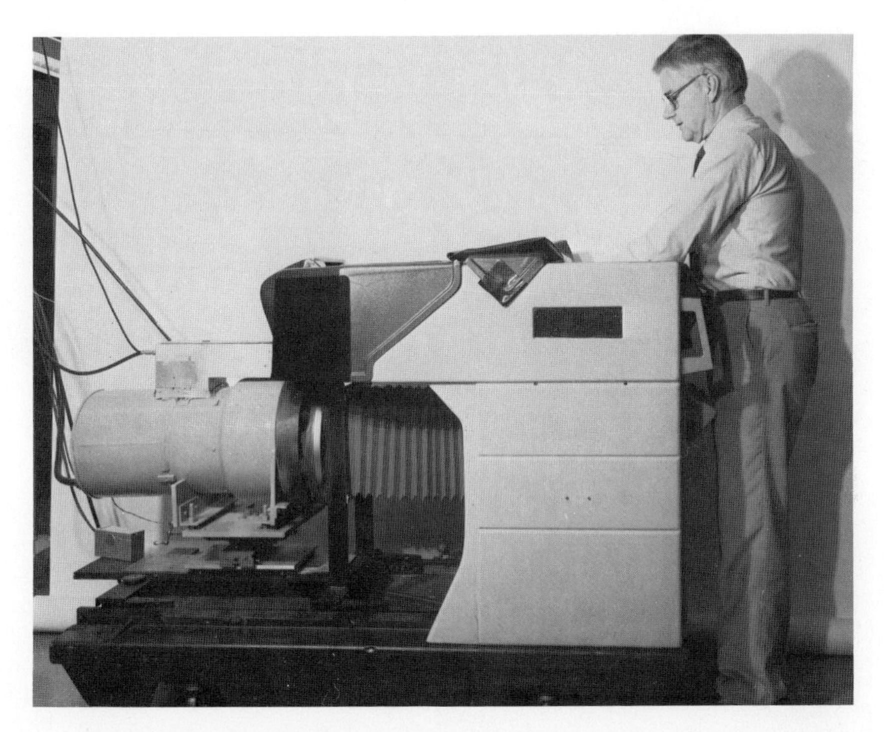

Fig. 6. Experimental autofluorographic camera built around an obsolete copy camera. Gel is loaded in original film chamber at top. The 150-mm-diam image-intensifier TV camera is seen at left. Lens and intensifier can be moved for size and focus adjustment.

digital data. For this the data could be transferred over parallel data lines from the memory processor to a larger computer for analysis by methods being used for analysis of film (Ref. 18).

7 RESULTS

The experimental camera shown in Fig. 6 was built around an obsolete copying camera (Ref. 19). The passage of the image through the camera was reversed. The intensifier-camera is placed at the original lens end of the bellows and the gel is placed on the horizontal glass plate in the light-proof chamber where the film was formerly put. Gels of up to 400 × 350 mm can be accommodated. Vignetting in the lens reduces the useful area for quantitative purposes. The camera lens and intensifier focal plane can be moved separately to cover the size of the gel. The

ORNL Photo 9018-81

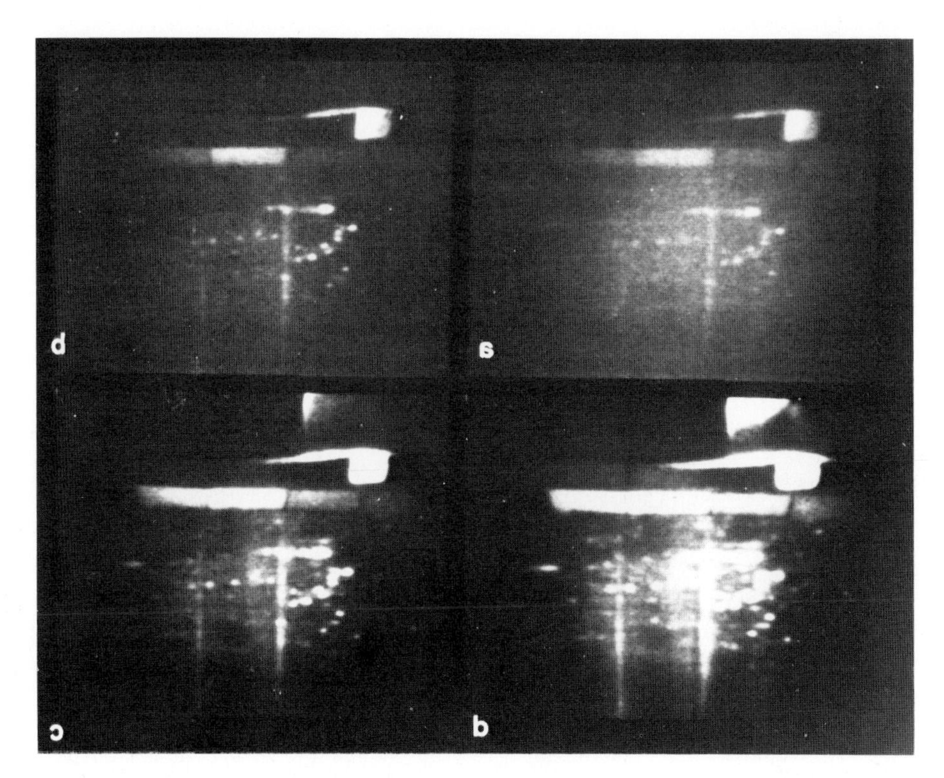

Fig. 7. Four exposures of ^{3}H containing gel and test strips: a = 1 min, b = 2 min, c = 4 min, d = 8 min.

camera mount was designed to accommodate the large original 150-mm input intensifier system shown in the figure as well as a smaller, more sensitive camera now under construction. The size of the system is constrained by the field of view and the focal length of the taking lens.

Figure 7 shows the image of part of a tritium-labeled gel and test strips recorded in four sections of memory at exposures of 1, 2, 4, and 8 min. The activity loaded on the gel strips ranged from 20 to 890 cpm/μl. The gel containing the scintillant PPO was placed in contact with the 150-mm image tube face plate. Figure 8 shows the response of the system to the activity in the test strips, determined by averaging the memory counts over an area of each strip. Using film and PPO, Laskey (Ref. 20) reported a minimum detectable activity for ^{3}H

ORNL-DWG 84-10952

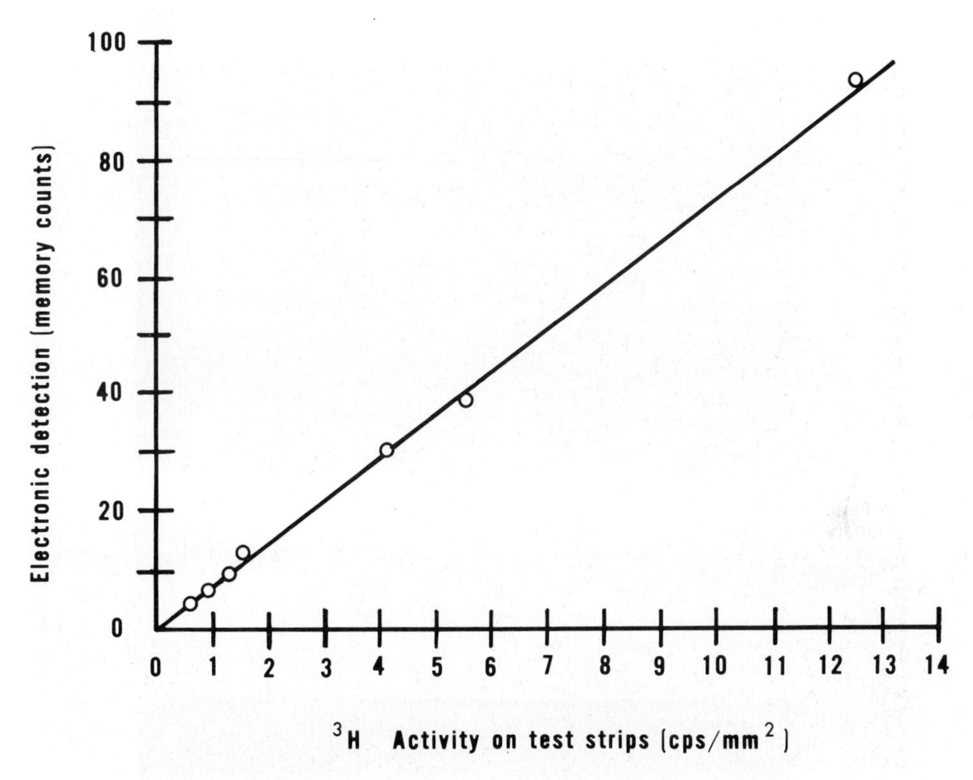

Fig. 8. Memory counts vs activity for ^3H test strips. Data averaged from 17 two-min exposures.

of 8000 dpm/cm^2 in 24 h or a total of 1.15×10^7 d/cm^2. Electronically 6000 dpm/cm^2 were detected in 2 min, or 7.2×10^3 d/cm^2.

The results shown in Fig. 9 were obtained using known concentrations of ^{32}P deposited on nitrocellulose. In Fig. 9a the sample was placed on an intensifying screen and the light was imaged onto the 150-mm-diam image intensifier. The field of view (not the sample) was approximately 350 × 250 mm, and the exposure was 5 min. The minimum detectable activity was 2 dpm/mm^2. Figure 9b shows the image when the sample and intensifying screen were put directly on the input face plate. The individual ^{32}P betas are clearly seen at the lower dilutions where the activity was .5-1 dpm/mm^2. When the sample was exposed for 18 h at -70°C on XAR5 film with an intensifying screen, these areas were just visible. Laskey (Ref. 20) found a minimum detectable ^{32}P activity of 50 dpm/cm^2 for 24 h exposure (72,000 d/cm^2). As discussed earlier, the

ORNL Photo 3133-84

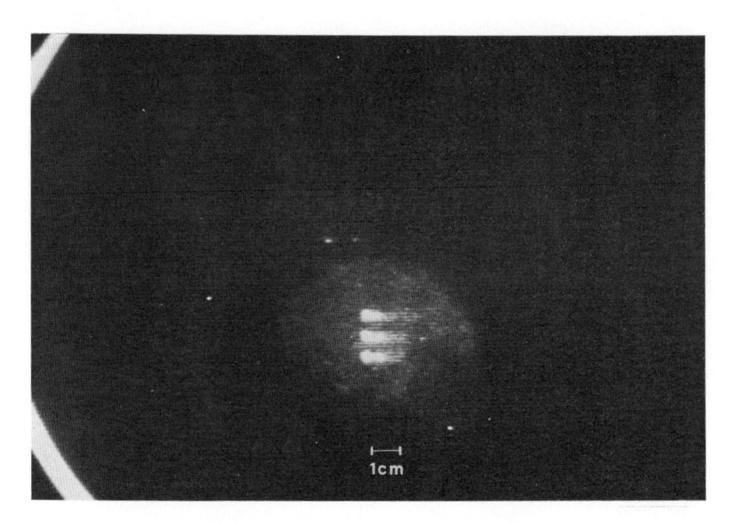

(a) Taken with lens coupling to 150-mm-diam image intensifier. Field of view was 200 × 250 mm and exposure was 5 min. Circle in center is glow from 150-mm-diam intensifying screen inadvertently exposed to daylight. Glow faded in ≈2 h.

ORNL Photo 3243-84

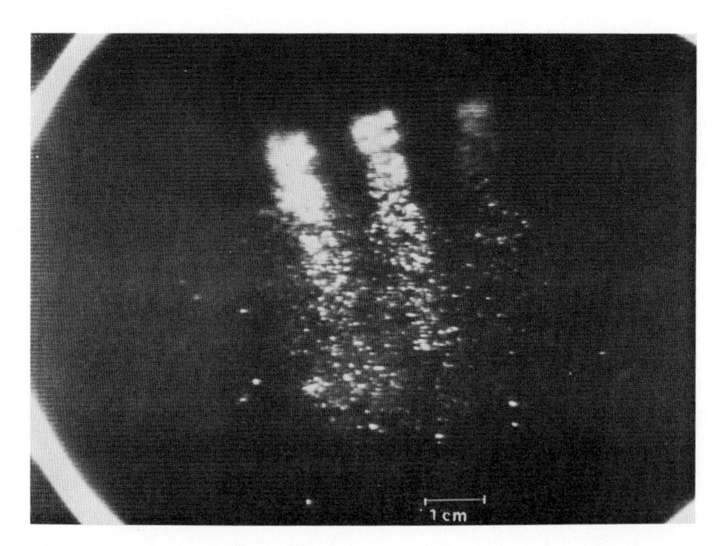

(b) Image of the same sample taken with intensifying screen in direct contact with image intensifier. Field of view 150 mm diam, exposure time 3 min. Intensifying screen: rare earth type 3M-TRIMAX. Small spots are single beta scintillations.

Fig. 9. Direct contact and lens imaging of ^{32}P on nitrocellulose

ability to resolve two images or determine the shape of a spot depends upon the counting statistics at the sensitivity levels indicated in Fig. 8. Resolution of the system at the center of the field of view was ≈2.0 mm.

The width of a single ^{32}P beta scintillation image stored in memory (Fig. 9b) was 0.5 mm full width at half maximum. When used in a counting mode in which only the position of the scintillation is stored using centroid-locating techniques (Ref. 13), the resolution of point images can be improved by a factor of 2 to 3. Because the counting mode requires continuous scanning of 30 frames/s, the decay time of the scintillator or intensifying screen must be shorter than this period (0.033 s) to avoid pileup of light in the subsequent frames resulting in the counting of an event more than once. For the same reason the response of the camera tube (target "lag") must be short so that each event is erased in a single scan.

8 PROSPECTS

The future of electronic autofluorography seems bright. The demonstration of ^{32}P detection in a large format removes the size limitation imposed by the small fiber-optic face plates and our original direct contact method. However, as gel sizes are reduced in the microelectrophoresis methods and, in general, as improved resolution is brought about by smaller starting samples, the direct contact method will be attractive since it eliminates the coupling lens while maintaining efficient light transfer and resolution. Location and quantitation of stained spots by their fluorescence should be straightforward using ultraviolet exciting light to which the intensifier camera does not respond. Prunell (Ref. 21) measured DNA on gels by photographing the fluorescence and using a densitometer on the film. Our system should be readily adapted to such a measurement. Since the intensity of the fluorescence can be made much greater than the light from autofluorography, instantaneous measurement can be obtained.

The continuing improvement of high-gain and high-resolution intensifier tubes as well as matching camera tubes seems likely. Already 1000 × 1000-line systems are practical. The resolution and sensitivity of solid-state imagers is increasing and soon will match that of conventional camera tubes. Their use could help reduce the size of the system. More important is their geometric stability. The resolution elements are fixed in position on the silicon wafer. Furthermore, these solid-state cameras lend themselves to digital scanning and readout into a computer memory.

The ready availability of digital memory processors makes image quantitation and storage practical and reasonably priced. These systems range from four- and six-bit systems for personal computers suitable for semiquantitative work up to elaborate 16- and 24-bit systems with full capability for image manipulation by integral computers. Archival storage and retrieval of images on disc will be easily accomplished with new high-speed devices capable of operating at TV rates.

9 ACKNOWLEDGMENTS

Thanks are due Drs. K. Isham and B. Mansfield of the ORNL Biology Division and Dr. E. Lester of the University of Chicago School of Medicine for samples and helpful discussions. The assistance of A. L. Case, Engineering Technologist, in early parts of the work is acknowledged with thanks.

10 REFERENCES

(1) J. B. Davidson, A. L. Case, Science, 215 (1982) 1398-1400.

(2) Nucl. Instrum. Methods 217 1-2 1983, Proc. of the Wire Chamber Conf., Vienna, Austria, Feb. 15-18, 1983, Eds. W. Bartl, G. Neuhofer.

(3) Laboratorium Prof. Dr. Berthold, Wildblad, W. Germany, Beta Camera LB292; see also H. Filthuth, paper presented at meeting on "Clinical and Environmental Applications of Quantitative Thin-Layer Chromatography," Philadelphia, Pa., December 2, 3, 4 (1980).

(4) S. Burbeck, Electrophoresis 4 (1983) 127-33.

(5) H. Hodara, W. H. Wells, Paper 5.2.1, Advisory Group for Aerospace Research and Development, Lecture Series No. 61, AGARD-LS-61, (Eds.) Halley and Hodara, North Atlantic Treaty Organization, 1973.

(6) G. W. Goetze, Adv. Electron. Electron Phys. 22A (1966) 219-227.

(7) C. M. Savage, P. D. Maker, App. Opt. 10 (1971) 965-968.

(8) A. Boksenburg, C. T. Coleman, Adv. Electron. Electron Phys. 52 (1979) 335-367.

(9) Photo-electronic Imaging Devices--(Proceedings of Symposia held Biennially at Imperial College, London) Adv. Electron. Electron Phys., Academic Press, N.Y.

(10) Photoelectronic Imaging Devices, Vols. 1 and 2 (Eds.) L. Biberman and S. Nudelman, Plenum Press, N.Y. (1971).

(11) D. L. Horrocks, Applications of Liquid Scintillation Counting, Academic Press, N.Y. (1974).

(12) N. S. Kapany, Fiber Optics Principles and Applications, Academic Press, N.Y. (1967).

(13) J. B. Davidson, J. App. Cryst. 7, (1974) 356-366.

(14) Old Delft Corp. of America, Fairfax, Va., Model Delcalix.

(15) Quantex Corporation, Sunnyvale, Calif., Model DS-20.

(16) Commodore Business Machines, Santa Clara, Calif., Model PET 2001-8.

(17) Tektronix, Inc. Beaverton, Ore., Model 4634.

(18) N. L. Anderson et al., Clin. Chem. 27 (1981) 1807-1820.
E. P. Lester et al., ibid. 26 (1980) 1379-1522.
J. I. Garrels, J. Biochem. 254 (1979) 7961.

(19) Visual Graphics Corp., Miami, Fla., Model SK-B.

(20) R. A. Laskey, Methods in Enzymol. 65 (1980) 363-371.

(21) A. Prunell, ibid., 353-363.

DETERMINATION OF MOLECULAR WEIGHTS AND STOKES' RADII OF NON-DENATURED PROTEINS BY POLYACRYLAMIDE GRADIENT GEL ELECTROPHORESIS

3. Determination of the largest and smallest entities of reversibly associating enzymes

Purkhanbaba, H. and Rothe, G.M.

Institut für Allgemeine Botanik der Johannes-Gutenberg Universität Mainz,
Saarstr. 21, 6500 Mainz, Federal Republic of Germany

1. INTRODUCTION

The high resolution capacity of polyacrylamide gradient gel electrophoresis (PAGGE) (1-3) together with its large separation range gave rise to use this method for the size determination of proteins (e.g. 4-8). We demonstrated that in PAGGE mol mass determinations are possible practically at any time of the separation process, provided a mathematical correlation between the size of proteins and their migration distances is known as well as the course of the gradient (6-8). Many enzyme proteins remain unaltered during the separation process, but some are degraded to smaller entities (7). In this paper we describe a method to determine the largest and smallest size of such proteins using the well known enzyme carbonic anhydrase (CA) (carbonate dehydratase, EC 4.2.1.1).

2. MATERIALS AND METHODS

For all investigations purified CA preparations from commercial sources (Sigma, Paesel) were used. Gradients were prepared essentially as described recently (6) but the thickness of the gels was 0.2 mm instead of 2.8 mm (6) or 0.8 mm (8). The ratio of acrylamide to BIS was 24:1, and the gradients ranged from ~ 7 to ~ 27% acrylamide + BIS (T). Under non-denaturing conditions a buffer of pH 8.4 containing 90 mM Tris, 80 mM boric acid and 2.5 mM $EDTA.Na_2$ was used as gel and electrode buffer. After a pre-electrophoresis of 30 min at 300 V (5^oC) 1-2 μl samples containing 1-2 μg protein (= 0.6-6 Wilbur-Anderson Units) were applied per sample well. Electrophoresis was performed at 300 V (5^oC) for various times. The marker proteins were the same as used recently (6-8). Enzyme bands of CA were visualized with the following substrate solution: 1 mg 4-methylumbelliferylacetate in 0.5 ml N,N-dimethylformamide plus 10 ml of 100 mM phosphate buffer of pH 6.5 (cf. 9). SDS-electrophoresis was performed as has been described in (8).

3. RESULTS

3.1 Enzyme patterns

The various CA preparations differ in the number of enzymatically active bands. Under the conditions of non-denaturing PAGGE we were able to localize three main bands by using CA from bovine, porcine, and rabbit erythrocytes. CA from human erythrocytes (Sigma C 4396)was the most purified enzyme and consisted of one single enzymatically active band. All enzyme forms were completely inhibitable by 1 mM N-(5-sulfamoyl-1,3,4-thiadiazol-2-yl)-acetamide (9), i.e. they all can be classified as true CA-enzymes. They have also in common that their migration velocity increases, the further they penetrate into the gradient gel. This separation behaviour indicated that they all exist in an associated state at the beginning of electrophoresis and dissociate to smaller entities when reaching smaller pore radii.

3.2 Estimation of the largest enzymatically active entities

When estimating this dimension we proceeded on the following assumptions: 1. the various CA-forms are associated to large entities before entering the gradient gel, and 2. the size of the dissociating molecules is hyperbolically correlated with the reciprocal value of the gel concentration. We therefore suggest the following equations relating the apparent Stokes' radius of a dissociating CA enzyme (R_{app}) and the gel concentration (T):

1) $(T + b) \cdot R_{app} = c$, or: 2) $1/R_{app} = 1/c \cdot T + b/c$

where b, and c are constants.

According to equation 2) the maximum size of an associated protein results from the point of intersection of the straight line in an $1/R_{app}$ vs. T-graph; the maximum mol mass (MM_{max}) can be taken from the point of intersection of the straight line obtained in a $1/(MM)^{1/3}$ vs. T-graph, assuming that $R_{app} = \alpha \cdot (MM)^{1/3}$.

3.3 Estimation of the smallest enzymatically active entities

The estimation of this size is based on the following assumptions: 1. The smallest possible size is obtained when $T \rightarrow \infty$, and 2. when the smallest Stokes'radius (R_{min}) has been reached then $R_{app} = R_{min}$. From both assumptions a hyperbolic correlation can be formulated according to the following equations:

3) $R_{min}/R_{app} = T/(T + b)$, or: 4) $R_{app} = (b \cdot R_{min})/T + R_{min}$

with b being a constant.

A straight line is obtained when R_{app} is plotted vs. 1/T. The point of intersection of that line equals R_{min}; the minimum mol mass (MM_{min}) can be obtained from the point of intersection of a straight line resulting from a $(MM)^{1/3}$ vs. 1/T-graph.

3.4 Sizes of the largest and smallest enzymatically active CA-forms

According to the procedures described we estimated the largest and smallest enzymatically active forms compiled in table 1.

Table 1

CA preparations obtained from:	Isozyme variant	Stokes'radius (nm) minimum	Stokes'radius (nm) maximum	mol mass minimum	mol mass maximum
Sigma (Munich, FRG) C 2273 C 5024 C 7500 and Paesel (Frankfurt, FRG) 102-01-03187	I	2.17 ± 0.16	7.35 ± 0.35	20 200 ± 3 740	527 000 ± 64 400
	II	2.34 ± 0.13	5.90 ± 0.16	24 200 ± 3 100	295 100 ± 30 900
	III	2.30 ± 0.07	5.14 ± 0.37	23 000 ± 1 800	216 300 ± 46 600
Sigma C 4396	IV	2.16 ± 0.17	9.14 ± 0.64	19 800 ± 3 800	973 500 ± 157 000

C 2273 : from bovine erythrocytes (for SDS-polyacrylamide gel electrophoresis)
C 5024 : from bovine erythrocytes (MM marker)
C 7500 : from bovine erythrocytes (dialyzed and lyophilized; 3000 Wilbur-Anderson units per mg protein)
C 4396 : from human erythrocytes (dialyzed and lyophilized; 400 Wilbur-Anderson units per mg protein)
Paesel : from bovine erythrocytes (2000 U/mg at 14°C)
± : standard deviations calculated from 4 (I-III) and 20 (IV) experiments

4. DISCUSSION

It has been concluded from equilibrium centrifugational and chromatographic experiments that carbonic anhydrase from mammalian erythrocytes exists as a monomeric enzyme having a mol mass of ~ 29 000 (10-12), while the size of various plant CAs was found to be 3-16 times larger (e.g. 13). An association of mammalian CAs has only been observed at pH-values ≪ 7 (10). In our experiments with PAGGE, however, we observed a reversible formation of complex entities with all the animal CAs used. Possibly the maximum size of the various polymeric forms depends on the isoelectric point of the monomeric form: The lower the isoelectric point, the lower the upper size limit. The dissociation into the monomeric forms is governed by the average pore size.

5. REFERENCES

(1) Margolis, J. and Kenrick, K.G., Biochem. Biophys. Res. Comm. 27 (1967) 68-73

(2) Wright, Jr. G.L., Farrell, K.B. and Roberts, D.B., Biochem. Biophys. Acta 295 (1973) 396-411

(3) Eposito, J. and Obijeski, J.F., Prep. Biochem. 6 (1976) 431-442

(4) Kopperschläger, G., Diezel, W., Bierwagen, B. and Hofmann, E., FEBS Letters 5 (1969) 221-224

(5) Lasky, M., in Catsimpoolas, N. (Ed.), Electrophoresis'78, Elsevier North Holland, Amsterdam 1978, pp. 195-210

(6) Rothe, G.M. and Purkhanbaba, H., Electrophoresis 3 (1982) 33-42

(7) Rothe, G.M. and Purkhanbaba, H., Electrophoresis 3 (1982) 43-48

(8) Rothe, G.M., Electrophoresis 3 (1982) 255-262

(9) Harris, H. and Hopkinson, D.A., Handbook of enzyme electrophoresis in human genetics, North Holland Publ. Comp., Amsterdam, Oxford 1976

(10) Rickli, E.E., Ghazanfar, S.A.S., Gibbons, B.H. and Edsall, J.T., J. Biol. Chem. 239 (1964) 1065-1078

(11) Righetti, P.G. and Caravaggio, T., J. Chromatography 127 (1976) 1-28

(12) Righetti, P.G. and Tudor, G., J. Chromatography 220 (1981) 115-194

(13) Rothe, G.M., Hum. Genet. 56 (1980) 129-155

ISOELECTRIC FOCUSING IN NARROW SMOOTH pH GRADIENT GENERATED BY BORATE-POLYOL SYSTEMS

P.D. Reshetov, L.A. Chupova, A.I. Lazarev

Shemyakin Institute of Bioorganic Chemistry, USSR Academy of Sciences, Moscow, USSR

A new technique to generate artificial pH-gradients for electrofocusing has been developed by G.V.Troitsky, G.Yu.Azhitsky et al. (1). In our previous work preparative IF of an antitumor protein, actinoxanthine, over the pH range 3.0-4.5 has been already reported (2).

In order to generate a smooth narrow pH-gradient over the range 5.0-6.5 this technique has been subjected to methodological improvements. A graph of pH-value against polyol concentration in different borate buffers was prepared. Based on this data "upper" and "lower" buffer compositions for generating pH-gradients have been optimized. By simply mixing these two solutions by means of a conventional gradient mixer narrow pH gradients can be produced. Conductivity of the buffer glycerol and glucose systems is shown to be varied over the ranges 1.83-2.45 10^{-4} $om^{-1}cm^{-1}$, 1.27-2.34 10^{-4} $om^{-1}cm^{-1}$, respectively. The pH gradients formed are stable under the voltage. To demonstrate

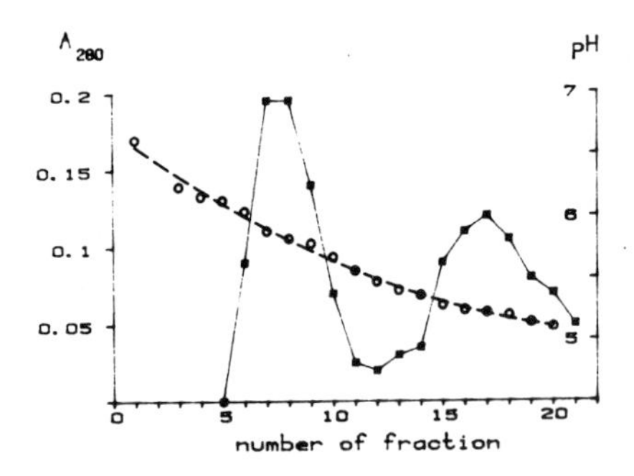

Fig. 1. Fractionation of catalase preparation in the glycerol-containing system. "Lower" buffer (in mixer): boracic acid 50 mM, sodium hydroxide 5 mM, glycerol 40%, pH 5-5.25; "upper" buffer (in reservoir): boracic acid 25 mM, sodium hydroxide 5 mM, glycerol 15%, pH 6.5. Column: 40 ml; sample: 5 mg; 700 V, 48 h.

the usefulness of this technique the fractionation of catalase preparation is reproduced in fig. 1.

The results indicate the IF in the borate polyol system can be powerful technique for protein separation.

REFERENCES

(1) G.V. Troitsky, G.Yu. Azhitsky et al., Biochim. and Biophys. Acta 400 (1975) 24-31.

(2) P.D. Reshetov, G.Yu. Azhitsky et al., Bioorga. Khim. (USSR) 6 (1980) 1476-1482.

TWO-DIMENSIONAL ELECTROPHORESIS WITH IMPROVED RESOLUTION USING NARROW pH GRADIENTS : APPLICATION TO HUMAN SERUM PROTEINS SENSITIVE TO ALCOHOL ABUSE

Thomas Marshall, Katherine M. Williams, Olof Vesterberg

Chemistry Division, National Board of Occupational Safety and Health, S-171 84 Solna, Sweden

1 INTRODUCTION

Previous application of the simplified version (1) of high resolution two-dimensional electrophoresis (2) to the analysis of serum proteins has involved isoelectric focusing (IEF, first dimension) in Ampholine of predominantly wide (pH 3.5-10) range (1,3). Whilst this relatively simple and economical approach successfully separates the major serum polypeptides, the size of the electrophoresis gels (75 x 75 x 3 mm) limits resolution. To improve resolution we have investigated IEF using Ampholine of narrow pH ranges. With this approach serum protein modifications associated with alcohol abuse (3) have been confirmed with increased clarity and additional changes detected.

2 METHODS

The polypeptides of pooled human sera from (a) 24 male alcoholics (sampled on the first day of admission to an alcoholics clinic) and (b) 24 male controls of the same age range, were compared by two-dimensional electrophoresis as previously described (1,3) but with the following modifications:

(i) The NP-40 content of the first dimension IEF gels was reduced from 2% to 0.5% (w/v) and SDS-PAGE (second dimension) performed without SDS equilibration (4).

(ii) The Ampholine (2%, w/v) comprised either the pH range 5.0-7.0 or a mixture of the pH ranges 2.5-4.0 and 4.0-6.0 (2:1, v/v).

(iii) The polypeptide patterns were detected with an improved methylamine-incorporating silver stain (5).

3 RESULTS AND DISCUSSION

The modified two-dimensional procedure gave reproducible polypeptide patterns with improved resolution over the pI ranges 3 - 6 (Fig. 1A,B) and 5 - 7 (Fig. 1C,D). Components 1-10 (Fig. 1) are numbered in accordance with reference 3 and correspond to polypeptides demonstrating either quantitative increases (large arrowheads) or decreases (small arrowheads) in association with alcohol abuse. However, improved resolution indicated:

(a) α_1-acid glycoprotein (component 2) is comprised of multiple polypeptides and alcohol abuse is predominantly associated with elevated levels of a lower molecular weight string of spots of slightly higher pI than the major components (Fig. 1A,B). This may reflect either enhanced synthesis of these components in alcoholics or liver damage with failure to remove partially de-glycosylated glycoproteins (6).

(b) The previously unidentified diffuse polypeptide zone 8 (3) is comprised of three parallel strings of spots, each containing at least five polypeptides (Fig. 1A,B). All tend to be increased in alcoholics' sera.

(c) The previously unidentified component 6 detected in close association with the α_1-antitrypsin (3) consists of at least three distinct polypeptides (Fig. 1C,D). All tend to be increased in alcoholics' sera.

(d) The previously identified apo A-I lipoprotein, component 9 (3) comprises at least four distinct polypeptides (Fig. 1C,D), all marginally enhanced in association with alcohol abuse.

Improved resolution and the comparison of pooled sera confirms all our previous findings (with the possible exception of the haptoglobins, component 7) but reproducibly indicates additional quantitative increases and decreases potentially associated with alcohol abuse. These include components 11 and 12 of lower pI than albumin, component 13 beneath the IgA heavy chains (component 4), component 14 of higher pI than transferrin and component 15 of similar pI to 14 but lower M_r. Whilst we believe that components 1-15 may prove of potential value in the diagnosis and clinical monitoring of alcohol abuse, further studies on a larger sample population are necessary to substantiate and follow up the findings.

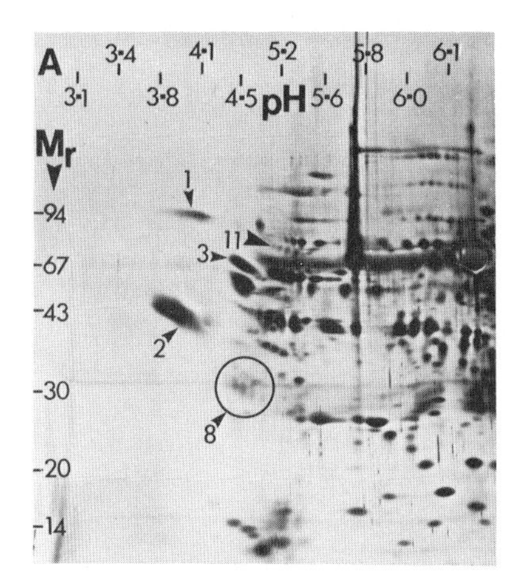

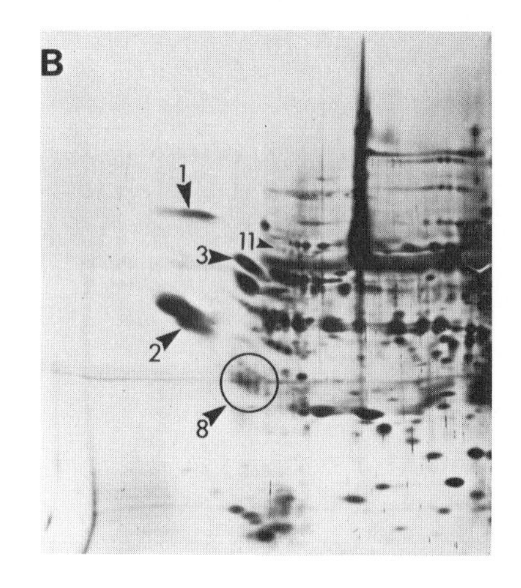

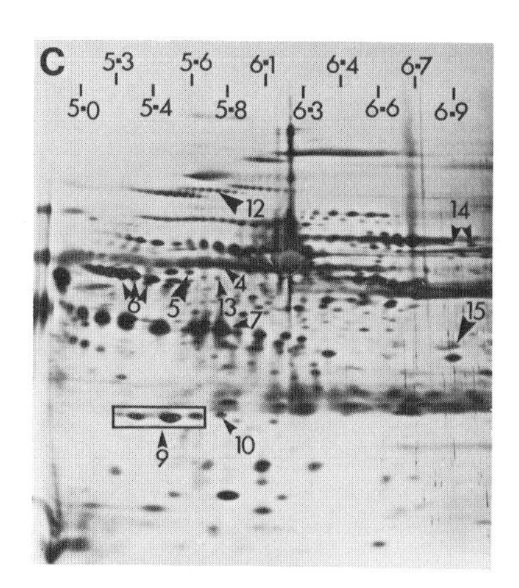

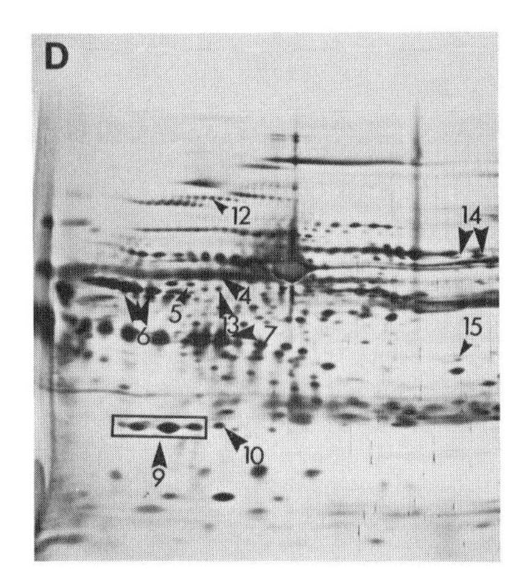

Figure 1. Two-dimensional polypeptide patterns of pooled human sera (0.25 µl) from 24 male controls (A,C) and 24 male alcoholics (B,D) following IEF in Ampholine of pH range 5.0-7.0 (C,D) or 2.5-4.0 and 4.0-6.0 (2:1, v/v; A,B). M_r indicates relative molecular mass x 10^{-3}. Previously identified components (reference 3) include α_1-acid glycoprotein (2), α_1-antichymotrypsin (3), IgA heavy chains (4), antithrombin III (5), haptoglobins (7) and apo A-I lipoprotein (9).

4 REFERENCES

(1) A. L. Latner, T. Marshall, M. Gambie, Clin. Chim. Acta 103 (1980) 51-59.

(2) P. H. O'Farrell, J. Biol. Chem. 250 (1975) 4007-4021.

(3) T. Marshall, O. Vesterberg, K. M. Williams, Electrophoresis 5 (1984) 122-128.

(4) T. Marshall, Electrophoresis 4 (1983) 436-438.

(5) T. Marshall, Anal. Biochem. 136 (1984) 340-346.

(6) G. Ashwell, A. G. Morell, Adv. Enzymol. Relat. Areas Biol. 41 (1974) 99-128.

THE USE OF TWO DIMENSIONAL GEL ELECTROPHORESIS TO MONITOR EARLY CHANGES IN THE LIVERS OF RATS TREATED WITH HEPATOCARCINOGENS

R. Ramasamy[1], S.P. Spragg[1], B. Elliott[2] and M. Stonard[2]

1 Department of Chemistry, University of Birmingham B15 2TT
2 Imperial Chemical Industries PLC, Central Toxicology Laboratory, Alderly Park, Macclesfield SK10 4TJ

1 INTRODUCTION

Two dimensional polyacrylamide gel electrophoresis (2D PAGE) is a very sensitive technique for separating individual proteins on the basis of (i) electric charge and (ii) molecular size. We have used 2D PAGE and silver staining to examine the changes in the relative concentration of normal proteins and the production of new proteins in the livers of male rats treated with different classes of hepatocarcinogens.

2 EXPERIMENTAL METHODS

The chemicals used were:

diethylnitrosamine (DEN, 500 ug/rat) which we have shown produces tumours in 6-7 months in the absence of overt hepatotoxicity;

di(2ethylhexyl)phthalate (DEHP, 1g/kg bodyweight) which is reported to be hepatocarcinogenic but for which no evidence of direct interaction with DNA has been shown (1);

6-p-dimethylaminophenyl)azobenzothiazole (6BT, 5 mg/kg bodyweight) which we have shown produces acute hepatotoxicity followed approximately 12 months later by hepatocarcinomas.

The chemicals were administered daily to male Wistar-derived rats and the liver microsomal and nuclei fractions were examined from treated and control rats at day 4 and 1, 2 and 4 weeks.

3 RESULTS AND DISCUSSION

Surprisingly few changes were seen in the protein profiles of the DEN and 6BT treated rats compared with their controls, however a

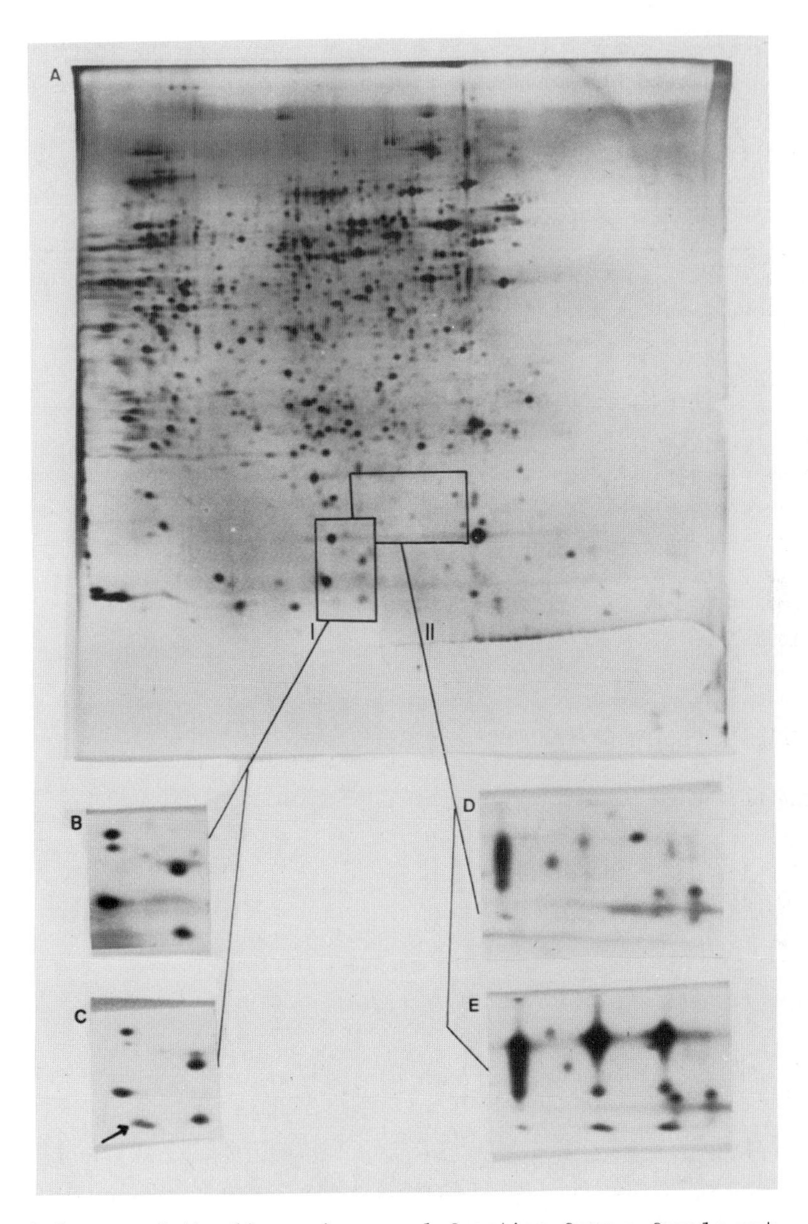

A=protein map of the liver microsomal fraction from a female rat. B=region 1 from a male control rat. C=region 1 of a male rat four days after treatment with DEHP, showing the spot characterising the treatment. Dα2uglobulin pattern (region 11) from a 4 week old male control rat. Eα2uglobulin pattern from an eight week old male control rat. The silver stained gels are orientated with the acidic side to the left.

clear treatment-related change in a single protein in the microsomal fraction was seen with the DEHP treated animals (see figures B and C). The protein of about 20000 daltons increased in relative concentration throughout the study and is clearly different to the PPA-80 protein previously observed in similarly treated animals (2).

Another interesting observation was the dramatic change in the protein profile of a group of proteins of 18-20000 daltons in the microsomal fraction that occurred as rats went from pre-puberty (4 weeks of age) to post-puberty (8 weeks). This change in proteins, which appear by antibody reaction to be the α2uglobulin fraction, was found in both test and control animals but not in fractions from female rats (see figures A, D and E). These results emphasise the need to use strictly appropriate control animals in investigations with such a sensitive technique, in order to discriminate protein changes arising as a result of chemical treatment.

4 REFERENCES

(1) National Toxicology Programme, Technical Report Series No. 217 (1983) National Institute of Health, Bethesda MD.

(2) J.K. Reddy, N.S. Kumar, Biochem. Biophys. Res. Commun. 77 (1977) 824-829.

TWO-DIMENSIONAL GEL ELECTROPHORESIS CHARACTERIZATION OF FIBRINOGEN " GRENOBLE "

O. Valiron[1], B. Polack[1,2], E. Concord[1], J.M. Freyssinet[1], G. Hudry-Clergeon[1].

1. U 217 INSERM, DRF and LETI/MCTE, Centre d'Etudes Nucléaires de Grenoble, 85 X, 38041 GRENOBLE CEDEX FRANCE
2. Laboratoire d'Hématologie, Centre Hospitalier Universitaire, 217 X 38043 GRENOBLE CEDEX FRANCE

1 INTRODUCTION

Fibrinogen is a 340,000 δ glycoprotein which is involved in the last step of the coagulation pathway. It is composed of three paired polypeptidic chains ($A\alpha$,$B\beta$,γ) held together by disulfide bridges (1). There are three kinds of heterogeneities in normal fibrinogen.
1. A post transcriptional modification which gives rise to a 1,500δ elongated γ-chain : the γ'-chain (2).
2. Post translational modifications which give rise to heterogeneities in isoelectric points. They involve different degrees of sulfatation, phosphorylation and differences in sialic acid content (3,4).
3. An in vivo proteolysis of the C-terminal part of the A -chain which gives rise to a heterogeneous population of lighter $A\alpha$-chains (5).

Fibrinogen "Grenoble" is an abnormal fibrinogen characterized by a decreased rate of fibrin monomer aggregation. Two-dimensional gel electrophoresis (2-D GEl) revealed abnormal γ-chains. A metrological study was performed on digitalized 2-D GEls to quantify the differences visually observed.

2 MATERIALS AND METHODS

2-D GEl was performed according to the method of Anderson and Anderson (6,7) with the ISO-DALT equipment from Electro-Nucleonics. Samples were either purified fibrinogen or whole plasma. Staining was either by Coomassie Blue or by the silver staining of Oakley et al (8). Digitalization was performed on vacuum dried gels with an Optronics film scanner using a 100 X 100μm grid. Each pixel yielded a byte (256 grey levels).

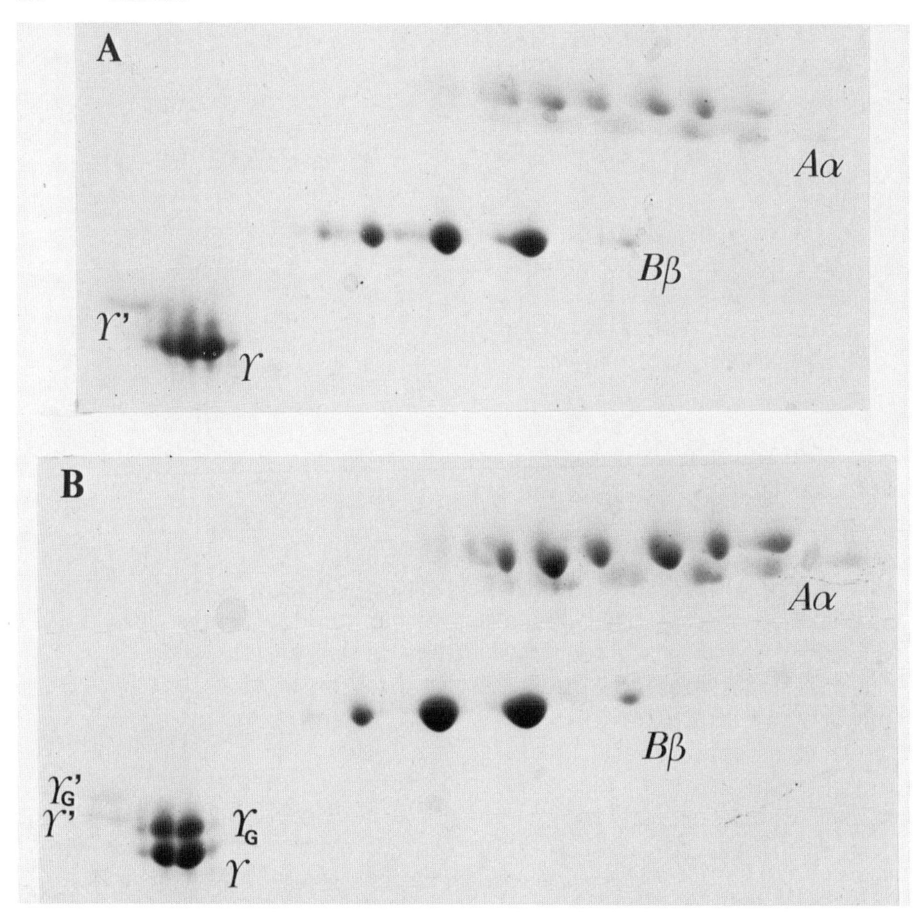

Fig. 1. 2-D GEl of normal fibrinogen (A) and fibrinogen "Grenoble" (B) showing abnormal γ_G and γ'_G-chains.

3 RESULTS

2-D GEl analysis did show important differences between normal fibrinogen and fibrinogen "Grenoble" (fig. 1). The A$\alpha$and Bβ-chains were almost identical with respect to their molecular weight and isoelectric points. The γ-chains were split into two, showing normal γ and γ'-chains as well as abnormal γ_G and γ'_G-chains. The abnormal $_G$ and γ'_G-chains showed an increase in molecular weight (1,250δ) without isoelectric point variation. Metrological analysis of fibrinogen "Grenoble" allowed a quantification of $\gamma$and γ_G-chains. There was about 60 % γ-chains and 40 % γ_G-chains. Such an analysis could not be performed on γ'-chains but, visually, seemed to be about the same as for γ-chains. The splitting of the γ-chains was also visible in 2-D GEl of whole plasma even if the A$\alpha$and Bβ-chains were not well resolved.

4 DISCUSSION

Fibrinogen "Grenoble" is an asymptomatic dysfibrinogen characterized by abnormal fibrin monomer aggregation. Fibrinopeptide A liberation, cross-linking by factor XIIIa and plasminic degradation are almost normal. Abnormal γ_G and γ'_G-chains result probably from an elongation of the polypeptidic sequence. As there is a polymerization defect, this elongation might be localized at the C-terminal part of γ-chains which is involved in fibrin polymerization. As there is a normal γ-chain cross-linking by factor XIIIa, the abnormal elongation should then be apart from the stabilization domain.

The presence of 60 % γ-chains and 40 % γ_G-chains would prove a heterozygotic status.

5 REFERENCES

(1) R.F. Doolittle. Fibrinogen and fibrin. In : Haemostasis and thrombosis, A.L. Bloom and D.P. Thomas (Ed.), Churchill Livingstone, New York 1981, pp. 163-191.

(2) C. Wolfenstein-Todel, M.W. Mosesson. Carboxy-terminal amino acid sequence of human fibrinogen γ-chain variant (γ'). Biochemistry 20 (1981) 6146-6149.

(3) F. Brosstad, B. Teige, B. Olaisen, K. Gravein, H.C. Godal, H. Stormorken. Two-dimensional electrophoresis characterization (ISO-DALT), of fibrinogen and fibrin subunit chains from four different genetic dysfibrinogen variants. In : Fibrinogen structure, functional aspect and metabolism, 2, W. de Gruyter, Berlin 1983, pp. 145-153.

(4) C. Kuyas, A. Haeberli, P.W. Straub. Sialic acid dependant polypeptide chain heterogeneity of human fibrinogen demonstrated by two-dimensional electrophoresis. Thromb. Haemost. 47 (1982) 19-21.

(5) D.K. Galanakis, M.W. Mosesson, N.E. Stathakis. Human fibrinogen heterogeneities distribution and charge characteristics of chains of Aα origin. J. Lab. Clin. Med. 92 (1978) 376-386.

(6) N.G. Anderson, N.L. Anderson. Analytical technique for cell fraction XXI. Two-dimensional analysis of serum and tissue proteins : multiple isoelectric focusing. Anal. Biochem. 85 (1978) 376-386.

(7) N.L. Anderson, N.G. Anderson. Analytical technique for cell fraction XXII. Two-dimensional analysis of serum and tissue proteins : multiple gradient, slab gel electrophoresis. Anal. Biochem. 85 (1978) 341-354.

(8) B.R. Oakley, D.R. Kirsch, N.R. Morriss. A simplified ultrasensitive silver staining for detecting proteins in polyacrylamide gels. Anal. Biochem. 105 (1980) 361-363.

MICRO-2D-ELECTROPHORESIS APPLIED TO IDENTIFY PATHOTYPES OF THE POTATO CYST NEMATODE GLOBODERA ROSTOCHIENSIS

J.P. Ohms

Landwirtschaftliche Untersuchungs- und Forschungsanstalt Hameln, Postfach 295, D-3250 Hameln 1, F.R. Germany

1 INTRODUCTION

The identification of species and pathotypes of the potato cyst nematode, the biotrophic parasite of potato, is of agricultural importance. The present method of analysis using bioassays on differential potato cultivars (1) is time consuming and cannot be used to recognize pathotypes exactly. Isoelectric focusing has been sucessfully used to distinguish the two species GLOBODERA ROSTOCHIENSIS and G. PALLIDA (2-4). However, one-dimensional electrophoretic methods do not allow the identification of pathotypes within both species.

2 ASSAY PRINZIPLE

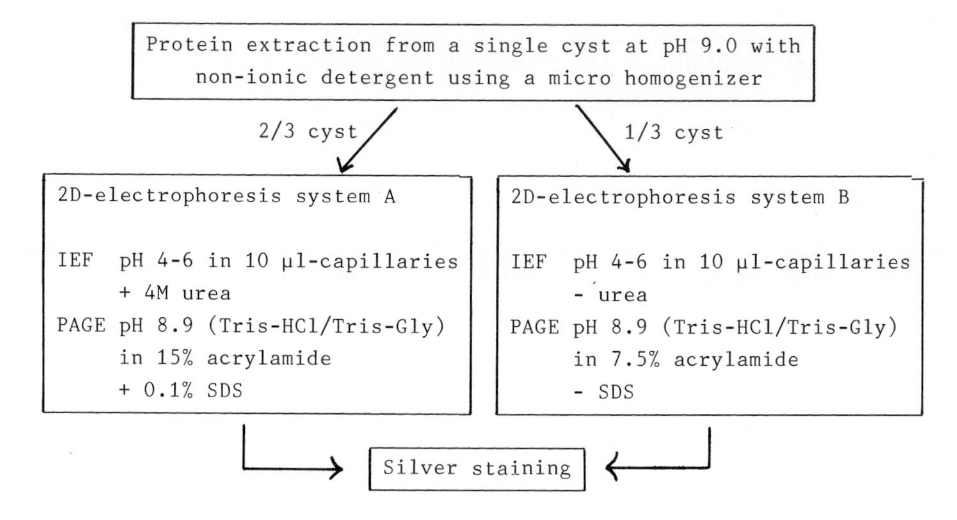

3 RESULTS

The cyst proteins separated by 2D-electrophoresis system A are classified into three groups termed "unspecific spots", "species spezific spots" and "pathotype specific spots". Compared to the species specific spots the pathotype specific spots are weak. Furthermore they are localized closely together in the electrophoretic pattern (IEF: pH 4.5; SDS-PAGE: Rf 0.4). Amongst the five European pathotypes of G. ROSTOCHIENSIS only Ro5 reveals a spot with relative high intensity (A5 in table 1), which is shifted to higher pH compared to the other spots. Ro4 can be distinguished from the other pathotypes by one specific spot (A4). Differences between Ro1, Ro2 and Ro3 appear only in cysts which are completely filled with eggs and larvae. Since discrimination between Ro1 and the other pathotypes is very important for plant protecting, the system B is used in addition to system A to recognize Ro1 in cysts partially filled with eggs and larvae. Routine tests of soil samples have shown that there is a high frequency of pathotype mixture in the potato fields. Therefore only the "single cyst technique" allows to determine the composition of mixed populations definitely.

Table 1: Distribution and intensity of pathotype specific spots

System	Spot	Pathotype				
		Ro1	Ro2	Ro3	Ro4	Ro5
A	A1	+	(+)	+	++	+
A	A2	(+)	+	+	++	+
A	A3			+		
A	A4				++	
A	A5					++++
B	B1	(+)	+++	+++	+++	+++
B	B2	+++	(+)	(+)	(+)	(+)

The intensity dereases from ++++ <medium> to (+) <very weak>

4 REFERENCES

(1) J. Kort, H. Ross, H.J. Rumpenhorst, A.R. Stone, Nematologica 23 (1977) 230-242

(2) C.C. Fleming, R.J. Marks, Ann. appl. Biol. 103 (1983) 277-281

(3) P.C. Fox, H.J. Atkinson, Parasitology 88 (1984) 131-139

(4) J.P. Ohms, D.H.K. Heinicke, Z. Pflanzenkrankh. u. Pflanzenschutz 90 (1983) 258-264

TWO-DIMENSIONAL ELECTROPHORESIS OF NAD-DEPENDENT MALATE DEHYDROGENASE IN BULL SPERMATOZOA

Georgi H.Georgiev, Margarita P.Grinko

Department of Biochemistry, Institute of Biology and Immunology of Reproduction and Development of Organisms, Sofia 1113, Bulgaria

1. INTRODUCTION

It has been found that malate dehydrogenase (MDH) has two separable forms - mitochondrial and cytozol MDH. The mitochondrial form of this enzyme represents a NADP-dependent and the cytozol one-NAD-dependent MDH. It is assumed that MDH is a dimer whose isoenzymes are under different gene control (1-4).

The aim of this study was to characterize the soluble NAD-dependent malate dehydrogenase in bull spermatozoa by means of two-dimensional electrophoresis.

2. MATERIAL AND METHODS

The isoenzyme pattern of NAD-dependent MDH was determined in the fraction of soluble proteins extracted by distilled water from washed ejaculated bull spermatozoa. The first dimensional electrophoresis of the extracted proteins was performed on 5.5 % polyacrylamide gel in tubes, and the second dimension one - on 7.5% polyacrylamide block (5,6). The MDH isoenzymes were demonstrated in a medium containing DL-malate (7).

3. RESULTS AND DISCUSSION

The first-dimension electrophoresis of NAD-dependent MDH produced maximum three isoenzymes (MDH_1, MDH_2 and MDH_3) with the following R_f values: MDH_1 - 0.54; MDH_2 - 0.22; and MDH_3 remained at the start. Data on two MDH isozymes in mammalian spermatozoa have been so far

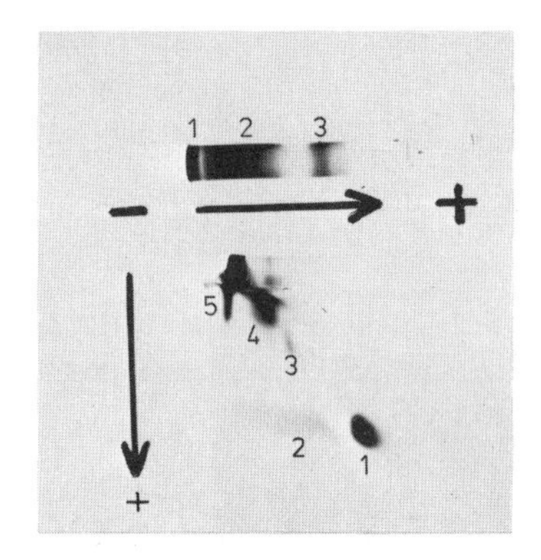

Fig. 1. Electrophoretic pattern of the first and second-dimension electrophoresis of soluble NAD-dependent MDH in bull spermatozoa.

reported in the literature (8,9).

The second-dimension electrophoresis revealed additional separation of each isoenzyme obtained from the first-dimension analysis. At least 5 protein fractions (bands) of malate dehydrogenase activity were recorded (Fig.1). It is suggested that the nature of NAD-dependent MDH is much more heterogenous in comparison with the characteristics based on the one-dimensional electrophoresis on polyacrylamide gel in tubes.

4. REFERENCES

(1) N.S.Henderson, Ann.N.Y.Acad.Sci. 151 (1968) 429-440.

(2) T.E.Wheat, G.S.Whitt, Experientia, 27 (1971) 647-648.

(3) G.Dolken, E.Leisner, D.Pette, Eur.J .Biochem. 47(1974) 333-342.

(4) J.L.Hodnett, J.E. Evans, H.B.Gray, A.H.Bartel, Comp. Biochem. Physiol.54 B (1976) 271-277.

(5) B.J.Davis, Ann.N.Y.Acad.Sci. 121 (1964) 404-427.

(6) E.Kaltschmidt, H.G.Wittmann, Analyt.Biochem. 36 (1970),401-412.

(7) H.J.Van der Helm, Lancet, 2(1961) 108-109.

(8) E.Goldberg, Science, USA, 139 (1963) 602-603.

(9) M.S.Mounib, FEBS Letters, 48 (1974) 79-84.

TWO-DIMENSIONAL ELECTROPHORESIS OF HUMAN CEREBROSPINAL FLUID

A. Thomas Endler, Donald S. Young, Rose M. Currie, Takehiko Yanagihara

Department of Laboratory Medicine and Department of Neurology, Mayo Clinic, Rochester, MN 55905, USA.

1. INTRODUCTION

Quantitative and qualitative protein analysis of cerebrospinal fluid (CSF) in patients with neurological and some systemic diseases can be used as a diagnostic tool. The production of CSF is complicated and only small volumes are available for investigation. Total protein, albumin, immunoglobulin G, and in some instances several other serum proteins have been investigated in CSF. Two-dimensional electrophoresis with subsequent silver staining offers the possibility of analyzing, in a small sample (50 µg protein), more than 1000 proteins simultaneously. A map of the protein pattern of normal CSF is a prerequisite for the recognition of disease related CSF protein patterns.

2. MATERIALS AND METHODS

2.1 Materials

CSF was investigated from 150 patients undergoing spinal tap for a variety of reasons. Patients' diagnoses were collected afterwards and CSF of patients with no neurological or systemic disease were classified retrospectively as normal.

2.2 Methods

Two-dimensional electrophoresis was performed on the ISO-DALT system as described previously (1). CSF specimens were desalted by dialyzing against 0.05 mol/L ammonium formate, and concentrated by freeze-drying. Proteins were dissociated by sodium dodecyl sulfate (SDS), β- mercaptoethanol, and heat at pH 9.5. Fifty µg protein were loaded on each gel. Isoelectric focusing was performed with ampholytes with a pH range of 3.5-10.0. Second dimension was performed on SDS-polyacrylamide with a gradient from 10% to 23%. Proteins were visualized by silver stain.

Figure 1. Two-dimensional electrophoresis protein map of normal CSF. Protein spots are marked according to a previously published serum map (2), a31 albumin, b10 transferrin, C8 αl-antitrypsin, d52 light chains, el apolipoprotein AI. CSF proteins which are also found in normal serum are al to a33, bl to b15, cl to c52, dl to d64, el to el2, fl to f5. CSF proteins which are not detected in normal serum are a34 to a36, b16 to b18, c53 to c70, d65 to d75, el3 to el5.

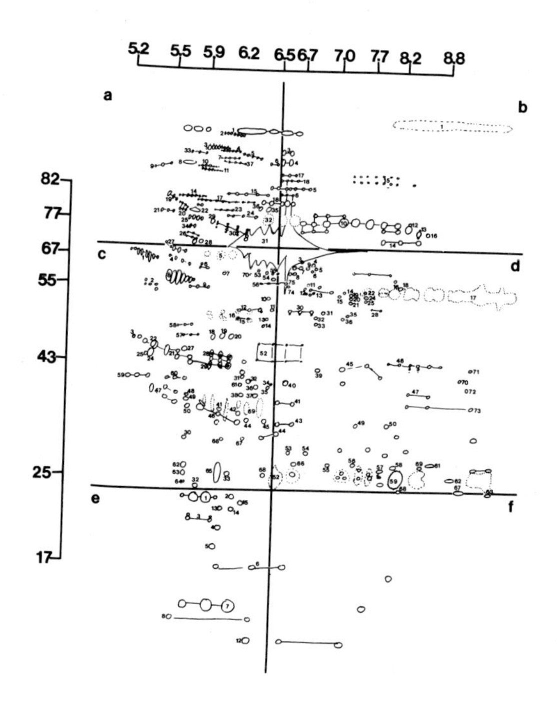

3. MAP OF NORMAL CEREBROSPINAL FLUID (Fig. 1)

A map of CSF proteins was made based on the proteins of CSF from five normal patients. For comparison a map of normal human serum designed by Tracy and Young (2) was used. Serum proteins were prominent, but additional protein spots not present in normal human serum were also found.

4. CONCLUSION

Serum has 2000 times more protein than CSF. To compare CSF from healthy and diseased patients and to achieve optimal resolution, the applied quantity of protein has to be 50 µg per gel and has to be constant. Different protein patterns in CSF were found in patients with different diseases. Multiple sclerosis, acute lymphatic leukemia and encephalitis were associated with differences in the protein composition of CSF. Further investigations have been done to determine if two-dimensional electrophoresis of CSF is a useful diagnostic device for neurological diseases.

5. REFERENCES

(1) R. P. Tracy, R. M. Currie, D. S. Young, Clin. Chem. 28 (1982), 890-899.

(2) R. P. Tracy and D. S. Young in Y. E. Celis, R. Bravo (Eds.), Two-dimensional gel electrophoresis of proteins, Academic Press, Orlando 1984, pp. 193-240.

2D GEL ELECTROPHORESIS OF LEAF PROTEINS : COMPARISON OF EXTRACTION PROCEDURES TO AVOID ADDITIONAL SPOTS DUE TO PROTEASE ACTION.

Catherine Colas des Francs, Hervé Thiellement, Dominique de Vienne

Laboratoire de Génétique des Systèmes Végétaux, GIS Moulon,
91190 GIF-SUR-YVETTE, France.

1 INTRODUCTION

The extraction of plant proteins raises the problem of *in vitro* degradation by proteases which results in additional bands or spots in electrophoresis. We chose the large subunit (LS) of the ribulose bisphosphate carboxylase oxygenase (Rubisco) from wheat leaf as a model to study this phenomenon.

In a previous work dealing with cytoplasmic genetic variability we showed that among several hundreds of spots revealed by two-dimensional (2D) gel electrophoresis, 24 appear structurally related to the LS of Rubisco : they exhibit an identical shift for isolectric point and molecular weight between the electrophoregrams of two cytoplasmic types analysed (1).

In order to know if these polypeptides are due to the action of proteases, we have performed various extraction experiments by using proteinase inhibitors or by heating the extract at 100°C in a sodium-dodecyl sulfate (SDS) and 2-mercaptoethanol solution.

We clearly show the proteolytic origin of 23 of the LS-associated spots, and propose a procedure to avoid degradation products on 2D gels, which are probably very frequent with the classical extraction methods.

2 MATERIALS AND METHODS

The expanded first leaf of an 8-day-old plant from *Triticum aestivum* L. constituted a sample.

2.1 *Tris extraction* (1). Hundred mg of leaf pieces were dry crushed in liquid nitrogen and resuspended at 0°C in 2ml Tris-Cl^- buffer pH 8.7 (30mM Tris, 1mM DTT, 1mM ascorbic acid, 1mM EDTA-Na_2 , 5mM $Mgcl_2$ and 12 mg insoluble PVP). The sample was twice centrifugated (35,300 g for 15 min and 10 min) and ice-cold acetone (8ml) with 10mM 2-mercaptoethanol was added to the supernatant, allowing the proteins to precipitate for 1h at -30°C. After centrifugation (10min at 35,300g) the pellet was air-dried and resolubilized in 200 µl of urea "lysis buffer" (2). The samples were stored at -80°C. This procedure is further referred to as control conditions.

2.2 *Extraction in the presence of proteinase inhibitors*. Proteinase inhibitors were added either in the Tris-Cl^- buffer or in the "lysis buffer" as further described.

- solution A : antipain 1mM
- solution B : antipain 1mM, leupeptin 1mM, pepstatin A 1mM
- solution C : chymostatin 1mM, elastatinal 1mM, pepstatin A 1mM
- solution D : PMSF 1mM, EDTA 2mM, pepstatin A 10^{-7}M
- solution E : α_2-macroglobulin 1mM

2.3 Extraction in the presence of SDS.

- SDS procedure : The leaf powder was suspended in 2ml of SDS solution (4 % SDS, 5% 2-mercaptoethanol, 5 % sucrose)(3) with 12 mg insoluble PVP, and heated at 100°C for 3 min. It was then centrifugated and further processed as described for control.

- Tris procedure followed by SDS procedure : The powder was suspended in 2ml Tris-Cl^- buffer with 12 mg PVP. After the second centrifugation, 4 % SDS, 5 % 2-mercaptoethanol and 5 % sucrose were added to the supernatant that was heated for 3 min. The subsequent procedure is as above mentionned.

2.4 Electrophoresis

The first dimension IEF was done according to Zivy et al. (1). The second dimension SDS PAGE was performed as described by O'Farrell (2) except for the acrylamide concentration of the gels (running gel : 11 % acrylamide ; stacking gel : 5 % acrylamide). The 2D gels were silver stained according to Oakley et al. (4) except for the revelator solution that was half concentrated. They were visually compared relatively to the control by superposing transparent films.

3 RESULTS AND DISCUSSION

3.1 Proteinase inhibitors

The 24 spots related to the LS of Rubisco (schematized in Figure 1) are not similarly altered according to the different proteinase inhibitors used. Fifteen of them show intensity decrease and 6 do not change whatever be the inhibitors added to the Tris-Cl^- buffer. Three spots have a different behaviour according to the proteinase solution used (A, B or C). Solutions D and E are ineffective.

These first experiments suggest that 18 of the 24 spots related to the LS of Rubisco are degradation products of this polypeptide. The inhibitors considerably limit the proteolysis but are not fully effective.

3.2 SDS procedures

After SDS procedure, all the spots but one (indicated by an arrow in Figure 1) show intensity decrease or desappear. After Tris procedure followed by SDS procedure the same 23 spots are much fainter than in the control. This means that proteases are much more active in urea than in Tris-Cl^- buffer.

We can conclude that the 6 spots that were not altered by the proteinase solutions used here also are degradation products of the LS. The question remains for one spot whose intensity decreased in only one of the antiprotease experiments but increased in the SDS procedure.

Apart from the 24 spots analyzed, many other spots of low molecular weight are lacking on the gels after the SDS procedure : they probably are degradation products too. The heat-treatment of the extract in the SDS and 2-mercaptoethanol solution alters quaternary and tertiary structures of proteins, including proteases. So it is likely that this drastic procedure avoids most of the protein degradation during their extraction.

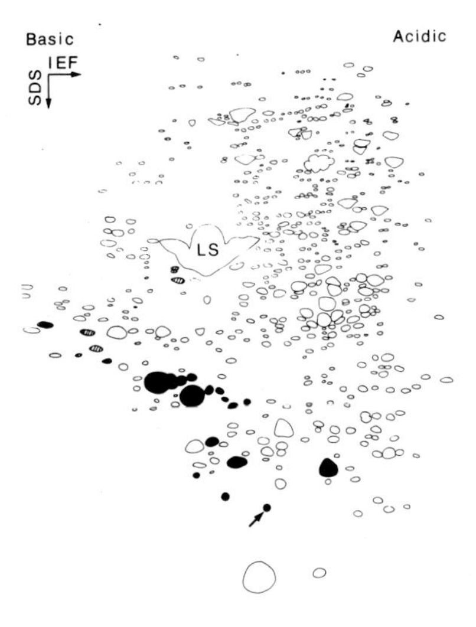

Fig. 1 : Map of wheat leaf proteins.
The 24 spots analyzed : black spots are affected by proteinase inhibitors and striped spots by SDS procedure only. The arrow indicates the spot unaffected by SDS procedure.

4 REFERENCES

(1) M. Zivy, H. Thiellement, D. de Vienne, J.P. Hofmann, Theor. Appl. Genet. 66 (1983) 1-7.

(2) P.H. O'Farrell, J. Biol. Chem. 250 (1975) 4007-4021.

(3) P.A. Harrison, C.C. Black, Plant Physiol. 70 (1982) 1359-1366.

(4) B.R. Oakley, D.R. Kirsch, R. Morris, Anal. Biochem. 105 (1980) 361-363.

TWO-DIMENSIONAL PROTEIN ELECTROPHORESIS OF GENE AMPLIFICATION PRODUCTS IN DRUG-RESISTANT TUMOR CELLS

Björn Dahllöf

Department of Genetics, University of Göteborg, Guldhedsgatan 23, S-413 46 Göteborg, Sweden

1 INTRODUCTION

In three separate experiments SEWA TC13 mouse ascites tumor cells were subjected to selection in stepwise increasing concentrations of methotrexate (MTX), actinomycin D (AMD) and vincristine (VCR), three drugs commonly used against neoplastic diseases. MTX is a competitive inhibitor of the enzym dihydrofolate reductase (DHFR) which is essential for DNA-replication, AMD binds to DNA and prevents transcription and VCR inhibits formation of the nuclear spindle. Resistance developed and was in all cases accompanied by the genesis of double minute chromosomes (1,2), a common cytogenetic sign of gene amplification.

2 EXPERIMENTAL PROCEDURE

Protein composition of the lines were compared using two-dimensional electrophoresis according to the method of O´Farrell (3,4). In the first dimension, tubes with NEPHGE gels (pH 7-10) for basic and IEF gels (pH 3-7) for acidic proteins were used. The second dimension consisted of a 12 % SDS-PAGE with a 3 % stacking gel and was stained with a silverstaining method developed by Ansorge and modified by Mose Larsen (5).

3 RESULTS AND COMMENTS

On NEPHGE gels the MTX-resistant line displayed highly elevated levels of a basic (pI approx. 8) 21,000 dalton protein, identified as DHFR (6). Thus, the cells responded to MTX selection by selective gene amplification of the DHFR gene causing an overproduction of DHFR, enough to overcome the MTX inhibition.

IEF gels of AMD and VCR resistant cells showed an acidic (pI approx. 5) 21,000 dalton protein, not detectable in neither sensitive nor

MTX-resistant cells (2). The function of this protein has not been determined so far, but it may be directly or indirectly responsable for the resistance. The two lines also displayed extensive cross-resistance and a reduced net-uptake of both AMD and VCR, i.e. they display the so called "pleiotropic drug resistance " phenotype.

As shown here and elsewhere, high-resolution two-dimensional electrophoresis has proved to be very suitable for the analysis of gene amplification on the protein level.

4 REFERENCES

(1) T. Martinsson, P. Tenning, L. Lundh and G. Levan, Hereditas 97 (1982) pp. 123-137.

(2) B. Dahllöf, T. Martinsson and G. Levan, Experimental Cell Research (1984), in press.

(3) P. H. O´Farrell, Journal of Biological Chemistry 250 (1975) pp. 4007-4021.

(4) P. Z. O´Farrell, H. M. Goodman and P. H. O´Farrell, Cell 12 (1977) pp. 1133-1142.

(5) P. Mose Larsen, S. Fey, R. Bravo and J. E. Celis, Electrophoresis 4 (1983) pp. 247-255.

(6) A-H. Jacobsson, B. Dahllöf, T. Martinsson and G. Levan, Hereditas 99 (1983) pp. 293-302.

ANALYSIS OF GENETIC NEUROMUSCULAR DISEASES BY 2D-PAGE: A SYSTEM FOR COMPARISONS

Michael J. Dunn, Arthur H.M. Burghes, Ketan Patel, Jan A. Witkowski and Victor Dubowitz

Jerry Lewis Muscle Research Centre, Department of Paediatrics and Neonatal Medicine, Royal Postgraduate Medical School, DuCane Road, London W12 OHS, U.K.

1 INTRODUCTION

2D-PAGE is potentially a powerful tool for use in studies of genetic diseases to detect the biochemical alterations that have occurred in various cells and tissues. However, there are certain limitations such as the consistent resolution of all the proteins expressed by cells, comparisons of samples both qualitatively and quantitatively, and whether the primary alteration is likely to be seen consistently. In this paper, we describe methods that overcome some of these problems when using 2D-PAGE and their application to studies of Duchenne muscular dystrophy (DMD).

2 2D-PAGE SYSTEM

The 2D-PAGE system that we have developed employs a flat-bed technique in which the first dimension IEF gel is bound to a plastic backing sheet. We also use mixtures of ampholyte and altered gradient shapes to enhance resolution. One of the most important features required for the successful use of this system is the reliable binding of the gel to a plastic sheet. We have reported a method for achieving this (1) involving treating the plastic with Dow Corning Prime Coat 1200, followed by reaction with silane A174. However, if the acrylamide-urea mixture was deionized before use, unreliable adherence of gels was obtained. We have also reported (2) that commercially available plastic supports did not bind to acrylamide reliably. However, more recently we have found that by increasing the catalyst concentration 2- to 3-fold (not to such a high concentration as to cause distortion), reliable binding of the polyacrylamide gel to GelBond PAG film was obtained, in the presence of 8M urea, 0.5% w/v NP-40 or CHAPS. This binding was more reliable than that to the plastic which we have previously described. Thus, gels containing 8M urea and 0.5% w/v CHAPS are now cast on GelBond PAG. In a further modification, the gels are set up such that the upper surface remains covered by a plastic sheet during the IEF run, thereby avoiding dessication, crystallization of urea, and effects of the atmosphere. The second dimension gradient SDS-PAGE gels are cast using the Ultrograd method described previously (1), but using the type of casting tower described in (3, 4).

3 DUAL LABELLING TECHNIQUE

Initially [^{35}S]-methionine-labelled samples from normal and DMD individuals were analysed visually by side-by-side comparison. Although variations in the 2D patterns were observed, no consistent differences were found. However, this method of comparison is so insensitive as to render it totally inadequate. Dual labelling methods have been developed which facilitate comparisons of pairs of samples. However, there are some major drawbacks in such dual labelling techniques. Firstly, if the amino acid analogs used for labelling are metabolized, then differences in 2D maps can arise due simply to differences in the position of radiolabel within the molecule rather than to differences inherent in the samples themselves. In addition, only a single pair of samples can be compared by this method, and comparison between pairs is no easier. Lastly, there is a loss of resolution when the positive image of the autoradiograph is made for overlay with the other autoradiograph. The first problem has been overcome using a combination of [^{35}S]-methionine and [^{75}Se]-selenomethionine, as the isotopes are in the same position and the two amino acid analogs are metabolized identically. The last problem can be overcome by resort to scanning densitometry and computerised image analysis. This latter approach is the only realistic solution to the problem of comparison of large numbers of samples.

4 COMPARISON OF SAMPLES

A genetic disease could involve a point mutation or a gene deletion. Indeed, it is possible that a variety of different changes within the same locus could result in clinically identical phenotypes. Recently, studies of Lesch-Nyhan syndrome indicate that this may be a general phenomenon as five variants of hypoxanthine-guanine phosphoribosyl transferase have been detected and the single amino acid changes responsible for four of these determined (5). Thus, diseases such as DMD could subdivide into distinct groups showing different protein changes. The situation would be further complicated by the presence of normal polymorphic variability and secondary, compensatory changes in response to the disease process. This complex situation makes it essential that there should be a satisfactory way of comparing between different diseased individuals. Our approach to this problem is to construct a so-called "super-normal" sample from a mixture of normal samples all labelled in the same way (e.g. with [^{35}S]-methionine). Each normal sample, labelled with the other amino acid analog (i.e. [^{75}Se]-selenomethionine), is compared to the "super-normal" sample by dual label 2D-PAGE to check for any dilution effects of any particular protein spot. The "super-normal" sample is then used for dual-label 2D-PAGE comparison with each individual DMD sample. In this way we should detect either a single, specific change in the DMD samples, or if DMD is polymorphic we would expect to recognize a set of changes in a specific area of the gel with a number of individuals showing each change.

5 COMPUTER ANALYSIS OF 2D-PAGE PATTERNS

It is extremely difficult to evaluate complex 2D-PAGE patterns by simple visual inspection. We believe that a computer-based analytical system is essential, especially in studies such as ours on DMD where the areas of interest on the gel are not known and the whole pattern must therefore be analysed. Several different groups have used a variety of approaches to tackle the problems involved in gel analysis and we have reviewed these in detail elsewhere (6). However, these systems are dedicated to the laboratories running them and sometimes involve custom-built hardware. These systems are therefore not readily accessible to the majority of workers using 2D-PAGE.

In our laboratory, we are attempting to establish a quantitative 2D-PAGE analysis system that can be implemented on computer systems that are generally available in research environments and the software is being designed for portability between operating systems. We believe that at present only scanning densitometers offer the resolution required for such analysis, although future developments using linear photodiode arrays may prove superior. We are at present using a Joyce-Loebl Chromoscan 3 flat-bed densitometer for analysis of small areas of 2D gels and a Joyce-Loebl Scandig 3 drum densitometer for digitization of complete gel images. We are evaluating these algorithms applied in the analysis of 2D-PAGE patterns for their efficiency in generating images that accurately reflect the biochemical data. We are also testing which stages of the analysis can run more efficiently on parallel processing machines than on serial "pipeline" machines.

6 SOME APPROACHES TO THE ANALYSIS OF CHANGES IN GENETIC DISEASE

High resolution 2D-PAGE detects changes in size or charge. However in a genetic disease like DMD it is possible that a point mutation is involved. This type of change could result in no charge change or only a small shift in charge that would be difficult to detect by 2D-PAGE. Moreover the change could be polymorphic with point mutations at various locations in the gene causing the same non-functional protein. Therefore some DMD individuals might show a change while other would not. Such a situation would be difficult to analyse using 2D-PAGE. In the case of X-linked DMD there are women who have balanced X autosome translocations and manifest X-linked DMD (7). The breakpoint in these translocations is found at Xp21, the precise location of the break may be found to alter. However, it is unlikely that the symptoms are due to a point mutation. Even if the translocation affected a controller sequence, it might be expected that protein coded for by the gene responsible for DMD would either not be produced or be extremely abnormal. Thus we are comparing fibroblasts derived from these patients to the "super-normal" using 2D-PAGE and dual labelling as discussed earlier.

In another approach we are preparing mRNA from normal and DMD cells and tissues, translating it in vitro and analysing the resultant protein products by 2D-PAGE. This has the advantage of avoiding any post-translational protein modification events. In addition, the use of mRNA may allow extension to cDNA cloning and possibly to a method whereby low abundance proteins can be satisfactorily analysed. Using a method of hybrid selection with available X-chromosome genomic libraries, it may be possible to obtain X-chromosome specific mRNA and hence, by in vitro translation, X-chromosome specific protein. This would obviously be of great usefulness in an X-linked disease such as DMD.

7 ACKNOWLEDGEMENTS

We thank Mrs. C. Trand for typing the manuscript. We acknowledge financial support from the Medical Research Council and the Muscular Dystrophy Group of Great Britain.

8 REFERENCES

(1) A.H.M. Burghes, M.J. Dunn, V. Dubowitz, Electrophoresis 3 (1982) 354-363.

(2) M.J. Dunn, A.H.M. Burghes, Electrophoresis 4 (1983) 97-116.

(3) N.L. Anderson, N.G. Anderson, Anal. Biochem. 85 (1978) 341-354.

(4) M.I. Jones, W.E. Massingham, S.P. Spragg, Anal. Biochem. 106 (1980) 446-449.

(5) J.M. Wilson, A.B. Young, W.N. Kelley, New Engl. J. Med. 309 (1983) 900-910.

(6) M.J. Dunn, A.H.M. Burghes, Electrophoresis 4 (1983) 173-189.

(7) P.A. Jacobs, P.A. Hunt, P.I.T. Mayer, R.D. Bart, Amer. J. Hum. Genet. 33 (1981) 513-518.

ANALYSIS OF GENETIC VARIANTS OF SOME PIG PLASMA PROTEINS (GC, α-PROTEASE INHIBITORS, POSTALBUMINS, TRANSFERRIN AND CERULOPLASMIN) BY HORIZONTAL TWO-DIMENSIONAL ELECTROPHORESIS

Bo Gahne, R. Kumar Juneja

Department of Animal Breeding and Genetics, Swedish University of Agricultural Sciences, S-75007 Uppsala, Sweden

1 INTRODUCTION

In pigs, genetic polymorphism is known for some plasma proteins viz. alkaline phosphatase, amylase I and II, ceruloplasmin, haemopexin, α-protease inhibitor 1 and 2, postalbumin 1 and 2, Sα_2-macroglobulin, transferrin and vitamin D binding protein - GC (1,2,3). Most of these proteins are phenotyped by using starch gel electrophoresis. GC variation was detected by using isoelectric focusing followed by autoradiography or immunofixation (3). We (2) reported a simple method of two dimensional (2-D) electrophoresis which resulted in improved separation of postalbumins and genetic polymorphism of postalbumin-2 (PO-2) was detected. The PO-2 variants have extremely valuable application in practical pig breeding as the *Po-2* gene is closely linked to *Hal*, the gene determining sensitivity to halothane (susceptibility to malignant hyperthermia) in pigs (2,4). The purpose of the present report is to describe and to illustrate the use of two simple methods of 2-D electrophoresis for improved and highly reproducible separation of plasma proteins with respect to studies of genetic polymorphisms.

2 MATERIALS AND METHODS

Heparinized plasma samples were obtained from about 100 complete families of pigs belonging to Swedish Landrace and Yorkshire breeds. These were analyzed by 2-D horizontal gel electrophoresis. The first dimension separation was done either with agarose gel electrophoresis or with isoelectric focusing in immobilised pH gradients. In the agarose gel electrophoresis (5), a continous buffer system with 0.05 M sodium acetate-EDTA pH 5.4 was used. The gel size was 220 x 220 x 1.2 mm. Sixty samples with bromophenol blue added were applied (7 µl each) in 4 rows on the surface of each gel (15 samples in each row and the rows being 2 cm apart from each other). The albumin zone was run up to 1.5 cm from the origin (running time - 1 h). Then the agarose strips (each 80 x 4 mm and containing 4 sample tracks - one sample from each row) were cut and used directly for the second dimension separation.

The polyacrylamide gels with immobilised pH gradients 4.0 - 6.0 were cast with Immobilines from LKB (Sweden) on hydrophilic plastic sheets (SERVA) according to the LKB application notes 321 and 322. The gel size was 180 x 115 x 0.5 mm with 18 gel pockets of the size 10 x 3 x 0.2 mm. The gels were washed and prefocused before plasma samples (18 μl) were pipetted into each pocket. Focusing with the power set at 5 W, the voltage at 3000 V and the current at 5 mA was performed for 5 h. The gels were stained in 0.1 % bromophenol blue in H_2O for 30 min and then washed shortly in H_2O. Gel strips were cut away with scissors.

The second dimension horizontal electrophoresis was done in polyacrylamide gels (260 x 220 x 1.2 mm) consisting of three layers of acrylamide concentration of 8, 4 and 12 % and of length 20, 40 and 160 mm respectively (6). The gel buffer was tris-citrate, pH 9.0 (0.1875 M in 12 % layer and 0.093 M in 4 and 8 % layers) and the electrode buffer was 0.065 M tris-borate, pH 9.0. Three agarose strips (total 12 samples) or three Immobiline gel stripes were applied on the surface of the 4 % gel layer of the polyacrylamide gel. The strips were removed after 15 - 25 min of electrophoresis when the borate boundary had reached near the agarose strips or just passed through the Immobiline gel strips. The run was stopped when the albumin zone had migrated 9 - 10 cm in the 12 % gel (running time - about 3 h). The gels were stained with Coomassie Blue G250 in 3.5 % perchloric acid solution (30 min), destained in 5 % acetic acid (30 min) and then vacuum-packed each in a transparant plastic bag for reading and storage.

3 RESULTS

Each of the two methods of 2-D electrophoresis used enable simultaneous typing of the genetic variants of the following proteins: α_1-protease inhibitor (PI-1, 2 alleles), postalbumin-1 (PO-1, 13 alleles), postalbumin-2 (PO-2, 2 alleles) and protease inhibitor-2 (PI-2, 5 alleles). In addition transferrin (TF, 2 alleles) and ceruloplasmin (CP, 2 alleles) were possible to type when agarose was used in the first dimension, and the vitamin D inding protein (GC, 2 alleles) when Immobiline gels were used. The 2-D protein patterns of some of the variants are demonstrated in Fig. 1.

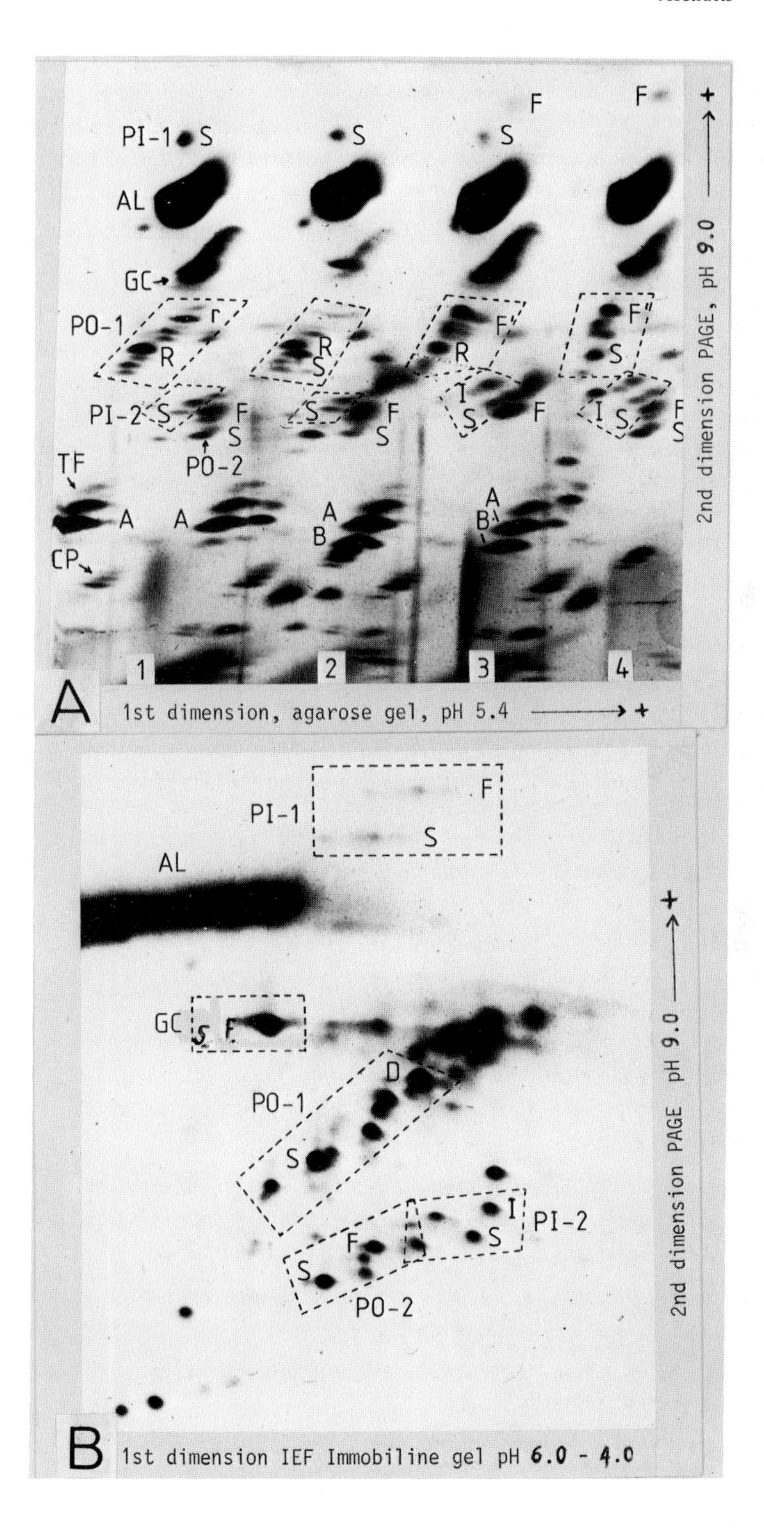

PI-1
S
F
AL
GC
PO-1
R
PI-2
PO-2
TF
A
B
CP
I
1
2
3
4
A
1st dimension, agarose gel, pH 5.4
2nd dimension PAGE, pH 9.0
D
B
1st dimension IEF Immobiline gel pH 6.0 - 4.0
2nd dimension PAGE pH 9.0

Figure 1. 2-D patterns of some pig plasma proteins using agarose gel electrophoresis pH 5.4 (A) and Immobiline isoelectric focusing pH 4.0 -6.0 (B) for the first dimension separation. Four samples are shown in (A) and one in (B). The symbols used are: AL, albumin; PI, protease inhibitor; PO, postalbumin; GC, vitamin D binding protein; TF, transferrin; CP, ceruloplasmin. The allelic variants of each protein are also marked.

The PO-1, PO-2 and PI-2 variants are separated from each other much more by using Immobiline gels than by using agarose gel electrophoresis. However, the 2-D agarose-polyacrylamide gel method is excellent for large scale screening of samples for typing of protein variants as it is cheap, extremely easy and rapid.

Each of the two PI-1 variants had 5 fractions in a row. The PI-2 variants gave 2 major fractions each. The PO-1 fractions occurred as groups of 4 fractions each (1 major and 3 minor). Most of the PO-1 variants showed one group of strong fractions and one group of weak fractions. A few PO-1 variants showed 2 groups of strong fractions. Further work is needed to determine if these extra fractions are due to duplication of the *Po-1* locus in some of the chromosomes or due to formation of complexes or breakdown products.

The family data clearly showed co-segregation of the alleles of PI-1, PO-1 and PI-2 systems and thus close genetic linkage between these systems is established. All tne animals studied showed at least one variant each of PI-1,PO-1 and PI-2. Further several animals were homozygous for the one system while they were heterozygous for the other systems. Our preliminary results indicate also the occurrence of recombination between *Pi-1* and *Po-1*, *Pi-2* loci in about 5 offspring.

4 REFERENCES

(1) L. Ollivier, P. Sellier, Ann. Génét. Sél. Anim. 14 (1982) 481-544.

(2) R. K. Juneja, B. Gahne, I. Edfors-Lilja, E. Andresen, Anim. Blood Grps biochem. Genet. 14 (1983) 27-36.

(3) L. Ljungqvist, J. Hyldgaard-Jensen, Anim. Blood Grps biochem. Genet. 14 (1983) 293-298.

(4) B. Gahne, R. K. Juneja, H. Petersson in Proceedings of the 5th Int. Conf. on Production Disease in Farm Animals, Swedish University of Agricultural Sciences, Uppsala, Sweden (1983) pp. 100-103.

(5) R. K. Juneja, B. Gahne, K. Sandberg, Anim. Blood Grps biochem. Genet. 10 (1979) 235-251.

(6) B. Gahne, R. K. Juneja, J. Grolmus, Anim. Blood Grps biochem. Genet. 8 (1977) 127-137.

IDENTIFICATION AND QUANTIFICATION OF HUMAN PLASMA LIPOPROTEINS BY LINE CROSSED IMMUNOELECTROPHORESIS(WITHOUT PRELIMINARY ULTRACENTRIFUGATIVE SEPARATION).

Quoc Quan Dang*, Rita Camaré**, Philippe Douste-Blazy***

* INSERM, U. 101, ** Biochimie I, *** Clinique Cardiologique, CHU Purpan, 31059 - Toulouse Cédex - France.

1 INTRODUCTION

Atherosclerosis and C.H.D (coronary-heart diseases)risks are highly correlated with the lipoprotein profile. (1, 2). In clinical analysis,usually the plasma cholesterol, triglycerides, are determined, then lipoprotein electrophoresis is carried out on paper or cellulose acetate (1), or on polyacrylamide discontinuous gradient (3, 4). For the phenotyping of the hyperlipoproteinemias, often complementary VLDL, LDL and HDL-cholesterol determinations are carried out after centrifugation and precipitation (4) and apo B and apo A are determined using immunoelectrophoresis with monospecific antibodies usually anti apo A and anti apo B (5). However, the PA electrophoreis of total plasma gives only qualitative results and the immunoelectrophoresis gives only the total apoprotein levels without insight into their distribution among the different subclasses. We describe here a crossed immunoelectrophoresis procedure allowing both the identification and the quantification of the plasma lipoproteins.

2 IMMUNOELECTROPHORESIS PROCEDURE

A first separation of the lipoproteins from human plasma was carried out by us on Sebia lipofilms, discontinuous polyacrylamide concentration gradient (2 % and 3 % PA) according to (3). Parallel migration was carried out both with Sudan black prestaining, as reference, or without it for subsequent second electrophoresis : four hours at 15 v/cm of gel and at 15°C on LKB multiphor electrophoresis cell, in a pH 8.6 barbituric buffer.

The second dimension electrophoresis (immunoelectrophoresis) was carried out essentially according to Kröll (6). The electrophoresis plate was divided into two parts, the first one (about 1/3) was covered with antibody-free agarose-gel; in this part a trench (5 x 60 mm) was digged out and filled with 600 µl of 1 % agarose solution containing 35 µl standard reference apo (Immuno) titrated in Apo B and Apo A, the second part (2/3) was covered with 10 ml agarose gel containing 200 µl of polyspecific antiserum (Behring) giving 2 mm thickness.

The migration band from the 1st dimension electrophoresis was cut offwith scissors and layed on the antibody free part of the 2nd gel between the trench and the cathode. The 2nd dimension electrophoresis was run at 1.2 v/cm gel for 20 hours using the usual pH 8.6 barbital buffer.

The gels were washed, dried according to the Biorad procedure, and stained using Sudan Black for two hours (Behring procedure). Only lipoprotein immunoprecipitation lines appeared : rockets (due to the plasma sample of 1st dimension) linked with the "platforms (horizontal lines due to the reference standard serum). Comparaison with an line immunoelectrophoresis of the reference standard plasma alone allowed identification of the nature of the apoprotein (B or A). The abscissas of the rockets corresponded to the lines of the first dimension band (Sudan Black prestained), and gave the nature of the different apo B containing lipoprotein subclasses : VLDL, LDL, Lp(a)... or of the apo A containing lipoprotein HDL. The areas under the rockets, compared to the areas under the "platforms" allowed a quantitative evaluation of the apoproteins of the different lipoproteins subclasses (6).

3 CONCLUSION

In conclusion, the modified crossed line immunoelectrophoresis with intermediate gel described above allows both the identification and the quantification of the whole human plasma lipoproteins without preliminary time consuming ultracentifugative separation. This new method gives on one plate the lipoprotein profile, and does not require either high cost apparatus or nonospecific antibodies.

The authors are grateful to Prof. G.M. Kostner (Graz, Austria) and Dr G. Peltre (Institut Pasteur, Paris, for fruitful discussion.

4 REFERENCES

(1) D.S. Fredrickson and R.S. Lees, Circulation, 31 (1965) 321-327.

(2) P. Alaupovic, Ann. Biol. Clin., 38 (1980) 83-93.

(3) C. Fievet-Desrumeaux et al., Clin. Chim. Acta, 95 (1975) 405-408.

(4) J.C. Fruchart and G. Sezille, Lipides et lipoproteines, Ed. Boehringer, 1979.

(5) J.C. Fruchart et al., Clin. Chem. 28/1 (1982), 59-62.

(6) J. Kröll, Crossed Line Immunoelectrophoresis in N.H. Axelsen et al., Quantitative Immunoelectrophoresis, Methods and Applications, Universitetsforlaget, Oslo, 1973.

SPONTANEOUS ENZYMATIC DEGRADATION OF IgD MYELOMA PROTEIN DEMONSTRATED BY TWO-DIMENSIONAL IMMUNOELECTROPHORESIS

Hocine Rabhi, Mohamed Ghaffor, Mohamed-Cherif Abbadi

Laboratory of immunochemistry. Pasteur Institute of Algeria. Algiers. Algeria.

M-component of beta mobility was detected in serum and concentrated urine of patient with clinical, haematologic and radiologic features of multiple myeloma. When analyzed by routine agar-gel immunoelectrophoresis, it reacted with anti-IgD antiserum but showed not convincing precipitation with anti-Kappa or anti-Lambda antisera. Similar negative precipitation with anti-Light chain antisera was noted using sensitive cellulose acetate-immunofixation procedure (1). Furthermore, both serum and urinary M-components gave abnormally heterogeneous precipitin lines with anti-delta antibodies. Although IgD myeloma proteins can bear "unreactive" light-chains (2) or show spontaneous enzymatic cleavage (3), it became necessary to rule-out the presence of true free H-chains as previously described in a case of delta-chain disease (4).

Rocket-immunoselection technique (5) using anti-Kappa and Lambda antiserum (6) revealed molecules bearing delta-chain specific but no light chain-specific antigenic determinants. A such result strongly suggested a pattern of delta chain disease.

However, two-dimensional immunoelectrophoresis (7) demonstrated the presence of two populations of molecules bearing delta chain determinants. The slowly migrating molecules were retained if not precipitated by anti-Kappa and Lambda light chain antiserum during the first electrophoretic run. They probably correspond to Fab fragments generated by enzymatic cleavage of complete IgD myeloma protein. The electrophoretic heterogeneity of Fc fragments could be due to multisite enzymatic degradation (3). It appeared from this study that degradative process of susceptible IgD myeloma protein resulted in pattern suggestive of delta disease.

REFERENCES

1. J. Kohn, P.G. Riches. J. Immunol. Meth. 20 (1978) 325-331.

2. J. Cejka, K. Kithier. Clin. Chem. 25 (1979) 1495-1498.

3. S.M. Goyert, T.E. Hugli, H.L. Spiegelberg. J. Immunol. 118 (1977) 2138-2144.

4. J.A. Vilpo, K. Irjala, M.K. Viljanen, P. Klemi, I. Kouvomen, T. Ronnemaa. Clin. Immunol. Immunopathol. 17 (1980) 584-594.

5. D.S.J. Gale, J.M.B. Versey, J.R. Hobbs. Clin. Chem. 20 (1974) 1292-1294.

6. H. Rabhi, M. Ghaffor, M.C. Abbadi. Arch. Inst. Pasteur. 54 (1983) in press.

7. A.O. Grubb. Scand. J. Immunol. 17, suppl. 10 (1983) 113-124.

IDENTIFICATION OF NERVOUS SYSTEM SPECIFIC PROTEIN, PGP 9.5, IN HUMAN NEUROBLASTOMA AND ASTROCYTOMA CELL LINES USING IMMUNOBLOTTING OF FIXED AND STAINED TWO-DIMENSIONAL POLYACRYLAMIDE GELS.

Peter Jackson, Lena Elfman, Michaela R. Torrance and R.J. Thompson.

Department of Clinical Biochemistry, School of Clinical Medicine, University of Cambridge, Addenbrooke's Hospital, Hills Road, Cambridge CB2 2QR, U.K.

1 INTRODUCTION

We have previously shown that fixed and stained two-dimensional polyacrylamide gels (2D-PAG's) can be blotted so that the Coomassie blue stain pattern is accurately transferred onto nitrocellulose coincident with the polypeptides. Anti-sera raised against specific purified polypeptides can be used to visualise cross-reacting polypeptides on a blot, using horseradish peroxidase coupled to a second antibody as the detection system. The brown peroxidase reaction product is deposited on top of the Coomassie blue spots and can be distinguished from non-reacting spots by use of a suitable filter (1)

We have used this method to precisely identify, in human neuroblastoma and astrocytoma cell lines, Coomassie blue stained spots on 2D-PAG's which cross-react with antisera raised against a nervous system specific polypeptide, protein gene product 9.5 (PGP 9.5), previously isolated from human brain (2).

2 MATERIALS AND METHODS

2.1 Cell Cultures.

The human glioma 138MG (3) and the human neuroblastoma TR14 (4) cell lines were grown in HAM-F10 and Dulbecco's modified Eagle's medium (1:1) containing 10% newborn calf serum and 2.5% fetal calf serum. Subcloning of the cells was performed by incubating in phosphate buffered saline (PBS), pH 7.5, containing 0.5 mM EDTA. The cells were then washed in medium and plated in Nunclon tissue culture flasks at a density of 10-20,000/cells/cm^2. Depending on the cell line, the cultures reached confluency after four to six days after plating at which time the cell growth was terminated. The cells were washed three times in PBS and harvested by incubation in solubilising solution (5) for 2h at room temperature. The protein extracts were kept at -20°C until use. The protein concentration was measured by the method of Lowry (6).

2.2 Electrophoresis and Immunoblotting

For electrophoresis, the cell line protein was precipitated from a suitable volume of harvested cell solution using 100 g/l aqueous trichloracetic acid solution, the precipitate resuspended in 100 ml/l formic acid solution and extracted with ether to remove the acid. To the aqueous layer (200 μl) containing the suspended protein was added 20 μl of 0.1 M tris HCl pH 8.0 containing 50 mM calcium chloride, 50 mM magnesium chloride, 10 mM EDTA and 1 μg of bovine pancreatic ribonuclease type 1-A (Sigma Chemical Co.) and 1 μg of bovine pancreatic deoxyribonuclease I (Sigma Chemical Co.). The suspensions were incubated at 22°C for 1 h, freeze dried and dissolved in isoelectric focusing solubilising solution (5) (9 M urea, 40 ml/l nonidet P40 (Shell Chemical Co.,) 20 ml/l ampholyte pH range 3.5 - 10 (LKB), 50 ml/l mercaptoethanol).

The ISODALT system of two-dimensional polyacrylamide gel electrophoresis (2D-PAGE) was used (5). Focusing was for 10,000 V.h. and the pH range was about 4 to 7. The fixing, staining, destaining, immunoblotting and photography were as previously described (1).

3 RESULTS AND CONCLUSIONS

Fig. 1a - c shows those sections of the Coomassie blue stained 2D-PAG's of the neuroblastoma, astrocytoma and mixture of the two containing the spots cross-reacting with rabbit anti-serum to human PGP 9.5. The patterns are similar but with significant differences between the two cell lines. In Fig. 1 d - f are photographs of immunoblots generated from the fixed and stained gels shown in Fig. 1a - c. They show the relevant sections of the blots with the replicated patterns of Coomassie blue dye together with the brown peroxidase reaction product deposited at the three arrowed spots in each blot. Peroxidase stain was found in no other areas of the blots. Fig. 1g - i show the blots in Fig. 1d - f photographed through a Wratten 47B (Kodak) blue filter with high intensity illumination. The three peroxidase stained spots can be seen alone differentiated from the Coomassie stain by the blue filter.

These data show the presence of three polypeptides cross-reacting with rabbit-anti-human PGP 9.5 serum in both the neuroblastoma and the astrocytoma cell lines. The blots on the co-electrophoretograms (Fig.1f-i)

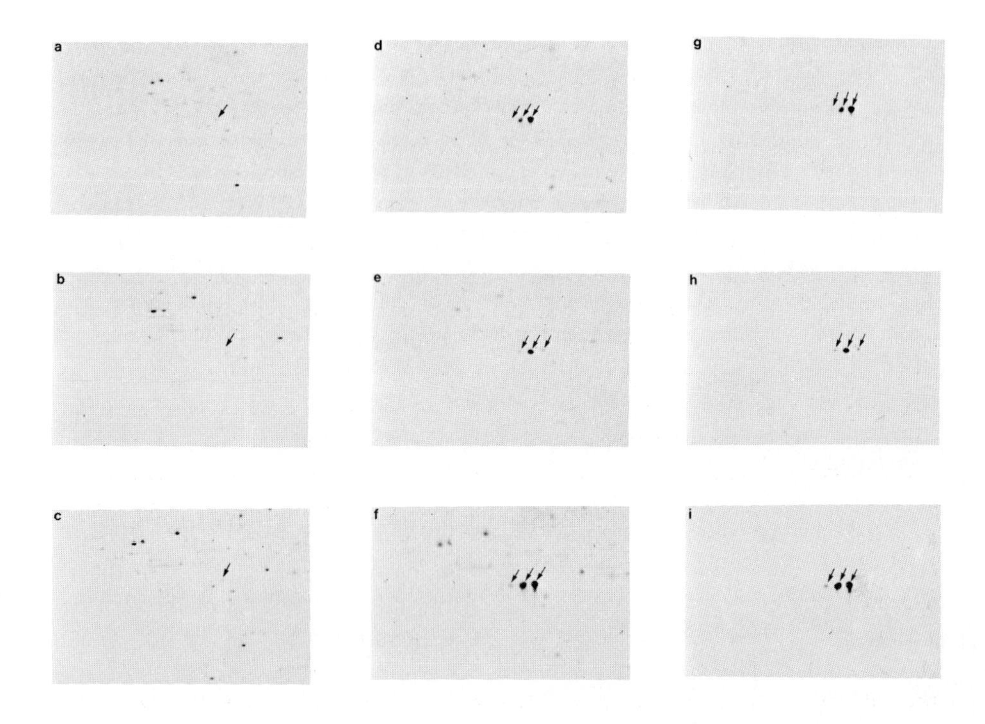

Figure 1. Photographs of the relevant sections of Coomassie blue stained gels and the blots generated from them.
Gels: (a) neuroblastoma (b) astrocytoma (c) neuroblastoma + astrocytoma
Blots: (d) neuroblastoma (e) astrocytoma (f) neuroblastoma + astrocytoma.
Blots photographed using a Wratten 47B filter: (g) neuroblastoma (h) astrocytoma (i) neuroblastoma + astrocytoma.
200 μg of protein from each sample was analysed on each gel. The acidic end of the first dimension is to the left and the pH range shown is approximately pH 4 to 5. Larger polypeptides are towards the top of the gels and the molecular mass range shown is about 30 KDa to 15 KDa. For an explanation of the arrows please see the text.

also show only three spots, which indicates that identical cross-reacting polypeptides are present in both cell lines. However, the intensity of the peroxidase reaction product differs, the most basic spot having the highest intensity in the neuroblastoma (Fig. 1g) and the central spot in the astrocytoma (Fig. 1h). These most intensely peroxidase staining spots can also be identified on the original gels and are marked with an arrow in Fig. 1a - c. The lesser peroxidase stained spots are below the level of detection by Coomassie blue staining.

All three spots have the same molecular mass of approximately 25 kDa and it is possible that these arise from a single polypeptide which is post-translationally modified. Alternatively each spot could be a single PGP. We have previously shown by immunohistochemical localisation in sectional tissue that PGP 9.5 occurs in neurones and APUD cells but not in glial cells (2,7). The finding of this protein in this astrocytoma cell line might depend on the fact that this cell line arose from a tumour and could have differentiated from normal astrocytes in such a way that PGP 9.5 is now expressed.

This work was supported by a grant from the MRC to R.J.T.

4 REFERENCES

(1) P. Jackson, R.J. Thompson, Electrophoresis 5 (1984) 35-42.

(2) J.F. Doran, P. Jackson, P.A.M. Kynoch, R.J. Thompson, J.Neurochem. 40 (1983) 1542-1547.

(3) J. Pontén, E.H. MacIntyre, Acta Pathol Microbiol. Scand. 74 (1968) 465-486.

(4) H.T. Rupniak, B.T. Hill, J.T. Kemstead, P.M. Warne, D.C. Bicknell, G. Rein, J. Pritchard, Second Int. Congress on Cell Biology, W. Germany (1980) p409.

(5) P. Jackson, R.J. Thompson, J. Neurol. Sci. 49 (1981) 429-438.

(6) O.H. Lowry, N.J. Rosebrough, A.L. Farr, R.J. Randall, J.Biol.Chem. 193 (1951) 265-275.

(7) R.J. Thompson, J.F. Doran, P. Jackson, A.P. Dhillon, J. Rode, Brain Res. 278 (1983) 224-228.

MICROCOMPUTER CONTROLLED 2-D DENSITOMETER FOR QUANTITATIVE 2-D PAGE

R. Amess, R. Ramasamy, S.P. Spragg

Department of Chemistry, University of Birmingham, Edgbaston, Birmingham, B15 2TT, England.

1 INTRODUCTION

A system has been developed for the quantative analysis of two-dimensional polyacrylamide gel electrophoresis (2-D PAGE) gels. This is suitable for direct measurement of 'wet' gels stained with either Coomassie Blue or silver, as well as autoradiographs. The system comprises a microcomputer controlled two-dimensional densitometer. A portion of a gel may be scanned and digitised for storage on a disk. The data may be examined later, using a graphics display. Individual, protein components may be analysed for total absorbance and hence relative amounts of proteins may be obtained. The system is easily adaptable to the analysis of one-dimensional gels.

2 DESCRIPTION AND SPECIFICATIONS

2.1 Densitometer

The light source and scanning device used is an oscilloscope (Hewlett Packard 1332A), this provides a spot of light, the position and intensity of which are controlled by a microcomputer. A combination of lenses and mirrors direct the light, first to a half-silvered mirror where a double beam is produced. A reference photo-multiplier measures the incident light, while a second, test photo-multiplier measures the light intensity after passing through the gel which is situated at the focal plane. Both photomultipliers are positioned at equal distances from the light source and at a point conjugate with the source. A log-amplifier and an analogue-digital converter contained within the interface are used to obtain an absorbance value in the range 0-2, directly and uninfluenced by variations in the incident light or detection performance.

2.2 Data collection

A small microcomputer (BBC Model 'B' Microcomputer fitted with a disk interface and a Cumana disk-drive) is used as a terminal for a larger microcomputer (Comart Communicator CP/M86 16-bit fitted with 8087 co-processor). A terminal emulator programme serves to link the two microcomputers (1). An assembly language programme controls the movement and intensity of the spot of light via a dedicated interface. The spot may be moved to any one of 256x256 positions on the oscilloscope. Currently, a maximum of 128x128 data points may be recorded, each at one of 256 grey-levels. The portion of the gel to be scanned is aligned manually and a choice of one of two lenses and various increment distances between readings is made. The measured data are stored in a sequential file on a disk, together with the identity and chosen limits for the scan.

2.3 Specifications

The size of the spot produced by the oscilloscope is <0.3mm this is reduced to <0.15mm or <0.2mm by 200mm and 150mm focal length lenses, respectively. Minimum distances between successive readings are <0.22mm and <0.3mm, respectively. The time required to collect 128x128 data points is only about 2 min. with each recorded value being the average of 16 readings taken at that point. Absorbance measured is linear up to at least 2.0 optical density units.

3 PRESENTATION OF DATA

3.1 General

The system is supported by a comprehensive interactive fortran programme for displaying the data and extracting information for quantitative evaluation of 2-D PAGE gels. The eight-colour graphics system of the BBC Microcomputer is utilized to display gel patterns on a RGB monitor (CUB Microvitec Model 1451/MS4).

3.2 Interactive display

The programme includes an index of file names relating to individual scans which may be set up at the beginning of a work session and changed later or output to the printer at any stage. The data from a scan may then be 'read-in' by selection of the appropriate index number.

One or two gels may be plotted on the monitor screen using the eight colours to represent eight grey levels; each representing one eighth of the maximum optical density for the scan. Using the cursor to pin-point a single pixel in the displayed gel, an enlarged cross-sectional view of the gel at that point can be drawn on the screen showing the variation in optical density. This may be either +/-8 or +/-16 data points. The picture area around the pixel may be duplicated alongside the cross-sectional view. Again, using the cursor, limits may be defined on the cross-sectional view to isolate peaks describing a spot. The absorbances within the total area of a spot may then be integrated using these limits. The integrated spot may also be plotted on a blank position at one side of the display and used as a progress record. The local background can now be subtracted at this stage by taking the average of four points at quadrants outside of the spot as the mean background optical density per unit area.

3.3 Image enhancement

A Fourier transform subroutine is included for the removal of noise (high frequency) and background absorbance (low frequency). This involves changing the raw data from the time domain in which it was collected to the frequency domain and applying a digital filter. The use of a simple orthogonal filter based on a Legendre polynomial (2) enables removal of noise in the time domain which is relatively fast compared with that in the frequency domain. A combination of one of the above techniques with a histogram equalization subroutine, in which the probability distribution of the seven highest order colours used in the display are equalized, is most effective for enhanced visualization of the graphically displayed data. For a detailed coverage on this type of numerical operation see Gonzalez and Wintz (3).

3.4 Hard copy

A copy of the screen output may be obtained from the printer (Epson MX-80 F/T III) via a 'screen-dump' facility which is an integral part of the terminal emulator programme. This is quick to produce and is useful for reference and note-making (i.e. 'scribbling on'). A more permanent hard copy may be obtained from a flat-bed multi-pen plotter (C.Itoh CX-6000). A choice of formats is available from two eight colour plots, 'filled-in' or contour, and two profile plots, oblique or isometric.

4 FURTHER POINTS

4.1 Densitometer

The use of neutral filters placed in front of the reference photomultiplier to reduce the amount of incident light measured enables the detectable absorbance range to be extended to between 1.0 and 3.0 optical density units. This is useful for gels with a high background where major spots exceed the normal optical density range.

4.2 Display system

Features of the terminal emulator programme (1) include the following: software hand-shaking; disk-file reading and writing for storage of events as they occur on the screen; printer toggle; page-mode toggle; change to mode 3 with green text; screen-dump with colour toning; baud rate and framing selection; exit terminal programme to return to BBC BASIC; listing of current definitions of function keys; define function keys; help message; line to BBC OS; control of cursor speed in graphics mode.

5 REFERENCES

(1) J. Campbell, J.M. Nelson, Department of Physics, University of Birmingham, England.

(2) W.D. Milne, 'Numerical calculus', Princeton University Press, Princeton, New Jersey 1949.

(3) R.C. Gonzalez, P. Wintz, 'Digital image processing', Addison-Wesley Publishing Company, Massachusetts 1977.

QUANTITATIVE ANALYSIS OF TWO-DIMENSIONAL ELECTROPHORETIC PROTEIN PATTERNS: COMPARISON OF VISUAL EVALUATION WITH COMPUTER-ASSISTED EVALUATION

Peter Jungblut, Werner Schneider, Joachim Klose

Institut für Toxikologie und Embryonalpharmakologie, Freie Universität Berlin, 1000 Berlin 33, FRG

1 INTRODUCTION

The evaluation of two-dimensional electrophoresis (2DE) patterns of proteins includes the detection of qualitative (changes in spot position) and quantitative (changes in spot intensity) differences between the patterns compared. A quantification of differences in spot intensity requires the measurement of the intensity of each spot with the help of a densitometer. In many cases, however, the simple visual observation that one spot is considerably "darker" than the corresponding spot may offer enough information for the investigation of a certain problem. For example, certain diseases or distinct genotypes of an individual or inbred strain are correlated with drastic alterations in the quantity of one or several proteins. Therefore we postulate that visual evaluation is sufficient for investigations for which drastic differences in protein amount are expected. To verify this postulate we investigated to what extent the eye is able to distinguish the intensity of two spots.

2 TWO-DIMENSIONAL ELECTROPHORESIS (2DE)

2DE was performed according to the method described by Klose and Feller (1). The proteins were stained with Serva blue R 250. Two sets of protein patterns were produced: 1) Single-spot pattern: Carboanhydrase (Serva, Heidelberg, FRG) was used as a model protein. 26 samples with different protein amount between 0,5 and 7,5 µg carboanhydrase were subjected to 2DE. 26 patterns each showing a single spot of defined intensity were obtained. 2) Multi-spot pattern: Complex protein samples from human fibroblasts of different individuals were separated by 2DE. The patterns consisted of several hundreds of spots.

3 COMPUTER-ASSISTED EVALUATION

We used the HTU C 1000-01 camera system (Hamamatsu TU Co., Ltd. 1126, Ichonocho, Japan) to get quantified intensities of the spots investigated. The camera was combined with a PDP 11/34A computer (Digital Equipment Co., Maynard, MA 01754) as described by Schneider and Klose (2).

Each spot of interest was surrounded individually on a monitor to get the precise spot area. The intensity (spot volume) was determined as sum of all digitized grey values within the measured spot area. The background volume was substracted. The spot volume increased linear with protein amount in the range 0.5 - 7.5 µg protein.

4 VISUAL EVALUATION

Four experienced and six unexperienced persons evaluated spots with known spot intensity. In single-spot patterns and multi-spot patterns all persons had to determine the differences only taking into account spot area and intensity. Then the experienced persons were to decide if they could accept the differences found in the multi-spot patterns taking into account the neighbour spots of the compared spots.

5 COMPARISON OF COMPUTER-ASSISTED WITH VISUAL EVALUATION

5.1 Single -spot patterns

13 pairs of carboanhydrase spots were compared in a lower (0.5 - 1.1 µg) and a higher range (3.2 - 5.6 µg) with differences between 0 and 50% (related to the upper value, upper value = 100%). In the lower range experienced persons took no wrong decisions down to 7% intensity difference. Down to 4% three wrong decisions resulted out of 48 decisions. Unexperienced persons came to 4 wrong decisions out of 72 decisions, whereby these wrong decisions were distributed in the range from 4 to 35%.

The higher range (3.2 - 5.6 µg) was more difficult to evaluate. Down to 18% two wrong decisions were made by experienced persons (20 decisions) and two wrong decisions by unexperienced persons (30 decisions). From 18% - 3% difference the experienced persons came to 22 wrong decisions out of 32 decisions. The unexperienced persons made 30 wrong decisions out of 48 decisions.

Therefore, reliable results from visual evaluation can be obtained down to 4% difference for the low intensity range and down to 18% difference for the high intensity range.

5.2 Multi-spot patterns

The patterns were grouped in pairs. 11 spot pairs were selected for comparison. The intensity of these spots was measured with the video densitometer. All spots selected were in the low intensity range (s. above).

By comparing spots in a complex protein pattern the difficulty arises that the surrounding spots may render the decision more difficult. Therefore we first tried to exclude this problem by asking only for differences not taking into account the neighbour spots. For 11 spots between 0 and 81% of difference, 84% of the decisions were correct (96% experienced persons, 74% unexperienced persons).

The correction of spot intensity in relation to a group of neighbour spots is the most relevant way for evaluating 2DE patterns quantitativly. The values obtained by computer assisted gel evaluation may be corrected by division of the absolute measured value of the spot through the sum of 5-10 neighbour spots. On the other hand, visual correction is difficult. Considering the surroundings 85% of the spot differences with differences above 45% were accepted. 25% were accepted in the range between 28 and 45%. Below 28% no difference was accepted.

For investigations restricted to the evaluation of drastic differences the visual evaluation shows sufficient reliable results for differences above 45%. To establish differences between 30 and 45% the evaluation of 5 - 10 gel pairs and by more than one person is necessary (experiments not mentioned above).

6 References

(1) J. Klose, M. Feller, Electrophoresis 2 (1981) 12-24.

(2) W. Schneider, J. Klose, Electrophoresis 4 (1983) 284-291.

EVALUATION OF PHEROGRAMS FROM MICROGELS BY DIGITAL SIGNAL PROCESSING

Klaus B. Mross, Dirk-Ingo Wolfrum

Medical Clinic University Göttingen Robert-Koch-Str.40, D-3400 Göttingen, FRG

1 INTRODUCTION

Analytical microgel-electrophoresis (micro-PAGE), developed by NEUHOFF (1), has proved to be an excellent method for the separation,qualification and quantification of proteins of biochemical interest (2).The micro-PAGE technique has been applied sucessfully in research (3) as well as in clinical evaluations (4).Protein amounts in the ng-range (comassie blue staining) or in the pg-range (silver staining) can be analysed with this technique.Molecular weight determinations from 10^5 - 10^7 Dalton are possible in gradient gels (5) as well as isoelectric point determinations from pH 2 - 11 (6). Semiquantitative evaluations of protein bands can be made by determination of the peak area (8).Limitations resulted because of different staining possibilities for staining of proteins depends on the structure,the molecular weight,the amount of protein and the dye-stuff (7).Estimation of MW,IEP,peak area,peak identification from proteins by densitometry and data processing with computer equipment is described.

2 METHODS

2.1.Microgel-electrophoresis

The technique is described extensive by RÜCHEL et al.(2) and WOLFRUM et al.(9) and NEUHOFF (1).The equipment for micro-PAGE is described by MROSS & WOLFRUM (10).

2.2. Densitometry

The evaluation of microgels has been tested using a double-beam recording microdensitometer 3CS from Joyce,Loeble & Co.LTD interfaced to a Tektronix 4051 grafic computer system.

2.3.Further equipment

The analog signals from the potentiometer coupled to the wedged gray filter of the densitometer are used for transformation into digital signals.This A/D converter was specially built for our system configuration.The grafic computer TEK 4051 has an effective capacity of 32 kbyte memory with an in-built tape drive with 300 or 450 kbyte capacity.A printer plotter from Integral Data System IDS 460 is connected for data listings and a plotter from Tektronix TEK 4662 for high quality densitograms.The program works only in combination with some additionally ROM's (read only memory) as the signal processing no.1 4051 R07 and 4051 printer interface ROM from Tektronix.

Additionally a joy stick TEK 4952 for exact positioning the cursur on the screen is necessary. (complete system configuration in fig.1)

2.4.Software

The program for evaluation of densitograms included the display of the pherogram on to the screen,norming the scan to the greatest peak (=1),filtering for smoothing the scan as option,baseline correction by use of the joy stick for setting the baseline points for each individual scan as option,maxima identification as option,peak area estimation by integration of the peak areas after two-sided fit of half-Gaussian profiles as option,determination of isoelectric points (IEP marker must be added to the sample) by cubic spline fit as option and determination of molecular weights (MW marker must be added to the sample) by linear logarithmic regression analysis as option.

3 RESULTS

3.1.Normal densitogram

Fig.2 shows a normal scan uneffected by the program.The densitogram shows some 'jumps' because of the limited number of data (n = 600; maximum 1000).

3.2.Densitogram after filtering

Fig.3 shows the same plot as in fig.2 after filtering (2x).This was done by forming the arithmetic mean of two adjoining points.After this procedure the scan seems to be smooth.

3.3. Densitogram from the area of interest

Because the area of interest is between 200 and 600 (x-scale) it is possible to reduce the scan to those areas which are of specially interest.Fig.4 shows this.

3.4. Determination of the isoelectric points

For determinations of IEP's it is necessary to add markers with known IEP's to the sample.This was shown in fig.5.Six markers with arbitrary IEP's between 2 - 8 were added.Such peaks with known IEP were marked on the screen and the value was given to the computer.The fitted pH gradient in the plot was calculated by cubic spline fit.

3.5. Determination of melecular weights

For determinations of the MW's of proteins it is necessary to add markers with known

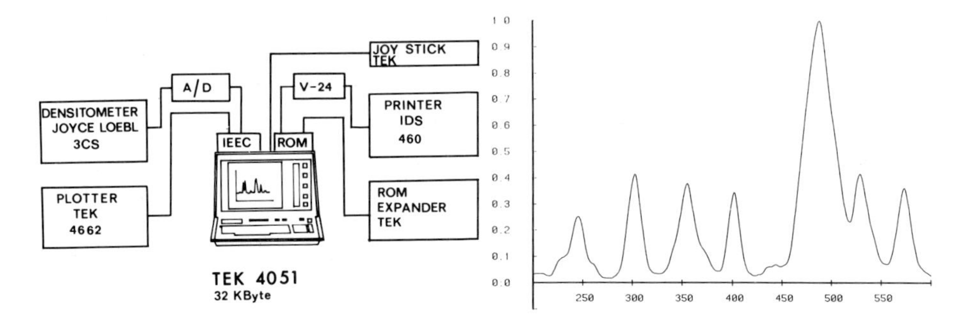

Fig.1: complete system configuration

Fig.4: 'zooming' of the area of interest

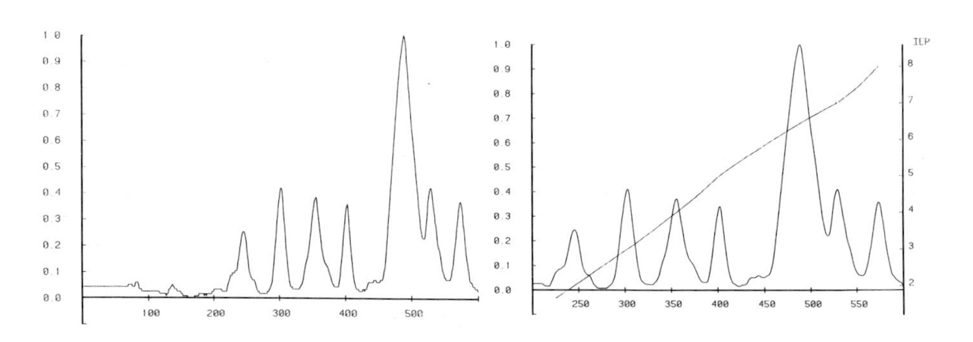

Fig.2: normal densitogram uneffected by the program

Fig.5: IEP determination with fitted pH gradient (cubic spline fit)

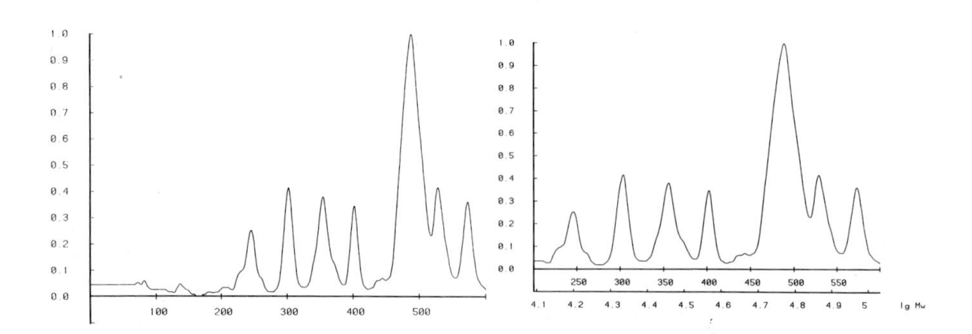

Fig.3: densitogram from fig.2 after using the filter (noise reduction) (2x)

Fig.6: MW determination with plotted molecular weights (log) (Dalton)

MW's to the sample.This was shown in fig.6.The procedure is the same as it is described in 3.4 .Because of the correlation between migration distance and molecular weight which are correlated by a logarithmic formula it is possible to define the MW in a satisfactory manner.The MW's of the added marker were given into the computer and from these data the MW's of the unknown protein bands were calculated by a linear logarithmic regression analysis.The calculated molecular weights are plotted into the densitogram as it is shown in the figure.

3.6. Molecular weight determinations (statistics)

Two series of MW determinations were performed with MW marker from Pharmacia.Five gels from one gel charge were run with the MW calibration kit.In a second series gels from five gels from different gel charges are used.The gels are running all at the same time in a 10-channel microgel power supply under identical conditions.The first series gives the following results listed in table 1, the second series is listed in table 2.

marker	1	MW	14400	VC	4,25%	SEM	0,60
"	2	"	20100	"	6,60%	"	0,58
"	3	"	30000	"	8,50%	"	0,83
"	4	"	45000	"	7,55%	"	1,40
"	5	"	67000	"	2,55%	"	0,35
"	6	"	94000	"	4,85%	"	0,69

Table 1:MW investigations with different gel charges

marker	1	MW	14400	VC	1,86%	SEM	0,21
"	2	"	20100	"	2,54%	"	0,21
"	3	"	30000	"	2,20%	"	0,19
"	4	"	45000	"	3,40%	"	0,59
"	5	"	67000	"	1,93%	"	0,26
"	6	"	94000	"	0,90%	"	0,10

Table 2: MW investigations with one gel charge

(VC = variation coefficient ; SEM = standard error of the mean)

4 DISCUSSION

In order to increase accuracy and precision of quantifying pherograms from microgels by digital signal processing, a software program was developed for use in experimental research laboratories.All gels used are stained with Coomassie Brilliant blue R-250 and scanned by a densitometer from Joyce-Loeble.600 measurement points are taken along the total length of about 18 mm.All steps of evaluating the pherogram took about 10 min. when all possibilities of the program are used.Most of the time will be needed by the section baseline correction,for this program segment is an interactive procedure, and the section peak area estimation with two-sided fit of half-Gaussian profiles.The last one will be used only if semi-quantitive analysis are necessary e.g. monitoring of degradation processes (3).Further tests have revealed that composite bands of up to three components are accurately fitted.Best results are obtained by carefully use of the baseline correction and symmetric peaks.Determinations of molecular weights are satisfactory when gels from one charge will be used,because the gradient gels should be nearly identical in their separation characteristic.The combination of a new developed 10-channel microgel-power-supply and a gradient mixer for production of microgels with nearly identical gradients (one gelcharge contains 100 - 200 gels) with this program for evaluation of densitograms from microgels seems to be a very attractive analytical method in biological research (10).

ACKNOWLEDGEMENT

We have to thank T.Simon (Dep.Clinical Chemistry) for the development of the A/D converter,Dr.D.Otten (Inst.of Physics) for much work on the computer and Prof.Söling (Dep.Clinical Biochemistry) for the disposition of the Joyce Loeble densitometer. This work was supported by grants of the Federal Ministry for Research and Technology (BMFT) 01 VH088-ZA/NT/MT 225a.

5 LITERATURE

(1) V.Neuhoff,Mitt.Dtsch.Pharmaz.Ges.40 (1970) 289 - 314

(2) R.Rüchel,S.Mesecke,D.I.Wolfrum,V.Neuhoff,Hoppe-Seyler's Z.Physiol.Chem. 354 (1973) 1351 - 1368

(3) B.Mross,K.Mross,D.I.Wolfrum,Cell electrophoresis in cancer and other clinical research Elsevier North-Holland (1981) 157 - 162

(4) J.M.Alt,M.Hacke,D.von der Heyde,H.Jänig,P.M.Junge,C.Olbricht,H.Schurek,H.Stolte, Klin.Wschr. 61 (1983) 641 - 648

(5) R.Rüchel,S.Mesecke,D.I.Wolfrum,V.Neuhoff,Hoppe-Seyler's Z.Physiol.Chem. 355 (1974) 997 - 1020

(6) G.Bispink,V.Neuhoff,Hoppe-Seyler's Z.Physiol.Chem. 357 (1976) 991 - 997

(7) M.H.Weber,T.Bittner,F.Scheler,Lab.Med. 7 (1983) 155 - 163

(8) H.Yakin,H.Kronberg,H.Zimmer,V.Neuhoff, Electrophoresis 3 (1982) 244 - 254

(9) D.I.Wolfrum,R.Rüchel,S.Mesecke,V.Neuhoff,Hoppe-Seyler's Z.Physiol.Chem, 355 (1974) 1415 - 1435

(10) K.Mross,D.I.Wolfrum,elektrophorese forum '83 Technische Universität München (1983) 158 - 163

The algorithms are presented as BASIC-programs and can be easily adapted to individual equipment.The programs are availible on request.

A 'GELLAB' COMPUTER ASSISTED 2-D GEL ANALYSIS OF STATES OF DIFFERENTIATION IN HEMATOPOIETIC CELLS

Eric P. Lester and Peter F. Lemkin*

Department of Medicine, University of Chicago, Chicago, IL, USA 60637 and *Image Processing Section, National Cancer Institute, Bethesda, MD, USA, 20205

1 INTRODUCTION

We have used a relatively global approach to the analysis of gene expression at the level of protein synthesis in an attempt to seek more meaningful classifications of human leukemias and a better understanding of their biology. The technique of two-dimensional polyacrylamide gel electrophoresis (2-D gels) allows us to examine the relative synthetic rates of up to 1000 of the major cellular proteins. The pattern of proteins displayed reflects both the underlying differentiation and the metabolic status of the leukemic cell population. From this pattern we are able to be able to subclassify human leukemias, both in terms of their differentiation and their state of growth, and to find sets of proteins whose genetic expression is regulated in common. Analysis of such data may permit a precise localization of blocks in the differentiation of leukemic cells.

2 METHODS

For these studies purified populations of cells have been biosynthetically pulse-labeled with [^{3}H]-leucine and cellular proteins have been subjected to 2-D gel electrophoresis and autoradiography (1, 2, 3). Each spot in the resulting pattern reflects the relative synthetic rate of a particular polypeptide during the labeling period. To quantitate and compare such images, we have developed the GELLAB computer system which is capable of accurately and automatically locating and quantifying over 90% of the spots in each image, comparing similar images, building a unified data base, and performing a variety of statistical analyses (4, 5, 6, 7).

3 RESULTS

Our initial studies characterized the sets of proteins whose relative synthetic rates are altered in normal lymphocytes during growth activation by lectins (1, 2). Subsequent work showed similar results in long-term human lymphoblastoid cell lines whose growth rates were modulated by varying culture durations. The synthetic rates of these proteins may serve as measures of the growth (cell cycle) status of leukemic cells. Additional work established that a GELLAB computerized analysis of 2-D gels could distinguish states of differentiation when a pair of autologous lymphoblastoid cell lines (T vs. B cell) were compared (3). Furthermore, differing pathways of myeloid differentiation (granulocytic vs. monocytic) during the induction of differentiation in the human promyelocytic cell line HL-60 may be defined using a GELLAB analysis of protein synthesis patterns (8). The identification of sets of proteins characterizing such differentiation is useful in the analysis of human leukemias (9).

Our most recent clinical data base contains 58 2-D gel images from leukemic cells from 26 patients (7 AML, 2 ALL, 5 CLL, and 12 HCL). Initial analysis suggests that approximately 10% of the proteins detected show significant qualitative or quantitative differences between these major classes of leukemia. The use of a correlation coefficient of the spot densities in each possible pair of gel images (a 'density/density' plot) provides a summary statistic expressing the overall relatedness of the various leukemic samples (9). Table 1 shows the average correlation coefficients obtained for the 3 major classes of samples.

Table 1. Average Correlation Coefficients of 2-D gel images of leukemic samples.

	AML	HCL	CLL
AML	.52	.42	.23
HCL	-	.68	.51
CLL	-	-	.87

The identification of individual proteins of particular interest in the 2-D gel studies permits the generation of monoclonal antibodies reactive with them (8). Such antibodies may then be used to explore the function of such proteins. Proteins showing increased relative synthetic rates in growth-activated normal cells show higher rates in most acute than in most chronic leukemias. The considerable variation in the 2-D gel patterns within each major category suggests that new and more meaningful subclassifications will be possible. Ultimately, correlation of genomic composition at the level of DNA (chromosomes) with genetic expression at the level of protein synthesis will be possible.

4 REFERENCES

(1) E. P. Lester, P. Lemkin, L. Lipkin, H. L. Cooper, J. Immunol. 126 (1981) 1428-1434.

(2) E. P. Lester, P. Lemkin, L. Lipkin, H. L. Cooper, Clin. Chem. 26 (1980) 1392-1402.

(3) E. P. Lester, P. Lemkin, L. Lipkin, Clin. Chem. 28 (1982) 828-839.

(4) P. Lemkin, L. Lipkin, Comput. Biomed. Res. 14 (1981) 272-297.

(5) P. Lemkin, L. Lipkin, Comput. Biomed. Res. 14 (1981), 355-380.

(6) P. Lemkin, L. Lipkin, Comput. Biomed. Res. 14 (1981), 407-446.

(7) P. Lemkin, L. E. Lipkin, E. P. Lester, Clin. Chem. 28 (1982) 820-849.

(8) E. P. Lester, P. Lemkin, L. Lipkin in J. E. Ultmann & J. Rowley (Ed.) Chromosomes and Cancer, Academic Press, New York, 1983, 225-245.

(9) E. P. Lester, P. F. Lemkin, J. F. Lowery, L. E. Lipkin, Electrophoresis 3 (1982) 364-375.

QUANTIATIVE MICRODENSITOMETRIC SCANNING OF FOOTPRINTING AUTORADIOGRAMS

Calvin Vary,* Michael J. Lane,* ** James C. Dabrowiak,** John N. Vournakis*

Departments of Biochemistry* and Chemistry,** Syracuse University, Syracuse, New York, 13210

1 INTRODUCTION

Recent advances in DNA sequencing technology and gel electrophoresis have made it possible to identify the binding sequences of anticancer drugs bound to heterogeneous DNA of defined sequence (1-3). For equilibrium binding drugs, quantitative footprinting analysis can be used to obtain kinetic and thermodynamic information as a function of sequence for a drug-DNA contact region. The footprinting method involves partial enzymatic digestion of a ^{32}P end labeled DNA restriction fragment in the presence and absence of a drug. The sites of drug induced enzymatic inhibition (the binding sites of the drug) are identified by analyzing the digestion products using polyacrylamide gel electrophoresis and autoradiography. Since quantitative footprinting analysis requires systematic variation of the input drug-DNA-bp ratio, r_t, the resulting autoradiogram is a two dimensional array of density data. The electrophoresing dimension is sequence while the second dimension quantitates drug induced enzymatic inhibition as a function of r_t. In view of the large number of images on a footprinting autoradiogram (~1000), quantitative analysis of the density data to obtain the relative concentrations of the oligonucletides produced in the digest is best accomplished through computer assisted data reduction and analysis.

2 QUANTITATIVE MICRODENSITOMETRY

The footprinting autoradiogram is cut into 10 cm wide strips in the direction of electrophoresis and scanned with a linear scanning Jarrell-Ash model 23-100 microdensitometer. The signal from the densitometer is outputed to a Nippon Electronic Corporation (NEC) computer for data reduction and analysis. The computer software, written in digital research personal basic, is functionally divided into four parts, data acquisition, peak identification and baseline establishment, peak integration and processed data output. The data from the densitometer are initially subjected to smoothing using a nine point Gaussian smoothing routine. The smoothing function eliminates data acquistion related noise without measurably degrading the desired peak information. Once the peaks are assigned by the operator, the program constructs a baseline by connecting the lowest density points between any consecutive pair of peaks. The baseline is subjected to editing by the operator. The calculated baseline is then subtracted from the data to produce a flat baseline from which the peaks areas are determined using the simple trapazoidal rule. The results of the peak analysis, presented on the graphics screen of the computer, can be copied to a plotter at any stage of the analysis.

The ability of the microdensitometer system to accurately measure the relative concentrations of the oligonucleotides present in the gel was examined. Various concentrations of ^{32}P labeled DNA restriction fragments were loaded into the wells of a denaturing polyacryamide gel and electrophoresed. After autoradiography a section of the gel containing the radiolabeled oligonucleotide was removed and subjected to scintillation counting. Plots of the scanned peak area versus the number of counts, Figure 1, were found to be linear in the O.D. range, $0 \leq$ O.D. maximum ≤ 1.0. Since all of the bands on the autoradiogram have identical shapes, scanning in the aforementioned manner indicates that the calculated areas are directly proportional to the concentrations of oligonucleotides in the gel. Scanning through a band at various points along its long axis (slit dimensions, 1.6 mm x 10 μm) gave areas reproducible to 2% indicating that the optical density (oligonucleotide concentration) is uniformly distributed within the bands. A three dimensional presentation of densitometric information collected from footprinting experiments involving the antitumor drug actinomycin-D and the self complimentary dodecanucleotide duplex having sequence 5'-TATAGCGCTATA-3' is showwn in Figure 2.

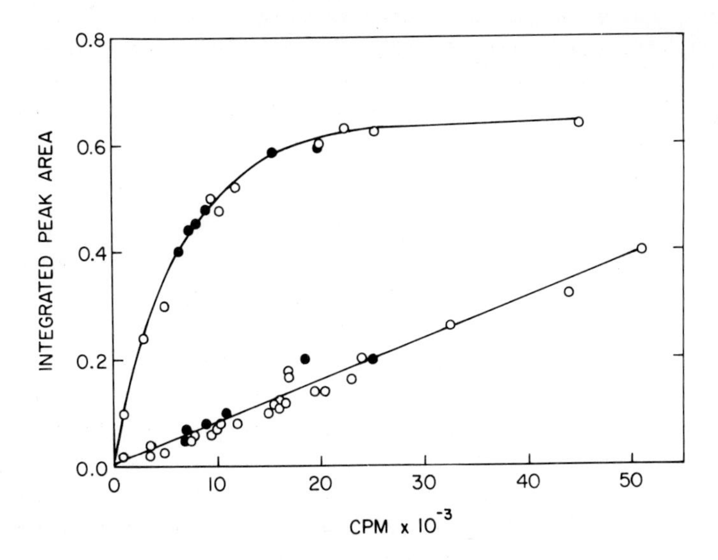

Figure 1. Plots of the intergrated peak areas determined by densitometry versus the the counts/min evaluated by scintillation counting for ^{32}P labeled DNA restriction fragments are shown. The nonlinear region corresponds to an O.D. maximum of >1.

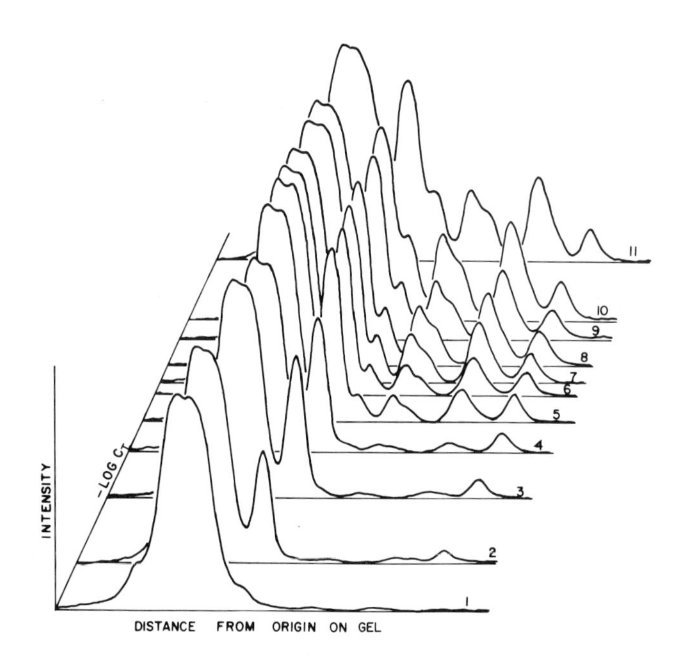

Figure 2. Microdensitometric data of footprinting experiments involving actinomycin-D and the duplex 5'-TATAGCGCTATA-3' are shown. Scan 1, $r_t = 0$; scans 2-10, $0.58 \leq r_t \leq 12.3$; scan 11, minus enyzme. The quantity C_T, the total drug concentration, is related to r_t through the expression, $C_T = 4.0 \times 10^{-6}M\ r_t$.

3 ACKNOWLEDGEMENT

We wish to thank Mr. N. Rich for his help with the computer software and P. Borer and N. Zanatta for assistance with DNA synthesis. This work was supported by a grant from the National Institutes of Health, GM31895.

4 REFERENCES

(1) M. J. Lane, J. C. Dabrowiak, J. N. Vournakis, Proc. Natl. Acad. Sci. USA 80 (1983) 3260-3264.

(2) M. W. Van Dyke, R. P. Hertzberg, P. D. Dervan, Proc. Natl. Acad. Sci. USA 79 (1982) 5470-5474.

(3) J. C. Dabrowiak, Life Sci. 32 (1983) 2915-2931.

A COMPUTER ALGORITHM FOR PATTERN MATCHING IN 2D-ELECTROPHEROGRAMS

Pardowitz, I., Zimmer, H.-G., Neuhoff, V.

Max-Planck-Institut for Experimental Medicine, Neurochemistry Research Group, Hermann-Rein-Str. 3, 3400 Göttingen

1. INTRODUCTION

An algorithm is presented for automatic spot identification in 2D methods. It is based on the minimalization of an "overlap-function" which depends on the pair distances between the centers of the spots in a sample and the spots in a master map. Apart from the preliminary marking of four fixed spots, the method is fully automatic.

2. THE ALGORITHM

As a result of the data acquisition and data reduction system /1,2/ the spot pattern on a chromatogram or on a 2D-gel is represented by a list which associates four parameters to each spot: the spot number, the x and y coordinates of the center of the spot with respect to an arbitrary rectangular coordinate system and a parameter linked to the quantity of substance contained in the respective spot /3/. The first four spots of this list represent predifined spots. The spot identification system has to compare this list with a similar list, called the master map, which contains all possibly occuring spots of interest. Spot identification means to establish a correspondence between the spots of the measured pattern and those of the master map.

The main feature of the iterative least square pattern matching is to determine a nonlinear transformation of the coordinates $\underline{r}_i^s$ of the sample pattern

$$T: \quad \underline{r}_i^s \rightarrow \underline{\tilde{r}}_i^s = T\,(\,\underline{r}_i^s\,) \tag{2.1}$$

which minimizes the "overlap function" /4/:

$$\psi = \sum_{i=1}^{4} (\,\underline{\tilde{r}}_i^s - \underline{r}_i^m\,)^2 + \sum_{i=5}^{S} \sum_{j=5}^{M} \varphi(\,\underline{\tilde{r}}_i^s - \underline{r}_j^m\,)^2 \tag{2.2}$$

Notice that the predefined spots (1-4) are treated differently from the others. Only the distances between the corresponding coordinates contributes to the sum ψ, whereas the second term evaluates the distances between all other spots in the sample and master map. The function is used to evaluate the overlap between the spots of the sample and the map. Its argument is the squared distance d_{ij} between the transformed point $\tilde{\underline{r}}_i^s$ of the sample and the reference point $\underline{r}_j^m$ of the map. It is required that $\varphi(d_{ij}^2)$ is a monotonically increasing function in order to minimize ψ for a perfect match. The shape of φ is uncritical. For computational convenience we have chosen

$$\varphi(d_{ij}^2) = - \exp-(\frac{\sqrt{d_{ij}^2}}{R}) \qquad (2.3)$$

where R is a typical diameter of the spots.

The nonlinear transformation T is established in the form of Taylor et. al. /5/

$$T : \underline{r}_i^s \rightarrow \tilde{\underline{r}}_i^s = \underline{r}_i^s + \sum_{k=1}^{n} \underline{a}^{(k)} \cdot f^{(k)}(\underline{r}_i^s) \qquad i=1,\ldots,S \; ; \; n \leq 10 \qquad (2.4)$$

where the functions $f^{(k)}$ are defined by

$$f^{(1)} = 1$$
$$f^{(2)} = x \qquad f^{(3)} = y$$
$$f^{(4)} = x^2 \qquad f^{(5)} = xy \qquad f^{(6)} = y^2$$
$$f^{(7)} = x^3 \qquad f^{(8)} = x^2 y \qquad f^{(9)} = xy^2 \qquad f^{(10)} = y^3 \qquad (2.5)$$

The vectors $\underline{a}^{(k)} = (a_x^{(k)} , a_y^{(k)})$ are the parameters of the transformation. They are determined by iteratively finding the minimum of the overlap-function ψ.

The transformed coordinates of the sample spots are used to get the most probable correspondence between sample and map spots. The function φ is used hereby as a measure of matching probability.

3. REFERENCES

/1/ Zimmer, H.-G., Neuhoff, V., Informatik-Fachber. 8 Springer (1977) 12-20

/2/ Zimmer, H.-G., Proc. 4th International Joint Conf. Kyoto (1978) 834

/3/ Kronberg, H., Elektrophoresis 81, de Gruyter Berlin, (1981) 413-423

/4/ Pardowitz, I., Clin. Chem. (1984) in press

/5/ Taylor, J., Elektrophoresis 81, de Gruyter Berlin (1981) 383-400

QUANTITATIVE ASPECTS OF PROTEIN STAINING BY COOMASSIE BLUE DYES

Volker Neuhoff and Reinhard Stamm
Max-Planck-Institut für experimentelle Medizin, Göttingen

For the first time it was possible to quantify the time-dependent staining and destaining of proteins in polyacrylamide gels using the newly developed high resolution scanning microphotometer with its more than 4000 available grey values (1). Polyacrylamide gels were prepared on silanized glass plates (2) (0.5 x 70 x 36 mm^3) with three wells of 0.5 x 8 x 34 mm^3 for three different proteins at various concentrations (BSA, transferrin and thyroglobulin) which were mixed into 12 % acrylamide in Tris/glycine buffer pH 8.8, plus 0,1 % SDS and polymerized within 30 min. These protein-containing gels were stained and destained under various conditions with Amidoblack 10B (Merck), Coomassie blue R-250, C.I. 42660 (Serva) and Coomassie blue G-250, C.I. 42655 (Serva). During staining and destaining in certain time intervals the integrated absorbance was measured at 589 ± 1 nm wavelength by scanning microphotometry (1) and expressed as the difference between protein and background staining.

Fig. 1 shows the result of different staining procedures for the same amount of BSA. The absolute values for transferrin and globulin are different but the staining characteristics are the same. Staining with Amidoblack 10B (0.5 % or 0.01 % in 7.5 % acetic acid) (3) results in a weak protein staining and a very high background, with maximal protein staining after 2 hrs. Clearing of the background requires 4 hrs shaking in 7.5 % acetic acid in which the protein-dye complex is stable for more than 240 hrs.

The most commonly used staining with 0.5 % Coomassie blue R-250 (4) in methanol / acetic acid H_2O, 50/10/40 v/v/v, followed by washing in 7.5 % acetic acid with 5 % methanol and 5 % glycerol (5) is not advisable as can be seen in Fig. 1. Maximal staining is reached after 3 hrs and will not increase within 300 hrs in the staining solution. Background staining is twice as high as protein staining. During destaining in the first few hours protein staining increases by 40 % which may be due to the omission of methanol and therefore higher pK value of the acid in the destaining solution. The presence of any alcohol in the staining solution leads only to intensified background staining and has neither a positive effect on the protein staining nor does it shorten the staining time. The addition or omission of glycerol is without any measurable effect on the staining. In the destaining solution the dye-protein complex is time-dependently destroyed resulting in drastically diminished protein staining which, on the other hand, can be reduced by adding 10^{-3}% stain (w/v) to the destaining solution but thereby leading to a more intense background staining.

Staining with Coomassie blue R-250 in 15 % acetic acid is superior in that protein staining is nearly twice as high as with the methanolic staining solution. Staining is maximal after 3 hrs and destaining with 15 % acetic acid leads to no further increase of protein staining and a clear background is obtained after 5 hrs. Stability of the protein-dye complex for more than 240 hrs is reached if 10^{-3} % dye (w/v) is added to the 15 % acetic acid. Even better protein staining, reaching a maximum after 10 hrs, can be obtained if 1-5 % $(NH_4)_2Fe(SO_4)_2 x 6H_2O$ is added to the staining solution. The results obtained so far lead to the conclusion that the intensity of protein staining is strongly dependent on the strength of the acid used for staining. However one has to take into consideration that in strong acid the dye itself can be destroyed.

Coomassie blue G-250 (6) forms colloid dye particles in solutions of low pH and a low background staining results if perchloric acid is used (7). Background staining is further dependent on the acrylamide concentration of the gel. As Fig. 1 shows maximal protein staining is obtained with 0.1 % Coomassie blue G dissolved in 1.5 % PCE (w/v) with very low background staining, but surprisingly enough even after more than 240 hrs staining a plateau is still not reached. Since the low background staining (which will not interfere with photometric evaluation) is undesirable for photographic documentation the plate was washed 30 min in 1.5 % PCA with the result that some of the protein-dye complex was destroyed. Thereafter the plate was transferred in a solution of 20 % ammonium sulphate in water in which the complex is irreversible precipitated and, if kept in the same solution, stable for more than 900 hrs (the time until typing this abstract) without any measurable loss of dye bound to the protein. This precipitation of the dye complex together with a dehydration may be the explanation for the observed increase of extinction which appears immediately after the plate is in the ammonium sulphate solution.

Conclusion: Since we have now available a scanning microphotometer allowing for quantitative measurements in the sensitivity range from 10^{-3} to 3 O.D in connection with automatic evaluation of one- or two-

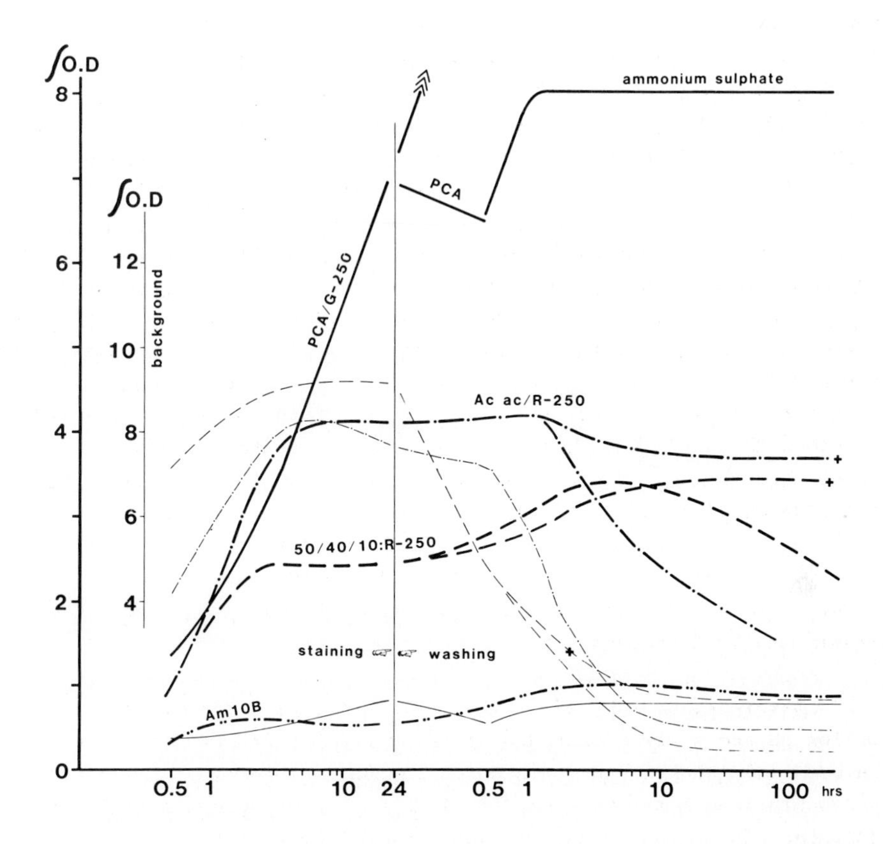

Fig. 1: Staining and washing of BSA (125 µg/ml) in 12 % Polyacrylamid gels

Thick lines: Staining and washing; corresponding thin lines: values of the background (Background for Am 10B is not shown). The washing solution has been changed after each measurement.

Am 10B: 0,01 % Amido black 10B (g/v) in 7,5 % acetic acid; 7,5 % acetic acid, 5 % Methanol, 5 % Glycerol.

50/40/10, R-250: 0,1 % Coomassie brilliant blue R-250 (g/v) in 50 % Methanol, 40 % H_2O, 10 % acetic acid (v/v/v); 7,5 % acetic acid, 5 % Methanol, 5 % Glycerol; + : $+10^{-3}$% (g/v) Coomassie brilliant blue R-250.

AC ac/R-250: 0,05 % Coomassie brilliant blue R-250 (g/v) in 15 % acetic acid; 15 % acetic acid; + : $+10^{-3}$% (g/v) Coomassie brilliant blue R-250.

PCA/G-250: 0,1 % Coomassie brilliant blue G-250 (g/v) in 1,5 % (g/v) Perchloric acid; for 0,5 hours in 1,5 % (g/v) Perchloric acid, storage in 10 - 20 % Ammonium sulphate $(NH_4)_2SO_4$.

dimensional gels (8.9) we need more information on the quality and quantitivity of protein staining to finally end up with relevant data. The results obtained so far clearly demonstrate that many further experiments have to be performed until an optimal recipe can be given. However, it is already clear that due to the lack of a reliable instrument almost every staining procedure has not been analysed carefully enough and used without sufficient critique. If the optimal quantitative staining procedure is once found the final step will be the combination with automatic evaluation of respective autoradiograms, including a suitable internal standard for calibration (10), for determining the specific radioactivity of a labled protein in a gel simply by two separate scans and combining the obtained quantitative data.

Acknowledgment: We like to thank Dr. Hansjörg Eibl and Dr. Hans-Georg Zimmer for many valuable discussions, Mr. Hans-Georg Klieber and Mr. Jens Schulz for skillfull technical assistance.

REFERENCES:

(1) Kronberg, H., Zimmer, H.-G, Neuhoff, V., Electrophoresis 83, 245 W. de Gruyter 1984

(2) Neuhoff, V., Electrophoresis, 4, (1984) in press

(3) Grassmann, W., Hannig, K., Klin. Woschrft. 32, 838 (1954)

(4) Fazekas de St. S., Groth, R., Webster, R.G., Datyner, A., Biochem. Biophys. Acta 71, 377 (1963)

(5) Meyer, TS., Lamberts, B.L., Biochim. Biophys. Acta 107, 144 (1965)

(6) Diezel, W., Kopperschläger, G., Hofmann, E., Analyt. Biochem. 48, 617 (1972)

(7) Reisner, A., Nemes, P., Buchholtz, C., Analyt. Biochem. 64, 509, (1975)

(8) Kronberg, H., Zimmer, H.-G., Neuhoff, V., submitted to Clin. Chem.

(9) Pardowitz, I., Zimmer, H.-G., Neuhoff, V., submitted to Clin. Chem.

DEVELOPMENT OF SILVER STAINS FOR THE RAPID VISUALIZATION OF PROTEIN ALTERATIONS WITH APPLICATIONS TO ANALYSIS OF CEREBROSPINAL FLUID IN DISEASES INVOLVING THE CENTRAL NERVOUS SYSTEM

Carl R. Merril, Michael Harrington

Section on Biochemical Genetics, Clinical Psychogenetics Branch, National Institute of Mental Health, Bethesda, Maryland 20205, U.S.A.

1 INTRODUCTION

Detection and characterization of proteins is of fundamental importance in the study of clinical disease. Recent advances in electrophoretic methods, particularly two dimensional electrophoresis (2 DE), have permitted the characterization of proteins from complex tissue and body fluid samples. When we utilized these methods to study diseases of the central nervous system (CNS) in 1978 the most commonly employed protein stain, Coomassie blue, took hours to perform and it lacked the sensitivity to detect less abundant but biologically important proteins (proteins which represent 10^{-4}% - 10^{-5}% or less of the total protein present in a sample). Sensitivities with heavy metal stains or fluoresent stains were, at best, equivalent to coomassie blue (about 10 ng of protein). By adapting a histological silver stain we achieved a hundred-fold increase in sensitivity (1,2). This histological silver stain took hours to perform and used considerable amounts of silver. However it permitted us to visualize over 300 proteins in cerebrospinal fluid (CSF), of which 26 were identified (3). In continuing our search to develop ultrasensitive methods for visualizing proteins we developed a series of simple "photochemical" stains which can be performed within one hour. These stains employ formaldehyde as a reducing agent for the silver ions in a solution made alkaline with sodium carbonate (4,5,6). The formaldehyde is oxidized to formic acid while reducing ionic silver to metallic silver (4). Many variations of chemical development silver staining methods have been derived over the past three years (7). We now report the development of a "photodevelopment" silver stain which utilizes light to initiate image development. An image can be obtained within 10 minutes after electrophoresis with this silver stain (8). The use of these stains has permitted us to detect both qualitative and quantitative alterations in CSF proteins in various disease states.

2 SILVER STAIN METHODS

2.2 A chemical development silver stain

Gels are fixed for 20 minutes in a solution containing 50% v/v methanol, 10% v/v acetic acid and 40% v/v water followed by 20 minutes in 10% v/v methanol and 5% v/v acetic acid. They are then treated for 5 minutes with a solution containing 3.4 mM potassium dichromate and 3.2 mM nitric acid followed by immersion in 12 mM silver nitrate for 20 minutes. The image is developed in a 280 mM sodium carbonate solution containing 0.5% v/v commercial formaldehyde.

2.3 A rapid photodevelopment silver stain

Gels are fixed for 5 minutes in a solution containing 50% v/v methanol, 10% v/v acetic acid, and 40% v/v water with 2% w/v citric acid and 0.2% w/v sodium chloride. After a rapid rince with deionized water to remove surface chloride the image is developed in a solution containing 50% v/v methanol, 10% v/v acetic acid, and 40% v/v water plus 2% w/v silver nitrate. Image formation is initiated by a uniform light source (A fluorescent 160-Watt grid lamp).

2.4 General staining comments

In most silver staining procedures considerable care must be taken to work with clean apparatus, pure reagents and deionized water with a conductivity no greater than 1 μmho. To preserve silver stain images photography of the stained gel is recommended.

3 RESULTS AND DISCUSSION

The use of high resolution 2DE and silver staining has revealed a number of disease specific protein alterations in CSF, from patients with multiple sclerosis, herpes simplex encephalitis, Creutzfeldt-Jakob disease and in 40% of schizophenic patients. We had previously demonstrated that we could visualize over 300 proteins in CSF and we identified 26 of these. Patients with multiple sclerosis, SSPE, and herpes simplex encephalitis all demonstrated additional immunoglobulin light chain species. We have also demonstrated that improved discrimination between MS and other neurological disorders may be achieved by quantitative assessment of the immunoglobulin light chains and quantitation of three additional proteins (9). Examination of CSF from Creutzfeldt-Jakob disease revealed two new proteins. These proteins have also been observed in experimental Creutzfeldt disease and Kuru. Patients with herpes simplex encephalitis have demonstrated two new proteins with charges similar to albumin but with lower molecular weights. These proteins were observed in 90% of herpes encephalitis patients and 40% of schizophenic patients.

4 REFERENCES

(1) C. R. Merril, R. C. Switzer, M. L. Van Keuren, Proc. Natl. Acad. Sci. U.S.A.

76 (1979) 4335-4339.

(2) R. C. Switzer, C. R. Merril, S. Shifrin, Anal. Biochem. 98 (1979) 231-237.

(3) D. Goldman, C. R. Merril, M. H. Ebert, Clin. Chem. 26 (1980) 1317-1322.

(4) C. R. Merril, M. L. Dunau, D. Goldman, Anal. Biochem. 110 (1981) 201-207.

(5) C. R. Merril, D. Goldman, S. A. Sedman, M. H. Ebert, Science 211 (1981) 1437-1438.

(6) C. R. Merril, D. Goldman, M. L. Van Keuren, Electrophoresis 3 (1982) 17-23.

(7) M. J. Dunn, A. H. M. Burghes, Electrophoresis 4 (1983) 173-189.

(8) C. R. Merril, M. Harrington, V. Alley, Electrophoresis, in press.

(9) M. G. Harrington, C. R. Merril, D. Goldman, X. Xu, D. E. McFarlin, Electrophoresis, in press

SILVER STAINING AFTER AGAROSE GEL ISOELECTRIC FOCUSING

R. McLachlan, D. Burns

Cancer Institute, 481 Lt. Lonsdale St., Melbourne, Australia 3000

1 INTRODUCTION

Numerous silver staining methods for the detection of trace proteins following polyacrylamide gel electrophoresis have been reported. However very few publications have described the use of these techniques for the detection of proteins in agarose gels. Of these, methods based on a procedure by Kerenyi and Gallyas (1) have been described for both electrophoresis (2) and isoelectric focusing (3). Lasne et al. (3) found that Kereyni & Gallyas stain was qualitatively more sensitive than Coomassie brilliant blue R-250 (CBB R250). However with their modification they claimed a sensitivity of 20 times CBB R250 (9 ng/mm^2 for β_2-micro-globulin), although from the data presented the background staining appears excessive.

This paper presents a modification of the method of Kerenyi and Gallyas (1). It has been optimized for staining of immunoglobulins and related fragments after ultrathin flatbed IEF in agarose gels containing non-crosslinked polyacrylamide. Sensitivity of staining for monotypic IgGs is approximately 10 times CBB R250 (2 ng/mm^2), with immune fixation 20 times (1 ng/mm^2). Furthermore background staining is negligible.

2 METHODS

2.1 IEF

The gels were composed of 1.0% IEF grade agarose, 0.5% non-cross-linked polyacrylamide and 2.0% carrier ampholytes pH 3-10. Batches of gels were formed between mylar films and perspex templates and were stored at 4°C. After removal of a 0.375 mm thick gel from its template, samples were added to precast sample wells (8 or 16/gel). The gel was inverted and placed onto water-moistened carbon rod electrodes in a simple humid chamber. Focusing conditions were 35 V.hr/cm at 17.5 mWatt/cm^2 gel surface area. No cooling was used. Final field strengths were about 80 V/cm. The gel was fixed (5 % TCA, 3,5% SAA, 33% Methanol) for

10 minutes, washed in water for 5-10 minutes, squashed, dried, washed (methanol: acetic acid: water, 4:1:4 v/v) for 5 minutes then stained in either CBB R250 or silver stain. If desired, proteins can be immune fixed after IEF (30 min.), washed (4 x 20 mins. saline, squashing between changes), dried and silver stained.

2.2 SILVER STAINING

The gels were stained horizontally in plastic or glass petri dishes placed on a "rocking" mixer. The silver stain reagent was composed of equal parts of filtered stock solutions. Solution A was 0.3 M Na_2CO_3 and solution B was 0.034 M NH_4NO_3, 0.016 M $AgNO_3$ and 0.25 M HCHO made 1.35% with respect to dodeca-Tungstosilicic acid. As described by Willoughby & Lambert (2) a white precipitate formed, which gradually became grey-brown and later black. The staining of the proteins was complete after approximately 7 minutes and before the black precipitate formed. The reaction was stopped by immersion of the gel in 5% acetic acid. The gel was then dried and analyzed. The method is ideally suited for overstaining CBB R250 stained gels.

Sensitivities were calculated by:
a) Ponceau S protein quantitation (4),
b) Laser densitometry (concentration of protein/band),
c) Photographic enlargement (area of band).

3 RESULTS

3.1 SENSITIVITY

Sensitivity studies were performed on four purified human monotypic IgGs. Staining sensitivities obtained were as follows (Fig.1):-

A) CBB R250	18 ng/mm^2
B) Silver staining	3.6 ng/mm^2
C) CBB R250/silver staining	2.2 ng/mm^2
D) Immune fixation/CBB R250/silver staining	0.9 ng/mm^2

To obtain maximum sensitivity and minimum background, a brief wash in the methanol-acetic acid solution prior to staining was essential. Omission of this step allowed development of a reddish-brown background, primarily at the cathode, resulting in impaired differentiation of protein bands from the gel matrix.

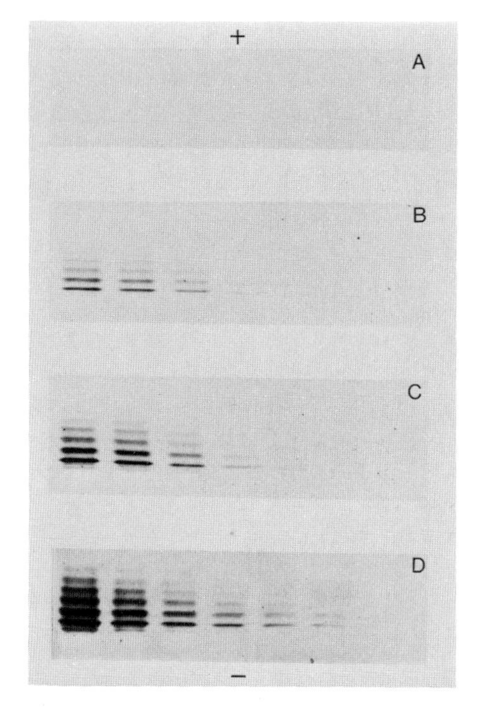

Fig.1 shows agarose IEF of dilutions of monotypic IgG stained with A) CBB R250, B) Silver stain, C) Silver stain following CBB R250, D) Silver stain following CBB R250 stain of proteins immune fixed with human gamma chain specific antiserum. The amount of IgG applied was, from left to right, 92, 46, 23, 12, 9, 5, 2, 1 ng respectively.

3.2 IMMUNOGLOBULINS IN BIOLOGICAL FLUIDS

The detection of oligoclonal IgG in cerebrospinal fluids (CSF) has been achieved in three of fourteen patients suspected of suffering from multiple sclerosis. Polyclonal or oligoclonal IgG was detected using only 1-2 μL of the respective unconcentrated CSF. In all cases, protein concentrations were less than 1 g/L and IgG/albumin ratios were normal.

The detection of monotypic light chains in urines has been achieved in several patients whose urinary protein concentrations were less than 0.1 g/L. Similar results have been obtained in sera for the detection of trace amounts of monotypic immunoglobulins and their fragments (IgD, IgA, IgM and free light chains). In these cases, specific antisera were used and silver staining was performed when CBB R250 staining failed to detect protein.

4 DISCUSSION

A reliable and inexpensive method for the detection and identification of trace amounts of immunoglobulins and related fragments in agarose IEF for the study of biological fluids has been established. Sensitivities achieved are approximately 10 times CBB R250 and when combined with immune fixation, 20 times CBB R250. These results compare favourably with Confavreux, et al. (5) who reported a sensitivity for immunoglobulins of 25 to 50 ng per band following polyacrylamide gel IEF. Our method is simple to perform, reduces the necessity of handling the neurotoxin acrylamide and can be accomplished in 80 minutes from the commencement of focusing. Immune fixations can be completed in 160 minutes, enabling full characterization of proteins in less than one working day.

5 REFERENCES

1. L. Kerenyi, F. Gallyas, Clin. Chim. ACTA 38 (1972) 465-467.

2. E.W. Willoughby, A. Lambert, Anal. Biochem. 130 (1983) 353-358.

3. F. Lasne, O. Benzerara, Y. Lasne, Anal Biochem. 132 (1983) 338-341.

4. M.A. Pesce, C.S. Strande, Clin. Chem. 19 (1973) 1265-1267.

5. C. Confavreux, E. Gianazza, G. Chazot, Y. Lasne, P. Arnaud, Electrophoresis 3 (1982) 206-210.

FREE SH-GROUPS ARE IMPORTANT FOR THE POLYCHROMATIC STAINING OF PROTEINS WITH SILVER NITRATE

Ernst Hempelmann, Matthias Schulze, Otto Götze

Department of Immunology, University of Göttingen,
Kreuzbergring 57, D-3400 Göttingen, FRG

1 INTRODUCTION

The long known histochemical silver staining method was modified by Hubbell et. al. (1) and Switzer et. al. (2) for the analysis of electrophoretically separated proteins. It has since found many applications for the study of proteins and nucleic acids. Two of the numerous variations of the method (3,4) result in the formation of coloured silver-protein complexes. So far no explanation for this phenomenon has been offered. It seems unlikely that the colouration is a consequence of the formation of (black) metallic silver. Our results show that complexes of silver ions which may form at near neutral pH with sulfhydryl, and possibly other negatively charged groups on proteins can be detected as coloured bands after a drastic rise in pH in the presence of paraformaldehyde.

2 RESULTS AND DISCUSSION

2.1 High resolution SDS-Polyacrylamide Gel Electrophoresis (SDS-PAGE)

Proteins were analysed on polyacrylamide gels employing linear gradients of acrylamide from 6% to 20% T. Buffers were prepared as described (5). Since for high resolution SDS-PAGE a separate stacking gel is not necessary all buffers were used at the same pH-value. In the electrophoretic system described here concentration and stacking of the SDS-proteins in the sample takes place at the boundary between glycine and chloride ions. Unstacking of the steady-state protein stack occurs continously in the gradient gel during the electrophoretic run because of the gradual increase in the frictional resistance. A limit gel concentration above 16% T was found to be necessary for complete resolution of stacks containing proteins with a mol. weight below 10 kD.

2.2 Polychromatic silver staining

The following procedure results in optimal staining of one 50 x 90 x 0.75 mm slab gel. The gel is sequentially soaked in 200 ml each of the washing- and staining solutions. Constant agitation throughout the procedure is required for reproducible staining patterns. All solutions were prepared with ion-exchange purified water of a resistance greater than 17 megohm.

Staining procedure	Time (min)
1) Prefix the gel in 10% (w/v) trichloroacetic acid	30
2) Soak the gel in ethanol, acetic acid, H_2O (20/5/75) containing 0.002% (w/v) DTT	30
3) Immerse in 0.5% (w/v) potassium dichromate solution	5
4) Place in H_2O	5
5) Immerse the gel in 0.1% (w/v) $AgNO_3$ solution	10
6) Place in H_2O	1
7) Transfer the gel to a freshly prepared solution of 3% (w/v) Na_2CO_3 containing 0.02% (w/v) paraformaldehyde	7
8) Store the gel in 1% (w/v) aqueous acetic acid	

The treatment of gels with dithiothreitol (DTT) results in highly reproducible patterns (6). The washing step with dichromate is essential for the prevention of a yellow background. The colours are fully developed after one day. Traces of background colour are completely washed out after one week of storage in acetic acid. The stained gels can be stored for at least 18 months in 1% acetic acid solution without detectable fading of colours.

FIG. 1. Comparison of different staining- and pretreatment procedures

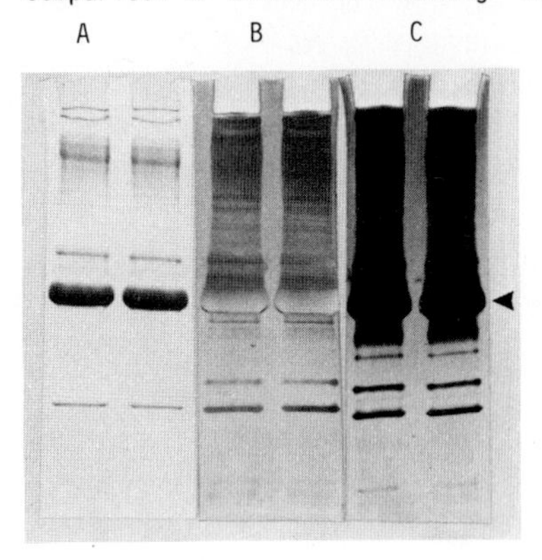

Samples consisted of human serum (20 µg protein)

A: stained with Serva Blue R (Serva, Heidelberg)

B: stained with silver nitrate. DTT in step 2 had been replaced by 0.02% (w/v) iodoacetamide.

C: stained with silver nitrate as described.

The dependence of the described polychromatic staining for proteins on the DTT-treatment step is shown by a comparison of the serum albumin patterns (arrow) in lanes B and C (Fig. 1).

FIG. 2. Examples of polychromatic silver staining of membrane proteins

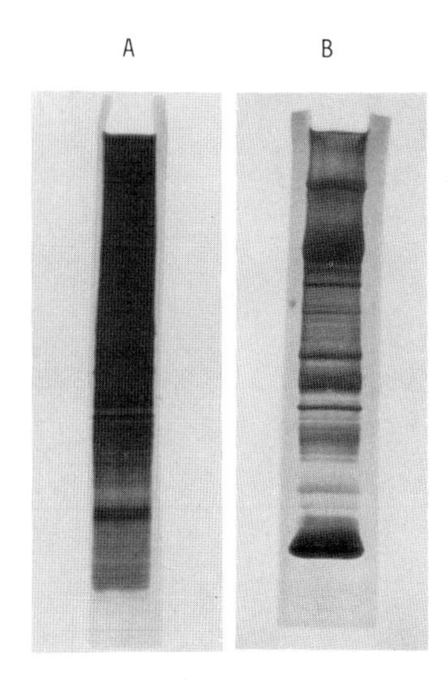

Samples consisted of membrane proteins (25 µg).

A: Membrane proteins of human erythrocytes.

B: Membrane proteins of human myelocytic cells (HL 60).

3 REFERENCES

(1) H.R. Hubbell, L.I. Rothblum, T.C. Hsu, Cell Biol. Inter. Rep. 3 (1979) 615-622

(2) R.C. Switzer, C.R. Merril, S. Shifrin, Analyt. Biochem. 98 (1979) 231-237

(3) D. Goldman, C.R. Merril, M.H. Ebert, Clin. Chem. 26 (1980) 1317-1322

(4) D. W. Sammons, L.D. Adams, E.E. Nishizawa, Electrophoresis 2 (1981) 135-141

(5) E. Hempelmann, Elektrophorese Forum '82 (1982) 111-116

(6) J.H. Morrissey, Analyt. Biochem. 117 (1981) 307-310

ATTACHMENT OF DTPA TO PROTEINS AND COMPLEXING OF METAL IONS TO DTPA-PROTEIN CONJUGATES STUDIED BY ULTRATHIN-LAYER ISOELECTRIC FOCUSING

Thomas Hausmann, Wolfgang Köhnlein

Institut für Strahlenbiologie, Westfälische Wilhelms-Universität, D-4400 Münster, FRG

1 INTRODUCTION

In nuclear medicine and physiology the attachment of radioactive metal ions to biological active macromolecules is used to measure biological functions or to locate specific target tissues, for example the detection of tumor tissue by radiolabeled monoclonal antibodies (tumor imaging). Covalent coupling of the bifunctional diethylenetriaminepentaacetic acid (DTPA) to proteins produces hexadentate chelating sites for metal ions on the protein. Protein labeling by chelation offers the advantage of rapid binding with a variety of metal ions which form very strong complexes with DTPA. Dispite of the loss of one carboxyl group due to the formation of the amid bond with the protein DTPA continues to form stable chelates with various radionuclides (1,2). To prevent the inactivation of the biological active proteins mild coupling conditions at the correct pH range are necessary. Therefore, the conjugation of DTPA to the protein was performed according to the method of Hnatowich et al. (2) by using the bicyclic anhydride of DTPA (cDTPA). We report here the changes of the isoelectric focusing pattern of horse myoglobin produced by covalent coupling with DTPA and by further chelation with metal ions of different oxidation states.

2 MATERIALS AND METHODS

Bicyclic DTPA acid anhydride was synthesized using the procedure of Eckelman et al. (3). Mechanical mixtures of horse myoglobin (1.5mg) with cDTPA anhydride (0.3; 3.0; 30.0mg) were prepared giving molar ratios from 10 to 1000 to minimize hydrolysis during dissolving and coupling. Two different buffers were tested: 0.1M HEPES pH 7 and 0.1M bicarbonate pH 8.2. Usually the mixure was agitated for 10 min at $4^{o}C$. For the chelation of metal ions DTPA and myoglobin were coupled in the molar ratio of 100. Metal ions were added at equimolar concentrations to DTPA ($8.43 \cdot 10^{-6}$ moles). The complexing time was 30 min. The coupling product was purified from low molecular weight contaminants by passage through a PD-10 column. The eluate was further desalted and concentrated by centrifugation with Amicon C-10 tubes for 90 min at 1500g.

Ultrathin-layer isoelectric focusing was performed in 50-100 μm polyacrylamide gels on silanized polyester films because of the high resolution and short focusing time of this analytical technique. Polyacrylamide gels (5% T, 3% C) containing 3% w/v carrier ampholytes were prepared by the flap technique of Radola et al. (4). A pH gradient of 4-8 with flat slope between pH 5-7 was obtained by mixing pH 3-10 "Pharmalytes" (Pharmacia) and pH 5-7 "Ampholines" (LKB) in the ratio 1:1 v/v. Marker proteins were used to calibrate the pH range of the gel. Fixation and staining was carried out as described by Radola et al. (4).

Focusing conditions are described in detail in the legend of figure 1.

3 PRINCIPLES

Horse myoglobin was chosen because of its simple focusing pattern with only two discret pI points at pH 6.8 and 7.3. CDTPA anhydride is covalently coupled to the protein molecule with one of its acetic acid groups by an amide linkage via a pH dependent acylation reaction at the ε-amine group of lysine residues (5,6). Due to the anhydride, producing four acetic acid groups, the pH of the buffer solution is slightly reduced. At a molar ratio of 1000 only 0.1M bicarbonate buffer ensured constant pH.

Assuming that the dissociation constants of the DTPA are not seriously influenced by the conjugation, two of the three imino groups are protonated at the focusing pH range (pH 5-7). Two additional negative charges from the DTPA are attached to the protein and one proton is eliminated from the amine group of lysine resulting in the addition of three negative charges per bound DTPA. Thus a shift of pI points is expected towards a more acidic pH region. Additional complexing of metal ions of different oxidation state to the DTPA protein conjugates is accompanied by the release of the two protons of the imino groups of DTPA. Therefore, the chelation of a bivalent metal ion should not alter the pI of the DTPA coupled protein. While the complexation of a trivalent ion results in a charge change of one unit ($\Delta e=1$) as compared to the DTPA-protein conjugate.

4 RESULTS

As demonstrated in Figure 1 the pI of horse myoglobin is shifted from pI 6.8 and 7.3 to the pH-region of 6.0-6.2 when conjugated to DTPA. At a molar ratio of 100:1 for DTPA to protein an additional banding pattern appears at a pH of about 5.3 - the pI-point of - lactoglobin (positions 5,6,7 in Figure 1).

The influence of metal ions to the banding pattern is shown in Figure 2. Divalent metal ions like Cu^{2+} and Zn^{2+} complexed to DTPA-protein conjugates do not change the pI points as compared to the metal-free compound (positions 6 and 7). Samples were applied in triplicate. With Zn^{2+} ions only a single band is seen (position 7). With trivalent metal ions Fe^{3+} and In^{3+} at the positions 4 and 5 respectively identical pI shifts were observed from about 6.1 to 6.6 as expected.

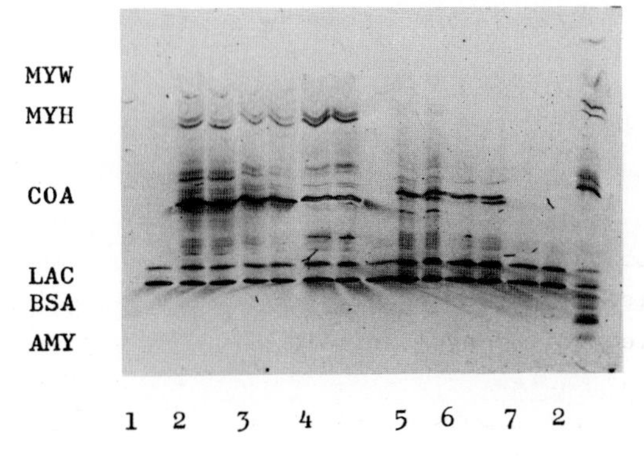

Figure 1: Ultrathin-layer (50 µm) polyacrylamid gel isoelectric focusing of DTPA coupled horse myoglobin (MYH). Separation distance:5cm. Prefocusing: 80 V/cm for 15 min. Focusing: for 500 V·h, final field strength 400 V/cm for 5 min. Sample volume: 1-3 µl. Temperature: 9°C. Sample positions: (1) marker proteins: MYW-whale myoglobin, pI 8.3; MYH-horse myoglobin, pI 7.3 and 6.8; COA-conalbumin, pI 5.9; LAC - β-lactoglobin, pI 5.2 and 5.3; BSA-bovine serum albumin, pI 4.7-4.9; AMY-amyloglucosidase, pI 3.5. (2) MYH. (3) cDTPA:MYH (10:1), coupled in 0.1M HEPES. (4) cDTPA:MYH (10:1) in 0.1M bicarbonate. (5) cDTPA:MYH (100:1), HEPES. (6) cDTPA:MYH (100:1), bicarbonate. (7) cDTPA:MYH (100:1) at a three fold higher concentration, bicarbonate.

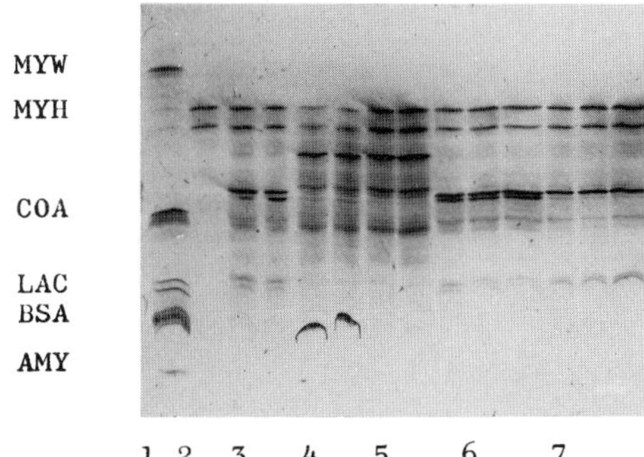

Figure 2: Ultrathin-layer isoelectric focusing of metal ions complexed to DTPA protein conjugates. Conditions as in Figure 1. Sample positions: (1), (2), (3) same as in Figure 1. (4) Fe^{3+}-cDTPA:MYH conjugate. (5) In^{3+}-cDTPA:MYH. (6) Cu^{2+}-cDTPA:MYH. (7) Zn^{2+}-cDTPA:MYH.

5 DISCUSSION

While informations about ligand binding and metal ion chelation so far were only obtained by gel chromatography, spectrophotometry and equilibrium dialysis, we have shown here for the first time to our knowledge that these informations are also obtainable with ultrathin-layer isoelectric focusing.

6 REFERENCES

(1) G.E. Krejcared, K.L. Tucker, Biochem. Biophys. Res. Comm. 77 (1977) 581-585.

(2) D.J. Hnatowich, W.W. Layne, R.L. Childs, J. Appl. Radiat. Isot. 33 (1982) 327-332.

(3) W.C. Eckelman et al., J. Pharm. Sci. 64 (1975) 704-706.

(4) B.J. Radola, Electrophoresis 1 (1980) 43-56.

(5) C.H. Paik, W.C. Eckelman et al., J. Nucl. Med. 24 (1983) 1158-1163.

(6) D.J. Hnatowich, B. Friedman, B. Clancy, M. Novak, J. Nucl. Med. 22 (1981) 810-814.

VISUALIZATION OF ELECTROPHORETICALLY SEPARATED LOW DENSITY LIPOPROTEIN BINDING MEMBRANE PROTEINS FROM BOVINE TISSUES

Hans Alois Dresel, Herbert Weigel, David Paul Via, Irmhild Otto, Gotthard Schettler

Medizinische Klinik, Abteilung Medizin I, Universität Heidelberg,
Bergheimer Str. 58, D-6900 Heidelberg, Fed. Rep. of Germany

1 INTRODUCTION

Radioligand blotting has been proved to be a sensitive method for the visualization of low density lipoprotein (LDL) receptor from bovine adrenal cortex membranes (1). We demonstrate in this contribution Ca^{++} dependent LDL receptor specific and unspecific binding of LDL to partially purified membrane fractions from a variety of bovine tissues. A highly sensitive anti-human-LDL ELISA with peroxidase-conjugated anti-goat IgG and 4-chloro-naphthol/H_2O_2 allowed rapid development of blue bands on nitrocellulose paper where LDL binds to electrophoretically separated membrane proteins. This highly sensitive and efficient ELISA avoids the need for continuous supplies of radiolabelled ligands and antibodies.

2 METHODS

2.1 LDL and antisera

LDL was prepared from healthy human plasma by preparative ultracentrifugation as described (2). Anti-LDL antibodies were raised in goats and purified by chromatography on DEAE cellulose and Sepharose-LDL as described (3). All chemicals and rabbit anti-goat horse raddish peroxidase (HRP) conjugate were purchased from Sigma, Munich, FRG.

2.2 Fractionation of membrane protein

Membranes from several bovine tissues were homogenized. A microsomal fraction was obtained as 10^7 gmin pellets. Membranes were solubilized with 1 % Triton X-114 (50 mM Tris, pH 8, 50 mM NaCl). Amphiphilic and hydrophobic proteins were separated according to Bordier (4). Acidic and basic proteins were separated by ion exchange chromatography on PEI cellulose at pH 7.8 eluting the acidic proteins with a salt step in presence of 40 mM ß-D-Octylglucoside.

2.3 SDS-PAA electrophoresis

Prior to electrophoresis fractions were desalted on Sephadex G 25 columns equilibrated with Laemmli buffer. The eluates were subjected to SDS-PAA electrophoresis in the BRL apparatus (200 V const. for 90 min.). The proteins were transblotted to nitrocellulose paper (Schleicher & Schüll, FRG) according to Towbin (5). Uspecific sites were blocked with a saturated solution of casein.

2.4 Anti-LDL-ELISA

For visualization of LDL binding proteins the paper strips containing the separated membrane proteins were incubated at 18° C with 50 mM Tris, pH 8, 2 mM Ca^{++}, 50 mM NaCl, 50 mg/ml BSA and 50 ug/ml LDL for 2 h. After extensive washes the paper strips were incubated with goat-anti-LDL IgG (1 mg/ml). Rabbit anti-goat HRP was used after several washes at a working dilution of 1:1000, the enzymatic reaction was started by addition of 0.018 ; 4-chloro-1-naphthol and 10 ul H_2O_2/50 ul buffer.

3 RESULTS AND DISCUSSION

Fig. 1 shows a typical result of one of our binding studies on various solubilized tissue membranes. LDL binding is demonstrated to

(a) the solubilized membrane fraction from bovine adrenal cortex containing the hydrophobic, acidic proteins,

(b) the solubilized membrane fractions from bovine spleen containing the amphiphilic, acidic proteins.

As seen in (a), an LDL binding protein with an apparent M_w of 140 000 - 160 000 is rapidly detected. LDL binding to this membrane component was inhibited by EDTA and thus Ca^{++} dependent. We conclude that this protein is the LDL receptor which was purified by Schneider (6) as a 160 000 D acidic glycoprotein. (b) identifies the LDL binding to the acidic amphiphilic proteins from the bovine spleen. LDL binding occurs predominantly to two components with a M_w of 60 000 - 80 000. LDL binding was not inhibited by EDTA and was thus "unspecific". These proteins might play a role in the unregulated tissue uptake of LDL and may be a part of a scavanger pathway (7).

4 REFERENCES

(1) T.O. Daniel, W.J. Schneider, L.J. Goldstein, M.S. Brown, J. Biol. Chem. 258 (1983), 4606-4673.

(2) R.J. Havel, H.A. Eder, J.H. Bragdon, J. Clin. Invest. 34 (1955) 1345-1353.

(3) N.F. Di Ferrante, P.V. Donelly, D.J. Di Ferrante, S. Toma, A.M. Gotto jr., Biochem. Biophys. Res. Commun. 84 (1978) 366-373.

(4) C. Bordier, J. Biol. Chem 256 (1981) 1604-1607

(5) H. Towbin, T. Staehelin, J. Gordon, Proc. Natl. Acad. Sci. 76 (1979) 4350-4354.

(6) W.J. Schneider, U. Beisiegel, J.L. Goldstein, M.S. Brown, J. Biol. Chem. 257 (1982) 2664-2673.

(7) L.J. Goldstein, M.S. Brown, Metabolism 26 (1977) 1257-1273.

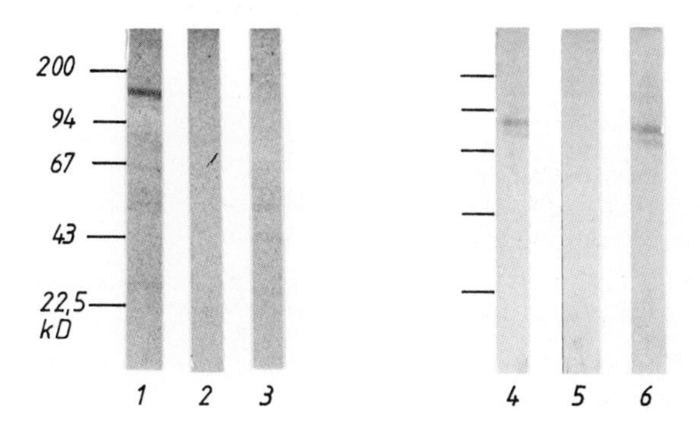

Fig. 1: Visualization of LDL binding membrane proteins

The PEI fraction of the detergent phase proteins of bovine adrenal cortex membrane (380 ug) and the PEI fraction with the amphiphilic proteins of bovine spleen membranes (500 ug) were subjected to SDS-PAA gel electrophoresis (9% PAA, 0.1% SDS) and transblotted to nitrocellulose. (a) contains adrenal cortex membrane proteins, (b) contains spleen membrane proteins.

(1) was incubated with 50 ug/ml LDL in presence of 2 mM Ca^{++}

(2) was incubated without LDL

(3) was incubated with 50 ug/ml LDL in presence of 10 mM EDTA

(4) was incubated with 50 ug/ml LDL in presence of 2 mM Ca^{++}

(5) was incubated without LDL

(6) was incubated with 50 ul LDL in presence of 10 mM EDTA

Blots were developed with goat anti-LDL (1 mg/ml) and rabbit anti-goat IgG HRP conjugate (1: 1000).

Symposium

Application – Clinical and Genetic

Chairmen:
K. Felgenhauer,
C. A. Saravis and K. Taketa

TISSUE ELECTROPHORESIS AND HUMAN TUMOR MARKERS

Calvin A. Saravis, Robert C. Allen, Peter Thomas, Norman Zamcheck

Gastrointestinal Research Laboratory, Mallory Institute of Pathology;
Departments of Surgery and Medicine, Harvard Medical School;
Department of Pathology, Boston University School of Medicine; Boston, Massachusetts 02118;
Medical University of South Carolina, Department of Pathology, Charleston, South Carolina 29425

SUMMARY

Improved resolution and analysis of proteins, including human tumor markers, separated by agarose direct tissue isoelectric focusing, result from the use of a mask overlay covering the gel surface during electrophoresis. This optimizes electrophoretic conditions and stabilizes agarose media during electrofocusing.

When agarose isoelectric focusing gels are cast on porous supports and used with the mask overlay, easier and more quantitative transfer of electrofocused proteins to nitrocellulose membranes is obtained, resulting in improved characterization of tumor markers and tumor associated antigens.

1 INTRODUCTION

Agarose electrophoretic techniques, in particular, agarose isoelectric focusing (IEF),(1), and direct tissue isoelectric focusing (DTIF),(2), are important techniques in the analysis of protein and glycoprotein heterogeneity especially those of molecular weights greater than 200,000 dalton. We have been using these techniques to study human tumor markers and tumor associated antigens (3,4,5). We found that results obtained using current procedures were not reproducible even following rigorous standardization of techniques; and thus improved procedures were necessary. Accordingly, technique changes have been made to simplify and increase reproducibility of IEF and DTIF analytical procedures for tumor markers and other trace components. These procedures can be used with serum, tissue extracts, solid tissues, tissue culture cells, and peripheral blood cells. The analytical procedures described in this paper are easy to do, give very good resolution, contribute to inter and intra laboratory standardization and reproducibility, and save time and reagents.

2. ISOELECTRIC FOCUSING AND DIRECT TISSUE ISOELECTRIC FOCUSING

Agarose isoelectric focusing (1) can show varability due to:

a. expression of fluid on the gel surface
b. formation of "hills and vales" on the gel surface indicating concentration zones of ampholytes in the gradient
c. evaporation of fluid from the gel
d. movement and collection of fluid at the cathodal wick
e. edge effects resulting in band distortions.

2.1 Mask

Improvements in IEF and DTIF can be made by using a mask overlay that covers the gel surface during electrophoresis, preventing or significantly decreasing the undesirable characteristics noted above. The mask is cut from 2 mil Mylar with cutouts for sample deposition and electrode wick placement. As a result of its use, a)wavy separation patterns are eliminated or greatly reduced, with increased resolution and easier comparison of samples, b) better contact of transfer membranes is made with improved resolution of the transferred proteins, c) thinner gels can be used, and d) preformed IEF media and 2-D gels have greater stability.

In addition, use of the mask results in accurate and reproducible placing of the wicks, and eliminates the danger of electrolytes dripping on the unprotected gel surface. The mask overlay is kept in position during IEF; and it is not necessary to turn off the electrical power supply for removal of an applicator mask as is frequently done.

2.2 Wicks

The usual electrophoretic conditions used during electrofocusing change with the use of the mask. Since evaporation is greatly minimized, the ratio of ampholytes to protein load does not increase during electrofocusing, and while a 4% ampholyte concentration is required, thinner gels can be safely used. When thick anodal wicks are used, wavy protein bands in the anodal region are obtained, probably due to fluid flow from the wick. Direct placement of the anodal electrode was found to be more satisfactory than the thick anodal wick. A thin wick (Schleicher and Schuell #577 filter paper) wet with ampholytes, most of which are in a pH range less than that of the separating gel, is now routinely used. As an example, when a 3.5-9.5 gel is used for electrofocusing, the anodal wick is wet with a solution of 2.5-4 ampholytes. This range of ampholytes is used in the anodal wick to minimize denaturation of proteins, such as prealbumins contacting acids used as anolytes.

A strong base, such as 1N NaOH in the thicker cathodal wick(S&S#470) prevents basic proteins from moving under the wick, with loss and/or waviness.

2.3 Electrophoretic Conditions

Initial application of 1 to 2 watts in electrofocusing and slow increases in wattage during the run, give better resolution than those obtained with rapid increase to the desired maximum wattage. Gel thickness is maintained during the run. As a result, zone sharpening at very high voltages for a short time can now be carried out at the end of the run, whereas previously, such high voltages often distorted the even gradient across the gel. With the use of the mask, higher voltages with better resolution can be applied to thinner plates (0.5mm instead of 0.75mm). Currently the highest voltage used with 0.75mm thick Isogel plates is 700 volts. The apparent higher resolution for a low voltage gradient is due to the improved electrochemical environment.

2.4 Direct Tissue Isoelectric Focusing

Eighty to one hundred thousand tumor cells may be placed in each mask sample cutout. After 60 volt hours (Pharmacia) at 2 watts, the residual cellular remains are swabbed from the cutout and electrofocusing continued to final conditions, (Figure 1). Interference with the established pH gradient by the buffer salts used to wash the cells is eliminated by washing of the cells with 0.15M ammonium bicarbonate buffer (pH 8) prior to counting them and their deposition in the mask cutout.

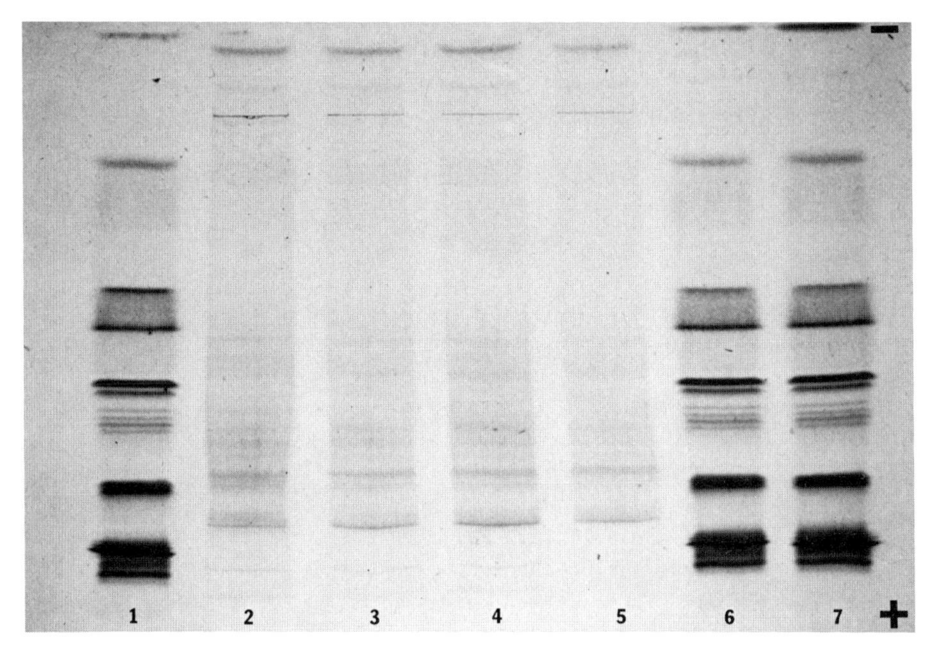

Figure 1: Direct tissue isoelectric focusing of tumor cells: One hundred fifty thousand tumor cells in 0.15M ammonium bicarbonate buffer, pH 8.0, were placed in each sample depot of the mask. Lanes 2,3,4,5, human tumor cells from more differentiated (2) to undifferentiated (5). Lanes 1,6,7, FMC pI Markers.

3 NITROCELLULOSE TRANSFERS AND FIRST DIMENSION GEL TRANSFERS IN TWO-DIMENSIONAL ELECTROPHORESIS

The elimination of hills and vales by use of the mask and Isogel (FMC) agarose electrofocusing medium significantly improves transfer of electrofocused components to immobilizing membranes since a flat surface is obtained. Similarly, two dimensional electrophoresis is made much easier where agarose is used as the first dimension and sealed to the second dimension. Formerly the wavy surface made gel transfer to the second dimension difficult especially when air was trapped in the gel waves.

3.1 Porous Gel Supports

Electroblot transfers and capillary blotting of separated components to immobilizing membranes are facilitated by casting the gel matrices on sintered porous polyethylene supports (6). This allows assembly of the transfer sandwich in air where previously it was necessary to asemble it under the buffer surface. Significant increases in resolution and retention of highly diffusible proteins results. The need for better immunodetection of tumor marker electroblot transfers has resulted in the further improvement of the sintered porous polyethlene gel support design. The use of a temporary solid plastic backing film attached with waterproof double sided tape (3M or Permafilm) to the thin reusable sintered support prevents agarose from passing through the support, resulting in a thin, uniform agarose layer. In addition, the sintered porous support with polycarbonate impregnated edges, has a raised border of solid polycarbonate welded to it, forming a frame for casting the desired gel. The support protects the fragile gels, maintains orientation, greatly increases resolution, and allows storage of preformed gels.

3.2 Transfers: Method of Operation

The sintered support can be used more than fifteen times reproducibly. It is deaerated in a suitable fluid for test, such as distilled water for isoelectric focusing, or buffer for molecular seiving. Alternatively, the support is wetted by capillary action by putting distilled water in one corner of the support. The amount of fluid taken up is constant and can be accounted for in achieving a constant concentration of gel. The plastic film with double sided tape is attached to the back of the porous support, which is at a temperature suitable for casting the gel, a cover of hydrophobic plastic or glass attached with clamps, and the gel cast in the sandwich consisting of top cover, gel, porous sintered support with border, backing film, and a rigid support such as a glass plate.

At the time of assay, the top cover is replaced with the hydrophobic plastic mask containing the sample cutouts, taking care to exclude air. Samples are placed, wicks with electrolyte or ampholyte applied, electrical connections made, and electrical current turned on. The plastic film backing is left in position to prevent contaminating the cooling plate, and to allow the use of a fluid film to conduct heat away from the reaction plate.

When separation is complete, the mask and the film backing are removed. Buffer-wet filter paper is placed back of the porous support and a buffer-wet nitrocellulose membrane placed on the gel surface, followed by a piece of wet filter paper. For capillary blotting, paper toweling is placed on the gel side removing material from the gel to and through the nitrocellulose membrane. For electroblotting, the sandwich just described is placed between compliant sponges, inserted into a cassette, and placed directly in an electroblot apparatus. Orientation of the gel is maintained, and breaking and distorting the gel is eliminated. In addition to a significant increase in resolution, there is a decreased loss of minor and diffusible components.

Following transfer of the proteins to the nitrocellulose membrane, or other immobilizing membranes, and blocking nonspecific binding of protein to the membrane with liquid gelatin (7), the proteins can be reacted with polyclonal or monoclonal antibodies, or molecular probes. Enzymes also can be immobilized without losing activity.

These procedures are useful in characterizing many of the tumor markers and tumor associated antigens being studied, as well as other clinically-important proteins. For example, carcinoembryonic antigen IEF profiles can be shown in patient plasma. We are examining human colon cancer cells by DTIF followed by immunological characterization to determine differences in protein profiles between cells of different degrees of differentiation.

We thank Dr. S. Wilhelm for providing the tumor cells, to FMC, Marine Colloids Division, for isoelectric focusing reagents, and to Mr. R. Morse at Schleicher and Schuell, for the nitrocellulose membranes. This work was supported in part by Research Grant CA-04486 from the National Cancer Institute, National Institutes of Health.

Note: Similar improvements are seen in polyacrylamide gel electrofocusing,in the cathodal region, particularly with the use of narrow range gradients such as 3.5-5, where the serum proteins cathodal to pH 4.8 are no longer wavy at voltage gradients up to 300 volts per cm.

4 REFERENCES

(1) C.A. Saravis, N. Zamcheck, J. Immun. Meth.29 (1979) 91-96.

(2) C.A. Saravis, M.J. O'Brien, N. Zamcheck, J. Immun. Meth.29 (1979) 97-100.

(3) R.C. Allen, C.A. Saravis, H.R. Maurer, Gel Electrophoresis and Isoelectric Focusing of Proteins:Selected Techniques, Walter de Gruyter, Berlin 1984.

(4) C.A. Saravis, C.G. Cunningham, P.V. Marasco, R.B. Cook, N. Zamcheck, Electrophoresis '79, Walter de Gruyter, Berlin 1980, pp. 117-122.

(5) C.A. Saravis, W. Cantarow, P.V. Marasco, B. Burke, N. Zamcheck, Electrophoresis 1 (1980) 191-193.

(6) C.A. Saravis, R.B. Cook, W.J. Polvino, C.E. Sampson, Electrophoresis 4 (1983) 367.

(7) C.A. Saravis, Electrophoresis 5 (1984) 54-55.

ENZYME ELECTROPHORESIS IN MUTATION ANALYSIS

Michael J. Siciliano, Ph.D.

Department of Genetics, The University of Texas System Cancer Center
M. D. Anderson Hospital and Tumor Institute, Houston, Texas, 77030, U.S.A.

Gerald M. Adair, Ph.D., Ronald M. Humphrey, Ph.D.

Science Park, Research Division, The University of Texas System Cancer Center
Smithville, Texas, 78957, U.S.A.

SUMMARY

Following exposure to either ultraviolet light (UVL), ethylmethane sulfonate (EMS) or ethylnitrosourea (ENU), Chinese hamster ovary (CHO) cells were cloned. Clones were expanded and examined by starch gel electrophoresis and histochemical staining for variation in the mobility and/or activity of ~45 isozyme loci. Variants were obtained at all loci and fell into three classes -- multiple-band shifts, single-band shifts, and nulls. These were verified as mutations induced at the test loci by subclone, subunit structure, gene mapping and dose response analyses. The most effective dose of mutagen inducing such mutations resulted in 10-20% cell survival. At that dose, EMS was shown to be the most effective of the three mutagens producing mutations at a frequency (f) of 5.21×10^{-3} per locus -- a mutation appearing in one out of every five clones tested. ENU was slightly less effective ($f = 3.70 \times 10^{-3}$/locus) and UVL the least effective ($f = 1.04 \times 10^{-3}$/locus) mutagen. The ability of the multiple locus screen to detect differential locus susceptibility to mutagens made it possible to reveal the considerable impact of induced mutation on mammalian cell variability, and the need to develop selectable mutation systems with multiple end points for effective mutagenicity testing. The system proved highly effective in introducing genetic markers into cultured cells.

1 INTRODUCTION

Mutation may generally be regarded as a stable change in the DNA of a gene. The simplest and most stable change in DNA is a nucleotide substitution since it effects only one of ~1000 nucleotides which may make up a gene and such a change will be eternally replicated (until the next mutation at that site). Identification of mutations and the measurement of the frequency of their occurence in mammalian cells have, for over 15 years, been very much the businesses of somatic cell geneticists.

Somatic cell assay systems to detect mutations in mammalian cells have been patterned after methods that have proven very successful in bacteria. Spontaneous or induced mutations that result in auxotrophic, drug-resistant, or temperature-sensitive variants have been selected through procedures designed to allow survival of cells that have become mutant at specific loci (for reviews see 1 and 2). Refinement of some of these procedures has produced systems considered useful in judging the mutagenic potential of physical and chemical agents. Examples are bromodeoxyuridine (BudR) resistance in mouse L5178Y cells designed to screen for mutations at the _thymidine kinase_ (_TK_) locus (3); 6-thioguanine (6TG) resistance in Chinese hamster ovary (CHO) cells to screen for mutations at the _hypoxanthine phosphoribosyl transferase_ (_HPRT_) locus (4); and ouabain resistance (OUA^R) in CHO cells to screen for mutations at the _Na+/K+ ATPase_ locus (5). Such systems select for cells in which a mutation results in the biological inactivation of the product of the target locus enabling the cells to survive under selective medium conditions. Hopefully, such systems give an approximation of what many really want to know -- the frequency of mutation induced by a test agent. Since the only mutations detectable by these systems are those that effect the enzymatic activity of the encoded protein, the approximations to the true mutagenic potential of the test agents may be rough indeed. In addition, the diploid nature of most loci in mammalian cells limits loci that may be studied to those that are hemizygous (HPRT) or have been rendered so (TK), or to systems that will select for dominant mutations (OUA^R). This limited range of testable target loci may have serious consequences in evaluating overall mutagenic activity if there are great differences in mutagenic susceptibility of loci to different mutagens. Therefore, our appreciation of the impact of mutation on somatic cell variability, as determined from data using selection systems, may be very innaccurate.

As an attempt to get an accurate view of mutation over a wide range of loci in somatic cells, we have developed a method for examining clones of cells, following mutagen exposure, for electrophoretic variations induced in the products of ~45 enzyme loci. Such variations may be viewed as the result of nucleotide substitutions producing an electrophoretically variant enzyme because of replacement of an amino acid residue with one of different charge (6). Approximately one third of amino acid substitutions should be electrophoretically informative (7). One might expect to detect electrophoretically informative mutations as much as six times more frequently than genetic alterations leading to enzyme inactivity because they are not restricted to regions coding for active sites of an enzyme molecule (8). Here we shall report our results using this approach.

2 METHODS OF PROCEDURE

All experiments were conducted using the Chinese hamster ovary (CHO) cell line. The CHO cell line, which has a modal chromosome number of 21 (9), an average generation time of 12 hr., and a plating efficiency of 70% to 90% (10), was cloned and all experiments were conducted with aliquots of cells derived from a cloned population. Cells (1×10^6) were plated into a 60-mm^2 Petri dish and incubated overnight. Cells were then exposed to varying doses of mutagen -- ultraviolet light (UVL), ethylmethane sulfonate (EMS), or ethylnitrosourea (ENU) -- and the percentage of survivors was determined (10). Incubation was continued in complete medium until the population had divided twice. The cells were then trypsinized and resuspended in medium at a dilution of one surviving cell per 0.25 ml. Each well of a 96-well Falcon Microtest plate then received 0.25 ml of culture. After 7-9 days of incubation, wells containing a single clone were picked (with trypsin) and each clone was expanded to 40-50 x 10^6 cells. This same procedure was followed for untreated cells to produce control clones. Cells of a clone were trypsinized out of bottles and then 2-3 x 10^6 cells were resuspended in medium and incubated until electrophoretic analysis of the remainder was completed. If a variant was detected in a clone, this sample was regrown for confirmation and then subcloned for heritability determination.

The remainder of the cells of a clone was homogenized. Cleared homogenates -- up to 30 at a time -- were subjected to vertical starch gel electrophoresis. A gel was sliced into as many as 10 slabs so that each could be histochemically stained for a different enzyme. Stained slices (zymograms) were then photographed and fixed. Staining was done for over 30 "housekeeping" enzymes. Methods for homogenization, starch gel electrophoresis, slicing, staining, photography, and fixing as carried out in our laboratory have been published (11). Because many of the enzymes studied have multiple forms (isozymes) coded by separate genetic loci (12), the products of 45 isozyme loci were studied for induced variation. For various reasons, every clone was not necessarily screened for the products of all 45 loci. Each clone was examined for the products of at least 30 loci and >95% of all clones were studied for 39-45 loci. After a cell homogenate containing a putative mutant gene product had been run a second time to verify that the variant was not an artifact of a particular electrophoretic run, the clone was regrown and retested to determine that the variant was not an artifact of sample preparation. Finally, the clone was subcloned with the recovery of the mutant phenotype.

3 RESULTS AND DISCUSSION

3.1 Phenotypes of Induced Variants

3.1.1 Possible Variants

A series of Chinese hamsters and Chinese hamster cell lines had been studied for variation at the same loci studied for mutation (13). Two facts relative to the present report emerged -- only two loci (ADA and AK2) were electrophoretically polymorphic in the Chinese hamster material available for study and none of the loci were electrophoretically heterozygous in CHO cells. The limited level of polymorphism present in Chinese hamsters used for research in the Western world is undoubtably due to the fact that colonies had been established and inbred from a limited number of animals (14). The lack of heterozygosity at any of the loci in CHO cells means that a mutation affecting the electrophoretic mobility of a gene product should result in one of two types of altered phenotype. For an autosomal locus which is functionally diploid in CHO cells, mutants should be multiple-banded having the product of the unaffected allele, the electrophoretically shifted product of the mutant allele, and the appropriate number of intermediately migrating heteropolymers consistent with the subunit structure of the enzyme (8, 15). For sex-linked loci or autosomal loci rendered hemizygous due to deletions or chromosomal rearrangements in CHO cells, electrophoretic variants should occur as single-band shifts. In addition to multiple- and single-band shifts, we might also recover nulls in which no enzyme activity for a particular gene product is detected.

3.1.2 Variants Obtained

Multiple-band shift, single-band shift, and null variants were obtained at the following loci (loci are identified and abbreviated according to the guidelines established for human gene nomenclature -- (16):

3.1.2.1 Multiple-band Shifts

ACP1, ACP3, ADA, AK2, ENO1, ES1, ESD, GAA, GAPD, GLO1, GOT1, GSR, HK1, IDH1, ITPA, LDHA, MDH1, MEI, MPI, NP, PEPA, PEPB, PEPC, PEPS, PGD, PGM1, PGM2, PGM3, SOD1 and TPI.

3.1.2.2 Single-band Shifts

ACP2, ES2, GOT2, G6PD, GPI, HAA, HK2, IDH2, MDH2, PEPD, PGAM and PGK.

3.1.2.3 Nulls

ACP2, ADA, ENO1, ES2, GAA, GOT2, G6PD, GPI, GUSB, HAA, HAB, HK2, IDH2, MDH2, PEPD and PGK.

3.2 Validation of Variants as Induced Mutations at Isozyme Loci

3.2.1 Were these variants due to mutational events? Heritability is the first characteristic of a variant phenotype that was due to true mutation. In our system heritability was determined by subcloning a clone shown to have a variant phenotype. Ten to 20 subclones were produced by the limiting dilution technique. Each subclone was then examined electrophoretically for the variant phenotype. Usually all subclones showed the variation indicating a true mutation. Occasionally only a sub-set of the subclones showed the variation. Such a result may have been due to an artifact in the original cloning -- more than a single cell may have been deposited in a cloning well following exposure to mutagen. Another reason for such a result may have been the delayed fixation of the mutant phenotype with wild type and mutant cells segregating after cloning. In either case, the true mutational nature of the variant was verified by further subcloning of one of the variant subclones and recovering 100% variants. Variants at all loci indicated above met these criteria and are, therefore considered the products of mutational events.

3.2.2 Were the mutations at the structural isozyme loci or at some second site leading to post-translational modification of isozyme gene products? There are two lines of evidence that support the former view.

3.2.2.1 Subunit structure argument for multiple-band shift mutants. If multiple-band shift mutations were the result of electrophoretic heterozygosity induced at formerly homozygous diploid loci, then the multiple-band patterns ought to be similar to heterozygousity found at these loci in nature and be consistent with the subunit structures of the encoded enzymes. This would be good evidence for the induction of mutant alleles at the specific test loci. Over the years it has been well demonstrated that heterozygosity for a monomeric enzyme results in a two-banded pattern -- product of the "wild" type allele and product of the mutant or variant allele with no intermediately migrating heteropolymer since, by definition, monomeric enzymes are composed of only a single polypeptide. For a dimeric enzyme, heterozygous patterns are 3-banded -- the two homodimers of the products of wild type and mutant alleles and the intermediately migrating heterodimer. Due to the random association of polypeptides into homo- and hetero-polymers, the ratio of activities of the three bands is 1:2:1. By the same principles, heterozygotes for trimeric enzymes are four-banded patterns with a 1:3:3:1 ratio of band activities, and heterozygotes for tetrameric molecules are five-banded in a 1:4:6:4:1 ratio (see 17 for a review and further discussion of these events). In all cases of our multiple-band shift mutants, the patterns were consistent with the subunit structures of the enzymes indicating heterozygosity at dizygous isozyme loci.

3.2.2.2. Concordance of loci producing multiple-band shift, single-band shift and null mutations with the ploidy and chromosomal location of the loci in CHO cells. As indicated above, multiple-band shift mutants should be limited to autosomal loci which remain functionally diploid in CHO cells while single band shift mutants should be restricted to hemizygous loci -- either sex linked, or autosomal (rendered hemizygous by chromosomal changes known to have taken place in CHO cells -- (18, 19). There should be a preferance for null mutations to have taken place at loci having only a single functional copy of the structural gene (hemizygous). These points are supported by inspection of the loci that fall into the three variant classes (see 3.1.2.1., 3.1.2.2., and 3.1.2.3. above). Consistent with the hypothesis, no loci that produced multiple-band shift mutants also produced single-band shift mutants. Also, of the twelve loci at which single band shift mutants were recovered, eleven also produced null mutants indicating the likely hemizygosity of those loci. Of the remaining loci that produced null mutants, two (GUSB and HAB) did not produce any shift mutants so they may be hemizygous but are uninformative in this analysis. Only three null mutants, one each at ADA, ENO1 and GAA were inconsistent with the remainder of the observations since several multiple-band shift mutants were recovered at these loci. The nulls at these loci may have been regulatory mutations, clones at which one of the alleles may have been lost and the second mutated to null, or clones at which two null mutations had taken place. The great bulk of the data is consistent with the idea that loci producing multiple-banded mutants are dizygous, whereas those producing single band shifts and nulls (with the exception of ADA, ENO1, and GAA) are hemizygous.

Definitive proof of this hypothesis comes from our gene mapping studies. Normal euploid Chinese hamster spleen or fibroblast cells, as well as CHO cells, were polyethylene glycol-fused with mouse C11D cells. Interspecific hybrid clones segregated hamster genetic material. In series of such studies (20-32) summarized in Siciliano et al (33) Chinese hamster isozyme loci were assigned to chromosomal elements. ACP1, ADA, AK2, ENO1, ESD, GAA, GAPD, GLO1, GSR, ITPA, LDHA, ME1, MPI, NP, PEPB, PEPS, PGD, PGM1, PGM2, PGM3, and TPI (21 of the 30 loci that produced multiple-band shift mutations) mapped onto Chinese hamster autosomes in euploid cells. In CHO cells, these loci were shown to have two alleles each mapping onto specific CHO chromosomes. The remaining loci producing multiple-band shift mutations have not yet been mapped. G6PD and PGK (two of the loci producing single-band shift and null mutations) were shown to be functionally hemizygous due to their X-linkage in both euploid and CHO cells. GOT2, GPI, IDH2, MDH2, and PEPD (five of the remaining nine loci producing single band shift and null mutations) were assigned to Chinese hamster autosomes, but were shown to have only a single functional allele in CHO cells because of the loss of the homologous allele due to deletion or monosomy. Remaining loci that produced single-band shift or null mutations have yet to be mapped.

Therefore, the available data confirm the genetic basis of the multiple-band shift, single-band shift and null mutations observed in CHO cells and indicate that the mutations observed were at the target isozyme loci.

3.2.3. Were the mutations at isozyme loci induced by mutagen treatment or were cells carrying mutations picked out of a heterogenous population of CHO cells? Since each experiment was started from a cloned population of CHO cells, reducing heterogeneity, it would appear unlikely that the mutations were anything but induced. However, the best evidence comes from dose response data generated from a series of UVL and EMS experiments. These data are shown in Table 1.

TABLE 1. Frequency of Electrophoretically Detected Mutant Clones Following UVL and EMS Exposure

Mutagen	% Survival	No. clones Tested	No. loci screened*	No. Mutants	Frequency of Mutants/Locus x 10^{-3}
None	100	383	16,086	1	0.06
UVL	30-50	288	10,231	5	0.49
	10-20	355	14,475	15	1.04
	~1	303	13,685	8	0.58
EMS	~50	107	4,340	9	2.07
	10-20	473	19,383	101	5.21

* Number of clones x number of loci screened/clone.

There is a clear and significant ($p < .001$) increase in the frequency of electrophoretically detectable mutations with the mutagenic dose as measured by cell survival indicating that the mutations were indeed induced by mutagen. The data also indicates that the most effective dose for producing such mutations results in 10-20% survival of the treated cells. This then has become our standard level of cytotoxicity in mutation experiments.

3.3 Induced Mutation Frequencies in Mammalian Somatic Cells

As was suggested in the "INTRODUCTION", the multiple locus screen for induced, electrophoretically detected mutations in mammalian cells was expected to give us a more accurate view of these events than was possible using the more classical, selective systems. Since the UVL dose response data indicated that the most effective mutagen treatment level was one that resulted in 10-20% survival of the cells (Table 1), we will look at the results of the three mutagens used at that dose point. EMS proved to be the most effective mutagen in the system. This is consistent with the results of Hsie et al. (34) obtained by screening CHO cells for mutations selected by 6TG. However, the frequency at which mutations were obtained, 5.21×10^{-3} per locus screened, is the highest ever obtained in a generalized mutation screen (one out of every five clones picked had a mutation!). The results with ENU were not much lower -- $f = 3.70 \times 10^{-3}$. Clearly, the impact of mutation on the induction of mammalian somatic cell variability is greater than one would have predicted on the basis of data from selective systems.

We believe this finding to be the result of differential locus susceptibility to mutagen which is only detectable by the multiple locus approach used here. For instance, in the UVL experiments (35), three loci were candidates for such differentially susceptible mutagenesis since more than two mutations were recovered at them in the irradiated groups. These include four *MDH2* shifts, three *IDH2* nulls, and five *HK2* nulls -- a total of 12 mutations out of 2838 loci screened (*MDH2*, *IDH2*, and *HK2* were each screened in all 946 UV-exposed clones). The fact that 12 of the 28 mutations obtained in the irradiated groups were at only three of the mean 41 loci screened/clone indicates that loci may be heterogeneous with respect to their susceptibility to UVL mutagenesis. This is consistent with the *in vivo* germ-line results of Johnson and Lewis (36) where six of the nine mutations were seen at only three of the 21 loci in their screen. For EMS, we recovered mutations at five loci (*PEPB*, *MDH2*, *HK2*, *PGM1*, and *PGM2*) in excess of 1% while for ENU *MPI*, *PEPB*, *ADA*, *MDH2*, *HK2*, *PEPD*, and *IDH2* mutations were recovered at frequencies of ~1% and above. Obviously some loci appear to be more generally susceptible to mutagenesis than others -- eg.: *MDH2*, *IDH2*, and *HK2*. Perhaps *PEPB* should also be in this category and the recovery of only one such mutation in the UVL studies (35) may be a reflection of the much lower mutagenic potential of that mutagen compared to the alkylating agents.

Of much greater interest are the results which indicate loci exquisitely sensitive to one mutagen, but not so to others. For instance, the high frequency of *PGM1* and *PGM2* mutations after exposure to EMS was not obtained with UVL and ENU, and the high frequency of *MPI*, *ADA*, and *PEPD* mutations after exposure to ENU was not obtained after exposure to UVL or EMS. The molecular bases of these differences has yet to be determined. However, for the present, the results indicate the need for caution in interpreting results on the mutagenic potential of agents where such potential is based on tests in which just one or a few loci were available for evaluation.

4 CONCLUSION

The multiple isozyme locus approach for detection of induced mutation in mammalian somatic cells is a valid system. Results using the system to screen for mutations after exposure to UVL, EMS, and ENU indicate that there is considerable differential locus susceptibility to mutagens and that the impact of somatic mutation on somatic cell variability, as a general phenomenon, appears to be much greater than previously suspected. While the systems may be inappropriate for large scale mutagen testing programs, results with it indicate the limitations of selective systems and point to the need to expand the base of selectable marker loci for use in such programs. Finally, results indicate that the system appears to be extremely effective in introducing genetic markers into mammalian cells.

5 ACKNOWLEDGEMENTS

The gene mapping aspects of these studies were carried out with the collaboration of Dr. Raymond Stallings presently in the Genetics Group, Los Alamos National Laboratories, Los Alamos, New Mexico, U.S.A. The research was partially supported by N.I.H. research grants CA4484, CA28711 and CA34797, and by a gift from the Exxon Corporation.

6 REFERENCES

(1) L. H. Thompson, R. M. Baker, Methods in Cell Biology, Vol. VI, Academic Press, New York 1973, pp. 209-281.

(2) L. Siminovitch, Cell, 7 (1976), 1-11.

(3) D. Clive, K. O. Johnson, J. F. S. Spector, A. G. Batson, M. M. M. Brown, Mutation Res. 59 (1979) 61-108.

(4) J. P. O'Neill, D. B. Couch, R. Machanoff, J. R. San Sebastian, P. A. Brimer, A. W. Hsie, Mutation Res. 45 (1977) 103-109.

(5) R. M. Baker, D. M. Brunette, R. Mankovitz, L. H. Thompson, G. F. Whitmore, L. Siminovich, J. E. Till, Cell 1 (1974) 9-21.

(6) U. Henning, C. Yanofsky, J. Mol. Biol. 6 (1963) 16-21.

(7) M. Nei, Molecular Population Genetics and Evolution, American Elsevier Publishing Company, New York 1975, pp. 26-28.

(8) M. J. Siciliano, R. Humphrey, E. Murgola, M. C. Watt, Isozymes IV (1975) 763-780.

(9) J. H. Tijo, T. T. Puck, J. Exp. Medicine 108 (1958) 259-268.

(10) R. M. Humphrey, B. A. Sedita, R. E. Meyn, Inter. J. of Rad. Biol. 18 (1970) 61-69.

(11) M. J. Siciliano, C. R. Shaw, Chromatographic and Electrophoretic Techniques, Vol. II, William Heinemann Medical Books Ltd., London 1976, pp. 185-209.

(12) C. Markert, Acad. Sci. 151 (1968) 14-40.

(13) R. L. Stallings, M. J. Siciliano, Somatic Cell Genet. 7 (1981) 295-306.

(14) G. Yerganian, J. Natl. Can. Inst. 20 (1958) 705-720.

(15) M. J. Siciliano, J. Siciliano, R. M. Humphrey, Proc. Nat. Acad. Sci. USA 75 (1978) 1919-1923.

(16) T. B. Shows, and 24 co-authors, Cytogenet. Cell Genet. 25 (1979) 96-116.

(17) H. Harris, The Principles of Human Biochemical Genetics, Elsevier/ North-Holland Biomedical Press, New York 1980.

(18) L. L. Deaven, D. F. Peterson, Chromosoma 41 (1973) 129-144.

(19) R. G. Worton, C. C. Ho, C. Duff, Somat. Cell Genet. 3 (1977) 27-45.

(20) R. L. Stallings, M. J. Siciliano, Somat. Cell Genet. 7 (1981) 683-698.

(21) R. L. Stallings, M. J. Siciliano, G. M. Adair, R. M. Humphrey, Somat. Cell Genet. 8 (1982) 413-422.

(22) M. J. Siciliano, R. L. Stallings, G. M. Adair, R. M. Humphrey, J. Siciliano, Cytogenet. Cell Genet. 35 (1983) 15-20.

(23) R. L. Stallings, M. J. Siciliano, J. Heredity, 73 (1982) 399-404.

(24) G. M. Adair, R. L. Stallings, K. K. Friend, M. J. Siciliano, Somat. Cell Genet. 9 (1983) 477-487.

(25) G. M. Adair, R. L. Stallings, R. S. Nairn, M. J. Siciliano, Proc. Natl. Acad. Sci. USA 80 (1983) 5961-5964.

(26) R. L. Stallings, G. M. Adair, J. Siciliano, J. Greenspan, M. J. Siciliano, Molec. Cell. Genet. 3 (1983) 1967-1974.

(27) R. L. Stallings, G. M. Adair, M. J. Siciliano, Somat. Cell & Mol. Genet. 10 (1984) 109-111.

(28) R. L. Stallings, G. M. Adair, J. Lin, M. J. Siciliano, Cytogenet. Cell Genet. (in press).

(29) G. M. Adair, R. L. Stallings, M. J. Siciliano, Somat. Cell & Mol. Genet. 10 (1984) 283-295.

(30) A. Westerveld, R. P. L. S. Visser, M. A. Freeke, D. Bootsma, Biochem. Genet. 7 (1972) 33-40.

(31) S. A. Farrell, R. G. Worton, Somat. Cell Genet. 3 (1977) 539-551.

(32) M. Rosentraus, L. A. Chasin, Proc. Natl. Acad. Sci. USA 72 (1975) 493-497.

(33) M. J. Siciliano, R. L. Stallings, G. M. Adair, R. M. Humphrey, In Molecular Cell Genetics: The Chinese Hamster Cell (in press).

(34) A. W. Hsie, P. A. Brimer, T. J. Mitchell, D. G. Gosslee, Somat. Cell Genet. 1 (1975) 383-389.

(35) M. J. Siciliano, B. F. White, R. M. Humphrey, Mutation Res. 107 (1983) 167-176.

(36) F. M. Johnson, S. E. Lewis, Proc. Natl. Acad. Sci. USA 78 (1981) 3138-3141.

CONCEPT AND APPLICATIONS OF DOUBLE ONE-DIMENSIOANL SLAB GEL ELECTROPHORESIS.

Klaus Altland, Rolf Hackler

Institute of Human Genetics, Justus-Liebig-University of Giessen, Schlangenzahl 14, D-6300 Giessen, Federal Republic of Germany

Summary

Double one-dimensional (D 1-D) slab gel electrophoresis has become a valuable tool for the study of interindividual sample variation where single one-dimensional electrophoretic techniques do not allow the recognition of the patterns of interest or their evaluation in qualitative and/or quantitative terms. The technical principle consists of a useful sequencial one-dimensional combination of two or more electrophoretic separations in slab gels. This paper demonstrates some of these combinations by examples of application performed in the author's laboratory. The resulting patterns of several human blood proteins are shown which are apolipoprotein AI, prealbumin, α_1-acid glycoprotein (orosomucoid), α_1-antitrypsin, 7S-β_1-glycoprotein, α_1B-glycoprotein and transferrin.

1 INTRODUCTION

1.1 Dimensions and Parameters

The study of individual proteins from body fluids or cell

Abbreviations: 2-D: Two-dimensional; D1-D: Double one-dimensional; CTAB: Cetyl trimethyl ammonium bromide; IEF: Isoelectric focusing; NP-40: Nonidet P-40; PAGE: Polyacrylamide gel electrophoresis.

homogenates and the demonstration of their heterogeneity patterns due to pre- and posttranslational modifications is mostly preceded by a varying number of sequential separation procedures based on different parameters like molecular size and shape, pI, solubility, electrophoretic mobility at varying pH, adsorptive properties, affinity to biological or artificial ligands, reactivity with detergents, etc.. At the end of such a multiparameter separation chain there is often the pure protein or one of its subunits or microheterogeneity components which can be further studied by functional tests or with regard to its chemical composition. As far as sequential electrophoretic separation steps are concerned and the parameters affecting separation are in fact different, some kind of one-, two-, three- or multiparameter electrophoresis is the basis of analytical or preparative isolation of the component of interest (1-5).

In addition to separation parameters spatial vectors are used to study the variability of proteins. Two-dimensional electrophoresis is the most frequently used example for this. As far as the same parameter is used the separated components will be located in a diagonal area with the exception for those which change their migration properties under the conditions of the experiment. If the parameters affecting the migration in both dimensions are independant of each other the spots of a two-dimensional pattern are located on a gel very similar to a set of uncorrelated data on a two-dimensional plot. The combination of two independant parameters with two spatial dimensions by the high resolution 2-D electrophoresis according to O'Farrell (6) has become the most powerful method to obtain a survey on what is the general composition of cells or body fluids but it is not very effective with regard to the information on an individual component of the sample due to the high proportion of redundant information on other proteins. It is the combination of a second separation parameter with a second spatial dimension which permits to obtain by one experiment a reliable set of comparable data on a high number of different individuals in a multicomponent sample. This is due to the fact that by including a second spatial dimension the test for the second parameter can be performed simultaneously for all components under identical experimental conditions.

1.2 THE CONCEPT OF D 1-D SLAB GEL ELECTROPHORESIS

The concept of D 1-D slab gel electrophoresis combines a sequential two parameter separation with the extremely advantageous effect of 2-D electrophoresis permitting the test for the second parameter to be performed under exactly identical experimental conditions for all components of interest. The conceptional difference is represented by the components under study. While these are all macromolecular components of one test sample in the 2-D experiment it is one individual component and its variability from many samples in the D 1-D slab gel experiment. The test principle for this concept consists in the sequential combination of two tests of electrophoretic parameters by slab gel techniques. A fraction from the first slab gel containing the test protein from all applied samples is transferred to the second slab gel and tested for the second paramater while the migration axis remains unchanged. As a result exactly comparable data are obtained on the sample to sample variability of single macromolecular components. Opposite to the test principle of 2-D analysis the number of sequential parameter tests under identical conditions for the test proteins is only limited by the number of useful slab gel techniques which can be combined with each other. In this sense the principle of D 1-D slab gel electrophoresis resembles very much the sequential combination of rod gel techniques used for the study of an individual component in an individual sample.

The first example of application of D1-D slab gel electrophoresis which has come to the author's knowledge was described in 1975 by Altland et al. (7). They used flat gel IEF to fractionate serum proteins from families of cystic fibrosis patients and transferred the gel strip containing the IgG fraction of all samples to the stacking gel of a horizontal disk electrophoresis system for basic proteins (8) to separate the low molecular size components from the bulk of IgG protein. An improvement of this technique was recently described (9).In 1978 Singer et al. (10) used the test principle in the sequence SDS-PAGE followed by IEF in the presence of 6 M urea and 2 % NP-40 to study genetic variants of E. coli proteins and in the same year we used the sequence of PAGE at pH 8.6 without urea and detergents followed by IEF in the presence of 4 M urea to selectively demonstrate genetic variants of human serum transferrin (11). The application of the sequence IEF in the presence of 4 M urea followed by electrophoresis in an agarose gel containing anti human transferrin IgG was described in 1979 by Altland et al. (12) and the combination of charge shift electrophoresis of CTAB-treated plasma samples in agarose followed by IEF in the presence of urea was described by Utermann in 1980 (13,14). More recently described examples of application will be mentioned later.

1.3 LIMITS OF USEFUL APPLICATION

For all methods there are limits for useful applications. D 1-D slab gel electrophoresis appears to be a valuable complementary experiment to provide a better understanding of the spots in a 2-D electrophoretic pattern as it presents the sample to sample variability of this spot due to pre- and posttranslational modifications by genetic and environmental influence. Its application makes no sense where a simple one-dimensional slab gel technique provides the same information. This would be the case where protein specific staining or immunofixation techniques are available. D 1-D slab gel electrophoresis permits the study of conformational changes of a test protein produced by variables that can be introduced into the slab gel matrix as for instance an urea concentration gradient. Protein specific titration curves affecting the conformation will present valuable information on protein structure, solubility as well as on the best condition for spatial and band resolution.

2 METHODS

The available space for this contribution does not allow to present the methods in detail. In principle any two slab gel techniques can be used for the combination in a D 1-D electrophoretic experiment. There are, however, certain limitations: [**1**] The transfer of one gel to the other is most easily performed by overlay. The thickness of the transferred gel should not exceed much the thickness of the gel to which it is applied since otherwise the field strength at the site of application will be too low for an effective protein transfer. The thickness relation of the transferred gel to the overlayed gel should not exceed a value of 1.5. Also the pore size of the transferred gel strip should be kept as large as possible to facilitate the migration of the testprotein into the second flat gel. [**2**] The electroendosmotic properties of the transferred and overlayed gel should be similar or identical to avoid water accumulation at the application site leading to contamination of neighboured sample material. [**3**] The site of application of the transferred gel on the overlayed gel should be optimized by prior experiments. It is often easily found by diagonal application of a test strip. [**4**] The localisation of the gel fraction with the testprotein in the unstained first slab gel is sometimes tricky. Stained marker proteins like hemoglobin could be applied to the extreme left and right sample wells. When discontinuous buffer systems are used the tracking dye boundary could be used as a reference zone. The extreme left and right sample lane could be cut out and submitted to a quick stain for protein. Singer et al. (10) used dansylated marker samples which could be observed by exposure to long wave UV-light. The extreme left and right samples could be overloaded with an unstained marker protein which can be located in the unstained gel by the Schlieren pattern of the zone boundaries. The test procedures could be calibrated and standardized to permit a blind metric localization of the fraction of interest. [**5**] The identification of the testprotein in the final pattern can be easiliy obtained by comparison with the pattern of a purified authentic protein sample or by the method of immunosubtraction or immunofixation by specific antibodies. [**6**] Sometimes the combination of two slab gel separations alone does not meet the requirements for a selective demonstration of the testprotein. In this case a special treatment of the samples might further help to reduce contaminating material in the final pattern. [**7**] The experience of 10 years of experimentation with this test principle has shown that there is no general optimum test condition for the demonstration of varying testproteins by D 1-D slab gel electrophoresis. As all proteins vary with regard to the parameters that can be tested by electrophoretic experiments and others like solubility, sensitivity to oxidation, cleavage into fragments or subunits, loss of ligands, reactivity with other molecules like free carrier ampholytes, etc., which all affect electrophoretic separations, the test conditions have to be adjusted to the specific properties of the protein by prior experiments.

3 RESULTS AND DISCUSSION

The first presented example of D1-D slab gel electrophoresis is very similar to that described by Singer et al. [10] for E. coli protein variants. The demonstration of the human plasmaprotein apolipoprotein AI by this procedure (15,16) which has been developed without the knowledge of the paper of Singer et al. is presented in Fig. 1 and 2. As can be seen from Fig. 1a the identification of the testprotein was performed by both a genetic and an immunological test. The evidence was provided by a deficiency of the testprotein in the plasmapattern of a patient with Tangier's disease as well as in a normal serum sample treated with an IgG-fraction of a specific antiserum against the apolipoprotein AI. The indicated gel strip was identified in the unstained gel by its location relative to the Schlieren pattern of the globin zones at the extreme left and right

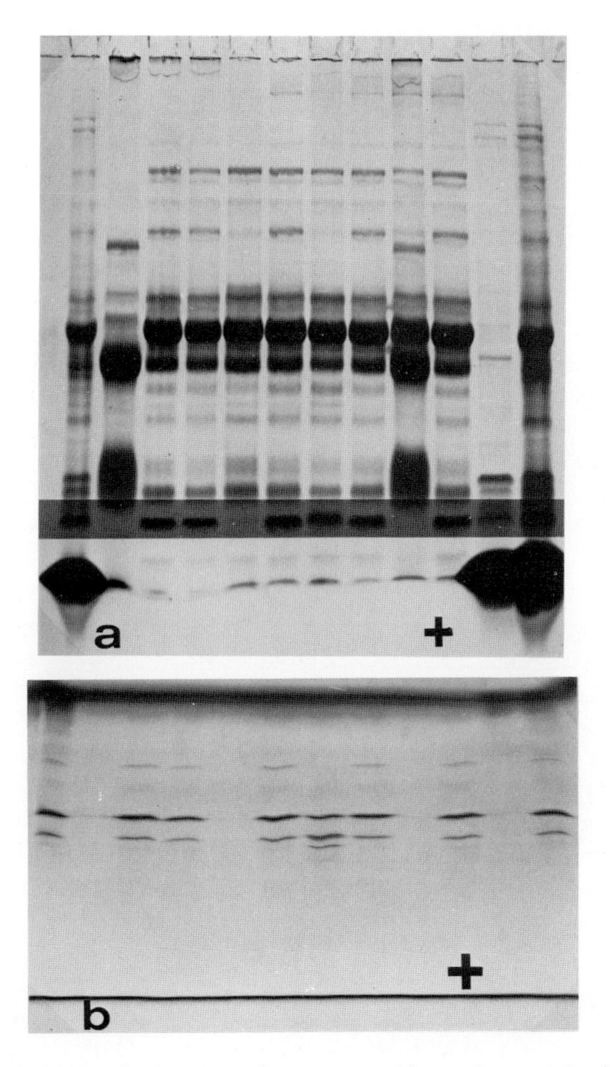

Fig. 1: a) SDS-PAGE of human plasma, erythrocytes and full blood stained with Coomassie R-250. The shaded area contains the apolipoprotein AI fraction. Sample no. 9 from left contains the immunosubtracted serum, sample no. 5 was from a patient with Tangier's disease. b) The final D1-D pattern of the shaded gel strip indicated in a). Note the charge variant in sample no. 7.

lane. The resulting pattern after slab gel IEF in the presence of 8 M urea shows the selective apolipoprotein AI pattern with a genetic charge variant in one sample. As expected the charge variant was in the SDS-gel pattern which means in other terms that by using this test combination charge variants don't get lost if the normal test protein is included in the gel strip transferred from the first gel. Fig.2 demonstrates how this procedure can be converted into a potent screening test. There are the patterns of 96 samples including 10 with a genetic charge variant. 5 of these variants were from different individuals identified among a total of 4,000 samples from midtrimester women.

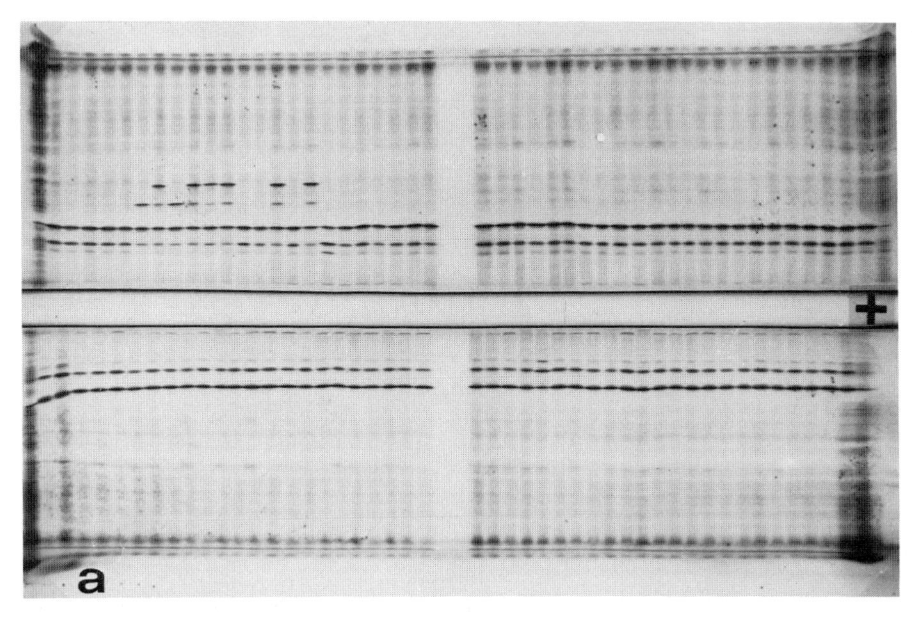

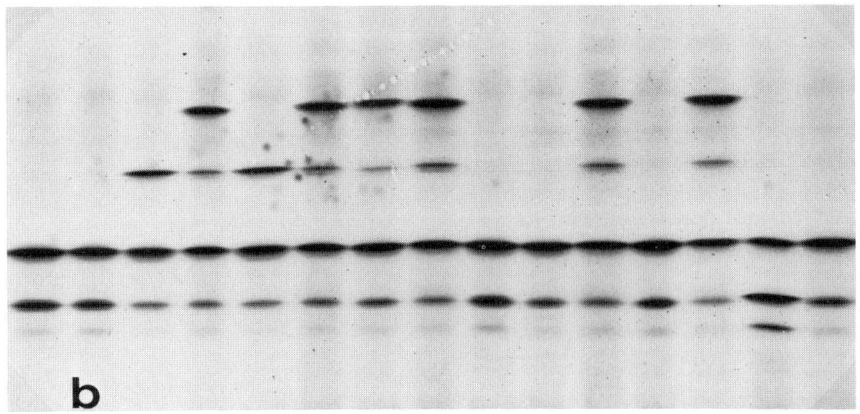

Fig. 2: a) D1-D screening gel with 96 samples containing several genetic variants. A detail of this gel is shown in b).

There are several other plasma proteins which can be tested following the same procedure with the only difference that gel strips with a different location on the SDS-gel are transferred to the IEF-gel. Among these proteins are the prealbumin, the haptoglobin β- and α_2-chains, α_1-antitrypsin, α_2HS-glycoprotein and others. The patterns of protein migrating in the SDS-gel with the albumin, however, are usually completely covered by the intense background produced by this latter protein on the IEF-gel. Also proteins with a size larger than 100,000 Daltons were found to be poor candidates for this procedure because of the high frictional resistance of the SDS-gel (T=5%) and low field strength at the site of overlay. Carbonic anhydrase I from human erythrocytes is fairly denatured by this procedure with the consequence that no sharp band could be obtained in the final pattern. In general it turned out that this procedure is very useful for the screening of charge variants of proteins with a molecular size smaller than 100,000 Daltons. There may be, however, the additional problem that rather small proteins like apolipoprotein AII (Mr 17,380) and haptoglobin α_1-chain (Mr 8,860) dissociate from their SDS-complexes with a minor proportion than larger components. We were not able at the present state of our art to demonstrate these components by this procedure when using standard Coomassie or silver stains in addition to increased acrylamide concentration (T=8%) in the final IEF-gel.

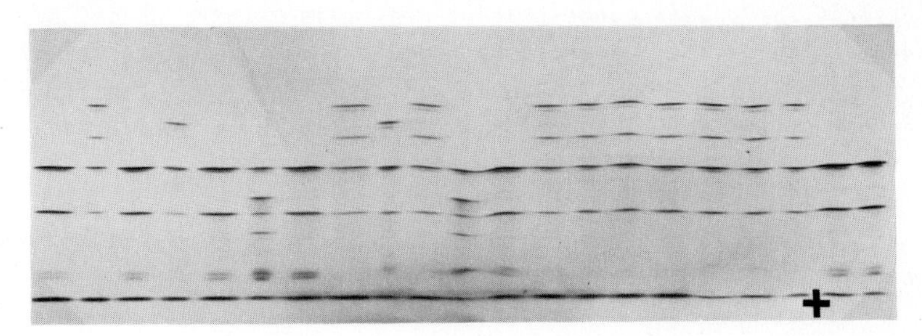

Fig. 3: A detail of a D1-D screening gel showing several genetic variants of prealbumin found among 4,000 tested serum samples.

The demonstration of genetic charge variants of prealbumin by D1-D slab gel electrphoresis in the sequence of discontinuous PAGE followed by IEF in a gel containing 8 M urea has been described in detail (17). Fig. 3 shows 3 different charge variants of this protein with one of them found in 6 copies among 4,000 serum samples. The patterns are those of the monomers visible in two major forms of different charge. In this case the first step of fractionation was a discontinuous PAGE without the addition of a detergent. The application of the test samples was preceeded by a prerun till the tracking dye boundary had entered the gel (T=5%; C=3%) by 4 cm. After sample application all proteins migrating faster than transferrin were also faster than the tracking dye boundary. The run was stopped at a distance of 2 cm between the blue stained cathodic boundary of the albumin zone and the tracking dye boundary. By preliminary experiments it was found that under these conditions a 7 mm wide gel strip with the tracking dye boundary in its center contained all prealbumin as a tetramer and part of the orosomucoid material but no albumin. The modified procedure provides a good control for all prealbumin variants migrating between the tracking dye boundary ond orosomucoid to be included in the final D1-D pattern and not lost by erraneous fractionation of the unstained gel used for the first separation step.

Orosomucoid or α_1-acid glycoprotein was selectively demonstrated by a rather similar procedure which has been described in detail (18). The comparative study of this protein pattern in plasma samples from patients with severe polytrauma revealed an interesting phenomenon (19). It can be seen from the patterns and their densitometric evaluation demonstrated in Fig. 4 that after a polytrauma there is a drastic change in the orosomucoid pattern with a shift of the center of density towards the cathode which is accompanied by the well known increase of the plasma concentration of this acute phase protein. However, a few days after the polytrauma the center of density of the pattern returns to its initial value while the total plasma concentration remains high. In this case the patient recovered rather fast from an accident. In others with slow recovery or even death within a few day's interval the center of density remained high. Further experiments are needed to explain these changes. Liver stress associated with incomplete biosynthesis of complex carbohydrate side chains or increased sialidase activity could be possible reasons. It should be emphasized that this observation could not be made by standard quantitative measurements of the plasma concentration and that the rather precise densitometric quantification of the changes in the orosomucoid pattern were only possible due to the electrophoretic demonstration of these patterns against a background free from contaminations.

The plasma samples of the same patient were also tested for variations in the microheterogeneity pattern of α_1-antitrypsin (19). To obtain a rather selective demonstration of this protein the samples were first run in a polyacrylamide gel containing Dextrane Blue. The

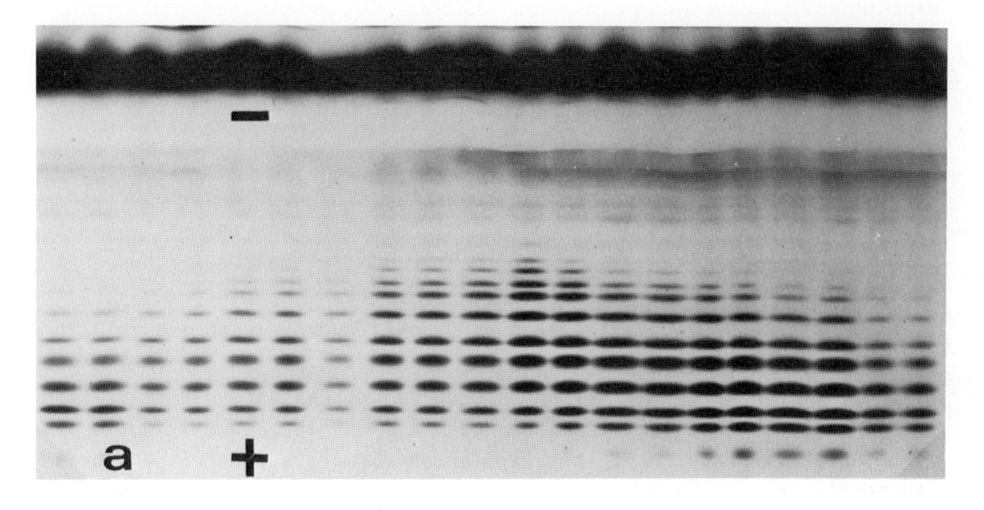

Fig. 4: a) The change of the orosomucoid microheterogeneity pattern in the plasma of a papient after a polytrauma. The densitometric evaluation (b)) revealed that the change of the center of density (•) is independant of the change of the total orosomucoid plasma concentration.

albumin absorbing dye Cibacron Blue F3G-A of this component is bound to high molecular weight (2,000,000) Dextrane which becomes fixed in the polyacrylamide gel matrix after polymerization. Thus, albumin is retained near the sample wells while α_1-antitrypsin with a usual migration rate almost identical with that of albumin is not retained and can be rather easily isolated by using this type of affinity PAGE as the first separation tep. The final pattern is seen in Fig 5. and demonstrates that the changes seen in the orosomucoid pattern are not found in the pattern of this protein which only varies by the total plasma concentration as expected.

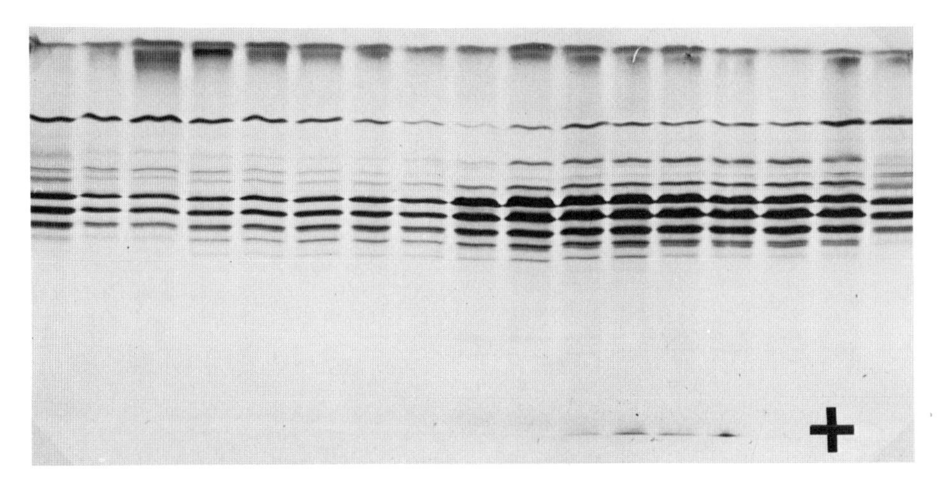

Fig. 5: The α_1-antitrypsin pattern of the same plasma samples used to demonstrate the orosomucoid patterns of Fig. 4.

By Fig. 6 it is demonstrated how the erythrocyte protein 7Sβ_1-globulin (20,15) and two genetic variants were identified by D1-D salb gel electrophoresis combined with immunosubtraction. Under the conditions of PAGE (T=5%; C=3%) at pH 8.6 this protein migrates together with hemoglobin. When the gel strip containing the hemoglobin fraction is submitted to IEF in the presence of 4 M urea the testprotein becomes clearly separated from the hemoglobin fraction and concentrated at a pI of about 5.6. The pattern of the two genetic variants found among 5,000 dried bood samples from newborns clearly demonstrate that this protein is a stable dimer under these conditions.

Sometimes, the use of 2 sequential electrophoretic techniques alone is not sufficient to demonstrate the testprotein against a background free of contaminants. Another additional measure takes advantage of the differnetial reactivity with detergents. This is shown by

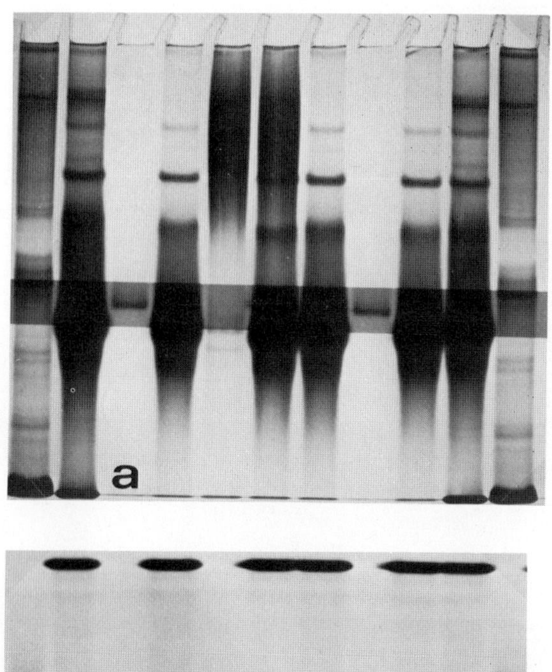

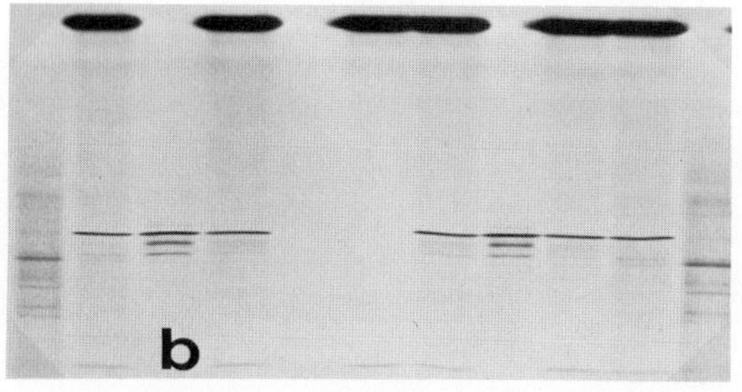

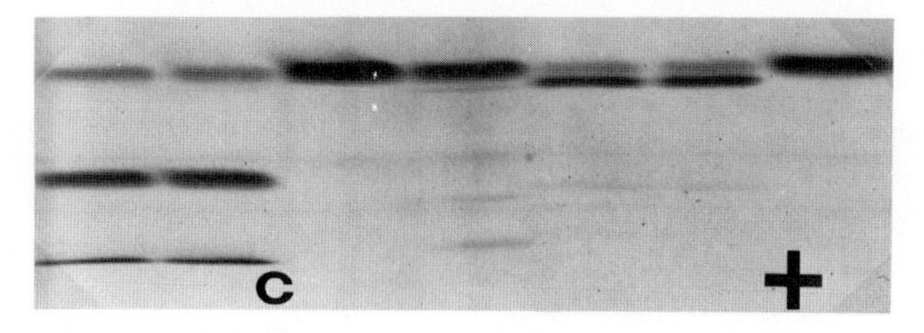

Fig. 6: a) The shaded gel strip with the PAGE pattern of serum, full blood, red cells, purified $7S\beta_1$-globulin and anti-$7S\beta_1$-globulin IgG-fraction was submitted to IEF in the presence of 4 M urea. The final D1-D pattern is shown in b). Note the result of immunosubtraction in lane 6. c) Two genetic variants of this protein were found by a screening among 5,000 dried newborn blood samples. The first 6 samples from the left are the two mother-child-father triplets demonstrating the transmittance of the variants.

pretreatment of plasma samples with the positively charged detergent CTAB which was used for separations by charge shift electrophoresis in agarose gels (21,14). As shown by Fig. 7 CTAB at a concentration of about 0.1 g% precipitates a lot of plasma proteins but does not react with others. Among these inert proteins is the α_1B-glycoprotein isolated by Schwick and Haupt (22). The study of about 200 CTAB-treated serum samples by D1-D slab gel electrophoresis revealed a genetic polymorphism for this glycoprotein at a heterozygote frequency of ca. 10 % in the German population (23).

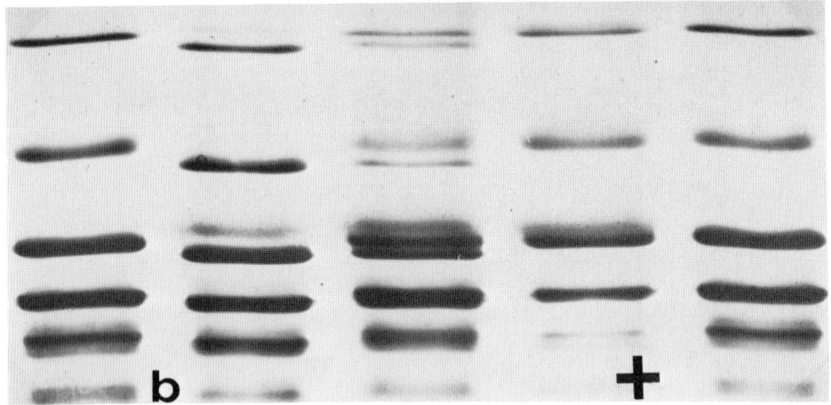

Fig. 7: a) The two 2-D patterns at the right show the effect of pretreatment of plasma with CTAB (the extreme right pattern was from untreated serum). The D1-D pattern of α_1B-glycoprotein is seen at the left and the three phenoptypes are shown in b).

Another interesting reaction of a detergent with plasma proteins modifying the electrophoretic pattern is shown in Fig. 8. When a human plasma sample is incubated in 0.2 % SDS for about 1 h at 37 °C and separated by PAGE as described for prealbumin there appears a protein fraction migrating even faster than prealbumin which contains apolipoprotein AI and AII plus some minor protein material. Collecting these proteins at the tracking dye boundary of a discontinuous PAGE system and transfering the corresponding gel strip to an IEF gel results in a simple alternative procedure for te demonstration of genetic apolipoprotein AI variants. Obviously the high density lipoprotein particles in human plasma are almost selectively destroyed by the pretreatment with SDS. Replacement of SDS by decylsulfate or Triton X-100 is by far not as effective in this reaction.

Fig. 8: The left 2-D pattern was from a serum sample treated with SDS as described. The indicated zones are the apolipoprotein AI material concentrated at the tracking dye boundary. The D1-D pattern at the reight shows two genetic variants of the testprotein.

A completely different type of application of D1-D electrophoresis is a type of titration curve for the denaturing activity of urea on a protein. This type of test was described by Hobart (24) in 1975. His test consisted of a pure protein sample solution soaked in a long paper strip which was applied on a flat IEF gel containing a urea concentration gradient perpendicular to the pH-Axis. The shift in pI

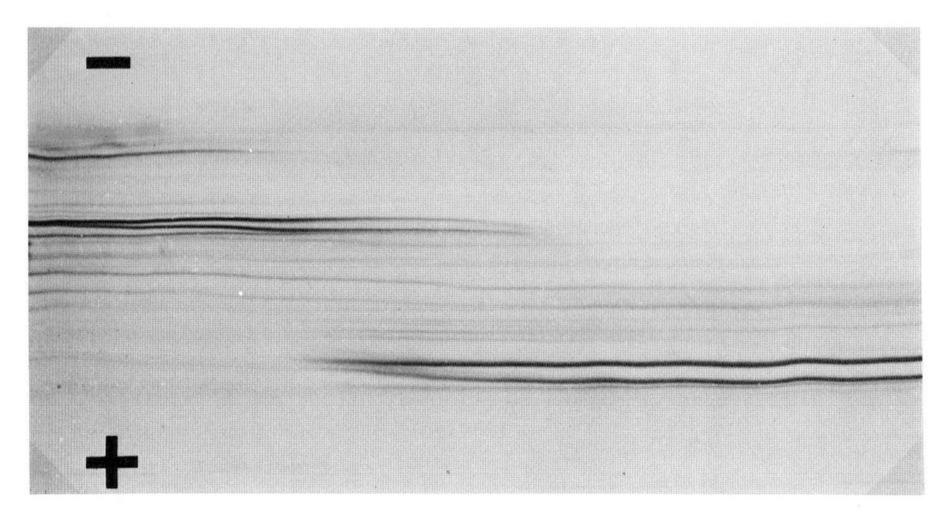

Fig. 9: Titration of a serum sample from a heterozygote for a transferrin B variant in an urea gradient between 0 (left) and 8 M (right). For further explanations see text.

of the testprotein due to conformational changes produced by the gradient can present interesting data on the structure of the protein. We have combined this test with the isolation of the testprotein by D1-D-salb gel electrophoresis to study the behaviour of several plasma proteins (17,18). One other example is given by Fig. 9. Human plasma from an individual heterozygote for a transferrin B variant was submitted to PAGE and the transferrin fraction was selected and transferred to an IEF-gel as described (25). The IEF gel contained a linear gradient between 0 and 8 M urea. The pattern obtained after IEF clearly demonstrates how both the normal and the variant transferrin protein change their pI in the range between 4 and 6 M urea which is associated by a loss of one ion of iron. Further increase of the urea concentration selectively affects the B variant which is converted to apotransferrin while the normal transferrin C protein remains in the Fe_1-transferrin form. This titration curve has shown to be specific for this variant and was not observed with several others. Such titration curves may, therefore, help in the characterization of genetic variants. We have also used this technique successfully to optimize the IEF-patterns in the sense of obtaining sharp bands (17,18).

ACKNOWLEDGEMENT:

A lot of the data presented in this summarizing paper have not been published in detail. The data were obtained by cooperation with the following coworkers: Ute Rossmann, Silke Rauh, Marlis Martin, Christa Kast, Petra Spoenemann, Brigitte Flesch, Thomas Sgraja, Thomas Roeder, Karl-Heinz Schultheiss, Arnd Petersen, and Arnold v. Eckardstein. The project was supported by the Deutsche Forschungsgemeinschaft (Grant No. Al 87/10-2). Fotos were made by Guenter Roehm.

4 REFERENCES

(1) V. Neuhoff in V. Neuhoff (Ed.), Micromethods in Molecular Biology, Springer Verlag, Berlin-Heidelberg-New York 1973, pp. 18-20

(2) R. Dernick, K. J. Wiegers, J. Heukeshoven in R.C. Allen, Ph. Arnaud (Eds.), Electrophoresis '81, Walter de Gruyter & Co., Berlin-New York 1981, pp. 245-256

(3) R. Dernick, K. J. Wiegers in B.J. Radola (Ed.), Elektrophoreseforum '82, TU Muenchen, pp. 207-217

(4) G. I. Danno, Anal. Biochem. 83 (1977) 189-193

(5) K. Bosbach in (3), pp. 344-348

(6) P. H. O'Farrell, J. Biol. Chem. 250 (1975) 4007-4021

(7) K. Altland, S.R. Schmidt, G. Kaiser, W. Knoche, Hum. Genet. 28 (1975) 207-216

(8) R. A. Reisfeld, U.T. Lewis, D.E. Williams, Nature 195 (1962) 281

(9) K. Altland, R. Hackler, Electrophoresis 2 (1981) 49-54

(10) B. S. Singer, H. Morrissett, L. Gold, Anal. Biochem. 85 (1978) 224-229

(11) K. Altland in B. J. Radola (Ed.), Elektrophoreseforum '78, TU Muenchen 1978, pp. 249-254

(12) K. Altland, R. Hackler in B.J. Radola (Ed.), Electrophoresis '79, Walter de Gruyter & Co., Berlin-New York 1980, pp. 53-66

(13) G. Utermann in B.J. Radola (Ed.), Elektrophoreseforum '80, TU Muenchen 1980, pp. 132-144

(14) G. Utermann, G. Feussner, G. Franceschini, J. Haas, A. Steinmetz, J. Biol. Chem. 257 (1982) 501-507

(15) K. Altland, Ch. Kast, S. Rauh, Th. Sgraja in H. Peeters (Ed.), Proc. XXXth Coll. Prot. Biol. Fluids 1982, Pergamon Press, Oxford-New York-Toronto-Sydney-Frankfurt 1983, pp. 595-598

(16) K. Altland, Th. Sgraja in (3), pp. 267-272

(17) K. Altland, S. Rauh, R. Hackler, Electrophoresis 2 (1981) 148-155

(18) K. Altland, Th. Roeder, H. M. Yakin, H. G. Zimmer, V. Neuhoff, Clin. Chem. 28 (1982) 1000-1010

(19) K. Altland, M. Martin, Th. Roeder, K. H. Schultheiss, H. M. Yakin, H. G. Zimmer, V. Neuhoff in (3), pp. 273-278

(20) S. Bhakdi, B. Bhakdi-Lehnen, O. J. Bjerrum, Biochim. Biophys. Acta. 470 (1977) 35-44

(21) H. Haupt, H. Bohn, Blut 35 (1977) 229-239

(22) H. G. Schwick, H. Haupt in D. H. Bing, R. A. Rosenbaum (Eds.), Plasma and Cellular Modulatory Proteins, Center for Blood Research, Inc., Boston, Mass. 1981, pp. 125-155

(23) K. Altland, M. Martin, A. v. Eckardstein, R. Hackler, U. Rossmann, P. Spoenemann in B. J. Radola (Ed.), Elektrophoreseforum '83, TU Muenchen 1983, pp. 203-208

(24) M. J. Hobart in J. P. Arbuthnott, J. A. Beeley (Eds.), Iseoelectric Focusing, Butterworths, London 1975, pp. 275-280

(25) K. Altland, R. Hackler, W. Knoche, Hum. Genet. 54 (1980) 221-231

ELECTROFOCUSING IN FORENSIC SEROLOGY:SOME FORMAL GENETIC AND METHODOLOGICAL ASPECTS OF ISOPROTEIN SUBTYPES

Peter Kühnl

Institute of Immunohematology , University Hospital,
Sandhofstrasse 1, D-6000 Frankfurt am Main 73 , FRG

SUMMARY

An increasing number of genetic markers is analyzed by isofocusing techniques in forensic serology.The application of IEF and its various modifications provided knowledge of a large number of inherited variants,unknown from conventional typing techniques so far and created conflicting nomenclatures in many systems.Formal genetic and methodological aspects of eight isoprotein systems with subtypic variation after IEF analysis are presented:Haptoglobin(HP),transferrin(TF),alpha$_1$-antitrypsin(PI), plasminogen(PLG),coagulation factor XIII subunit B(FXIIIB),amylase 2(AMY2-EC 3.2.1.1),the sixth component of complement (C6), properdin factor B(BF).

INTRODUCTION

The rapidly increasing spectrum of blood group systems,whose analysis by IEF procedures yields additional information compared with conventional electrophoretic separation techniques includes at least 16 isoprotein and 9 isozyme markers:Haptoglobin(HP),group-specific component(GC),transferrin(TF),alpha$_1$-antitrypsin(PI),the complement components C2,C4,C6,C8 and BF,coagulation factor XIIIB, apolipoproteins E,A1 and A4,antithrombin III, and the glycoproteins A2HS and A1B;plasminogen(PLG),amylases(AMY1,2),PGM1,ESD,FXIIIA,GAA, FUCA and GDH.The current status of eight systems is reviewed here.

Haptoglobin subtypes (HP). The extended HP system comprises five common alleles, as HP*1 is split into the subtypes HP*1F and *1S, and HP*2 into *2SS, *2FF and *2FS (= *2SF + *2FS). A pretreatment of sera with urea and reduction with mercaptoethanol is required for a detection of different pI values of the cleaved chains (HP peptides) by IEF (SHIBATA et al., 1982). In a modified one-dimensional separation system the recovery of purified HP was controlled after examination of the protein by IPAGE. Each peptide chain was present as a single band, providing a clearcut differentiation of αS, α_2SS, α_2FS, αF, and α_2FF and of two new mutants HPαvar and HP$\alpha_2$var. The formal genetic model of five alleles and 15 phenotypes (NANCE and SMITHIES, 1963) was confirmed in a sample from SW France (n=202), where the frequencies differed only marginally from those reported in Denmark by THYMANN, 1977. In contrast, *2FF (0.006) and *2SS (0.002) were found well below the 1% limit in Spain (Barcelona) by MORAL and PANADERO (1983), thus yielding a smaller additional information of HP splits than in Central European populations (SHIBATA et al., 1982, France): HP*1F = 0.139, *1S = 0.245, *1V = 0.005, *2FF = 0.012, *2FS = 0.547, *2SS = 0.045, and *2V = 0.007. Despite the somewhat critical feasibility of the proposed standard HP subtyping technique and the still limited population data, the inclusion of HP subtypes in the "basic blood group expertise" of affiliation cases is desirable in view of the increased exclusion chances.

Transferrin C subtypes (TF). Whereas TF B and D heterozygotes can be readily distinguished from TF C (common) homozygotes by AGE at pH 8.6, isofocusing is required for the detection of one of the three polymorphic C subtype alleles *C1, *C2 and *C3 in Caucasians (KÜHNL and SPIELMANN, 1978, 1979). IEF in narrow pH ranges of 4-6.5 or 5-6.5, the use of iron-pretreated sera (1:5 incubation of serum in 0.15% ferrous ammonium sulfate solution for 18h at +4°C in stoppered tubes) and a reduction of gel thickness to 0.2 or 0.4 mm yielded not only a clearer distinction of the six common phenotypes TF C1, C2-1, C2, C3-1, C3-2, and C3, but also of hitherto 12 additional C subtypes (CONSTANS et al, 1980; KÜHNL et al., 1980; DYKES et al., 1982; KÜHNL and SPIELMANN, 1983; YUASA et al., 1983; WALTER et al., 1981; KAMBOH and KIRK, 1983; WEIDINGER et al., 1984; KRÜGER and HUMMEL, 1984; KÜHNL and PATZELT, 1984, in preparation). TF*C5, *C6, *C7, *C9 were observed rarely in Caucasians with frequencies ranging between 0.00025 to 0.001; *C4 is common in North and South American Indians, *C5 and *C8 were primarily detected in Blacks. TF C10 is a variant band intermediate to C2 and C6, TF C11 is focused between C4 and C1 ("C4-like"). TF*P (Pangwala) was observed by WALTER et al. (1981) in Indian populations and is obviously identical with TF*C Nepal, for which the numerical designation is TF*C12.This allele has a frequency of slightly over 1% in Nepalese but is absent in Whites,according to published data. A further split of C was encountered in low frequency in Australian Aborigines by KAMBOH and KIRK(1983),who described the variant band in a position anodal of C12;the proposal for this allele,(which was originally called TF*C6 by these authors)is *C13.Still anodal to C13 another TF phenotype was recently confirmed as C14 (KRÜGER and HUMMEL,1984).Family data are still lacking for two other variants,which appear as regular C after AGE at 8.6 and 9.0, but disclose bands anodal to C14 and cathodal to C7,respectively.The array of subtypes in the TF system,starting with the position closest to the anode comprises TF C14,C13,C12,C9, C4,C11,C1,C8,C3,C5,C2,C10,C6,and C7.The "old" allele TF*C seems to be atomized in a similar manner by IEF, as this was the case in the GC and PI system.Concerning the allele frequencies of the common splits,we recently calculated TF*C1 at 0.76975, *C2 = 0.1635, and *C3 = 0.0565 (n=2,000;Hessen,Germany; KÜHNL,1984) and confirmed previous data form our population.

Alpha$_1$-antitrypsin (PI). The history of PI*M subtypes started with the description of microheterogeneities of PI M (LAURELL and PERSSON,1973) and CONSTANS and VIAU (1975),who named the second commonest subtype PI*N(=PI*M2).A third polymorphic allele,PI*M3 appeared two years later,it was split from both *M1 and *M2 frequencies(KLASEN et al.,1977;GENZ et al.,1977).Separator isofocusing (SIEF) using ACES improved the distinction of the six common PI phenotypes (FRANTS and ERIKSSON,1978), if the separation was carried out in a pH range of 4-6.In addition,a fourth subtype PI*M4 could be split from the *M3 gene product,which was located in an intermediate position of the M1/M2 corridor(CHARLIONNET et al.,1979;CONSTANS et al.,1980).Ultra-thin-layer SIEF and narrow pH ranges still posed the problem of creating a clearcut M3/M4 corridor, which was indispensable for the recognition of the formal genetic four-allele M subtype system with ten phenotypes.Like in M3, where technical problems led to significant discrepancies of allele frequencies(0.05 to 0.1124; FRANTS and ERIKSSON;KLASEN et al.,1977), the published data on *M4 range from 0.0146(Central Spain) to 0.0179(Southern Germany),0.0308 (Southern Italy),0.037(Northern Italy),0.037(Southern France)to 0.0476(Netherlands).The fact,that *M4 frequencies in Southern Germany reach only 40% of that in Netherlands is probably not due to a true ethnic variation of these populations in terms of a North-West/South-East trend,but rather reflects actual problems of PI M4 phenotype identification.Even less well established are the possible subgroups PI*M5 and *M6,whose gene products are assumed between M1 and M3(M5), and cathodal to M2(M6;CONSTANS,1981).Unlike M4,both splits appear to be rare.Repeated comparisons of M4-1 and M4-S reference samples with appropriate M3-1 and M3-S controls in our lab proved them as indistinguishable in pH 4-6 and also in commercially available pH 4-5 gels (1 mm gel thickness;LKB PAGplates^{R}).Standard PI M subtyping techniques therefore carry little risk of mistyping either M3-2/M4-2 or M3-1/M4-1 as M2 or M2-1,respectively(M4 is found slightly cathodal to M3).M4 therefore should be considered as M3-split,at least until convincing patterns of the phenotypes M4-3 and M4 are obtained,*M4 frequencies are in better accordance and family data justify its inclusion in routine cases of forensic serology. The loss of information caused by a preliminary renunciation of M4 is outweighed by a safer phenotype assignment within a reduced three allele/six phenotypes system of PI*M splits.The situation resembles strikingly the problems of the most useful genetic marker system HLA (human leukocyte antigens),where the availability of monospecific antisera against split antigens (and less well defined w-antigens) presents the central problem of routine serology.Even the use of immobilized pH gradients (IPG) has not resulted in a major breakthrough in the problem of PI*M subtypes.The zones 4 and 6 can be readily identified in ultra-narrow pH 4.4-4.7 IPG(see fig.below), the M3/M4 distance however remains rather small(KÜHNL et al.,1984). The PI*M4 gene product in zones 4 and 6 has an almost identical pI value as M3.Better distinctions can be performed in zone 8 closer to the cathode (CLEVE and WEIDINGER,1984).Heterozygotes for *F,*I, *L and *N were seen with the expected extension of their IPG isoproteinograms so far.

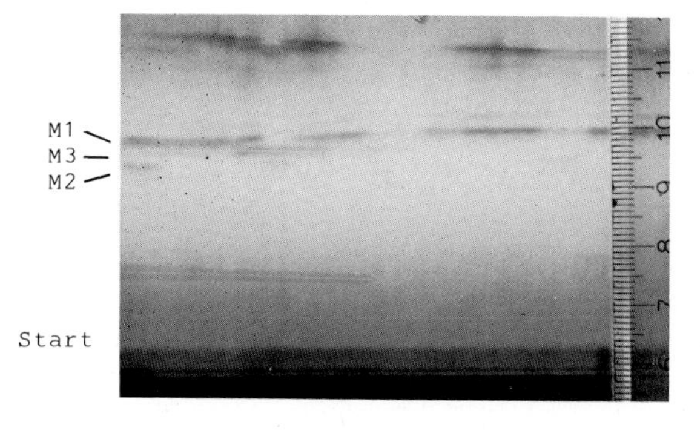

Fig.1. PI M subtypes in an ultra-narrow pH 4.4-4.7 IPG gel.From left: M2-1,1,1,3-1,3-2,3-1,1, 3-1,1,1,1,2-1,and 1. PI zones 4 and 6 at top

Plasminogen (PLG). Neuraminidase treatment of sera, separation by IEF in a pH 3-10 or 5-8 gradient and subsequent detection of PLG (plasmin after urokinase activation) in a functional caseinolytic assay is considered the method of choice for PLG allotyping. Distinct patterns appear after Coomassie Brillant Blue R 250 stain of the separation gel, in which the plasmin-digested casein areas reveal specific activity. Besides the common alleles PLG*1(0.71),*2(0.27),*3 (0.015) and the rare(below 0.005) *4,*5 and *6, a subtype of PLG*2 was encountered and named PLG*8. The corresponding gene product was at first observed in an African Black, later also in Caucasians. The atypical fraction is located 1/2 mm (pH 5-8 gel) anodally to PLG 2, in an asymmetrical intermediate position of the PLG 2/6 corridor (see fig. below). PLG*8 was observed twice among 500 individuals from Germany, adding another variant to the array of PLG alleles. Starting from the anode, PLG 3,4,1,5,6,8,2 and 7 are the designations in the extended numerical nomenclature(HOBART,1979;SPIELMANN and KÜHNL,1982; HOFFMANN,1984;KÜHNL et al.,1984). Two other nomenclatures are used in USA and Japan, where at least two additional variants in the PLG 1/2 corridor were observed, together with a silent gene PLG*QO (DYKES et al.,1983;NAKAMURA and ABE,1982;NISHIMUKAI et al.,1981;IKEMOTO et al. 1982).

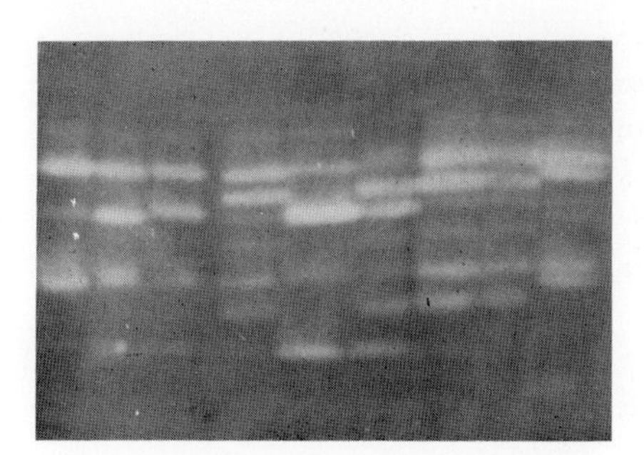

Fig.2. PLG phenotypes in a pH 3-10 IEF gel after caseinolytic assay. The subtype PLG 8-1 in channel 3 resembles closely PLG 2-1. From left: PLG 1,2-1,8-1,6-1,2, 6-2,6-1,6-1, and 5-1; anode at top(KÜHNL et al., 1983, HOFFMANN, 1984).

Coagulation factor XIII subunit B (FXIIIB). Like in the PLG system, desialylated sera proved to be the optimal material for the investigation of the polymorphism of the B subunit of coagulation factor XIII. After the confirmation of BOARD's three-allele model, which was later contradicted by the two-allele model of KERA et al.(1981), we compared immunofixation procedures after agarose gel electrophoresis (IAGE) and isofocusing(IAGIF/IPAGIF)(KÜHNL et al.,1981;KRECKEL and KÜHNL,1982;KRECKEL et al.,1983;KÜHNL et al.,1984). It became clear, that besides the three common alleles B*1(0.74),B*2(0.09), and B*3(0.16), three rare alleles occurred in Whites, namely B*4,B*5 and B*6. A seventh type, B*7 was first described in a Black(KÜHNL et al.1983)

Whereas B5 was located cathodally to B3 , and B7 anodally to B1 , the two subtypes of the B*2 allele (splits B4 and B6)could only be reliably determined by IAGIF from the desialylated B2 band.After conventional electrophoresis, only minimally differing migration rates of B2,B4 and B6 were noted.IEF shifted B2 drastically towards the B1 band,leaving a 1/2 mm wide B2/1 corridor in pH 5-7 gradient gels.B4 and B6 remained in a rather symmetrical position of the B1/3 corridor,corresponding to the electrophoretic separation patterns.This deviating characteristics of B2 concerning pI and mobility are reflected by the FXIIIB IAGE sequence B7,B1,B6/B4 ,B2,B3,and B5,whereas the IAGIF/IPAGIF sequence is B7,B1,B2,B6,B4,B3(and B5,which still has to be tested by IEF procedures to our knowledge).We believe,that the assumed absence of the common B*2 in Japanese(KERA et al.,1981), and the hypothesis of a race-specific common allele B*B'(NAKAMURA and ABE(1982) both can be explained by this above-mentioned phenomenon of the "asialo-FXIIIB2-shift" after IEF(KÜHNL et al.,1984).

Amylase 2(AMY2-EC 3.2.1.1).The amylase patterns of human serum separated by IEF at pH 5-8 and stained with the iodine-starch reaction,reveal the genetic polymorphism of the second AMY locus on chromosome 1.Besides the gene products of the two common alleles AMY2*1 (0.949) and AMY2*2 (0.050),two rare alleles *3 and *4 were described by KÖMPF et al.,1979.Variant bands were observed cathodally to the common AMY2 1 fraction.We recently encountered an unusual enzyme pattern in the serum of a Caucasian woman with an activity zone intermediate to the bands AMY2 2 and 3(see fig. below.Continuing the numerical nomenclature,this phenotype would have to be called then AMY2 5-1,providing its confirmation in the family study.

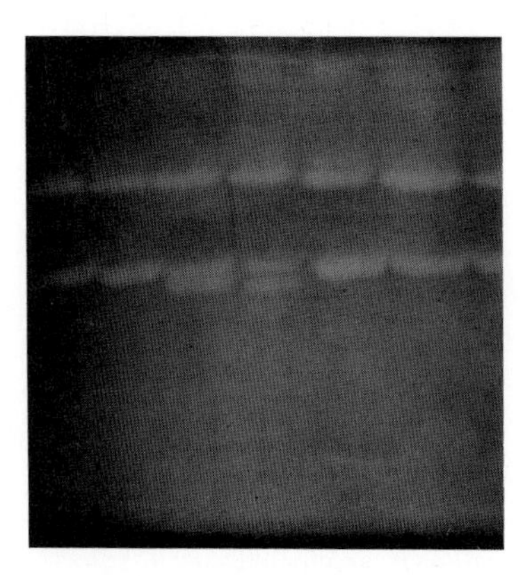

Fig.3. Amylase 2 phenotypes after separation in a pH 5-8 IEF gel and amyloclastic activity stain/iodine starch reaction.From left: AMY2 1, 1,2-1,5-1,1,and 1.Anode at top.The width of the corridor of the new phenotype 5-1 is slightly wider than that of a AMY2 2-1 reference sample

Sixth component of complement (C6). Discrepancies in the reported frequencies of C6 alleles in Caucasians induced us to reassume the investigation of this polymorphism.Instead of the usual hemolytic ("functional") detection system, C6 antiserum was used after separation of sera in a pH 5-7 polyacrylamide gel (IPAGIF).The antibody was diluted 1:2 and spread evenly on the surface of the gel. After incubation for 90 min the gel was washed in saline overnight, dried and stained.Compared with replica techniques on CAF foils, the in-situ immunoprecipitates were stronger and allowed clear phenotype assignments.Particularly C6 AB vs.B differentiation was facilitated;preliminary frequency calculations indicate,that the C6*B frequency is closer to the value of 0.346 (KÜHNL and KRECKEL,1980), than to 0.379 (RITTNER et al.,1979).The combined frequencies of the rare variants amount to 0.009.

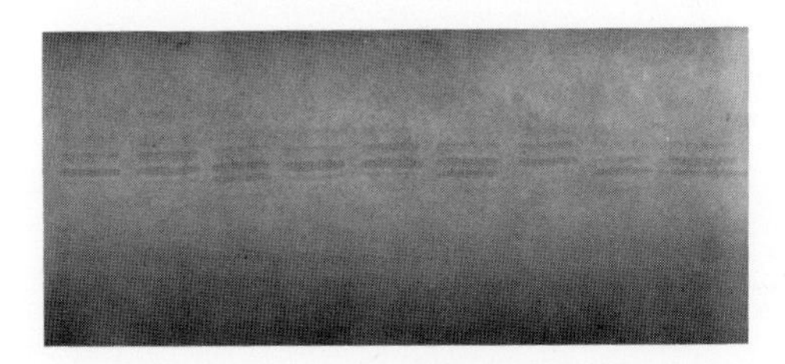

Fig.4.C6 allotypes in the IPAGIF system, using monospecific C6 antiserum (Cappel,USA).From left:C6 A,A, AB,A,A,AB,A,B,and AB.Anode at top(KÜHNL,1984).

Properdin factor B (BF). The question of the existence of subtypes in the BF system,as postulated by TENG and TAN,1982, and GESERICK et al.,1983 for the common allele BF*F, as well as for BF*S by DAVID et al.,1983 motivated us to revisit this genetic marker by IPAGIF.Using a similar technique as in the C6 system(see above), clear phenotype distinctions were possible in all fresh serum samples, corresponding to the patterns seen after IAGE(ALPER et al., 1972).The *F1 gene product disclosed an unexpected cathodal extraband.No evidence was found however for further IEF splits of either BF*F or BF*S so far in our technique.In a previous report evidence was obtained for a epigenetic(posttranslational) modification of partly converted B molecules in the Bb fragment region after IAGIF (KÜHNL,1983).

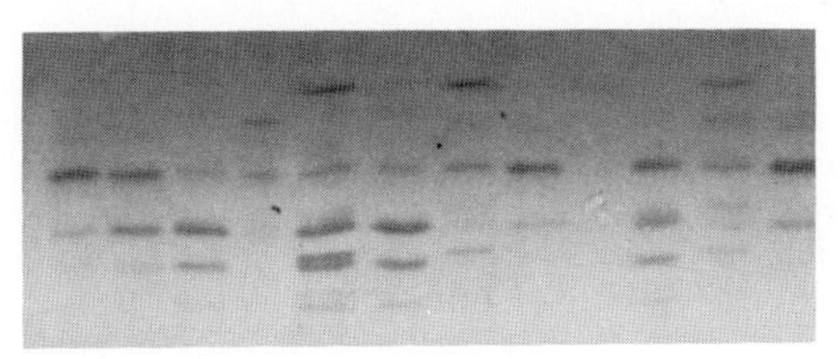

Fig. .BF allotypes in the pH 5-7 IPAGIF system with monospecific BF antiserum (ATAB,USA).From left:BF S, F1S,FS,S,F1S,F,F1F,SSO7,F, FS,and S.Anode at top(from KÜHNL and KUBIN,1984)

In conclusion,it becomes evident from these few examples of modified IEF procedures,particularly the combination with immunologic detection systems,that isofocusing is of increasing importance in the field of forensic serology.Hitherto only a few genetic markers have been analyzed by immobilized pH gradients, the majority remains to be analyzed by this promising new tool for geneticists.

Literature by request from author

MULTIPLE REPLICA TECHNIQUE AND QUANTITATION OF HUMAN SERUM PROTEINS ON THE IMMUNOREPLICAS

Takashi Manabe, Tsuneo Okuyama

Department of Chemistry, Faculty of Science, Tokyo Metropolitan University, Setagaya-ku, Tokyo 158, JAPAN

SUMMARY

An apparatus for electrophoretic transfer of proteins from four micro polyacrylamide slab gels has been developed. It is designed to obtain multiple blots from each gel. Electrophoretic conditions were adjusted so that all of the blots obtained sequentially from one slab gel were successfully used to visualize specific proteins irrespective of their molecular weight. The transfer technique was combined with the technique of parallel micro two-dimensional electrophoresis. Five blots can be obtained from one slab gel, so the total number of the blots obtained was forty from eight slabs by the single processing. The quantitation method of immunologically visualized spots were also described.

INTRODUCTION

We have reported a two-dimensional electrophoretic technique in which no denaturing agent is used, for the analysis of proteins in biological fluids and in tissue extracts (1-3). A microscale multisample version of the technique (4) enabled us to reduce the protein amount required and to study multiple protein samples comparatively (5,6). For the quantitation of proteins dye-stained on the micro slab gels, we have developed a quantitation system, using a television camera for data acquisition and a microcomputer for data analysis (7). Then we intended to develop a system for immunological identification of proteins to obtain as much information from the multiple micro two-dimensional gels as possible.

Towbin et al. (8) described a technique for electrophoretic transfer of proteins from an SDS-polyacrylamide slab gel to a nitrocellulose sheet and specific proteins were identified by treating the nitrocellulose sheets (blots) with specific antibodies. The technique was adapted by many workers. Anderson et al. (9) identified 30 human plasma proteins on blots of SDS-two-dimensional electrophoretic gels. Legocki and Verma (10) reported "multiple immunoreplica technique", which provided several blots of one gel by partial transfer of proteins. Since there is an increasing number of specific antibody available and on the other hand, only one or at most a few proteins may be identified on one blot, we wanted to adopt the multiple replica technique for electrophoretic transfer of proteins on micro two-dimensional gels. Conventional apparatus ever designed were not suited for this purpose, then a new apparatus was designed. This apparatus was designed for four slab gels at one processing. Thus in one regular procedure, we combined one set of micro two-dimensional electrophoresis apparatus with two sets of electroblotting apparatus, so we could obtain forty blots from eight gels in one serial processing. Then we could test 35 commercially available specific antisera against human serum (plasma) proteins simultaneously and could identify 28 serum proteins in one experiment.

MATERIALS AND METHODS

Materials. Antisera against human serum proteins were obtained from Behring. Peroxidase-conjugated goat anti-rabbit IgG was from Miles. Nitrocellulose sheets (0.45 µm pore size) were obtained from Schleicher and Schüll.

Micro two-dimensional electrophoresis. Microscale-multisample two-dimensional elecrophoresis of human serum, plasma or cerebrospinal fluid proteins was performed as described previously (4). Eight gels were run in parallel. First dimension isoelectric focusing was run for 40 min and second dimension polyacrylamide

gradient gel electrophoresis was run for 120 min.
Electroblotting Apparatus. Apparatus for electroblotting (Fig. 1) was newly built and is now manufactured by Fuji Riken Co., Bunkyo-ku, Tokyo 113, Japan. It is made of Plexiglas and consists of a lid and a buffer reservoir each with a platinum wire serving as electrode. The lid holds a Scotch-Brite pad and a Plexiglas projection is glued to the lid. A Plxiglas plate is glued to the inside bottom of the buffer reservoir and a Scotch-Brite pad is put on the plate. Four micro slab gels (38 x 38 x 1 mm) are set horizontally in the apparatus. The whole apparatus is slanted to help removal of gas bubbles produced by electrolysis.

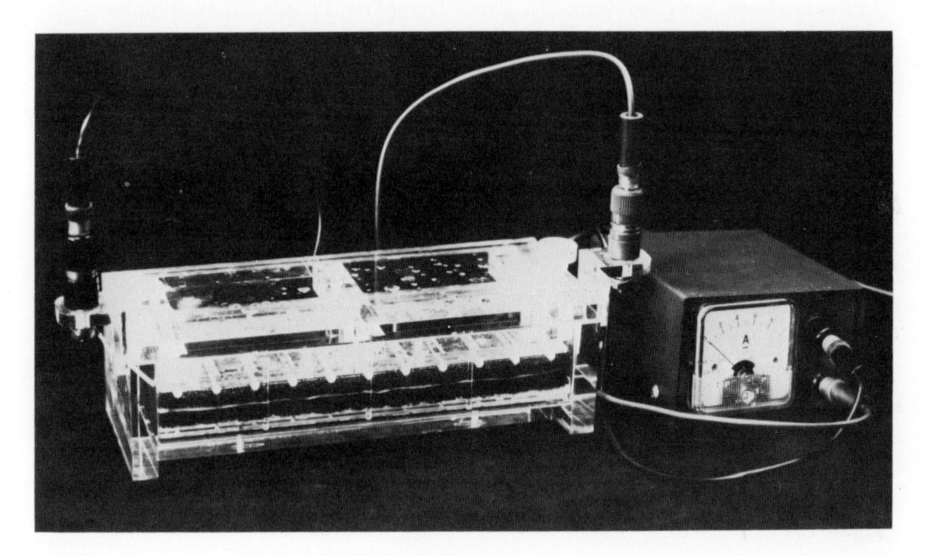

Fig. 1. The electroblotting apparatus.

Procedure of electroblotting. Buffer for electrophoretic transfer (0.025M Tris-0.19M glycine, pH 8.3, 100 ml) was poured in the reservoir of the apparatus. The buffer level was just above the top surface of the Scotch-Brite pad in the reservoir. A Whatman 3MM filter paper (cut in 40 x 168 mm) was set on the Scotch-Brite pad. After two-dimensional electrophoresis, each slab gel (4-17% polyacrylamide gradient gel) was scooped with a stainless-steel plate (35 x 80 x 0.3 mm) and set on the filter paper. One of the nitrocellulose sheets (0.45 µm pore size, cut in size of 40 x 40 mm), which had been soaked with the buffer, was laid on one slab gel using tweezers. Specific cautions were reqired not to trap any air bubbles in the interface between the gel and the sheet. Very close contact between the gels and the sheets was also required. To ensure reproducible patterns, precise setting of the sheets was necessary. An edge of the nitrocellulose sheet was touched with a side wall of the apparatus and the position of the sheet was determined by a Plexiglas guide rod which had been attached to the side wall. When the lid was put on the reservoir, the projection of the lid sinked in the buffer, then the buffer level raised above the top surface of the upper Scotch-Brite pad. The lid was fixed to the reservoir with two screws. Electrophoresis was performed at 150mA constant current (initial voltage 15V), replacing new nitrocellulose sheets every 10 min. Five replicas (blots) were routinely obtained from one slab gel, thus 40 blots from 8 slab gels, employing two sets of the blotting apparatus.

Immunochemical staining of proteins on blots. After blotting, the blots were treated as described by Towbin et al. (8) with some modifications: 1) Each blot was put in a plastic container with a lid (64 mm W x 58 mm L x 21 mm H), soaked in 5 ml of 3% bovine serum albumin (BSA) in saline (0.9% NaCl, 0.1% NaN_3, 10mM Tris-HCl, pH 7.4) for 2 h at room temperature; 2) Specific rabbit antiserum (10 µl, 1:500 dilution) was added to the BSA solution and kept at room temperature for 30 min; 3) Washed in saline (five changes during 30 min); 4) Soaked in peroxidase-conjugated goat anti-rabbit IgG (2.5 µl, 1:2000 dilution) in 5 ml saline for 60 min at room temperature; 5) Washed in saline (five changes during 30 min); 6) Stained in 10 ml of 0.2mM diaminobenzidine-saline + 0.1 ml 3% H_2O_2 for 15-30 min. During the whole staining procedure, the container was gently shaken on a gyrotory shaker.

Dye-staining of proteins. Polyacrylamide slab gels were stained in 0.1% Coomassie Brilliant blue R-250 (CBB)-50% (v/v) methanol-7% (v/v) acetic acid for 15 min and destained in 20% (v/v) methanol-7% (v/v) acetic acid for 2 h. In some cases, the blots were stained with the same CBB staining solution for 5 min and destained in three changes of 80% (v/v) methanol-7% (v/v) acetic acid for 10 min. The gels and the blots were shaken during staining and destaining.

Quantitation of staining density on blots. The density of protein spots on an imunochemically stained blot was quantitated using the television camera-microcomputer system (7). The composition of the system is illustrated in Fig. 2. The general procedure of quantitation was almost the same as the case of dye-stained spots on a polyacrylamide slab gel, except the spot density under reflecting light was measured. The magnification rate of the camera could be adjusted to meet the purposes. The resolution of the system employed in this study was 200 x 160 µm.

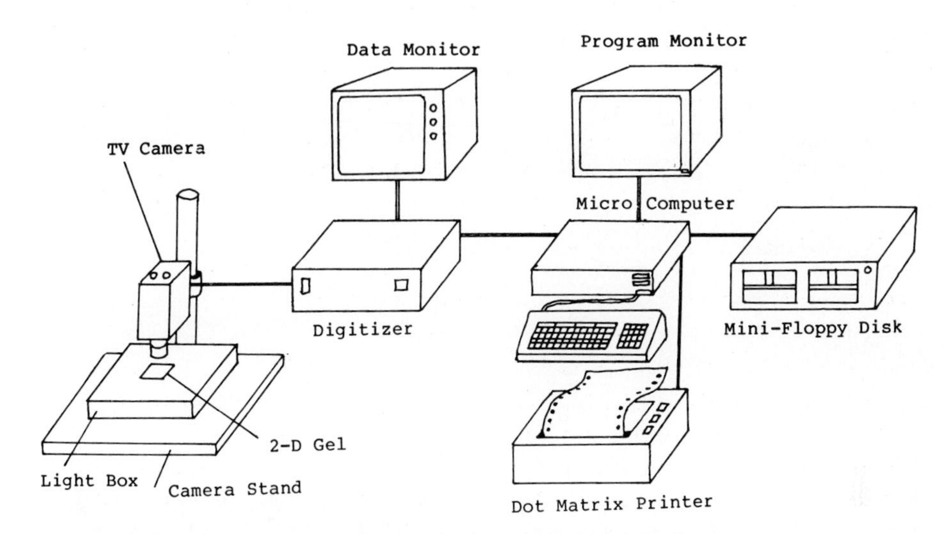

Fig. 2. A TV camera-microcomputer system for quantitation of spot density.

RESULTS

Electrophoretic transfer of proteins from polyacrylamide gradient gels to nitrocellulose sheets. The changes of protein pattern of human serum on the slab gel during electrophoretic transfer were examined. A human serum sample was subjected to parallel micro two-dimensional electrophoresis in the absence of denaturing agent. One of the two-dimensional gels was stained with Coomassie Brilliant blue R-250 (CBB) (Fig. 2 A). Four two-dimensional gels were set in the apparatus shown in Figure 1 and electrophoresis was run at 150mA constant current. After various time intervals, the gels were stained with CBB. Some of the slab gels, after 50 min and 100 min electroblotting, were shown in Fig. 2 B and C, respectively. Before electroblotting (Fig. 3 A), more than 100 spots of human serum proteins, which have isoelectric point between pH 8 and pH 4 and apparent molecular weight between 1,000,000 and 50,000, were detected on the gradient gel (4-17% acrylamide gradient and 0.2-0.85% N,N'-methylenebisacrylamide gradient). Apparent molecular weight of serum proteins were calculated using the mobilities of

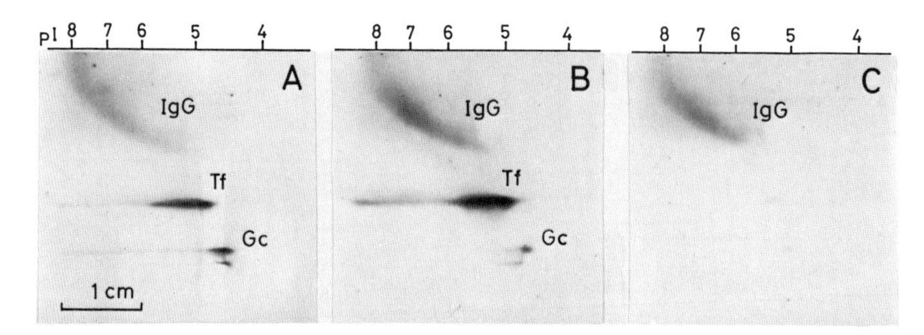

Fig. 3. The changes of protein pattern during electrophoretic transfer. A human serum sample (2 µl) was subjected to micro two-dimensional electrophoresis in the absence of denaturing agent and the gels were stained with Coomassie Brilliant blue R-250. A, before electrophoretic transfer; B, after 50 min transfer at 150mA constant current; C, after 100 min transfer at 150mA. Total acrylamide concentration (acrylamide plus N,N'-methylenebis-acrylamide) of the gradient gel is shown by T(%).

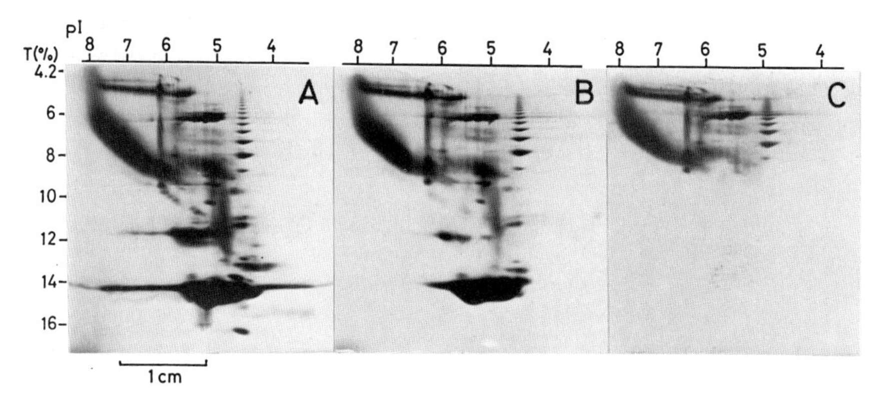

Fig. 4. Some of the nitrocellulose blots sequentially obtained from one micro two-dimensional gel. Ten-fold diluted human serum (2 µl) was subjected to two-dimensional electrophoresis. The blotting cycle (150mA, 10 min) was repeated ten times. The blots were simultaneously treated with rabbit antisera mixture, anti-IgG, anti-transferrin (Tf), and anti-Gc-globulin (Gc). A, the first blot; B, the fifth blot; C, the tenth blot.

haptoglobin 2-2 polymers and albumin. After 50 min electroblotting (Fig. 3 B), proteins of apparent molecular weight below 120,000 decreased in level and after 100 min (Fig. 3 C), most of the small proteins (smaller than IgA, MW 170,000) disappeared from the gel. These results showed that smaller proteins migrate more rapidly, although the pore size of polyacrylamide gel is smaller at the gel positions of small proteins.

The conditions of electrophoresis to obtain multiple replicas from one slab gel were examined by staining nitrocellulose blots serially obtained from one slab gel. Ten-fold diluted human serum, 2 µl, was subjected to micro two-dimensional electrophoresis, the gel was set in the blotting apparatus, and the blotting cycle (150mA constant current, 10 min) was repeated ten times. Ten blots thus obtained were simultaneously treated with rabbit antisera mixture, anti-IgG, anti-transferrin (Tf), and anti-Gc-globulin (Gc), and stained with peroxidase conjugated goat anti-rabbit IgG in diaminobenzidine-H_2O_2. Figure 4 A, B, and C show three blots out of ten, obtained in the first, fifth, and tenth blotting cycle, respectively. The spot area of Gc decreased on the fifth blot and both Tf and Gc were not stainedtenth blot.

Quantitation of spot density on the blots. Staining density of protein spots on the blots was quantitated by a television camera-microcomputer system (7). In the former report, we quantitated dye-stained spots using penetrating light. For stained spots on the blots, we used reflecting light and the gray levels of the digitizer were adjusted to match the density of diaminobenzidine-stained spots. Figure 5 A shows a gray scale contour map of the blot shown in Fig. 4 A, a print-out image. A spot to be quantitated was selected by keyboard control (Fig. 5 B) and "integrated density" of the spot was calculated. Figure 6 summarizes the results of quantitation of protein spots on the ten blots serially obtained. As shown in Fig. 6, the density of Gc spot decreased to zero on the sixth blot and that of Tf peaked on the fifth blot then decreased to zero on the tenth blot. The density of IgG spot on the tenth blot remained at almost the same level as the first blot. From the results shown in Figs. 4 and 6, we assumed that most of the serum proteins would be present on the first to the fifth blots under the electrophoretic conditions.

Identification of serum proteins. A human serum sample was subjected to micro two-dimensional electrophoresis and resulting eight slab gels were set on two blotting apparatus. Forty blots were sequentially obtained from the eight gels and each blot was used to

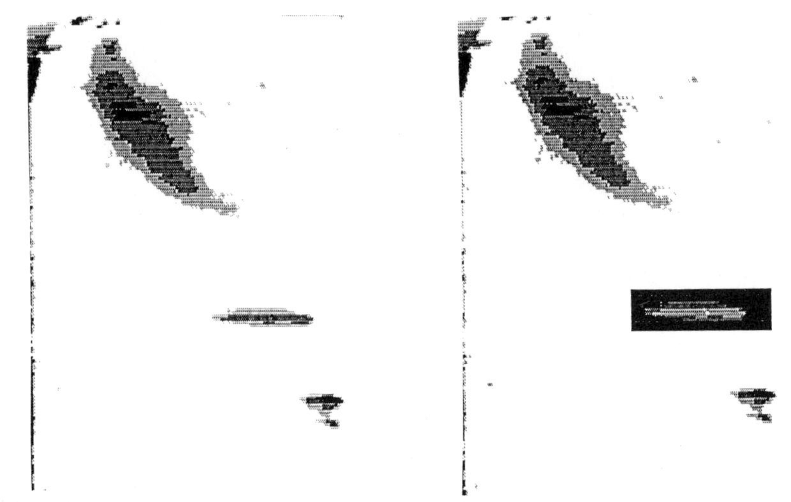

Fig. 5. A gray scale contour map of the blot (40 x 40 mm) shown in Fig. 4 A. The resolution was 200 x 160 µm. The print-out image is expanded 1.3-fold in the vertical axis. A, before calculation of integrated density; B, after quantitation of transferrin spot.

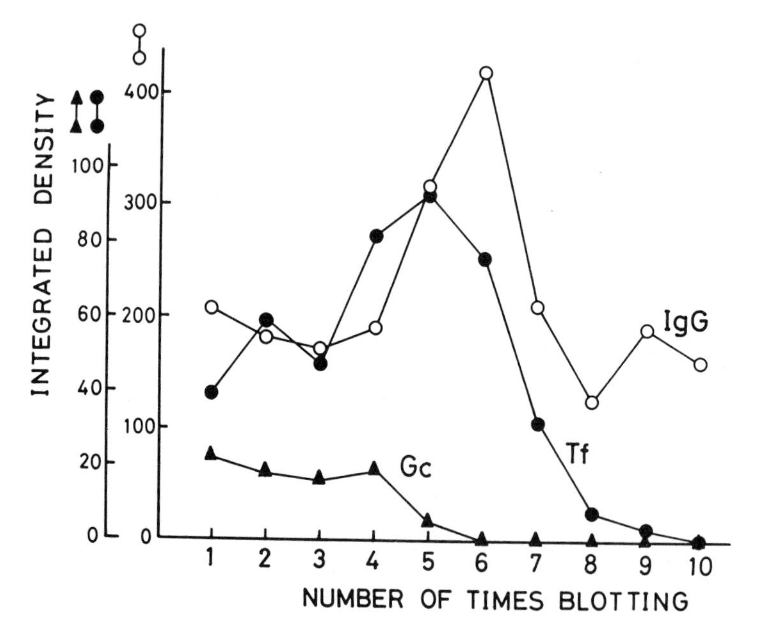

Fig. 6. Quantitation of spot density on nitrocellulose blots. A TV camera-microcomputer system (Fig. 2) was used to quantitate the staining density of proteins on nitrocellulose blots. o, Integrated density of IgG spot; ●, transferrin; ▲, Gc-globulin.

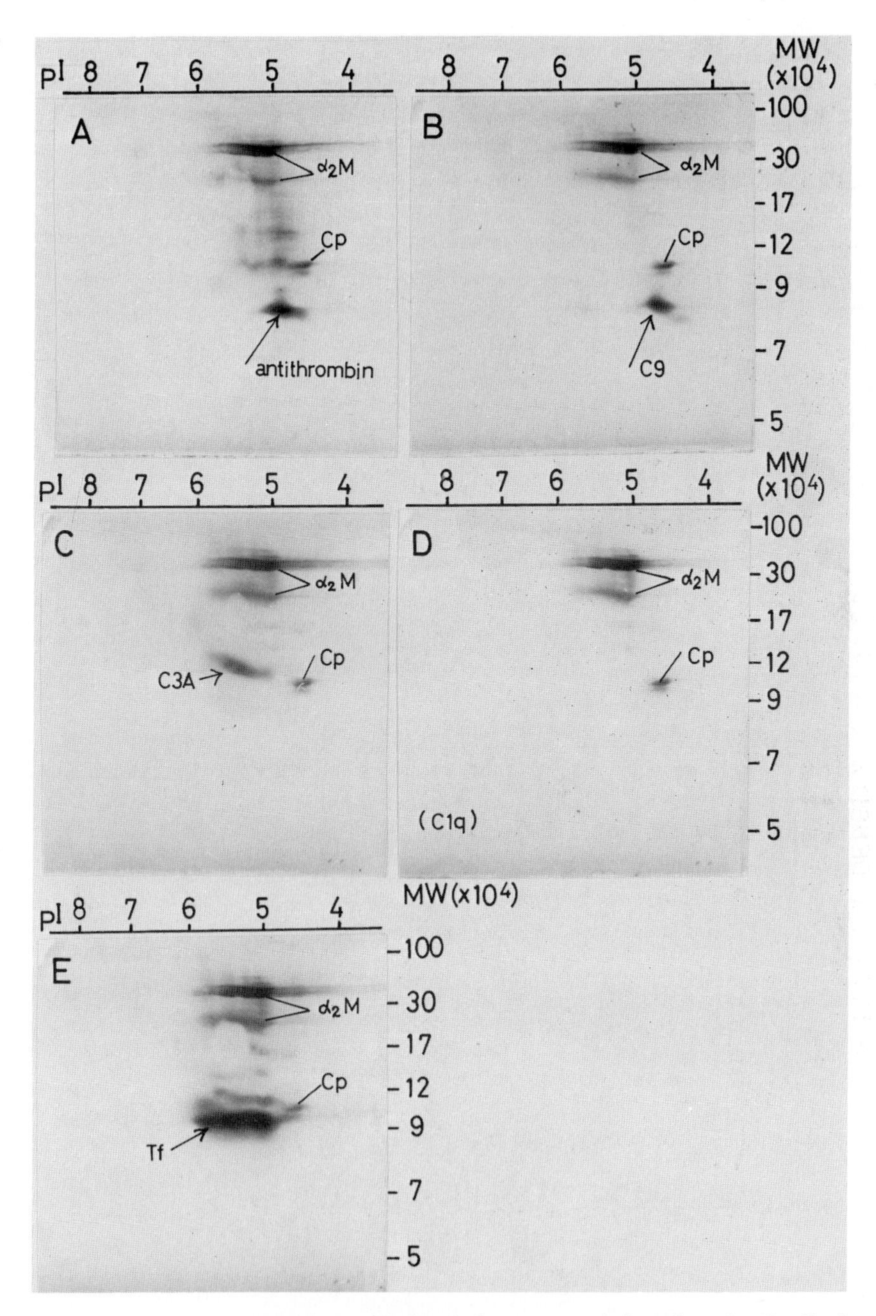

Fig. 7. A Series of blot obtained from one slab gel. A, B, C, D, and E represents the first, second, third, fourth, and the fifth blot, respectively. Each blot was treated with a mixture of antisera (anti-$_2$M, anti-Cp, and a specific antiserum).

identify a specific serum protein. Figure 7 A-E show a series of blot obtained from one slab gel, A is the first blot and E is the fifth blot. In order to determine the position of a serum protein precisely, each blot was treated with a mixture of anti-α_2 -macroglobulin (α_2M), anti-ceruloplasmin (Cp), and a specific antiseum. The positions of α_2M and Cp were used as standards. The positions of serum proteins were shown in Fig. 5: A, antithrombin; B, C9 component (C9); C, C3 activator (C3A); D, C1q component (C1q); E, Transferrin (Tf). C1q was not stained on the blot, possibly because it shows a isoelectric point more basic than 8. As shown in Fig. 7, α_2M and Cp were stained on all the five blots. Likewise, 35 commercial antisera were tested using the blots. Twenty-eight serum proteins were identified on the blots serially obtained in one experiment. Antisera against α_1-acid glycoprotein, retinol binding protein, carboanhydrase, fibrinogen, C-reactive protein, β_2 III-glycoprotein, and C1q component did not give clear spots. However, β_2III and fibrinogen were clearly stained when human plasma proteins were subjected to two-dimensional electrophoresis and resulting replicas were treated with the peroxidase staining. The differences of the protein distribution between serum and plasma will be fully described elsewhere.

Sensitivity of the immunochemical staining technique. In order to know the level of sensitivity of the immunochemical staining technique, we performed spot tests. Ten µl of human transferrin solution, which contained 10 pg to 100 ng of transferrin, was dropped on a nitrocellulose sheet and was treated for immunochemical staining as described in 'Materials and Methods". As shown in Fig. 8, transferrin spot of 10 pg/6 mm^2 could be stained by the peroxidase staining.

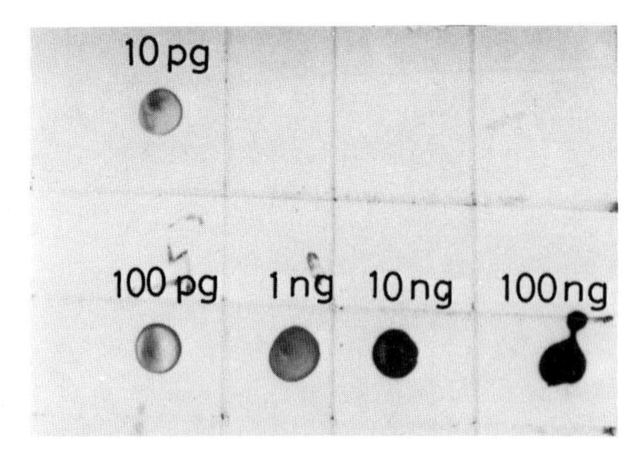

Fig. 8. Spot tests to stain transferrin. Human transferrin, 10 pg, 100 pg, 1 ng, 10 ng, and 100 ng in 10 µl solution, was dropped on a nitrocellulose sheet and stained employing anti-transferrin.

DISCUSSION

Many apparatus designs have been reported for electrophoretic transfer of proteins (8,9,11-14). Generally, one gel and one nitrocellulose sheet are sandwiched with supporting porous pads, the "gel plus sheet plus pads" are supported with solid grids, and then the whole assembly is set vertically in an electrophoresis buffer tank. However, when we tried to obtain multiple blots from one gel using such an apparatus, we found that the procedure to change the nitrocellulose sheet was too complicated; the steps described above must be repeated very precisely the same way for every blotting cycle. The apparatus shown in Fig. 1 was designed to make easy to change the nitrocellulose sheets which were set on multiple slab gels. After short time of electrophoresis, the lid was removed from the buffer reservoir, then the sheets could be changed to new ones with a tweezers. One plausible disadvantage of the apparatus design shown in Fig. 1 was that gas bubbles produced by electrolysis might be trapped between the electrode and the Scotch-Brite pad in the buffer reservoir and might interfere the migration of proteins. However, we have overcome this defect by giving suitable slant to the apparatus, most of the bubbles moved off the pad. Further, the interference was not noticeable on the stained blots as some examples were shown in Figs. 4 and 7. Possibly, low current and short transfer time employed might be helpful to minimize the artifact.

In order to obtain multiple replicas from a gel, uniform transfer of proteins to nitrocellulose sheets is most desirable. As shown in Fig. 3, the rate of transfer of proteins was larger for low-molecular weight proteins. Further, each protein was not uniformly transfered during the course of electrophoresis; there was a peak of quantity of transfered protein (Fig. 6). However, the results shown in Figs. 3 and 4 also indicated that within a determined electrophoresis time, the proteins on a gel could be detected on multiple nitrocellulose sheets irrespective of their molecular weight. As some examples are shown in Fig. 7, multiple replicas obtained from one gel could be successfully utilized for qualitative purposes, e.g. protein identification.

The number of replicas available should depend on the amount of antigen in the gel. We performed spot tests on nitrocellulose sheets and found that the sensitivity of the immunochemical staining technique for human transferrin was about 10 pg, using 1:500

diluted commercial antiserum and 1:2000 diluted anti-IgG-peroxidase. The sensitivity of Coomassie blue staining was 10 ng for proteins on micro two-dimensional gels, then the immunochemical staining is about 1000-fold more sensitive. The number of replicas we obtained, five, should have been too small since the calculated amount of antigen proteins, for which we tried antisera, ranged from about 100 ng (Znα_2-glycoprotein) to about 30 µg (IgG) per one micro two-dimensional gel.

The locations of 28 serum proteins were simultaneously determined. Combining the technique of micro two-dimensional electrophoresis with the multiple replica technique, identification of proteins in human body fluids, plasma, cerebrospinal fluid (15), abdominal fluid, urine, etc. is in progress. The techniques were also applied for the simultaneous examination of cross-reactivity of human antibodies with serum proteins from various animal species. Another promising application of the combined technique is the screening of specific monoclonal antibodies produced from hybridoma cells.

Although the apparatus shown in Fig. 1 is specifically for micro two-dimensional gels, the apparatus design was applicable for larger sized gels, by proportionally enlarging the horizontal dimensions. We successfully used an apparatus for four 8 x 8 x 0.1 cm gels. However, the conditions of electrophoretic transfer to obtain multiple replicas should be reexamined, when the slab gels which differ in thickness or in pore size from ours are used. Further, in the case of slab gels of larger thickness, cooling of the transfer buffer might be necessary to maintain reproducible transfer of proteins.

The technique of electrophoretic transfer followed by immunochemical staining is most suited for qualitative purposes, but it may also be used for quantitation of proteins on the blots as shown in Figs. 6 and 8, when the conditions of the immunochemical staining were clearly defined. Various factors may affect the color development; the titor of antibody, volume and times of washing, temperature, etc. When these factors are fixed, the technique will be useful for quantitative purposes because of its high sensitivity and wide detection range.

REFERENCES

1. T. Manabe, K. Tachi, K. Kojima, T. Okuyama, J. Biochem. 85 (1979) 649-659.
2. T. Manabe, K. Kojima, S. Jitzukawa, T. Hoshino, T. Okuyama, J. Biochem. 89 (1981) 841-853.
3. T. Manabe, S. Jitzukawa, N. Ishioka, T. Isobe, T. Okuyama, J. Biochem. 91 (1982) 1009-1015.
4. T. Manabe, E. Hayama, T. Okuyama, Clin. Chem. 28 (1982) 824-827.
5. T. Manabe, Y. Takahashi, T. Okuyama, Y. Maeda, G. Chihara, Electrophoresis 4 (1983) 242-246.
6. T. Manabe, Y. Takahashi, T. Okuyama, Electrophoresis 4 (1983) 359-362.
7. T. Manabe, T. Okuyama, J. Chromatogr. 264 (1983) 435-443.
8. H. Towbin, T. Staehelin, J. Gordon, Proc. Nat. Acad. Sci. USA 76 (1979) 4350-4354.
9. N. L. Anderson, S. L., Nance, T. W. Pearson, N. G. Anderson, Electrophoresis 3 (1982) 135-142.
10. R. P. Legocki, D. P. S. Verma, Anal. Biochem. 111 (1981) 385-392.
11. M. Bittner, P. Kupferer, C. F. Morris, Anal. Biochem. 102 (1980) 459-471.
12. W. Gibson, Anal. Biochem. 118 (1981) 1-3.
13. T. McLellan, J. A. M. Ramshaw, Biochem. Genet. 19 (1981) 647-654.
14. R. T. Vaessen, J. Kreike, G. S. Groot, FEBS Lett. 124 (1981) 193-196.
15. T. Manabe, Y. Takahashi, T. Okuyama, A. Hiraoka, I. Miura, O. Murao, Electrophoresis '83 (Proceedings of the 5th International Congress of Electrophoresis Society, Tokyo) Walter de Gruyter, Berlin 1984, pp. 179-187.

IDENTIFICATION AND IN VITRO SYNTHESIS OF NERVOUS SYSTEM SPECIFIC PROTEINS IN OPTIC NERVES OF MYELIN DEFICIENT (*mld*) MUTANT MICE

Jean-Marie Matthieu[1], Guillermina Almazan[1], Thomas V. Waehneldt[2].

[1]Laboratoire de Neurochimie, Service de Pédiatrie, Centre Hospitalier Universitaire Vaudois, CH-1011 Lausanne, Switzerland.
[2]Forschungsstelle Neurochemie, Max-Planck-Institut für Experimentelle Medizin, D-3400 Göttingen, West Germany.

Myelin deficient (*mld*) mutant mice are affected by an important myelin deficit with extremely low myelin basic protein (MBP) content (1,2). Proteins specific of oligodendrocytes, CNS myelin (MBP and proteolipid protein, PLP) and astrocytes (glial fibrillary acidic protein, GFAP) were studied in optic nerve homogenates of 17-day-old *mld* and control mice. Protein synthesis was investigated by incubating optic nerves for 30 or 60 min at 37°C in 0.5 ml Earle's medium containing 0.25 mCi of[L-]^{35}S methionine in a humidified atmosphere of 5% CO_2-95% O_2. The nerves were homogenized and aliquots were immunoprecipitated using different polyclonal antisera prepared in our laboratories (3). Total homogenate proteins or immunoprecipitated proteins were separated by SDS-polyacrylamide slab gels. Autoradiography was performed with dried gels which were pretreated with 1 M sodium salicylate. Autoradiographs were scanned on a densitometer. Slab gels were stained with Fast Green.

In *mld* optic nerves, the amount of MBP identified by immunoblotting of total homogenates was extremely low. PLP which is mainly concentrated in compact myelin sheaths was detectable but in reduced amounts. This can be explained by the scarcity of myelinated axons present in *mld* optic nerves. In contrast, GFAP levels were increased in *mld* optic nerves confirming our morphological data showing astrocytes with larger and more extended branches which were more intensely immunostained than in controls (4). The synthesis of MBP, an extrinsic protein synthesized on free ribosomes was severely reduced in *mld* optic nerves indicating that the low levels measured with our radioimmunoassay were not caused by a defect of incorporation into the membrane and degradation (3,5). In contrast, an intrinsic myelin protein, PLP was normally synthesized in *mld* mice suggesting that the protein synthesis on membrane-bound ribosomes and the post-translational modifications are not affected by the mutation.

These results and our developmental study (5) suggest that *mld* mutants are affected by a defect of gene regulation.

Supported by grants from the Swiss National Science Foundation (3.176.82), the Multiple Sclerosis Society of Switzerland and the Deutsche Forschungsgemeinschaft.

REFERENCES

(1) J.M. Bourre, C. Jacque, A. Delassalle, J. Nguyen-Legros, O. Dumont F. Lachapelle, M. Raoul, C. Alvarez, N. Baumann, J. Neurochem. 35 (1980) 458-464.

(2) J.-M. Matthieu, H. Ginalski, R.L. Friede, S.R. Cohen, D.P. Doolittle, Brain Res. 191 (1980) 278-283.

(3) H. Ginalski-Winkelmann, G. Almazan, J.-M. Matthieu, Brain Res. 277 (1983) 386-388.

(4) J.-M. Matthieu, F.-X. Omlin, O. Reymond, Experientia, in press.

(5) J.-M. Matthieu, F.X. Omlin, H. Ginalski-Winkelmann, B.J. Cooper, Develop. Brain Res. 13 (1984) 149-158.

MICRO - SLAB ELECTROPHORESIS OF MYELIN PROTEIN. APPLICATION IN ANALYSIS OF CHANGES OCCURRING DURING MYELINATION IN DIFFERENT CNS STRUCTURES OF THE RABBIT

Bozena Zgorzalewicz, Volker Neuhoff*, Hans H. Poehling*, Maria Dambska**

Department of Developmental Neurology, School of Medicine, 60-355 Poznań, Poland

* Max-Planck-Institut für experimentelle Medizin, Forschungsstelle Neurochemie, 3400 Göttingen, F. R. G.

** Medical Research Center Polish Academy of Sciences, 02-093 Warsaw, Poland

1 INTRODUCTION

The developing mammalian brain undergoes major morphological changes during postnatal development. Histological examination shows that the onset myelination occurs at different times in various structures of the CNS. Because of small quantities of available tissue biochemical studies of myelinogenesis in particular anatomical structures require a sensitive micromethod for protein estimation and myelin isolation and analysis with high degree of resolution using micro-slab electrophoresis. In a continuation of our previous studies on protein composition of various regions of the developing nervous system /1, 2/ the protein pattern of myelin sheath in optic nerve internal capsule cerebral peduncle and corpus callosum was estimated by means of above mentioned techniques. In the present investigation we have also attempted to extend correlations between the alterations occurring in the myelin proteins and the appearance and maturation of myelin sheats observed in morphological studies of these four developing structures.

2 MATERIAL AND METHODS

The studies were carried out on Chinchilla rabbits of both sexes aged 6, 12, 16, 32, 48 and 180 days. The rabbits were decapitated and the different structures were dissected for biochemical and morpholo-

The work was partially supported by research grant of the Alexander Humboldt Foundation.

gical examination as described previously /3/. The myelin fraction was prepared on a microscale by the procedure of Fagg et al. /4/. The protein content was estimated by the micromethod of Neuhoff et al. /5/ and the protein composition was determined by means of one-dimensional electrophoresis in micro-slab-gels according to Poehling and Neuhoff /6/.

3 RESULTS

3.1 Myelin protein content during development in different structures.

The rate of accumulation of total myelin protein in the developmental stages was different depending on the structure examined. Myelin was obtained by ultracentrifugation from the optic nerve and cerebral peduncle as early as 6th day after birth, the internal capsule on the 10th day and from corpus callosum not untill the 12th day of extrauterine life. The greatest myelin accumulation appeared in the optic nerve between the 16 and 32 day of life. Internal capsule and cerebral peduncle attained parallel values. The lowest yield in the time span studied was found in corpus callosum /Fig. 1/.

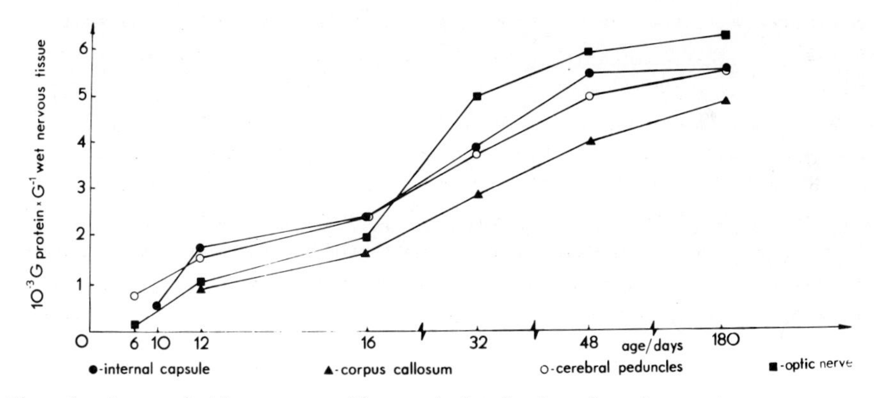

Fig. 1. Accumulation on myelin protein during development

3.2 Changes in composition of myelin protein

During development of these four structures changes in the relative proportion of myelin proteins were estimated /Fig. 2/. The early myelin sheath was found to contain a significant amount of high molecular weight protein identified as Wolfgram protein whose relative content decreased with development and was associated with an increase in the percentage of the basic and proteolipid proteins. The most evident changes appeared in the optic nerve, which has the greatest percentage of basic protein, constituting at 48 days about 45% of all protein components. The least obvious changes in protein pattern were observed in corpus callosum. Although there was a similarity in protein composition in the internal capsule and cerebral peduncle, myelination started earlier in the latter. This pattern did not undergo further significant changes until maturity.

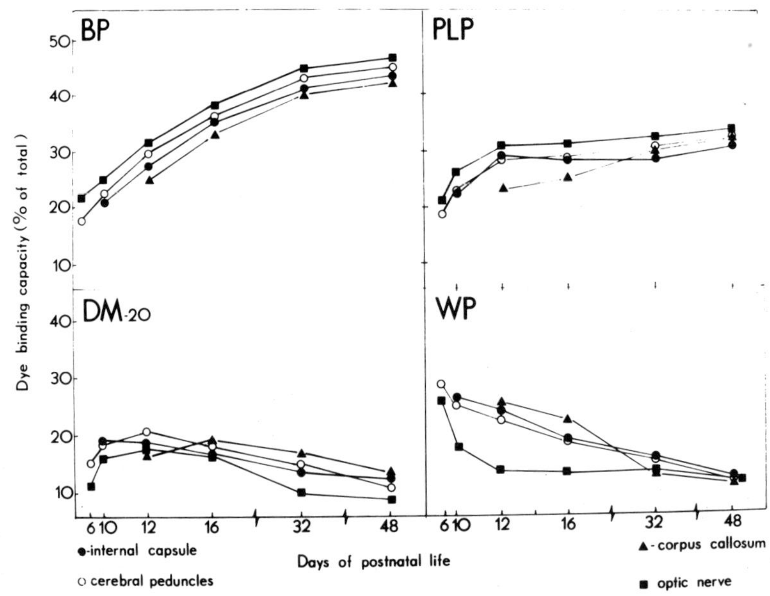

Fig. 2. Protein composition of myelin from different structures of the developing rabbit brain. The ratios were calculated for the following proteins: BP basic protein, DM-20 intermediate protein, PLP proteolipid, WP Wolfgram protein. Each sign represents the average of six determinations.

3.3 Morphology

Myelination started in the optic nerve about the 6th day of life, in corpus callosum not earlier than the 12th day. In the four structures the number of myelinated fibres gradually increased between 16th and 48th day. On the 16th day the thickness of myelin sheaths differed from very thin, composed of only few myelin lamellae, to the rather thick. During further development the number of myelin lamellae in the sheaths evidently increased /Fig. 3/. On the 48th day of life apart from corpus callosum, optic nerve, internal capsule and cerebral peduncle appeared to be well myelinated.

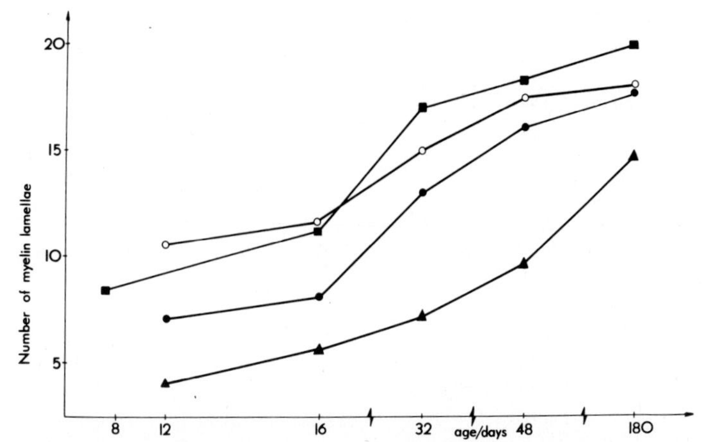

Fig. 3. The average number of myelin lamellae around the axons in particular developmental stages.
● internal capsule ▲ corpus callosum ○ cerebral peduncles ■ optic nerve

4 DISCUSSION

Micromethods for protein estimation and electrophoresis permitted estimation of changes occurring in the myelin sheath in the very early stages of myelination, when only minute amounts of nerve tissue were available. Myelin deposition has been found to proceed in rabbit at an exponential rate fo at least 180 days of life and the rate of myelin accumulation varies in different structures of the CNS. The ultrastructural studies confirm the different rates of myelinogenesis in optic nerve, cerebral peduncle, internal capsule and corpus callosum, as regards the number of sheaths as well as their thickness. This morphological progress of myelination correlated well with the increase of total myelin protein obtained from these structures in the time span studied. Although in all four structures during maturation the relative Wolfgram protein content decreased with a simultaneous increase mainly of the basic protein, the values and age differed. Therefore in developmental studies attention must be concentrated on the sequence of myelination of investigated structures of the CNS.

4 REFERENCES

/1/ B.Zgorzalewicz, V. Neuhoff, T. Waehneldt, Neurobiology 4 /1974/ 264-276.
/2/ B.Zgorzalewicz, V. Neuhoff, H. Zimmer, Neuropat. Pol. 21 /1983/ 161-168
/3/ M. Dambska, B. Zgorzalewicz, Neuropat. Pol. 21 /1983/ 27-33.
/4/ C. Fagg, T. Waehneldt, V. Neuhoff, Adv. Exp. Med. Biol. 100 /1978/ 135-145
/5/ V. Neuhoff, K. Philipp, H. Zimmer, S. Mesecke, Z. Physiol. Chemie 360 /1979/ 1657-1670.
/6/ H. Poehling, V. Neuhoff, Electrophoresis, 1 /1980/ 90- 302.

EFFECT OF EtOH (PERMANENT & FILIAL ALCOHOLISM: "A.G. RATS") ON MITOCHONDRIAL CNS PROTEIN

ENRIQUE EGAÑA & MARINA ACORIA

University of Chile - Faculty of Medicine; Institute of Experimental Medicine - Laboratory of Neurochemistry; Hospital J.J. Aguirre - Santiago 7 - Chile.

1. INTRODUCTION

In previous electrophoretic study on CNS protein in "A.G." rats we showed some differences in the protein pattern compared with normal (1). These results refered to CNS mitochondria, microsoma & citosol protein. See also (2). In order to identifier the altered "A.G." rats CNS proteins we began to study them in mitochondria fractions.

2. MATERIAL & METHODS

Adult albino Wistar rats. Four experimental groups: normal and three "A.G." groups: "A.G./12" rats drinking as exclusive fluid intake 12% (v/v) ethanol (EtOH) solution since 1948 (at present 77 generations); "A.G./25" rats drinking 25% (v/v) EtOH (11 generations since 1979); "A.G./H_2O" rats who drank 12% (v/v) EtOH solution until the 42th generation ("A.G./12") and thereafter separated to drink water (33 generations). Four CNS' submitochondrial fraction were obtained by digitonin and lubrol WX treatement & differential centrifugation (Schnaitman and Greenawalt methods 3, 4) outer membrane, soluble intermembrane protein, inner membrane and soluble matrix protein. Electrophoresis in poliacrilamide SDS gel (5) at room temperature by 4-5 hours; 3% stacking gel at 15 mA and 14% runing gel at 30 mA; staining coomassie blue 0.25%, methanol 50%, acetic acid 10%; destaining: metanol 45% and acetic acid 7%. 50 ug of protein per sample in the diverse experimental condition, by Lowry et. al. method.

3. RESULTS

The results showed major change in the outer membrane of the "A.G. groups" compared with normal. The intermembrane was similar in Normal & "A.G. groups". Inner membrane presented some differences among the "A.G. groups". Matrix showed the most noticeable alteration in the "A.G./12" group compared with normal.

These results let us to think that mitochondria altered protein band could correspond to enzimatic systems involved in EtOH (& AcCHO) metabolism.

4. REFERENCES

(1) Egaña, E., Ramirez, M.T. & Llona, I. "Ionizing Radiation effect on the CNS' Electrophoretic protein profile in special experimental alcoholism model". 9th International Meeting of the International Society for Neurochemistry. Vancouver, B.C. Canada - Julio 10-15, 1983.

(2) Tewari, S. & Noble, E.P. "Biochemistry and Pharmacology of Ethanol" Majchrowicz & Noble E.P. editors, Plenum Press New York, 1979 Vol. 2.

(3) Schnaitman, C. & Greenawalt J.W. , J. Cell. Biol. (1968) 38: 158-175.

(4) Greenawalt J.W. In "Methods in Enzymology", S. Fleischer and L. Packer editors; Academic Press Inc., New York 1974 Vol. 31 Part A: 310-323.

(5) Vos, J. & Vander Helm, H.J., J. Neurochem. (1964) 11: 309-314.

2D-ELECTROPHORESIS OF CEREBROSPINAL FLUID

Felix Wiederkehr, Allan Ogilvie, Dieter J. Vonderschmitt

Medizinisch-chemisches Zentrallaboratorium, Universitätsspital Zürich, CH-8091 Zürich, Switzerland

1 INTRODUCTION

Cerebrospinal fluid (CSF) is relatively low in protein content compared with serum. However, in essential most individual protein fractions correlate qualitatively. Proteins in CSF may change in the presence of various diseases as seen in inflammatory processes of the central nervous system (CNS). Immunoglobulins are synthesized intrathecally. Two-dimensional electrophoresis (2-D) on polyacrylamide gel was used to demonstrate oligoclonal zones in the light chains area of immunoglobulins in several patients with multiple sclerosis (MS), viral myelitis, neurolues etc.. In addition, we followed the pattern in the light chain area of immunoglobulins from one individual patient during one year.

2 METHODS

2.1 Sample preparation

CSF and serum samples were simultaneously obtained from the same patient by the standard procedure. CSF samples were concentrated 10-20 fold. CSF gamma globulin was measured by routine agarose electrophoresis. The samples for 2-D electrophoresis were prepared according to the method of Anderson and Anderson (1).

2.2 Analysis

Iso-dimension was carried out in capillary gel columns (14 cm x 0,15 cm i.d.). The gels contained 35 g/l acrylamide, 9 mol of urea, 20 g/l NP-40 surfactant, 20 g/l of 3 1/2 - 10 ampholytes, and 5 g/l of 5-7 ampholytes. The separation was allowed to run under 9000 volt.h.

DALT-dimension was carried out in slab gels (155 mm high x 140 mm wide x 1,5 mm thick) consisting of a running gel containing 100 g of polyacrylamide per liter. The equilibration buffer used to introduce

SDS into the system and to remove ampholytes from the ISD gels was prepared without 2-mercaptoethanol. The capillary gels were applied onto the slab gels immediately after an equilibration time of exactly 8 minutes.

We compared several different silver staining procedures (2-6). The silver staining according to Oakley et al (2) produces the best patterns. The gel was equilibrated for 30 seconds in a 0,02% sodiumthiosulfite solution to eliminate non-specific high background staining before developing in the citrate-formaldehyde solution.

3 RESULTS AND DISCUSSION

3.1 Serum versus CSF

Several CSF specific proteins (non-existent in sera) are noticeable when comparing 2-D patterns of sera versus CSF. The protein group with m.w. of 38,000 shows variations in each CSF pattern in contrast to protein groups m.w. 30,000 and m.w. 77,000.

3.2 CSF with elevated gamma globulins

All CSF-samples with elevated gamma globulins show oligoclonal zones (pin point patterns, spots) in the light chains region. The points are uniformly distributed over the entire pH range in all cases pertaining to MS. The oligoclonal zone appears isolated and is not detected in serum. Patients suffering from viral myelitis show a slightly different basic pattern in the oligoclonal zone than the MS patients. A totally different pattern is displayed from a patient diagnosed with brain atrophy. Five clearly visible clones, produced intrathecally in CSF, are present in the light chains area.

3.3 Constant patterns of light chain clones in the course of a disease

All four CSF-samples with elevated gamma globulin fraction from a patient suffering from viral myelitis have shown a constant pattern in the region of the light chains of immunoglobulins during one year. In the acute stage, the first 2-D electropherogramm showed a definite pattern of points in the light chain area. The pattern was not detectable in the second CSF sample obtained during clinical remission. The third to fifth CSF sample, collected during several relapses, reverted to the original pattern. This observation suggests that the same cell-clones are always being activated.

4 REFERENCES

(1) Anderson, N.L., Anderson, N.G., proc. Natl. Acad. Sci. USA 74, 5421-5425 (1977)

(2) Oakley B.R., et al., Anal. Biochem. 105, 361-363 (1980)

(3) Adams, L.D., Sammons, D.W., Electrophoresis 81, 155-165, Walter de Gruyter, Berlin (1981)

(4) Wray, W., et al., Anal. Biochem. 118, 197-203 (1981)

(5) Ansorge, W., Electrophoresis 82, 235-242, Walter de Gruyter, Berlin (1983)

(6) Merril, C.R., et al., Anal. Biochem. 110, 201-207 (1981)

DIFFERENCES IN AGAROSE GEL PROTEIN ELECTROPHORESIS OF NATIVE UNCONCENTRATED AND CONCENTRATED CEREBROSPINAL FLUID (CSF).
(Experiments with a commercially available system.)

Tilmann O. Kleine, Rainer Althen

Funktionsbereich Neurochemie im Zentrum für Nervenheilkunde der Universität, D-3550 Marburg a.d. Lahn, G.F.R.

1 INTRODUCTION

Previous experiments with the agarose gel electrophoresis system Paragon from Beckman Instruments have shown that the system can be adapted to native unconcentrated cerebrospinal fluid (CSF) (1,2). Thus a concentration of the CSF sample up to 7 g protein per liter is not needed as it is proposed by the manufacturer. In this paper, comparative experiments were done with CSF samples before and after concentration in order to exclude the effect of different protein concentrations on the pherogramm pattern. For comparison, concentrated samples rediluted to the starting protein concentration of the native samples, were examined, too.

2 MATERIALS AND METHODS

Fresh CSF samples, free of cells, were concentrated with microconcentrator Centricon 10 from Amicon Corporation, Danvers, MA, USA. Protein concentration was examined with a modified Bradford method before and after concentration using Total Protein Test from BIO-RAD, Anaheim, CA, USA. Concentrated samples were diluted with saline.
The agarose gel electrophoresis system Paragon, commericially available from Beckman Instruments (Brea, CA, USA) was applied as follows:
SPE I gels were used for concentrated CSF samples as described by the manufacturer utilizing the Paragon Blue Stain. The procedure was modified for native samples as follows (cf. 2): 5-10 µl sample was applied 3 times with 3 min interval each, using a 0.8 mm slot. After a 25 min electrophoresis step the gel was fixed with a solution of acetic acid-ethanol-water (1:3:1; v/v) for 10 min.
SPE II gels were used for concentrated CSF samples as indicated by the manufacturer utilizing the Paragon Violet Stain. For native samples the procedure was modified as follows (cf. 2): 5-10 µl sample was applied 3 times with 3 min interval each using a 0.8 mm slot.

The stained gels were scanned with the computing Densitometer System CDS-200 from Beckman Instruments at 600 nm. Kontrollogen L (Behringwerke Marburg/Lahn) diluted 1 + 199 with saline served as control.

3 RESULTS AND DISCUSSION

3.1 Electropherogramms with concentrated CSF samples (by a factor of 15 to 22) yielded at least one prealbumin, albumin and γ-globulin band and two α_1-globulin-, α_2-globulin- and β-globulin bands each (Fig. 1). However, different electropherogramms were obtained with Paragon SPE I and SPE II: they differ in area and relative percent of pherogramm fractions (Table 1). This indicates that the results obtained with both systems were not comparable.

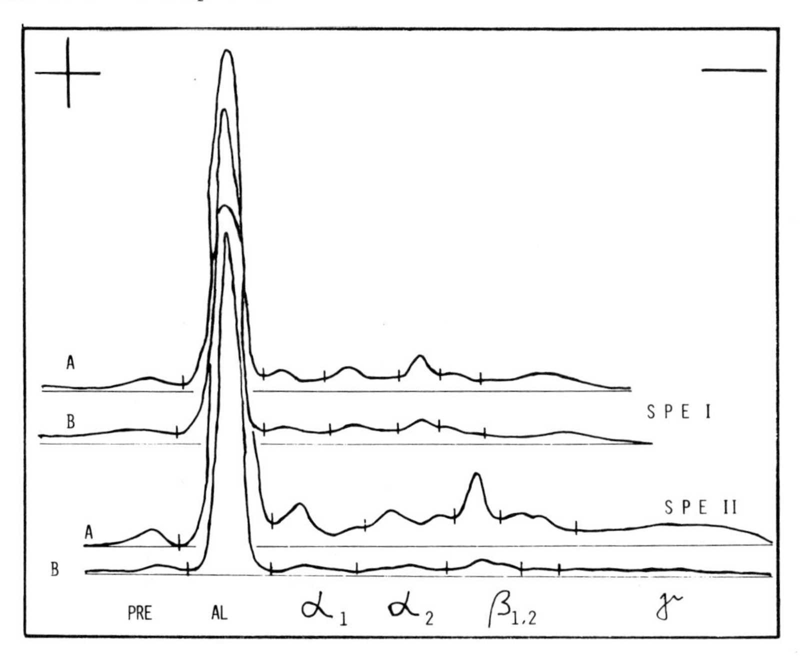

Fig. 1. Pherogramms of a CSF sample obtained with the Paragon system SPE I and SPE II. (Total protein 0.8 g/l.)
A: concentrated sample by a factor of 23. B: native unconcentrated sample. For further details see Material and Methods.

3.2 Electropherogramms with native CSF samples yielded at least one band of prealbumin, albumin, α_1-, α_2-, β- and γ-globulin (Fig. 1). Second globulin fractions were only indicated probably on account of their smaller concentrations (Fig. 1). Moreover, areas and relative percent of the fractions were clearly lower with SPE II than with SPE I,

Table 1. Electropherogramms of two native CSF samples and after their concentration and redilution using the electrophoresis system Paragon SPE I and SPE II.
Results indicate the mean of 2-4 experiments. Only these results were considered having coefficients of variation < 15% of each fraction.

Procedure	Gel	Total protein g/l	Total area+	Fractions of Electropherogramm: Prealbumin area+ %	Albumin area+ %	α_1-Globulins A area+ %	α_1-Globulins B area+ %	α_2-Globulins A area+ %	α_2-Globulins B area+ %	β-Globulins 1 area+ %	β-Globulins 2 area+ %	γ-Globulins area+ %
Sample I	SPE I	0.38	7119	605	3331	778		5o1		831	517	556
native	modified			8.5	46.8	1o.9		7.0		11.7	7.3	7.8
unconcen-	SPE II		4641	77	2898	134	58	357	81	285	296	455
trated	modified			1.7	62.4	2.9	1.3	7.7	1.8	6.1	6.4	9.7
Sample I	SPE I	5.25	8120	951	3550	319	291	736	244	754	514	761
concentrated				11.7	43.7	3.9	3.6	9.1	3.0	9.3	6.3	9.4
by factor 15	SPE II		4646	182	3029	159	103	184	99	339	264	287
				3.9	65.2	3.4	2.2	4.0	2.1	7.3	5.7	6.2
Sample I	SPE I	0.35	7025	1128	3223	485	266	382	260	666	200	415
rediluted	modified			16.0	45.9	6.9	3.8	5.4	3.7	9.5	2.9	5.9
	SPE II			606	3414	183	6.1	166	134	315	356	344
	modified			10.8	61.2	3.3	1.1	3.0	2.4	5.6	6.4	6.2
Sample II	SPE I	0.66	6418	812	3371	355	152	438	220	431	275	364
native	modified			12.6	52.5	5.5	2.4	6.8	3.4	6.7	4.3	5.7
unconcen-	SPE II		3893	179	284o	97	26	78	67	294	105	207
trated	modified			4.6	72.9	2.5	0.7	2.0	1.7	7.6	2.7	5.3
Sample II	SPE I	12.1o	4553	133	3222	138	67	194	105	275	162	257
concentrated				2.9	70.8	3.0	1.5	4.3	2.3	6.0	3.6	5.6
by factor 22	SPE II		9050	265	5105	427	124	269	386	1090	663	721
				2.9	56.4	4.7	1.4	3.0	4.3	120	7.3	8.0
Sample II	SPE I	0.55	6071	788	3405	426	213	243	133	348	306	209
rediluted	Modified			13.0	56.1	7.0	3.5	4.0	2.2	5.7	5.0	3.4
	SPE II		4330	267	3152	122	36	68	65	293	102	225
	modified			6.2	72.7	2.8	0.8	1.6	1.5	6.8	2.4	5.2

+ arbitrary units

especially with the prealbumin fraction. Cause for this phenomena are an elevated zero line with the prealbumin region and a longer pherogramm with SPE II, thus diluting the fractions. Moreover, different pherogramms were found with the unconcentrated native and concentrated CSF sample (Table 1). The data were not comparable probably on account of higher protein concentration of the concentrated CSF samples. Thus, the bands became overstained.

3.3 Electropherogramms with concentrated CSF samples rediluted to the starting protein concentration differed to some extent with those of native samples (Table 1). This indicates that during the concentration process a loss of various proteins and their denaturation occured. Total protein content of the samples was also lower in the rediluted samples (Table 1).

3.4 In conclusion, the results presented indicate differences in pherogramms with the electrophoresis systems Paragon SPE I and SPE II for the native unconcentrated and concentrated CSF samples. The differences may be caused by the methodical design and changes during the concentration process of CSF samples. Thus, separate reference values have to be established for each system.

4 REFERENCES

(1) T.O. Kleine, R. Althen, Hoppe Seyler's Z.Physiol.Chem. 364 (1983) 1159.

(2) T.O. Kleine, R. Althen in B.J. Radola (Ed.), elektrophorese forum '83. München 1983, p. 121-128.

Supported by Deutsche Forschungsgemeinschaft (Kl 193).

HETEROGENEOUS OLIGOCLONAL PATTERN OF CSF IMMUNOGLOBULINS ANALYSED BY ISOELECTROFOCUSING ON POLYACRYLAMIDE GELS: DUE TO ACTION OF DIFFERENT PROTEINASES IN CENTRAL NERVOUS SYSTEM (CNS) ?

T.O. Kleine, Bernhard Haak

Funktionsbereich Neurochemie im Zentrum für Nervenheilkunde der Universität, D-3550 Marburg a.d. Lahn, F.R.G.

1 INTRODUCTION

Previous experiments with purified immunoglobulins have shown that the action of neuraminidase and endo-β-N-acetylglucosaminidases yielded additional subfractions placed at the alkaline pH-range of isoelectrofocusing in polyacrylamide gels (1). These findings suggested that the removal of oligosaccharide redidues from immunoglobulins changed their electrical charges. Glucose stavred cells produced precursor forms of glycoproteins with incomplete oligosaccharide chains (cf. 1); similar states may be present with lymphocytes accumulated in CNS under inflammatory conditions. With inflammatory processes of CNS, especially with multiple sclerosis, proteinases are increased (2,3). In CSF, at least three distinct proteolytic enzymes have been characterized having pH optima at acid, neutral and alkaline pH (4). In this paper purified immunoglobulins were treated with four proteinases cleaving at different sides of the peptide chain and analysed by isoelectrofocusing.

2 MATERIAL AND METHODS

Purified monoclonal IgG, IgA and IgM were kind gifts from Behringwerke Marburg/Lahn and dissolved in saline or as indicated. All purified proteinases were obtained from Sigma Chemical Company St. Louis, USA.

Cathepsin D from bovine spleen (EC 3.4.23.5) was incubated at pH 3.0 with 0.1 M sodium citrate-phosphate buffer.

Chymotrypsin from bovine pankreas (EC 3.4.21.1) was incubated at pH 7.o with o.1 M sodium-phosphate buffer.

Plasmin (human, EC 3.4.21.7) was incubated at pH 7.5 with o.o5 M Tris-HCl buffer.

Trypsin from bovine pankreas (EC 3.4.21.4) was incubated at pH 7.5 with o.o5 M Tris-HCl buffer.

All incubations were done at 37°C for 0.5 or 1 h. Controls with the enzymes, preincubated for 10 min at 100°C, together with the immunoglobulins or with saline were performed as indicated.
Isoelectrofocusing of the samples was performed with Ampholine PAG plates 1804-101, pH 3.5-9.5, using Multiphor apparatus, all from LKB, Sweden. The samples (20 to 25 µl) were applied into holes of a plastic foil placed on the polyacrylamide gel with 3.5 cm distance from the anode. Samples were focused 3 h at 1000 volts and 6°C and silver stained according to the LKB instruction paper of H. Kruse, H. Reiber and H.L. Schipper.

3 RESULTS AND DISCUSSION

Monoclonal IgG dissolved in saline, was placed with more than 12 silver-stained bands to the alkaline pH gradient only of low alkaline pH range using the isoelectrofocusing technique described here (Fig. 1 C,Q). However, this distribution of the bands appeared to be influenced by acid buffer solutions (e.g. 0.1 M sodium citrate-phosphate buffer, pH 3.0; Fig. 1A) producing additional bands; buffer solutions of the neutral pH range had not such effects (Fig. 1B,R). Moreover, the presence of heat-inactivated enzyme protein also changed the band pattern of monoclonal IgG, especially in case of cathepsin D (Fig. 1E) and trypsin where two additional bands appeared in the strong alkaline pH range (Fig. 1O). This finding indicates some aggregation between IgG and the inactivated cathepsin D. Heat-inactivated chymotrypsin and plasmin did not show such effects (Fig. 1H,L).
Nevertheless, our incubation experiments with four different proteinases indicated changes of the band pattern of monoclonal IgG which differed significantly from the band pattern of controls described above:
Cathepsin D which cleaves preferentially peptide bonds with the hydrophobic amino acids phenylalanine and leucine, produced some loss of bands and additional small distinct bands as well at low alkaline pH region (Fig. 1D). Chymotrypsin which cleaves also peptide bonds with other hydrophobic amino acids (e.g. tyrosine, tryptophan), made additional bands at high alkaline pH region (Fig. 1G).
Plasmin which cleaves peptide bonds with basic amino acids (e.g. arginine, lysine) produced some additional distinct bands over the whole alkaline pH region (Fig. 1K), whereas with trypsin which has similar cleavage properties, only few additional distinct bands at low and high alkaline pH region appeared (Fig. 1N).
These findings indicate that incubation of monoclonal IgG with four proteinases having different cleavage properties and pH optima, caused

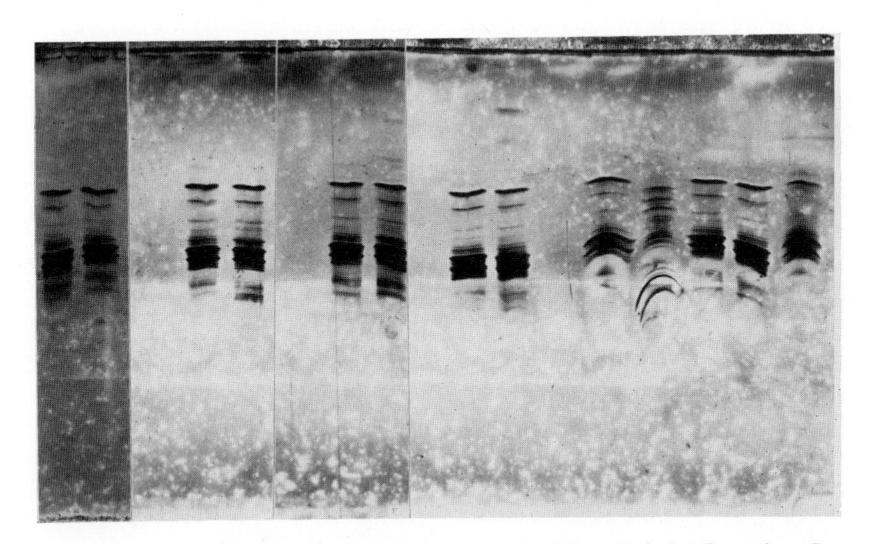

Fig. 1. Isoelectrofocusing of purified monoclonal IgG treated and untreated with different enzymes and buffers.

A: 1 µg IgG in 0.1 M sodium citrate-phosphate buffer pH 3.0;
B: 1 µg IgG in 0.1 M sodium phosphate buffer pH 7.0;
C: 1 µg IgG in saline;
D: 1 µg IgG incubated with cathepsin D (5 mU) for 1 h as indicated under A;
E: 1 µg IgG + heat inactivated cathepsin D (5 mU) in buffer like under A;
F: heat-inactivated cathepsin D (5 mU) in buffer like under A;
G: 1 µg IgG incubated with chymotrypsin (5 mU) for 1 h as indicated under B;
H: 1 µg IgG + heat-inactivated chymotrypsin (5 mU) in buffer like under B;
I: heat-inactivated chymotrypsin (5 mU) in buffer like under B;
K: 1 µg IgG incubated with plasmin (4 mU) for 1 h as indicated under R;
L: 1 µg IgG + heat-inactivated plasmin (4 mU) in buffer like under R;
M: heat-inactivated plasmin (4 mU) in buffer like under R;
N: 1 µg IgG incubated with trypsin (7 mU) for 1 h as indicated under R;
O: 1 µg IgG + heat-inactivated trypsin (7 U) in buffer like under R;
P: heat-inactivated trypsin (7 U) in buffer like under R;
Q: 1 µg IgG in saline;
R: 1 µg IgG in o.o5 M Tris-HCl buffer, pH 7.5.

For further details see Materials and Methods.

the appearence of different additional bands using an isoelectrofocusing technique. These additional silver-stained bands probably represent IgG fragments because they could not be detected in the presence of the heat-inactivated enzymes. Similar findings were observed after incubating IgA and IgM with these proteinases (not shown here). Thus, it appears very likely that hetereogeneity of the oligoclonal immunoglobulin pattern, well known in CSF from patients suffering from certain inflammations (cf. 5), can be caused by the action of some proteinases present in CNS and/or CSF. It has been shown, that fresh plaques in CNS from patients with active multiple sclerosis had increased proteolytic enzyme activities (2,3) as also did leucocytes from patients of various inflammatory disease (6). Plasminogen levels were also elevated in CSF under such conditions (7).

In conclusion, evidence is presented here that additional bands of the oligoclonal immunoglobulin pattern as it is obtained by isoelectrofocusing on polyacrylamide gel, can be produced by the action of some proteinases.

4 REFERENCES

(1) T.O. Kleine, B. Haak in H. Peeters (Ed.) Protides of the Biological Fluids XXXII Colloquium. Brussels 1983 in press.

(2) P.J. Riekkinen, J. Clausen, H.J. Frey, T. Fog, U.K. Rinne, Acta Neurol.Scandinav. 46 (197o) 349-353.

(3) R.E. Einstein, J. Csejtey, K.B. Dalal, C.W.M. Adams, O.B. Bayliss, J.F. Hallpike, J.Neurochem. 19 (1972) 653-662.

(4) P.J. Riekkinen, U.K. Rinne, J.Neurol.Sci. 7 (1968) 97-1o6.

(5) K.G. Kjellin, A. Sidén in J.H. Wood (Ed.) Neurobiology of Cerebrospinal Fluid, Plenum Press, New York 1983, p. 369-386.

(6) M.L. Cuzner, W.I. McDonald, P. Rudge, M. Smith, N. Borshell, A.N. Davison, J.Neurol.Sci. 26 (1975) 1o7-111.

(7) K. Kun-yu Wu, C.D. Jacobsen, J.C. Hoak, Arch.Neurol. 128 (1973) 64-66.

Supported by the Deutsche Forschungsgemeinschaft (Kl 193)

CHROMATOFOCUSING OF CEREBROSPINAL FLUID AND SERUM IMMUNOGLOBULIN G: ANALYTICAL POTENTIAL AND UTILITY FOR COMBINATION WITH TWO-DIMENSIONAL GEL ELECTROPHORESIS

Paolo Gallo, Åke Sidén

Department of Neurology, Huddinge Hospital, S-141 86 Huddinge, Sweden

1 INTRODUCTION

Chromatofocusing (1) is a chromatographic analogue of isoelectric focusing. The method is based on the elution of an ion exchanger with a self-generated pH-gradient which gives a separation and focusing of the sample molecules on the basis of their respective isoelectric points. In the present study this technique has been used for analytical examinations of relatively low amounts of normal and oligoclonal immunoglobulin G (IgG) from cerebrospinal fluid (CSF) and serum. In addition, the utility of chromatofocusing for combination with two-dimensional gel electrophoresis was investigated.

2 MATERIALS AND METHODS

2.1 Materials

Twenty paired CSF and serum samples (10 paired normal samples and 10 paired samples from subjects with intrathecal IgG-synthesis), 20 serum samples with oligoclonal IgG-components and five normal sera were examined by chromatofocusing. The IgG-concentration of the sera was 6-32 g/l and that of the CSF samples 16-113 mg/l. These samples had also been examined by thin-layer isoelectric focusing followed by Coomassie-staining as well as detection of IgG by immunofixation.

2.2 Methods

Chromatofocusing was performed by using the Pharmacia FPLC system with a Mono P column or a specially designed small column based on the same medium and prepared by the manufacturer according to instructions from the authors. The start buffer was 0.025 M diethanolamine-HCl, pH 9.5, and the eluent 10% Polybuffer 96-HCl, pH 6.0. The sera were diluted to an IgG-concentration of 1 mg/ml and the CSF samples were concentrated to the same level. A chloroform-extraction was performed in order to eliminate the lipids. The samples were diluted 1:5 in start buffer and filtered through a sterile 0.2 µm disposable filter. A total amount of 0.1 mg IgG was applied to the column. The separation was performed at a flow rate of 0.25 ml/min with 5 ml

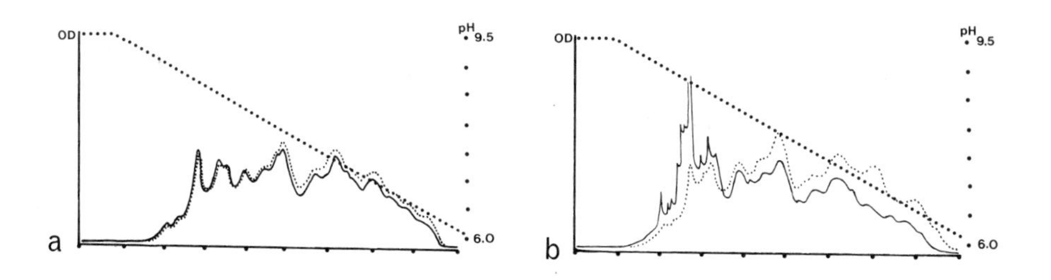

Fig. 1. Chromatofocusing of CSF (continuous line) and serum (dotted line) with normal IgG (a) and from a subject with intrathecal IgG-synthesis (b). The elution volume (5 ml between each dot) is shown along the x-axis and the optical density (280 nm) of the eluate along the y-axis. The pH-gradient is indicated by large dots.

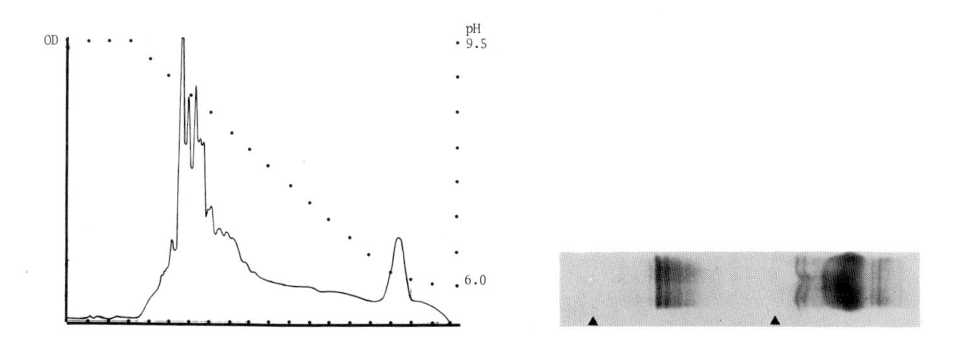

Fig. 2. Chromatofocusing of serum (continuous line) with oligoclonal IgG performed with the small column. Each dot along the x-axis corresponds to an elution volume of 1 ml. The corresponding thin-layer isoelectric focusing run is shown to the right (cathodic end to the left); the pH-interval of 9.5-6.0 is indicated by arrow-heads.

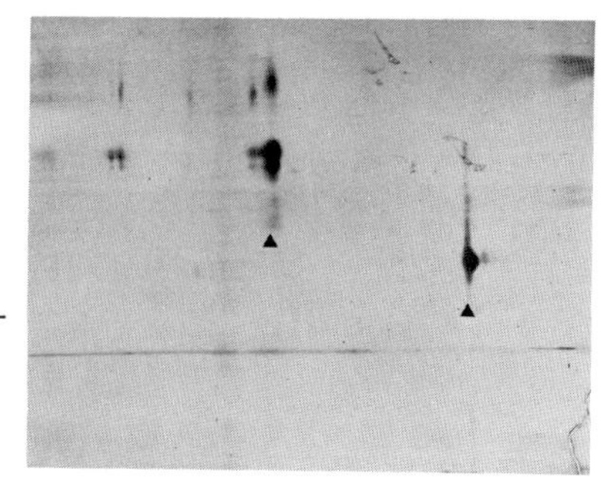

Fig. 3. Two-dimensional gel electrophoresis of the serum sample in Fig. 2. The cathodic end of the first dimension isoelectric focusing run is to the right and the second dimension electrophoresis was performed from top to bottom. The heavy and light chain positions are indicated by arrow-heads.

of start buffer followed by 35 ml of Polybuffer 96 and finally 5 ml of start buffer; the corresponding volumes used for the small column were 2, 15 and 2 ml. The optical density of the eluate was measured at 280 nm and the oligoclonal IgG-components were collected by a FRAC-100 fraction collector. Two-dimensional gel electrophoresis was performed as previously described (2) with some minor modifications. An Ampholine (pH 3.5-10.0) concentration of 2% was used for the first dimension and the second dimension was performed in 10% SDS-acrylamide gels. The protein components were detected by silver staining (3).

3 RESULTS AND DISCUSSION

The chromatofocusing program gave linear pH-gradients and regularly performed duplicate separations of the samples exhibited no significant run to run variation. Fig. 1 shows the chromatofocusing findings of two paired CSF and serum samples which were analysed by the Mono P column. All samples with normal CSF and serum IgG gave profiles with a number of relatively smooth peaks. Since the IgG of normal CSF emanates from serum both curves were very similar. Samples from subjects with intrathecal synthesis of IgG all exhibited distinct differences between the serum and CSF profiles. The CSF gave a number of distinct peaks corresponding to the oligoclonal IgG-fractions. Fig. 2 gives the results from chromatofocusing of a serum sample with oligoclonal IgG performed on the specially designed small column. All 20 sera with such abnormal components gave profiles which differed from those of the 5 normal samples. Flow rates of 1.0 ml/min could also be used as well as IgG-amounts of 0.05 mg. The present chromatofocusing programs were found to be well suited for isolation of oligoclonal IgG-components prior to two-dimensional gel electrophoresis (Fig. 3). Chromatofocusing exhibits promising capacities for studies of heterogeneous proteins like IgG in CSF and serum. Abnormal IgG-components are easily detected and the method is a valuable first-step procedure prior to two-dimensional gel electrophoresis.

4 REFERENCES

(1) L. A. AE. Sluyterman, J. Wijdenes, Proc. Int. Symp. Electrofocusing and Isotachophoresis, Walter de Gruyter, Berlin - New York 1977, pp. 463-466.

(2) P. H. O'Farrell, J. Biol. Chem. 250 (1975) 4007-4021.

(3) C. R. Merril, D. Goldman, M. L. Van Keuren, Methods in Enzymology 96 (1983) 230-239.

QUANTITATIVE CROSSED IMMUNOELECTROPHORESIS OF CEREBROSPINAL FLUID

Karin Lenger, Marion Blunk, Krystyna Warecka

Laboratorium für Neuroimmunochemie und Liquordiagnostik der Klinik für Neurologie, Medizinische Hochschule Lübeck, D - 2400 Lübeck (FRG)

1 INTRODUCTION

Quantitative analysis of particular proteins of cerebrospinal fluid (CSF) is of great importance for diagnosis of neurological diseases. However, such investigations are rare because of two main difficulties: firstly, only small quantities of CSF are available and secondly the protein content of CSF is approximately twohundredfold lower than that of serum, which has to be simultaneously analysed. Generally speaking, similar composition of proteins do exist in both liquids (1,2), although the blood/brain barrier does exist. It is supposed that the quantities of various protein components of CSF might be changed especially in neurological diseases and that these changes should be of importance not only for diagnosis, as mentioned above, but also for treatment and prognosis. This paper represents an adaptation of the "crossed immunoelectrophoresis" (3), which is usually for determination of serum proteins, to quantitative evaluation of CSF proteins.

2 PRINCIPLES OF OPERATION AND POSTULATES

2.1. METHODS

In the first dimension 5-10 µl of CSF is separated in 1% agarose-gels on 9 x 11 cm glass-plates (250V/1 h), in the second dimension the 1% agarose-gel contained 0,1 ml (1 ml) antihuman serum (DAKO, Denmark). Electrophoresis is performed in Tris/Na-barbituric acid-buffer pH 8,6 (0,07 M Tris). After electrophoresis, the gels were washed and stained with Coomassie Blue. The areas (mm^2) under the precipitation lines were then calculated by morphometrical measurement.

3 ANALYSES OF CSF WITH LOW PROTEINCONCENTRATION

In both body fluids i.e. in serum as in CSF albumin consists about

60% of total protein. Fig. 1: two standard curves are shown in the protein range of 156,2 mg/dl - 2 500 mg/dl, using albumin as a "leading protein" of the human standard serum (a) and pure albumin (b). The gel contained 1 ml of antihuman serum. The height of the precipitation lines corresponds to the increasing protein contents. Using gels containing 1 ml antihumanserum, the detection limits are 100 mg/dl and 2 500 mg/dl. The same phenomen was observed for serum proteins such as $alpha_1$-antitrypsin, haptoglobin, orosomucoid , prealbumin and so on for which unique protein a standard curve was done. The amount of their antibodyconcentration was sufficient for getting precipitation lines, which, as known, depends on increasing concentration of these particular antigens. For each protein the quantities were separately calculated.
Because of the fact that the proteinconcentration of CSF is about 40 mg/dl it could not be analysed in agarose gels containing 1 ml of antihuman serum, even when the antihuman serum was diluted to 0,1 ml in the gels. But a standard curve could not be obtained with diluted standard humanserum when used as antigen. Therefore, humanserum was replaced with increasing albumin concentrations of 5 mg/dl to 156,2 mg/dl (Fig. 2): the area under the precipitation lines is linear with increasing albumin quantity.
For example, the area of 120 mm^2 corresponds to 36 mg/dl of albumin, a value which meets the albumin concentration of CSF. Comparing this area with the albumin standard curve of Fig. 1 the albumin concentration was calculated to be 360 mg/dl, corresponding to the tenfold higher concentration of the antihuman serum in the gel. In Fig. 3 a native CSF i.e. without any concentration is shown: the agarose gel contains 0,1 ml antihuman serum, the albumin concentration was at first calculated (Fig. 2) to be 50 mg/dl by means of the albumin standard curve. However, when using human serum standard curve (Fig. 1) the calculation was 52 mg/dl when divided by ten. Therefore, it was justified to calculate the concentration of CSF proteins with adequate proteins of serum for which, as described above, separate standard curves were done. The obtained protein values are in agreement with those of literature. Summarizing these data, a quantitative method for determination of particular proteins of CSF was developed.

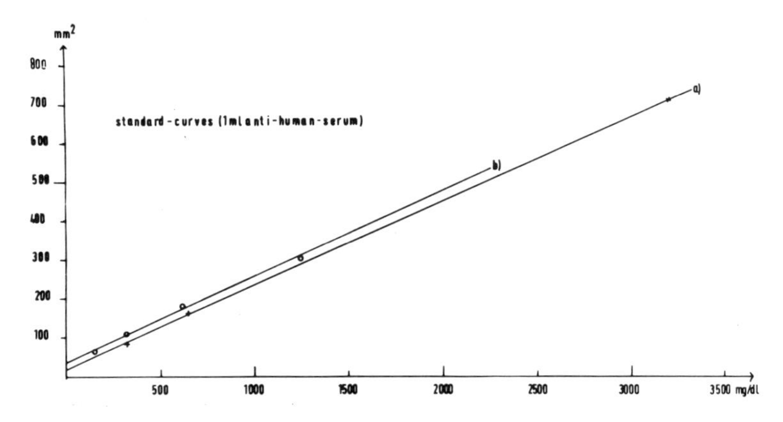

Fig. 1: Standard curves for a) albumin in human serum and for b) pure albumin (156,2 mg/dl - 2 500 mg/dl) by crossed immunoelectrophoresis using 1 ml of antihuman serum.

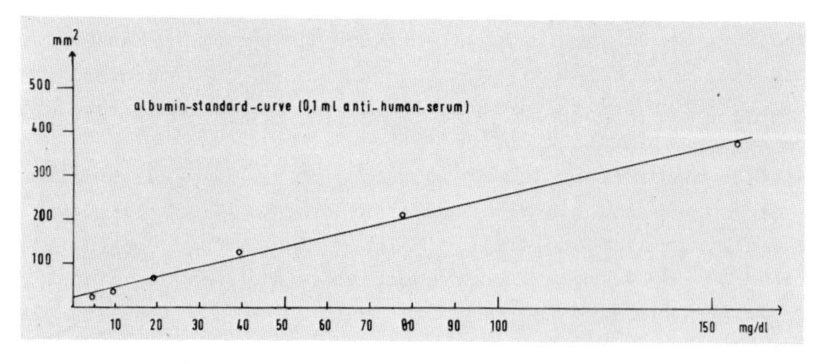

Fig. 2: Standard curve for pure albumin (5 mg/dl - 156,2 mg/dl) by crossed immunoelectrophoresis using 0,1 ml of antihuman serum.

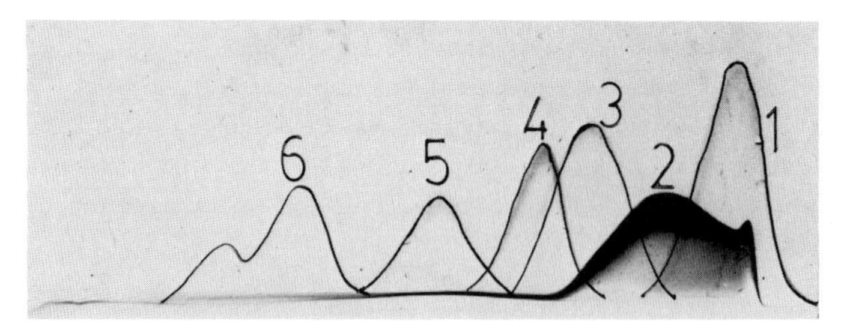

Fig. 3: Crossed immunoelectrophoresis of 10 µl CSF (protein concentration: 38 mg/dl) using 0,1 ml of antihuman serum: 1) prealbumin, 2) albumin, 3) orosomucoid, 4) $alpha_1$-antitrypsin, 5) haptoglobin, 6) C3-complement).

4 CONCLUSION

1) Without any concentration of CSF small quantities of particular proteins could be analysed by crossed immunoelectrophoresis.
2) This method is not very expensive and can be routinely used for researching the quantitative protein pattern of CSF in the various neurological diseases.
3) Although this method is limited to proteins, which do exist in both body fluids as serum and CSF, it has a clinical relevance especially in neurological diseases with blood/brain barrier changes.
4) The exact concentration of the various proteins might give a lot of information concerning the diagnosis, course, therapy and prognosis of neurological diseases.
5) Studies using antihuman CSF are under investigation for determining specific CSF components.

5 REFERENCES

(1) C.-B. Laurell, Scand.J.clin.Lab.Invest. 29 (1972) Suppl. 124, 71-81.

(2) P. Grabar, P. Burtin, Immunoelectrophoretic Analysis, Elsevier, Amsterdam 1964.

(3) H.G.M. Clarke, T. Freeman, Clin. Sci. 35 (1968) 403-413.

MICROHETEROGENEITY OF HUMAN SERUM AND CEREBROSPINAL FLUID PREALBUMIN

Françoise Lasne *, Yves Lasne **

Centre Européen d'Informatique et d'Automation/Département Recherche
51 boulevard des Belges, 69006 LYON/France *
Laboratoire Central des Isotopes 21411 M, Hôpital Edouard Herriot,
Place d'Arsonval, 69374 LYON Cedex 03/France **

The microheterogeneity of human serum prealbumin (PA) has been previously studied by Altland et al. (1) who used a double one dimensional slab gel electrophoresis. This technique required a previous electrophoretic separation of PA from the other serum proteins before isoelectric focusing (IEF) of PA. So far, no study concerning the microheterogeneity of cerebrospinal fluid (CSF) PA has been reported.

We report an immunofixation technique which allows of studying the microheterogeneity of the native serum and CSF prealbumins without any prior purification. The prealbumin isotypes are first recognized by specific antibodies to human PA and revealed by their fixation of ^{125}I labelled thyroxine so that they are shown to present immunological and biological properties of thyroxine-binding prealbumin (TBPA).

This technique establishes that there is no evident polymorphism of TBPA either in serum or in CSF in humans but that there is a striking difference between the serum and the CSF TBPA isoelectric focusing patterns (respective pI ranges : 4.7 - 5.0 and 4.7 - 4.8) in individuals. This difference is shown to be related to interactions between TBPA and β lipoproteins occuring in serum but not in CSF on account of its low β lipoproteins level, and maintained during IEF in a pH gradient 4 - 6.

REFERENCE

(1) Altland, K., Rauh, S. and Hackler, R. Electrophoresis, 2, 148-155 (1981)

EVIDENCES FOR A STRUCTURAL MICROHETEROGENEITY IN CRYSTALLINE YEAST ASPARTYL-tRNA SYNTHETASE

Bernard Lorber, Daniel Kern and Richard Giégé

Laboratoire de Biochimie, Institut de Biologie Moléculaire et Cellulaire du C.N.R.S., 15, rue René Descartes
F - 67084 Strasbourg, France

Yeast aspartyl-tRNA synthetase (or ligase, E.C. 6.1.1.12) is an enzyme involved in protein synthesis. It has three substrates: one macromolecular substrate, $tRNA^{Asp}$ (Mr = 24,160 daltons) and two smaller ligands, ATP and aspartic acid. The free enzyme, an α_2 dimer of Mr ≃ 125,000 daltons, and the complex formed between the enzyme and two tRNA molecules could be crystallized (1,2) and crystallographic studies are underway on both types of crystals. When analyzed by electrophoretic and isoelectric focusing separation methods, the highly purified active enzyme, stored in solution or recovered from crystals, presents a peculiar behavior.

In polyacrylamide gel electrophoresis under native conditions the enzyme can be separated in three populations of identical molecular weight but differing by charge. Under denaturing conditions in the presence of SDS (with or without urea) or in the presence of cetyl-trimethylammonium bromide two protein bands can be visualized when the gels are run in the Tris buffer system of Laemmli. On the other hand only a single band is seen in the phosphate buffer system of Weber and Osborn.

Gel isoelectric focusing under native conditions reveales with a better resolution the charge microheterogeneity of pure aspartyl-tRNA synthetase. Up to eight distinct populations of active enzyme can be counted. Similar results are obtained in immobilized pH gradients. This pattern is reduced to four bands when the focusing experiments are done under denaturing conditions in the presence of urea.

In O'Farrell's two dimensional separation method four distinct spots can be visualized by protein staining as well as by immunological detection methods.

The previous results (PAGE and IEF under native conditions) are found again on the electrophoretic titration curve pattern.

Moreover liquid chromatography experiments confirm the charge heterogeneity observed by the electrophoretic methods. For example, low pressure and high performance liquid chromatofocusing experiments allowed to separate the enzyme populations observed in isoelectric focusing. High performance ion exchange liquid chromatography revealed as well the microheterogeneity of the enzyme.

Similar heterogeneities have been observed in several other aminoacyl-tRNA synthetases (3) and other proteins. Yeast aspartyl-tRNA synthetase could be a candidate of choice for an extended study of such peculiar structural properties of proteins.

1) A. Dietrich, R. Giégé, M.B. Comarmond, J.C. Thierry and D. Moras J. Mol. Biol. 138 (1980) 129-135.

2) B. Lorber, R. Giégé, J.P. Ebel, C. Berthet, J.C. Thierry and D. Moras, J. Biol. Chem. 258 (1983) 8429-8435

3) B. Lorber and R. Giégé, FEBS Letters 156 (1983) 209-216

HORIZONTAL ULTRATHINLAYER SDS POREGRADIENTGEL ELECTROPHORESIS FOR THE DIFFERENTIATION OF URINARY PROTEINS. A HIGH RESOLVING, RAPID AND SENSITIVE METHOD FOR ROUTINE ANALYSIS.

H.W. Schiwara[1], J. Weser[2], W. Postel[2] and A. Görg[2]

[1]Klinisches Labor Schiwara, v. Winterfeld und Pfanzelt, D-28oo Bremen (F.R.G.)

[2]Lehrstuhl für Allgemeine Lebensmitteltechnologie der Technischen Universität München, D-8o5o Freising-Weihenstephan (F.R.G.)

1 INTRODUCTION

The molecular mass analysis of urinary proteins is of great interest for the diagnosis of renal and extrarenal deseases. The ratio of high to lower molecular mass proteins in urine is a useful indicator of kidney status. The pathogenetic difference between glomerular leakage and disturbed tubular reabsorption is expressed by the molecular mass of urinary proteins: tubular proteinurias are composed of micromolecular plasma proteins (<7o ooo daltons) while glomerular proteinuria is characterized by macromolecular proteins (>6o ooo daltons). Additionally glomerular and tubular proteinurias of different selectivity are specified (1,2). Other proteinurias are differenciated with respect to the molecular mass of their pathologic components (myoglobin, paraproteins etc).

In clinical laboratories electrophoretic molecular mass analysis of urinary proteins is usually performed in gel rods (2,3), vertical gel slabs (4) and micro gels (5).

In this study the usefulness of horizontal ultrathinlayer SDS poregradientgel electrophoresis (6,7) in combination with a simple silver stain (8) has been explored for routine analysis of urinary proteins in clinical laboratories.

2 MATERIAL AND METHODS

Tris (hydroxymethyl)-aminomethane was from Merck (Darmstadt, FRG), all other chemicals were from Serva (Heidelberg, FRG). Electrophoresis was run horizontally using the Multiphor chamber and the constant wattage power supply from LKB Produkter AB (Bromma, Sweden). For casting the ultrathin gradient gels, the LKB gradient kit and Gel-Bond-PAG-film were used.

Urine samples were used directly or diluted to contain 1oo-3oo mg/L protein. SDS was added to a final concentration of 1 %. SDS electrophoresis was performed in gel rods according to Boesken et al. (3) and in ultrathin poregradientgels according to Görg et al. (6,7). Microproteins were identified by immunodiffusion (9).

Gel casting (12ox25oxo.36 mm; 4 % to 22.5 % T, 4 % C const). For the set up see Ref. 6, 7. (Vertical cassette: one glass plate coated with Gel Bond PAG film, other glass plate with slot formers (8x2xo.1 mm from two layers Tesafilm), U-gasket from three layers Parafilm; micro-gradient mixer with both chambers open for linear mixing). The mixing vessel of the gradient mixer is filled with 4.8 ml of heavy solution and the reservoir with 4.8 ml of light solution. 2.5 ml of heavy solution is pipetted into the cassette and after its even distribution over the bottom the pouring of the gradient is started and finished within 5 min. Leave the cassette for 1o min at room temperature. Polymerization at 5o^{o}C for 3o min. Heavy solution: 4 % T, 4 % C in 3o % glycerol. Light solution: 22.5 % T, 4 % C, 0 % glycerol. Both solutions are buffered with 375 mM Tris-HCl, pH 8.8, and contain o.1 % SDS, o.o3 % Temed and o.o4 % ammonium persulphate.

Separation Run. 3 μl of each sample solution is pipetted into the gel pockets. Electrode buffer: 25 mM Tris/192 mM glycine and o.1 % SDS. A starting current is set at 5o mA, the power is limited to 3o W and the voltage to 6oo V. 2 hrs at 5°C.

Staining. Coomassie Staining: 3o min in 2o % TCA, 2o min o.1 % Coomassie BB R 25o (in 45 % methanol/1o % acetic acid) and 6o min in destaining solution (35 % methanol/ 1o % acetic acid). Silver staining (8): Coomassie stained gel is washed 2x5 min with 1o % ethanol, 3x3 min with water, incubated in o.1 % $AgNO_3$ for 3o min, rinsed with water for 1o sec, developed with 3 % Na_2CO_3 containing o.o2 % formaldehyde for 5 - 1o min, stopped with 1 % acetic acid for 1o min, washed 3x3 min with water, incubated for 3o sec in a solution containing 1 % $K_3\{Fe(CN)_6\}$ and 1.6 % $Na_2S_2O_3 \cdot 5 H_2O$, rinsed with water for 1 min, washed 5x3 min with water. Recycling: start again with o.1 % $AgNO_3$ for 3o min.

Drying of the Gels. The stained gel, still adhering to the plastic foil, is impregnated in an aqueous 3 % glycerol/7o % methanol solution for 1 min, mounted on a glass plate and wrapped with a water soaked cellophane foil. After air drying the cellophane with the acrylamide gel is peeled off from the plastic foil.

3 RESULTS AND DISCUSSION

Urine samples of different proteinuric deseases were analyzed by horizontal ultrathin-layer SDS poregradientgel electrophoresis (6,7). As shown in Fig. 1 the electrophoresis of urinary proteins in ultrathin gradient gels displays an extremely high resolution and sharpness of the protein bands. First results were obtained

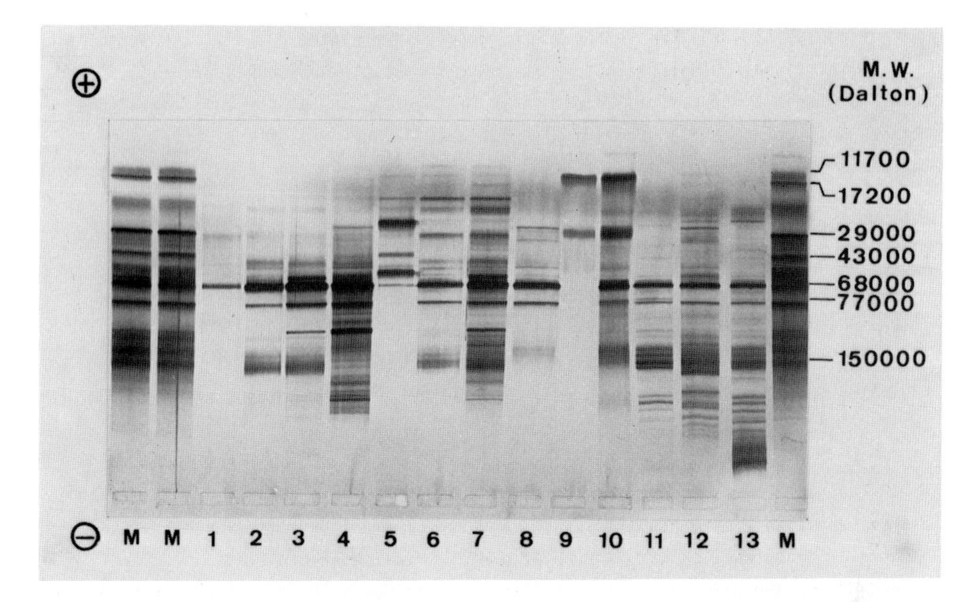

Fig. 1 Ultrathinlayer SDS poregradientgel electrophoresis of unconcentrated urine samples (1oo-3oo mg/L urinary protein). Linear gradient (4 % to 22.5 % T, 4 % C const.) 36o µm gel thickness. Running conditions: 2 hrs, 5 °C, 6oo V (max.). 3 µl of each sample were filled into the gel pockets. Samples: 1 physiological urine, 2-8 urines of different proteinuric deseases, 9 erythrocyte hemolysate, 1o blood hemolysate, 11 serum with IgG, 12 serum with IgA, 13 serum with IgM, M Markerproteins.

Tab. 1 Comparison of the results obtained by (A) ultrathinlayer SDS poregradientgel electrophoresis (6,7), (B) immunoanalysis (9) and (C) SDS electrophoresis in gel rods (2,3).
I-VI Proteinuria types. Typing according to Boesken (2,3).
+, - Immuno analysis of the microproteins (9)

samples (see Fig. 1)	1	2	3	4	5	6	7	8
A	O	I	II	III	IV	V	V	VI
B	O	I	II	III	IV	V	V	VI
C	O	I	VI	III	IV	I	II	VI
β_2-microglobulin	-	-	-	-	+	+	+	-
retinol binding protein	-	-	-	-	+	+	+	-
α_1-microglobolin	-	-	-	-	+	+	+	-
α_1-acid glycoprotein	-	-	-	+	+	+	+	+
α_2 HS glycoprotein	-	-	-	-	-	-	+	-
α_1-antitrypsin	-	-	-	+	-	-	-	+

after 4 hours (electrophoretic run 2 hrs, Coomassie Staining 2 hrs), after completion with silver staining (8), including one recycling step, the results are ready to evaluate within 7 hours. This is one sixth of the time needed for the conventional methods with gel rods (3) or vertical gel slabs (4). Because of the very low gel thickness (24o µm or 36o µm), the gradient gels are easily and rapidly dried on their supporting films and thus transparent permanent pherograms are obtained for densitometry and documentation.

Due to the high sensitivity of electrophoresis in ultrathin gels (1o) and the silver staining, pathologic urines (>1oo mg/L protein) are not to concentrate. Avoiding the concentration step is not only time saving but also of great advantage for the reproducibility of the results. Different concentration methods cut the protein spectrum at different places (11).

In Tab. 1 the results obtained by SDS electrophoresis in ultrathin gradient gels and gel rods and by immunoanalysis are compared. There is no difference in typing of glomerular proteinurias, but in tubular proteinurias. Microproteins, which are important for the differentiation of tubular proteinurias or extrarenal proteinureas are better detected in ultrathin gradient gels than in gel rods. This is confirmed by immuno analysis.

4 CONCLUSION

Horizontal SDS electrophoresis in ultrathin layer pore gradient gels on foil supports in combination with an easy silver staining has proved to be a useful tool for separating large series of unconcentrated urine samples because of its easy handling, short separation and staining time, high resolution and sensitivity.

5 REFERENCES

(1) A.J. Pesce, I. Boreisha, V.E. Pollak, Clin. chim. Acta 4o (1972) 27-34.
(2) W.H. Boesken in H. Losse, E. Renner (Eds.), Klinische Nephrologie, Thieme Verlag, Stuttgart 1982, p. 136.
(3) W.H. Boesken, K. Kopf, P. Schollmeyer, Clin. Nephrol. 1 (1973) 311-318.
(4) A.E. Lison, V. Herold, Nieren- und Hochdruckkrankheiten 11 (1982) 137-141.
(5) V. Neuhoff, Micromethods in Molecular Biology, Springer Verlag, Berlin 1973.
(6) A. Görg, W. Postel, R. Westermeier, E. Gianazza, P.G. Righetti, J. Biochem. Biophys. Methods 3 (198o) 273-284.
(7) A. Görg, W. Postel, R. Westermeier, Z. Lebensm. Unters. Forsch. 174 (1982) 282-285.
(8) J. Heukeshoven, R. Dernick in B.J. Radola (Ed.) Elektrophorese Forum '83, München 1983.
(9) Ouchterlony, Ö. in D.M. Weir (Ed.) Handbook of Experimental Immunology, Blackwell Scientific Publications, Oxford 1967.
(1o) A. Görg, W. Postel, R. Westermeier in B.J. Radola (Ed.) Electrophoresis '79, de Gruyter, Berlin 198o, p. 67-78.
(11) N.G. Anderson, N.L. Anderson, S.L. Tollaksen, Clin. Chem. 25 (1979) 1199-121o.

ENZYME VISUALIZATION AFTER ISOELECTRIC FOCUSING WITH CARRIER AMPHOLYTES AND IMMOBILINES. OPTIMIZATION WITH ULTRATHIN POLYACRYLAMIDE PRINT GELS WITH SUBSTRATE AND PH GRADIENTS.

A. Görg, W. Postel, J. Weser and P. Johann

Lehrstuhl für Allgemeine Lebensmitteltechnologie der Technischen Universität München, D-8050 Freising-Weihenstephan (F.R.G.)

1 INTRODUCTION

For enzyme detection after electrophoresis or isoelectric focusing direct visualization by immersing the running gel into substrate solution or indirect visualization by using substrate-containing matrices (agarose, membranes, paper etc.) for contact printing are applied. Recently, a new print technique with substrate-containing ultrathin polyacrylamide gels on plastic film was described (1). Ultrathin polyacrylamide prints have proved to reproduce exactly the resolution of enzymes obtained by ultrathinlayer isoelectric focusing (2,3) and ultrathinlayer gradientgel electrophoresis (4,5). Based on this print technique (1) and the casting technique for ultrathin gradient gels (4,5), we developed ultrathin polyacrylamide print gels with pH gradients or concentration-gradients of different substrates, inhibitors or buffers in order to demonstrate the influence of these parameters for enzyme activities in an attempt to optimize enzyme visualization after electrophoresis and isoelectric focusing with carrier ampholytes or Immobilines. By focusing in narrow or ultranarrow immobilized pH gradients (6,7) resolution is increased 10 times. Proteins with pI differences as little as 0.001 pH units are separated. Enzyme visualizations after IEF in immobilized pH gradients are performed directly (7) or with print techniques (this paper). Additionally we investigated in enzyme staining procedures which are interfered by carrier ampholytes but not by Immobilines.

2 MATERIAL AND METHODS

2.1 Materials

Ampholine carrier ampholytes pH 3.5 - 10, pH 4 - 6 and Immobilines^R pK 3.6, 4.6 and 6.2, acrylamide, N,N'-methylenebisacrylamide, ammoniumpersulphate, TEMED were from LKB (Bromma, Sweden). Pectinol B 20 from Röhm (Darmstadt, F.R.G.), Ultrazym 100 G from Suisse Ferment AG (Basel, CH), pectolytic enzymes with cellulolytic activities were supplied by several companies. Sodium pectate was from Obi Pectin (Bischofszell, CH), Carboxymethylcellulose (CMC) from Hercules (Neu-Isenburg F.R.G.). The IEF experiments were carried out using the LKB Ultrophor apparatus and the constant wattage power supply from LKB. For casting ultrathin gradient gels (Ref 4,5), the LKB gradient kit and Gel-Bond-PAG-film were used.

2.2 Preparation of ultrathin polyacrylamide gels

2.2.1 IEF gels

With carrier ampholytes. 24o µm PAA gels (5 % T, 4 % C), containing 2 % w/v Ampholines were cast on plastic film (3), e.g. Gel-Bond-PAG-film, by clamp technique (2,3).
With Immobilines. All gradient gels were cast according to Görg et al. (4,5). For preparing an immobilized pH gradient gel pH 3.5 - 5.o see Ref. 8.

2.2.2 Print gels

Homogeneous gels. Ultrathin (12o µm) PAA gels (8 % T, 4 % C) were cast on Gel-Bond-PAG-film by clamp technique (2,3). Gels were impregnated with low molecular reactants by equilibration. High molecular substrates were incorporated by polymerization (e.g. o.35 % carboxymethylcellulose for cellulase detection).
Gradients gels. Ultrathin (24o µm) PAA gels (5 % T, 4 % C) on Gel-Bond-PAG-film.
I Substrate gel with pH gradient (o.75 % Na-pectate, pH 2.5 - 6.5). Heavy solution: 5 % T, 4 % C, o.1 M citrate/NaOH buffer pH 6.5, 15 % glycerol, 1o µl Temed, 1o µl persulphate (4o %). Light solution: 5 % T, 4 % C, o.1 M citrate/HCl buffer pH 2.5, 1o µl Temed, 2o µl persulphate (4o %).
II Buffer gel with substrate gradient (pH 4.3, o.2 - 1.6 % Na-pectate). Heavy solution: 5 % T, 4 % C, 1.6 % Na-pectate in o.1 M citrate/HCl buffer pH 4.3. Light solution: 5 % T, 4 % C, o.2 % Na-pectate in o.1 M citrate/HCl buffer pH 4.3. In both solutions 1o µl Temed, 2o µl persulphate (4o %).

5 ml of heavy solution is filled into the mixing chamber and 5 ml of light solution into the reservoir of the micro gradient mixer. The vertical cassette is filled by linear mixing (both chambers open). Leave the cassette for 15 min at room temperature. Polymerisation for 1 hr at 5o^{o}C. For set up see Ref. 4,5,9.

2.3 Enzyme visualization

Polygalacturonase: Staining of the print gels I and II with Ruthenium Red (o.o2 % aqu. solution) or Methylene Blue (o.o1 % aqu. solution). Destaining with water (1).
Cellulase: Staining of the print gels (o.35 % CMC) after IEF with carrier ampholytes or with Immobilines with o.o5 M iodine (1o).

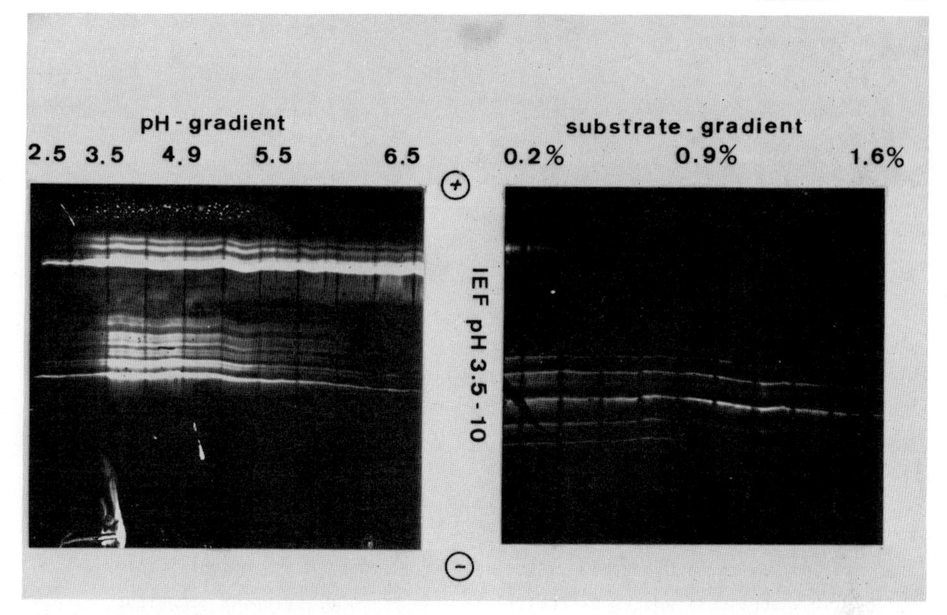

Fig. 1 Visualization of polygalacturonases (Ultrazym) with an ultrathin PAA print gel, containing o.75 % Na-pectate and a buffer generated *pH gradient* 2.5-6.5. IEF with Ampholine 3.5-1o. Incubation of the gel-gel sandwich: 4 min at 4o °C. Staining of the print gel with Ruthenium Red.

Fig. 2 Visualization of polygalacturonases (Pectinol 2o) with an ultrathin PAA print gel containing a *substrate gradient* of o.2-1.6 % Na-pectate, pH 4.3. IEF with Ampholine 3.5-1o. Incubation of the gel-gel sandwich: 3o sec at 4o °C. Staining of the print gel with Methyleneblue.

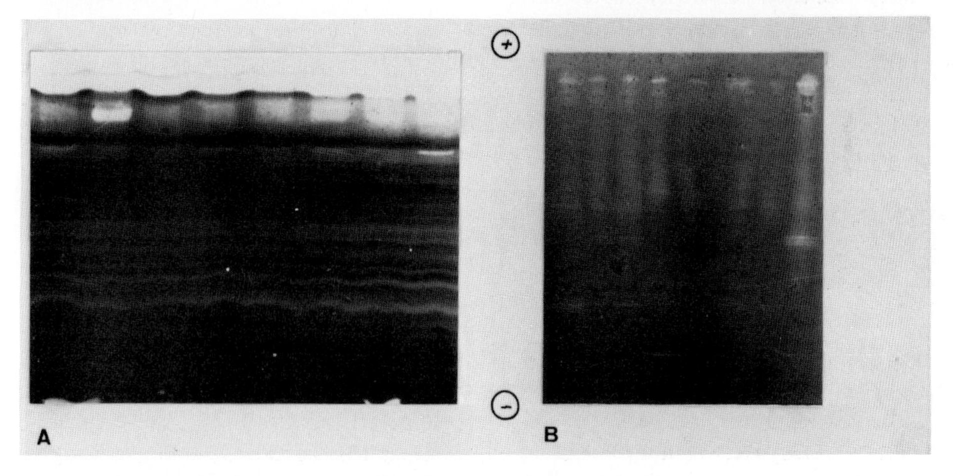

Fig. 3 Staining for cellulase activities in different commercial pectolytic enzymes with an ultrathin PAA print gel containing o.35 % CMC, pH 3.5.
(A) IEF with Ampholine 4-6: Incubation of the gel-gel sandwich: 3 min at 4o °C. Rinsing with water. Staining of the print gel with iodine.
(B) IEF with Immobilines 3.5-5.o. Incubation of the gel-gel sandwich: 3 min at 4o °C. Staining of the print gel with iodine without prewashing.

3 RESULTS AND DISCUSSION

In Fig. 1 an ultrathinlayer polyacrylamide print gel, containing o.75 % Na-pectate and a buffer generated *pH gradient* from 2.5 to 6.5 is shown in order to demonstrate the influence of the pH on enzyme activity. The print was made from an ultrathinlayer focusing gel, where polygalacturonase was applied over the whole gel width and separated with Ampholines pH 3.5-1o. For Ultrazym^R-polygalacturonase the highest enzyme activities are observed in the pH range from 3.5-4.9.

Different substrate concentrations reveal different isoenzyme pattern. This is demonstrated by an ultrathinlayer polyacrylamide print gel containing a *substrate gradient* (Fig. 2). The influence of other reactants is investigated in the same way (poster).

Isoelectric focusing of enzymes with Immobilines offers many advantages. With narrow or ultranarrow immobilized pH gradients microheterogeneties in enzyme pattern are detected, which have not been described before (7). Enzyme stainings are performed in conventional way by direct visualization (7) or by print techniques (poster). Moreover, enzyme stainings which are interfered by carrier ampholytes are not disturbed by Immobilines. In Fig. 3 iodine stained prints from different pectolytic enzymes with cellulase activities focused with carrier ampholytes (Fig. 3A) or Immobilines (Fig. 3B) are shown. Prints from running gels with immobilized pH gradients are stained with iodine without prewashing, therefore very sharp isoenzyme pattern are obtained. Carrier ampholytes have to be removed before staining. On continued washing of the print gel, the isoenzyme pattern diffuses, whereas the remaining carrier ampholytes still interfere with enzyme staining.

4 REFERENCES

(1) E. Günther, G. Haßelbeck, E. Bürger, Z.Lebensm.Unters.Forsch. 178 (1984) 93-96.
(2) A. Görg, W. Postel, R. Westermeier, Anal. Biochem. 89 (1978) 6o-7o.
(3) A. Görg, W. Postel, R. Westermeier, Z.Lebensm.Unters.Forsch. 168 (1979) 25-28.
(4) A. Görg, W. Postel, R. Westermeier, E. Gianazza, P.G. Righetti, J. Biochem. Biophys. Methods 3 (198o) 273-284.
(5) A. Görg, W. Postel, R. Westermeier, Z.Lebensm.Unters.Forsch. 174 (1982) 282-285.
(6) B. Bjellqvist, K. Ek, P.G. Righetti, E. Gianazza, A. Görg, W. Postel, R. Westermeier, J. Biochem. Biophys. Methods 6 (1982) 317-339.
(7) A. Görg, W. Postel, J. Weser, R. Westermeier, in H. Hirai (Ed.) Electrophoresis '83, de Gruyter, Berlin 1984, p. 525-532.
(8) Application Note 324, LKB Produkter, Bromma (Sweden), 1984.
(9) A. Görg, W. Postel, R. Westermeier, P.G. Righetti, K. Ek, Application Note 32o, LKB Produkter, Bromma (Sweden) 1981.
(1o) R. Goren, M. Huberman, Anal. Biochem. 75 (1976) 1-8.

THE DETERMINATION OF ANIONIC AND CATIONIC CONSTITUENTS IN UNPROCESSED URINE BY ISOTACHOPHORESIS

Patrick Pei, Wolfgang Häfliger, Dieter J. Vonderschmitt

Medizinisch-chemisches Zentrallaboratorium, Universitätsspital Zürich, CH-8091 Zürich, Switzerland

1 INTRODUCTION

Human urine contains a number of anionic and cationic constituents. Isotachophoresis is an electrophoretic separation technique that allows quantification of the separated sample ions of urine at nanomol levels by measuring the zone length formed in a capillary. It offers a great degree of freedom from the point-of-view of manipulation of the operational systems. Thus, variation in the counterionic constituent or pH of the leading electrolyte (1), changing of the solvent (2) or the use of complex forming equilibria (3) can result in the separation of compounds which form mixed zones under other conditions. We show here that it is possible to obtain quantitative results for chloride, sulfate, phosphate, citrate, hippurate, benzoate, acetate, ammonium, potassium, sodium, magnesium, calcium and creatinine in urine.

2 MATERIALS AND METHODS

2.1 Samples

No pretreatment of urine was found necessary, except a 5-fold predilution. Each sample was kept frozen until used.

2.2 Instruments

A Shimadzu IP-2A isotachophoretic analyzer (capillary type) equipped with a potential gradient detector and a UV-detector (254 nm) was used. The isotachophoretic separations were carried out in a two-stage migration tube system, 1.0 mm I.D. x 40 mm + 0.5 mm I.D. x 300 mm which was maintained at a constant temperature of 20°C.

2.3 Isotachophoretic procedure

	cation system	anion system
Solvent	95% methanol	H_2O
Leading electrolyte	10^{-2}M TMA*/CH_3COOH pH 5,13	$2x10^{-3}$M HNO_3/$3x10^{-3}$MCd $(NO_3)_2$/β-alanine/0.04% HPMC** pH 3,0
Terminating electrolyte	$2x10^{-2}$M Cd $(NO_3)_2$ pH ca. 6,0	$2x10^{-2}$M capronic acid
Migration current	200 µA (8 min.) → 75 µA	300 µA (8 min.) → 100 µA
Sample volume	1 - 6 µl	1 - 6 µl

* TMA = Tetramethylammoniumhydroxide

** HPMC = Hydroxypropylmethylcellulose

3 RESULTS AND DISCUSSION

3.1 Separation of cations in urine

The mobility ($cm^2/V \cdot sec$) of K^+ and NH_4^+ in water is about the same but in methanol their mobility differs considerably. We use $(CH_3)_4$ NOH as leading electrolyte in methanol so cationic species such as K^1, NH_4^+, Na^+, Mg^{2+}, Ca^{2+} and creatinine-H^+ with mobilities less than that of $(CH_3)_4N^+$ can be determined and separated. The pH of the leading electrolyte must be adjusted between 5.08 and 5.20 for the optimal separation of the main cationic species in urine. Total run time is about 40 minutes.

3.2 Separation of anions in urine

Human urine contains high concentrations of chloride and sulfate, which have almost identical mobilities in water and are difficult to separate using the generally applied operational conditions. In an aqueous system Bocek et al. separated the halides quantitatively together with sulfate, using cadmium (II) as the counter ion and nitrate as the leading ion (3).

We have observed that only Cd(II) as counter ion is not efficient enough for the separation of anionic species in urine. We added β-alanine as a second counter ion in the leading electrolyte thus maintaining a "steady state".

4 REFERENCES

(1) Everaets, F.M., Beckers, J.L., Verheggen, Th.P.E.M., Journal of Chromatography Library, Vol 6, Elsevier, Amsterdam, 1976

(2) Beckers, J.L., Everaets, F.M., Journal of Chromatography 68, 207-230 (1972)

(3) Boček, P., Miedziak, I., Deml, M., Janàk, J., Journal of Chromatography 137, 83 (1977)

ISOELECTRIC POINTS OF URINARY ALBUMIN. CHARACTERIZATION OF A MICRO-HETEROGENEOUS GLYCOSYLATED VARIETY WITH HIGH ANIONIC CHARGE.

Giovanni Candiano, Gian Marco Ghiggeri, Gerolamo Delfino, Pier Giorgio Righetti*, Carlo Queirolo.

Hemodialysis Service, Hospital of Lavagna, Genova, Italy.
*Chair of Biochemistry, Faculty of Pharmacy, University of Milano.

1 INTRODUCTION

Renal handling of albumin (alb.) is influenced in rats by the net charge on the molecule, being the passage of positive alb. more facilitated compared to the more anionic compound (1,2). Cationization of human serum alb. has been shown to occur in diabetic patients (3), making new suggestion available for a role of pI of glycosyl albumin (GA) in determining a high urinary excretion of alb. in diabetes mellitus. This aspect was focused here by determining the pI of total alb. and GA in urine of 5 diabetic patients with diabetic functional nephropathy.

2 METHODS

Albumin was purified by pseudo-ligand chromatography on Affi Gel Blue (4) and GA resolved from the unmodified species with Concanavalin A Sepharose (3). IEF was carried out in polyacrylamide ultrathin gels (240 µm) (5) containing glycerol and urea, and precoated on silanized glass plate (13 x 13 cm). Proteins were stained with the photochemical silver method of Merril (6) and immunochemical characterization was carried out either with bidimensional immunoelectrophoresis or immunoelectrophoresis according to Grabar and Williams (7).

3 RESULTS AND DISCUSSION

3.1 Composition of urinary albumin

In all urines studied, alb. was constituted by a main peak with a pI of 4.7 (which is the pI of native alb.) and a broad spectrum of more anionic bands (pI 4.0-4.7) (Fig.1a) which reacted with anti-alb. antibodies when subjected to a two layers bidimensional immunoelectrophoresis. When urinary alb. was fractionated on Concanavalin A Sepharose and the unbound (unmodified) and bound (glycosylated) peaks were analyzed by IEF the pattern shown in Fig.1b was observed: unreacted alb. focuses as a single band in the pH interval ca 4.7-4.9, while the glycosylated compound accounts for all the more anionic bands (pI 4.0-4.7) with some minor others co-focusing in the region of the native protein.

3.2 Conclusive remarks

While the high anionic charge of urinary GA is consistent with the saturation by circulating monosaccharides of positive ε-amino groups of lysine (which are the sites of glycosylation), there is no reason available to explain the high amount of these urinary anionic GA in the light of current views on mechanisms subserving the renal filtration of macromolecules (1,2). The characterization of high anionic urinary GA could give new insights about the pathophysiology of renal deposition of macromolecules in diabetic nephropathy.

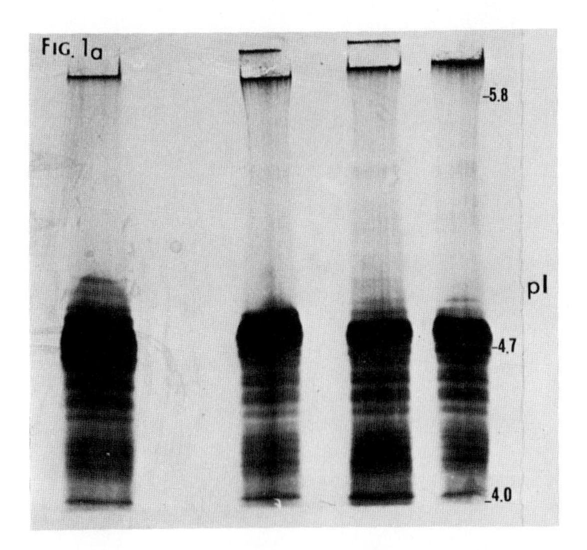

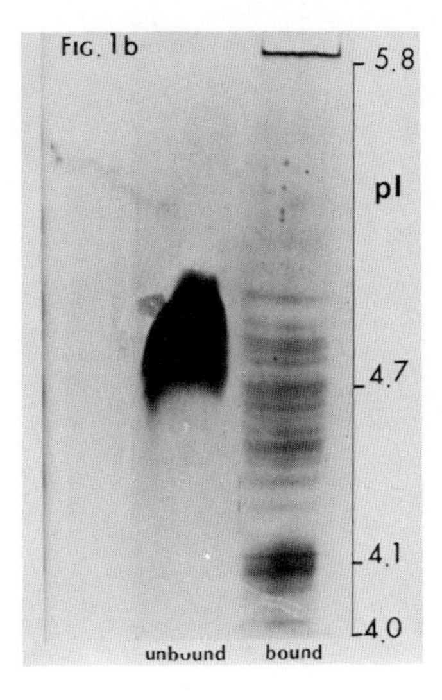

Fig.1 (a) IEF of urinary alb. from diabetic patients.

(b) IEF of urinary alb. as resolved by Concanavalin A Sepharose in two fractions: unmodified (unbound) and glycosylated (bound).

4 REFERENCES

(1) B.M. Brenner, T.H. Hostetter, H.D. Humes, N. Engl. J. Med. 298 (1978) 826-833.

(2) J.N. Purtell, A.J. Pesce, D.H. Clyne, W.C. Miller, V.E. Pollack, Kidney Int. 16 (1979) 366-376.

(3) G. Candiano, G.M. Ghiggeri, G. Delfino, F. Cavatorta, C. Queirolo, Clin. Chim. Acta 128 (1983) 29-40.

(4) J. Travis, R. Pennel, Clin. Chim. Acta 49 (1973) 49-52.

(5) A. Gorg, W. Postel, R. Westermeier, Anal. Biochem. 89 (1978) 60-70.

(6) C.R. Merril, D. Goldman, H.L. Van Keuren, Electrophoresis 3 (1982) 17-23.

(7) P. Grabar and C.A. Williams, Biochim. Biophys. Acta 10 (1953) 193-194.

REACTION OF ALBUMIN WITH GLYCERALDEHYDE "IN VITRO". CHARACTERIZATION OF SCHIFF-BASE AND AMADORI PRODUCTS BY ISOELECTRIC FOCUSING.

Gian Marco Ghiggeri, Giovanni Candiano, Gerolamo Delfino, Elisabetta Gianazza*, Carlo Queirolo.

Hemodialysis Service, Hospital of Lavagna, Genova. Chair of *Biochemistry, Faculty of Pharmacy, University of Milano, Italy.

1 INTRODUCTION

Most mammalian proteins undergo a nonenzymatic condensation with aldehydic groups of monosaccharides (1) and give as final result the so called "browning products", so far implicated in the pathogenesis of diabetic microangiopathy (2). Although the thesis is based upon an hypothesized alteration of the physico-chemical characteristics of the glycosylated compounds, there is no evidence for a direct effect of such a reaction on either stability or functions of proteins.
We describe here an alteration of the electrical charge of albumin (Alb.) induced by the reaction with glyceraldehyde which could lead to a new interpretation of the effects of nonenzymatic glycosylation on proteins.

2 METHODS

Serum Alb. purified from normal donors by Affi-Gel Blue (3) was reacted (1 mg/1 ml) with 20 mM glyceraldehyde in a 10 mM phosphate buffer pH 7, inducing in some case the reduction by 100 mM $NaCnBH_4$ which selectively blocks the reaction at the stage of the Schiff base. IEF was performed in ultrathin gels (240 µm) (4) polymerized on silanized glass plates and proteins were stained with the photochemical silver method of Merril (5).

3 RESULTS AND DISCUSSION

The formation of a yellow product was readily obtained within 24 hours by reacting Alb. and glyceraldehyde without $NaCnBH_4$, although the kinetic of incorporation of the sugar was similar for either the reduced (with $NaCnBH_4$) or the unreduced mixture. Fig. 1 (tracks a,b) illustrates the patterns at IEF of the glyceraldehyde-Alb. adduct rearranged as an Amadori compound together with the same product blocked as a Schiff base linkage (tracks c,d). The rearrangement of the linkage produces a fall of pI of Alb. from the original 4.7-4.9 to 4.0-4.1, with a broad spectrum of bands in the anionic area, which are not detectable in the non rearranged product.

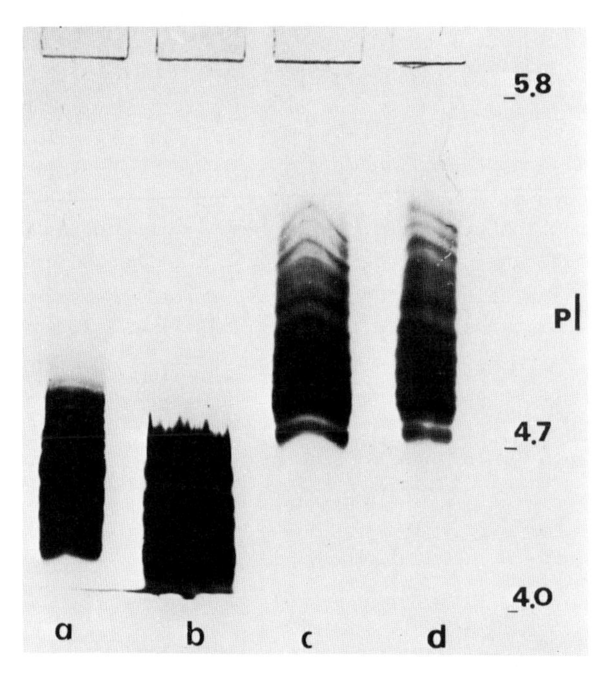

Fig. 1. IEF of Alb. reacted with glyceraldehyde for 1 and 7 days without $NaCnBH_4$ (a,b) and with $NaCnBH_4$ (c,d).

These observations indicate that the shift of the pI of Alb. is not related to a saturation of Σ-amino groups of Lysine by glyceraldehyde "per se", but it's induced by the passage of a H^+ from the second to the first carbon of the skeleton of glyceraldehyde, main characteristic of the Amadori linkage. In this view an alteration of the structural conformation of Alb. or the formation of new charged groups in glyceraldehyde molecule become the most probable candidates for explaining this perturbation. The chemical characterization of these compounds would aid the understanding of the mechanisms of macromolecular deposition along membranes in diabetes mellitus.

4 REFERENCES

(1) R. Dolhofer, O.H. Wieland, FEBS Lett. 85 (1978) 86-90.

(2) V.J. Stevens, C.A. Rouzer, V.H. Monnier, A. Cerami, Proc. Natl. Acad. Sci. U.S.A. 75 (1978) 2918-2922.

(3) J. Travis, R. Pennel, Clin. Chim. Acta 49 (1973) 49-52.

(4) A. Gorg, W. Postel, R. Westermeier, Anal. Biochem. 89 (1978) 60-70.

(5) C.R. Merril, D. Goldman, H.L. Van Keuren. Electrophoresis 3 (1982) 17-23.

DIFFERENTIATION OF URINARY PROTEIN PATTERNS AFTER SDS-GRADIENTGEL-ELECTROPHORESIS BY POLYCHROMATIC SILVER STAINING

Ulrich Wurster[1], Friedrich Krull[2], Jochen H. H. Ehrich[2]

Divisions of Neurology[1] and Pediatrics[2], Hannover Medical School, P.O. Box 61 01 80, D-3000 Hannover-61, FRG

1 INTRODUCTION

Since the kidney handles the proteins of the plasma like a molecular sieve, the appearance in the urine of proteins with a molecular weight greater than albumin indicates glomerular damage, while a preponderance of micromolecular proteins would signify defects in tubular resorption. Based on this principle, molecular weight dependent electrophoretic methods like (micro) gradient electrophoresis (1) or SDS-PAGE (2) or a combination thereof (3) are becoming increasingly popular for the differentiation of proteinurias. Most users interpret the urinary protein patterns obtained after staining with Amidoblack or Coomassie-Blue by visual inspection, taking albumin as the borderline between high and low molecular weight proteins. Incorporation of internal mass standards is usually omitted and identification of the individual bands is deemed superfluous (4).

This present situation is unsatisfactory for several reasons. Firstly, most urines still require concentration prior to electrophoresis, a time-consuming procedure which is also prone to (selective?) loss and aggregation of proteins. Secondly, the considerable degree of variation in migration distances between different gels carries a potential risk of misinterpreting atypical micromolecular proteins as indicators of tubular disease. Finally, if it were known which individual proteins are actually present during proteinurias, further classification of subtypes could be achieved and the hitherto largely ignored influence of charge on elimination investigated.

The use of a polychromatic silver stain abolishes the need for concentration, allows the identification of certain proteins by their characteristic color (even when they are overlapping) and reduces the protein load resulting in a better separation of bands.

2 METHODS

Centrifuged native morning urines (5 µg total protein) were run overnight on 0,75 mm thick, 8-21 % T, 6 % C vertical (13 x 14 cm) gradient slab gels in a Laemmli system. The proteins were fixed in 20 % TCA and silver stained as described previously (5) with an additional wash in 7 % MeOH, 5 % HAc. LKB Laemmli molecular weight markers as well as a standard mixture of five urinary proteins (Behring Nr. 7321) were included on each gel.

3 RESULTS AND DISCUSSION

Urinary proteins were identified by either co-electrophoresis with purified proteins, identical position and color with known plasma proteins, immunodeletion or immunoblotting. 12 proteins could be identified definitely, another three tentatively. Tamm-Horsfall glycoprotein (THP) appeared at 80 - 90 000 D as a diffuse brownish spot which stained negatively at higher concentrations. Considerable amounts ot THP together with other, preferably basic plasma proteins were also found in the urinary sediments.

A survey of 50 pathological urines showed different patterns of selectivity similar to the types proposed by Boesken (1981). Electrophoresis is thus superior to determination of a single protein, i.e. β_2-microglobulin (MW 11 600) which will fail to detect tubulopathy if only greater (40 - 70 000) microproteins are excreted.

In some instances micromolecular proteins appeared which did not coincide with the usual array of small plasma proteins (retinol binding protein, α_1-microglobulin, β_2-microglobulin) regarded as markers for tubular damage. Likewise these proteins bore no resemblance to overflow proteins like hemoglobin, myoglobin or IG light chains. They may originate from any of the seven sources compiled by Anderson et al. (6), but in view of the underlying diseases a renal origin seems most likely.

4 REFERENCES

(1) W. Reichel, D. I. Wolfrum, R. Klein, F. Scheler, Klin. Wschr. 54 (1976) 19-24.

(2) W. H. Boesken, Electrophoresis '81, W. de Gruyter, Berlin, New York 1981, pp. 453-462.

(3) A. Görg, W. Postel, J. Weser, R. Westermeier, LKB application letter, 1983.

(4) J.M. Alt, M. Hacke, D. von der Heyde, H. Jänig, P.-M. Junge, Ch. Olbricht, H.-J. Schurek, H. Stolte, Klin. Wschr. 61 (1983) 641-648.

(5) U. Wurster, Electrophoresis '82, W. de Gruyter, Berlin, New York 1983, pp. 249-259.

(6) N.G. Anderson, N. L. Anderson, S. L. Tollaksen, Clin. Chem. 25 (1979) 1199-1210.

THE INFLUENCE OF CYTOSTATICA ON THE ISOENZYMEPATTERN OF URINARY ALANINAMINOPEPTIDASE

Adrianus J. van Triet, with technical assistance of AnneMarie Grijpma and Wijnand Giese

Department of Clinical Chemistry : Researchlaboratory for Isoenzymes , Academic Hospital of the Free University , de Boelelaan 1117 , Amsterdam , The Netherlands.

More or less severe kidney damage is a well known complication of the treatment of tumor patients with cis-platinum or its analogs. This drug nephrotoxicity causes an elevated urinary excretion of several enzymes (1), under which Alaninaminopeptidase has caught our special attention for two reasons: (i) this enzyme is a sensitive indicator for tubular injury as it is located superficially in the brush border of the renal tubulus (2, 3); (ii) the determination of the total activity of Alaninaminopeptidase as well as the electrophoretic separation of its isoenzymes are easily to perform (4, 5).
In this poster the alterations in the isoenzymepatterns will be shown after administration of cis-platinum or J.M.40. It is obvious that isoelectric focusing gives more details than one-dimensional electrophoresis. Overlooking the changes in the isoenzymepatterns a return to the original pattern will be seen after some time. This fact indicates the recuperative power of the kidney when a rather low dose of the drug is administered.

References

1) U. Diener, E. Knoll, D. Ratge, J. Clin. Chem. Clin. Biochem. 20 (1982) 615-619.

2) R.J. Haschen, Enzymdiagnostik (2 Ed.) Gustav Fischer Verlag, Stuttgart 1981.

3) J.E. Scherberich, F.W. Falkenberg, A.W. Mondorf, H. Müller, G. Pfleiderer, Clin. Chim. Acta 55 (1974) 179-197.

4).A.J. van Triet, in B.J. Radola (Ed.), Elektrophorese Forum '83, Technische Universität München, 1983, p. 153-157.

5) A.J. van Triet, Electrophoresis, submitted.

ISOELECTRIC FOCUSING OF SERUM ISOAMYLASES

Helena Geada, Rosa Espinheira, Carlos Manso

Physiological Chemistry Institute, Medical School of Lisbon, 1600 Lisbon

Fernando Piteira Barros, Miguel Carneiro de Moura

Center of Gastroenterology, Medical School of Lisbon, 1600 Lisbon, Portugal

1 INTRODUCTION

The development of methods for separating organ-specific isoenzymes provides a potential means for identifying the origin of enzymes. Characterization of serum isoamylases was possible through the use of a variety of methods that involved cellulose acetate electrophoresis, polyacrylamide electrophoresis and isoelectric focusing (1-4). Isoamylases have two major isoenzymes - a salivary and a pancreatic type.

Hyperamylasemia due to increased activity of salivary isoamylase is a non-specific finding, occuring in several situations besides salivary gland disorders. In acute pancreatitis, hyperamylasemia is characterized by an increased of pancreatic isoamylase (5).

Hyperamylasemia also occurs during the course of some liver diseases (6), but one cannot account for its origin using current chromogenic methods. Besides, the mechanisms for the elevated levels of serum amylase in liver patients is unclear. We have applied isoelectric focusing to the study of hyperamylasemia origin associated with liver disease, and to detect any pancreatic involvement in various disease cases.

Serum was obtained from 82 blood donors and 95 patients with biopsy-proven liver diseases with no clinical evidence of pancreatic, salivary or renal disease. Serum from children with cystic fibrosis or celiac disease were also studied, as well as serum from patients with acute pancreatitis. α-amylase levels in serum were determined using a chromogenic technique (Phadebas Isoamylase Test). The upper limit of normal was 310U/L (mean $\pm$ 2 SD).

Isoenzymes were separated by a modification of the method of Rosenmund et al (7). LKB Ampholines pH 5-8/pH 3.5-10 (10:1) were used. Ten microliters of sample was applied directly on the gel. Electrofocusing was performed for two hours with a 1100V maximum voltage. Serum α-amylase isoenzymes were detected using a modification of the starch-iodine zymogram procedure of Scully et al (8).

2 RESULTS AND COMMENTS

Serum samples from liver disease patients and blood donors were studied by isoelectric focusing (Table 1). Four electrophoretic patterns can be detected - a normal (N), a salivary/pancreatic (S/P), a pancreatic (P) and a double pancreatic (dP) pattern. In pancreatic pattern (P), we can see an increase of S/P and specially of P bands, and in S/P pattern we have only an increase of S/P band. No salivary pattern was obtained.

Table 1. Isoamylase patterns in patients with liver diseases and blood donors

Isoamylase pattern	Patients with hyperamylasemia		Patients without hyperamylasemia		Blood donors	
	No	(%)	No	(%)	No	(%)
Normal (N)	6	(27.3)	47	(64.4)	57	(69.5)
Pancreatic (P)	3	(13.6)	1	(1.4)	0	(0.0)
Salivary/Pancreatic (S/P)	13	(59.1)	19	(26.0)	19	(23.2)
Double Pancreatic (dP)	0	(0.0)	6	(8.2)	6	(7.3)
Total	22		73		82	

The incidence of these electrophoretic patterns was similar in blood donors and in patients with normal values of amylase, being N pattern the prevalent in both. Patients with hyperamylasemia have a different pattern - S/P pattern, different from the salivary (S) or the pancreatic (P) pattern. The inhibitor assay yielded a predominant increase in type P (15 out of 22), 5 S sera and 2 with both P and S type. With isoelectric focusing, only 3 serum samples have a pancreatic pattern, 6 being normal and all the others have a S/P pattern. We have found a poor correlaction between the inhibitor assay method and isoelectric focusing.

Our findings show that in most cases hyperamylasemia occuring in hepatic diseases has a different electrophoretic pattern. This different pattern may be caused by a modification of salivary or pancreatic isoenzymes, or may have a different origin.

The development of isoelectric focusing method to study organ-specific isoamylases provides a potencial means for identifying amylase sources. We have also used this method to study any pancreatic involvement in children with cystic fibrosis and celiac disease or in patients with pancreatitis, and to study the salivary type in children with parotitis. Since isoenzyme separation has been found to be useful in differential diagnosis, the isoelectric focusing method used is a good one for routine clinical chemistry analysis.

3 REFERENCES

(1) D.R. Benjamim, M.A. Kenny, Am. J. Clin. Pathol. 62 (1974) 752-758.

(2) T. Takeuchi, T. Matsushima, T. Sugimura, T. Kezu, T. Takeuchi, T. Takemoto, Clin. Chim. Acta, 54 (1974) 137-144.

(3) A.D. Merritt, M.L. Rivas, D. Bixler, R. Newell, Am. J. Hum. Genet. 25 (1973) 510-522.

(4) G. Cassara, E. Gianazza, P.G. Righetti, S. Poma, L. Vicentini, V. Scortecci, J. Chromatogr. 221 (1980) 279-291.

(5) M. Otsuki, H. Yuu, M. Maeda, S. Saeki, K. Okano, T. Yamasaki, T. Kanda, C. Sakamoto, S. Baba, Clin. Chim. Acta, 89 (1978) 159--164.

(6) I.L. MacGregor, D. Zakim, Gastroenterol. 72 (1977) 519-523.

(7) H. Rosenmund, M.J. Kaczmarek, Clin. Chim. Acta, 71 (1976) 185-189.

(8) C. Scully, P.D. Eckersall, R.T.D. Emond, P. Boyle, J.A. Beeley, Clin. Chim. Acta, 113 (1981) 281-291.

COMPARISON OF PURIFICATION OF A FUNGAL PROTEINASE BY ISOELECTRIC FOCUSING, ELECTROPHORESIS AND GEL FILTRATION

Maria Giulia Menesini Chen, John S. Chen, Giuseppe Pompucci[§], Mario Bari and Carlo Ricci[*]

U.O. Progetto Finalizzato IPRA del CNR, c/o * Istituto di Chimica Biologica dell'Università di Siena. § Istituto di Fisiologia Generale e Chimica Biologica dell'Università di Sassari, Italy

1 INTRODUCTION

Enzyme purification is an important and difficult task. In spite of the considerable volume of technical information which is available for isolation and purification of proteins in general nowadays, purification of proteinase EL25-79 (1) is still difficult due to the fact that this enzyme is contaminated by other proteins. The purpose of this study is to compare the results of the purification of EL25-79 using three different methods for protein separation.

2 MATERIALS AND METHODS

2.1 Gel filtration

Sephadex G-75 from Pharmacia in a LKB L62-70 column was equilibrated in 0.1 M phosphate buffer pH 7.4. The flow rate of 9/ml/h was monitered by a peristaltic pump. Fractions were collected, pooled dialyzed and liophylized as usual.

2.2 Electrophoresis

Agarose HL (Litex, Denmark) was used. Electrophoresis of EL25-79 in 1 % Agarose in 0.1 M citrate-phosphate buffer pH 5.5 was performed with a LKB Multiphor 2117. Three corresponding bands were cut off and then centrifuged with a Beckman Ultracentrifuge at 127.000 xg for 20 min. at 4°C. The supernatant (about 60-80 % recovery) was dialyzed against distilled water and liophylized.

2.3 Isoelectric focusing

LKB Preparative IEF apparatus (LKB 8100-1) and Ampholyte (Bio-Rad)

3.5-10 were used for this study. The separation procedure was that described in the instructions supplied by the Company. Fractions were collected and the pH measured. They were dialyzed against distilled water for 3 days in a cold room.

Analytical IEF was carried out using LKB Multiphor 2117.

2.4 Enzyme assay and others

Proteolytic activity was assay as described (2). Protein was determined according to Lowry et al (3). The enzyme specific activity, Es, was expressed as O.D.280 nm x $min.^{-1}$ x mg $protein^{-1}$. Gels were stained by Coomassie R 250 (4).

3 RESULTS AND DISCUSSION

By gel filtration, 100 mg EL25-79 in 1 ml 0.1 M phosphate buffer pH 7.4 were loaded into a LKB L62-70 column. We obtained 4 protein peaks, fractions I, II, III and IV. Their enzyme specific activities, Es, were 396.3, 1022.2, 1916.7 and 0 respectively. Only fraction III showed enzyme activity slightly higher than EL25-79. With the exception of fraction IV each fraction contained many protein bands when they were analyzed by analytical IEF (Fig. 1A).

In the case of agarose electrophoresis, 6 mg EL25-79 in 260 µl in 0.1 M citrate-phosphate buffer pH 5.5 was loaded into 0.5x5x11 cm agarose gel. 4 major bands were obtained after electrophoresis (240 mA for 45 min.), from which three were cut off and studied. The Es of these three bands, fraction I, II and III, were 725.3, 1737.3 and 700 respectively against 1696.9 for EL25-79 (Table 1). IEF analysis of these fractions is shown in Fig. 1B.

For preparative isoelectric focusing, 100 mg of EL25-79 were applied to the column. After the electrophoresis, from 8 fractions with major protein peaks, we chose 4 fractions, I, II, III and IV with pI 11, 9.2, 8.2 and 7.2 respectively, for the enzyme assay. We found two of these have an Es higher than that of EL25-79, specifically pI 8.2 and 7.2. The value of fraction III is twice that of the unpurified enzyme. This fraction presents one major band in analytical IEF (Fig. 1C).

From these data we conclude that only isoelectric focusing provides a valid method for further purification of EL25-79

Table 1. Enzyme specific activities of various fractions obtained by different methods of purification.

	EL25-79	Fraction			
		I	II	III	IV
IEF		0	0	3298.5	2310.0
Agarose electrophoresis	1696.9	725.3	1737.3	700.0	-
Gel filtration		396.3	1022.2	1916.7	0

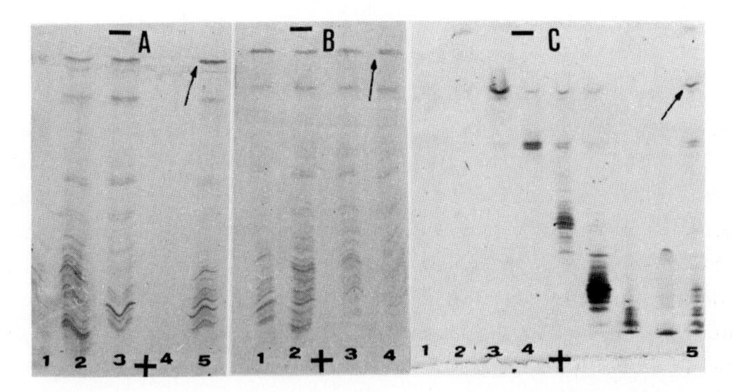

Fig. 1 IEF of various protein fractions isolated by different method of separation: A Gel filtration: 1=I; 2=II; 3=III; 4=IV; 5=EL25-79: B Agarose electrophoresis: 1=I; 2=II; 3=III; 4=EL25-79: C IEF: 1=I; 2=II; 3=III; 4=IV; 5=EL25-79. Arrows indicate pH 8.2.

4 REFERENCES

(1) M.G. Menesini Chen, V. Micheli, and J.S. Chen. In the Proceeding of the II Italy-ROC Seminar on New Aspects of Biotechnol. and Biomed. Res. March 29-30, 1983, Sassari. (in the press).

(2) J.S. Chen, M.G. Menesini Chen and G. Pompucci. Riassunto del 29° Congresso Nazionale della Società Italiana di Biochimica. Saint Vincent 26-28 Settembre 1983, pp 142-143.

(3) O.H. Lowry, N.J. Rosebrough, A.L. Farr and R.J. Randall. J. Biol. Chem. 193 (1951), 265.

(4) LKB Application Note 250, p 8. (December 1977).

A SIMPLE METHOD FOR PROTEIN PURIFICATION IN POLYACRYLAMIDE GEL BY ANALYTICAL ISOELECTRIC FOCUSING

John S. Chen, Maria Giulia Menesini Chen, Annalisa Santucci, Patrizia Pontani, Giuseppe Pompucci§

U.O. Progetto Finalizzato IPRA del CNR, c/o Istituto di Chimica Biologica dell'Università di Siena, 53100 Siena. § Istituto di Fisiologia Generale e Chimica Biologica dell'Università di Sassari, Sassari, Italy

1 INTRODUCTION

Isoelectric focusing (IEF) is known to be a valid method for both analyses and purification of proteins. As stated by Radola in 1976 (1) "-- the many efforts aimed at scaling-up of PAGE, one of the most successful analytical methods, reflect the difficulties in passing from analytical conditions to preparative scale work--". Up to date the proliferation of devices would indicate that the words of Radola are still echoing. Observing the protein migratory behaviour in polyacrylamide gel used for IEF we noted that there are possibilities of exploiting the analytical IEF for preparative purposes.

2 MATERIALS AND METHODS

2.1 Materials

Acrylamide and n-n-methylene-bis-acrylamide were purchased from Sigma. Human hemoglobin (Hb) was isolated from normal subjects: heparin treated blood was washed in three changes of physiological saline (NaCl 0.142 M in 12 mM Potassium phosphate buffer pH 7.4). Hemolysis was performed adding 2 vol. distilled water. After centrifugation at 1000xg, supernatant was chromatographed in a Bio-gel P 100 column. The resulting Hb solution was then dialyzed against distilled water overnight in a cold room. Hb (70 mg/ml) solution was then stored at 4°C in 0.02 % sodium azide and used within 10 days. The Hb so prepared presented one major red band (more then 90 %) in IEF (Fig. 1) with maximum absorbance at 415 nm. Fungal proteinase EL25-79 was kindly supplied by Rohm GmbH, Darmstadt and carrier Ampholyte 6/8 and 3.5/10 were purchased from Bio-Rad. LKB Ampholine Plate 3.5-9.5 was also used. For IEF a LKB Multiphor 2117, 6 % polyacrylamide gel slab (110x45x1.9 mm) was cast according to the LKB and used 12 hrs later.

2.2 Runnig conditions

Hb or other protein samples were applied to polyacrylamide gel slab as indicated in the brochure of LKB. 20 µl with various protein concentrations was applied to 5x10 mm Whatman 3MM filter paper. The positions of the sample loading paper were varied according to results desired.

For the determination of the positions of Hb at various times, a sample was applied on gel near the cathode. The running of the Hb due to its red color, was followed with semplicity and accuracy. The initial current was set from 2.65 mA to 4.5 mA per cm gel (for easier calculation, as the length and the thickness of the slab are constant). The watts were then kept constant and ampers and volts were permitted to fluctuate as the IEF proceeded. pH was measured and gels were photographed without staining, using a green filter.

2.3 Purification and recovery of human hemoglobin and a proteinase

1.4 mg in 20 µl Hb was applied on the 5x10 mm Whatman 3MM filter paper which was positioned on the Hb focusing site. The 3.4 mA/cm gel was set for the initial run. After 2 hrs of electrophoresis, the filter paper was detached from the gel and eluted with 800 µl distilled water. The Hb was either quantitated by Drabkin's method (2) or read at 415 nm.

From preparative IEF, the enzyme under study found in EL25-79 was localized at pH 8.2 (3). For purification of EL25-79, we used the method described above. Enzyme activity was assayed using denatured BSA as substrate at pH 6 (4).

3 RESULTS

3.1 The final positions of the major hemoglobin band

Fig. 1 shows that the final position of hemoglobin is usually resolved at 4 cm from the starting point near the cathode, when the Ampholine 6/8 was used. The current applied did affect the time required to attain the steady state. Higher energy resulted in distortion of the bands (5). Prolonged focusing, in this case over 7 hrs, results in a "cathodic shift" (6).

3.2 Hemoglobin recovery after electrophoresis

In short, the experiment might be summarized in Fig.2. Here 2 % Ampholine 3.5-10 was used. A and B (Fig. 2) are the same gel. The positions of the filter paper indicate where the Hb solutions have been applied. Initial current was 3.4 mA/cm gel. After 2 hrs of electrophoresis, Hb was focused at final positions a and b (Fig.2): a on the filter paper and b in the gel (Fig.2A). The arrow indicates the residue of Hb in the gel after the removal of the filter paper (Fig. 2B). The Hb remaining on the filter paper was easily eluted by distilled water or a buffer with a pH near its pI. In this case the quantityof Hb recovered from the filter paper after electrophoresis is 70.34 ± 10.97 %. The loading capacity of each filter paper (5x10mm) is up to 1.4 mg. The same gel can be reused for at least 3 consecutive runs until the cathodic shift occures. Thus the Hb might provide a valid indicator for the whole course of operation.

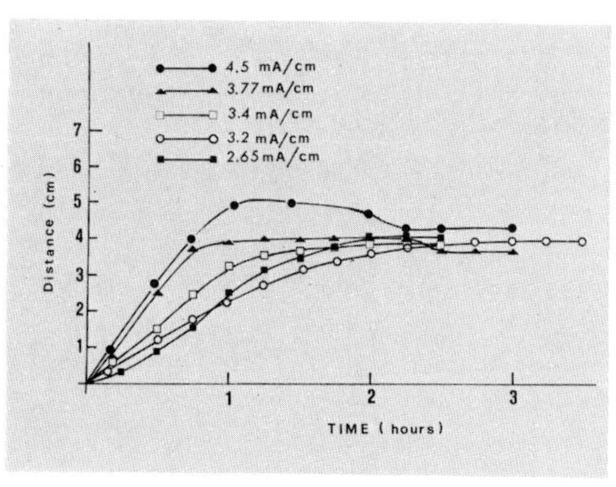

Fig. 1 The positions of the major Hb in the gel at various powers and times

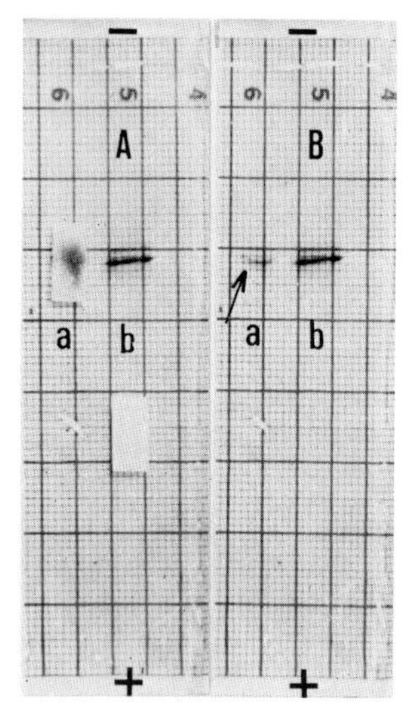

Fig. 2 Focusing of Hb on filter paper (b) and in gel (a). Arrow indicates the residue of Hb after the removal of filter paper.

3.3 Purification of EL25-79

Usually, EL25-79 resolved in 8 major bands with analytical

IEF using Ampholine 3.5-10 (3). For the purification of EL25-79 the method described above was used. 1 mg enzyme in 20 µl was applied to a filter paper (5x10mm) which was placed in a pre-established position at pH 8.2. In this case Ampholine 3.5/10 was used. The initial current,3.0 mA/cm gel, was applied. After 2 hrs the filter paper was removed from the gel and eluted with 400 µl distilled water. This solution was then dialysed against distilled water overnight in a cold room. The protein was determined by the method of Lowry et al(7). The enzyme specific activity(O.D.280nmxmin.$^{-1}$xmg protein^{-1})for purified enzyme is 4430 against 1463 for EL25-79. The purified enzyme presents one band in analytical IEF. The data seem to confirm the result obtained from the preparative IEF as described eleswhere (3).

4 DISCUSSION

We have devised a simple and reliable method for protein purification in polyacrylamide gel by analytical IEF. The method is useful to those who with to purify 100 mg scale proteins or greater quantities. Theoretically, our procedure is applicable to the use of Immobiline which is currently the most promising method for both analytical and preparative IEF (8). The advantages of using Immobiline are many and the purified protein (enzyme) is free from Ampholine contamination and it should increase the preparative scale.

5 REFERENCES

(1) B.J. Radola, in Isoelectric Focusing, edited by N. Catsimpoolas,Academic Press Inc. New York,San Francisco, London 1976, pp 119-171.

(2) D.L. Drabkin, J. biol.Chem. 185 (1950) 231-242.

(3) M.G. Menesini Chen,J.S.Chen, G.Pompucci,M.Bari,C.Ricci(this Proceed).

(4) J.S. Chen, M.G. Menesini Chen, G. Pompucci, riassunto del 29° Congr. Naz. della Soc. Italiana di Biochem. S. Vincent Sept.1983,p 142-143.

(5) M. Jonsson, Electrophoresis 3-4/80: 141-149.

(6) P. Righetti, J.W. Drysdale, BBA 236 (1971) 17-28.

(7) O.H. Lowry, N.J. Rosebrough, A.L. Farr, R.J. Randall, J. Biol. Chem. 193 (1951) 265-275.

(8) B. Bjellqvist, K.EK, P.G. Righetti, E. Gianazza, A. Gorg, W. Postel, in Electrophoresis '82, Stathokos, D. ed. de Gruyter, Berlin, 1983, pp 61-74.

ANALYSIS OF MEMBRANE POLYMERS FORMED BY DIVICINE ACTION ON G6PD-DEFICIENT ERYTHROCYTES

Franco Turrini°, Gian G.Pinna°, Anna Sisini°, Gian P.Pescarmona*

Istituto di Chimica Biologica°, Facoltà di Medicina e Chirurgia, Università di Sassari, 07100 Sassari, Italy and Istituto di Igiene, Cattedra di Chimica*, Facoltà di Medicina e Chirurgia, Università di Torino, 10123 Torino, Italy

INTRODUCTION

The aglycone divicine(D) of the glycoside vicine contained in Vicia faba seeds has been reported(1) to induce high molecular weight polymer formation in erythrocyte membranes of glucose-6-phosphate dehydrogenase(G6PD)-deficient subjects.We refer on the analysis of these polymers by an apparatus based on preparative electrophoresis principles.

METHODS

The action of D was tested in two different conditions:i)incubation of erythrocyte ghosts at 37°C for 30 min with D concentration ranging from 0.1 to 0.5 mM and ii)incubation of intact erythrocytes with D for a maximum of 24 hours as already described (1). Red blood cells and ghosts were obtained from normal and G6PD-deficient(Mediterranean variant) subjects.Samples of erythrocytes under incubation were collected after 6 and 24 hours for ghosts preparation.Analytical SDS-PAGE was made in glass rods containing 2.5% acrylamide,0.05% bis-acrylamide and 0.3% agarose.2-mercaptoethanol(ME) was at 0.5 M final concentration when included in the samples.To evaluate the formation of polymers not completely reducible by ME as revealed by SDS-PAGE (see further) we devised the apparatus illustrated in fig.1.

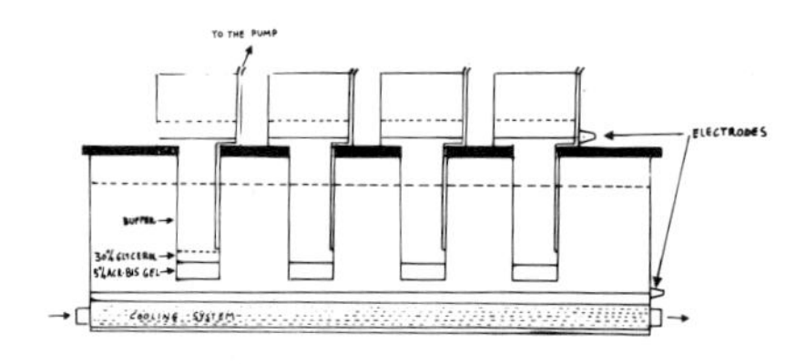

Fig.1-Scheme of the preparative electrophoretic apparatus.

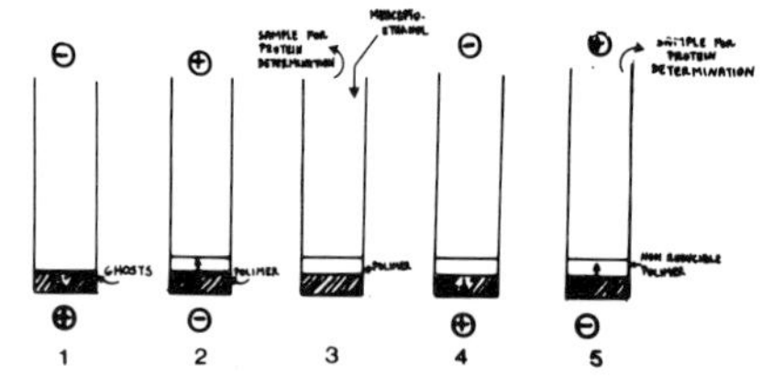

Fig.2-Scheme of operation for the quantitation of polymers.

A perspex rectangular box provided with cooling system contains four glass tubes of 1.7 cm i.d. and 7 cm long.Tubes are cast with 5% acrylamide/0.1% bis-acrylamide to obtain 1 cm high gels.Usually 3 to 4 mg protein in 0.5 ml volume were applied to each gel and electrophoresis carried out for 2 hours at 80 mA per gel(fig.2.1).Electrode buffer was then drained off and replaced by 0.5 ml of 33% glycerol and enough buffer to reach the upper electrode;polarity was then reversed and electrophoresis continued for 45 min(fig.2.2).Buffer was again drained off by means of a small bore tube ending to obviate the capillary phenomenon,about 2 mm above the glycerol layer(fig.1) and 20 µl of this collected for protein determination(2)(fig.2.3).At this point 20 µl of ME were added and operation as in fig.2.4 and 2.5 carried out again as explained before(fig.2.1 to 2.3).

RESULTS

The incubation of D directly with ghosts from normal and G6PD-deficient erythrocytes induces the formation of high molecular weight polymers at a D concentration of 5 mM;these polymers are -S-S- crosslinked because they are totally reducible by ME(fig. 3.3 and 3.4);ghosts obtained following a 6 to 24 hours incubation with D of G6PD-deficient erythrocytes show the formation of both reducible and non reducible polymers as a a function of time(table 1 and fig.3.1 and 3.2).

Table 1-Polymer formation in ghosts from G6PD-deficient erythrocytes after 6 and 24 hours incubation with divicine.

Time	Polymer protein recovered in the glycerol layer		
	without ME	with ME	%
hours	mg/ml		
6	1.016	0.055	5.4
24	2.076	0.356	17.0

Finally,no polymer formation is observed in ghosts from 24 hours incubated normal red blood cells.The polymers that are not reducible by ME could be formed,as in other cases(3),by action of a transamidase(EC 2.3.2.13) that might be activated following prolonged exposure of red blood cells to D in the presence of physiological calcium concentration.

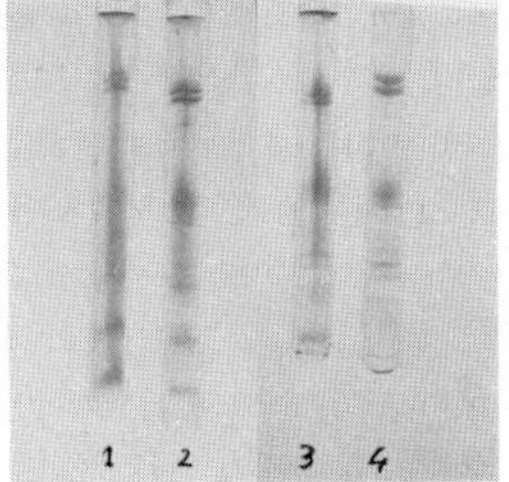

Fig.3-SDS-PAGE analysis of polymer formation(see text); gels 2 and 4 are with ME,gels 1 and 3 without.

REFERENCES

(1) P.Arese et al.,Advances in Red Blood Cells Biology,D.H.Weatherall,G.Fiorelli,G. Gorini,eds.,P.59,Raven Press,New York,1982.

(2) M.Bradford,Anal.Biochem.,72,(1976),248

(3) L.Lorand et al.,Proc.Natl.Acad.Sci.USA,73,(1976),4479-4481.

APPLICATION OF MICROELECTROPHORESIS FOR THE KINETIC INVESTIGATIONS OF LIPOPHILIC CATIONS TRANSPORT THROUGH THE RED BLOOD CELL MEMBRANE

Paweł Krysiński

Laboratory of Electrochemistry, Department of Chemistry, University of Warsaw, 02-093 Warsaw, Pasteura 1, Poland

1 INTRODUCTION

Besides its routine analytical applications electrophoresis has started to be used as a tool in the investigations of cell deseases and membrane phenomena. In form of cell electrophoresis which allows us to determine the surface charge density of living cells, this technique has been used as diagnostic tests in medicine /1,2/. It is also a very important method in the investigations of membrane structure /3-6/ and bioelectrochemical phenomena at the cell membrane-electrolyte solution interface /2,7,8/. Cell electrophoresis in all these applications has an important advantage: it can be aplied to the in vitro measurements of intact cells.

In our Laboratory, under Prof.Dr.S.Minc guidance, cell electrophoresis is used for the in vitro studies of the electrical double layer structure at the cell membrane-electrolyte interface as well as for adsorption and transport processes in the case of human erythrocytes and their ghosts to distinguish the role of cell interior in these phenomena /7-9/. In our previous work /9/ on the basis of microelectrophoretic measurements and extensive literature data /10,11/, we suggested quaternary ammonium cations transport through the erythrocyte membrane. The cations of lipophilic character: tetramethylammonium /TMA^+/, tetraethylammonium /TEA^+/ and tetrabuthylammonium /TBA^+/ were chosen for our investigations. This paper presents the first approach to the kinetic model of observed process.

2 EXPERIMENTAL

2.1 Apparatus and procedure

The apparatus we have used for our investigations was constructed in our Laboratory. It is a classical version of microelectrophoretic apparatus with rectangular measuring cuvette. The electrochemical measuring system is the cell:

Ag,AgCl | $NaCl_{sat.}$ || cell suspension || $NaCl_{sat.}$ | Ag,AgCl

The whole apparatus is located in a thermostat. The potential gradient was applied by a d.c.-power supply controled by two probe /sampling/ electrodes in the both sides of the cuvette. The erythrocytes were observed under the microscope /250 x magnification/ during the experiments. The electrophoretic mobility data were obtained as described in details in our previous work /7-9/. On the basis of these data the values of surface charge density changes were calculated for the red blood cells influenced by TMA^+, TEA^+ and TBA^+ as function of cation concentration and interaction time. We assumed the standard surface charge density and cell surface according to Donath at al. /6/ to be equal 2×10^{-2} C x m^{-2} and $1.4 \times 10^{-10} m^2$ respectively.

3 OUTLINE OF A MODEL

The calculated from our microelectrophoretic data changes of cell surface charge density Δq as a function of time are presented in Fig.1.

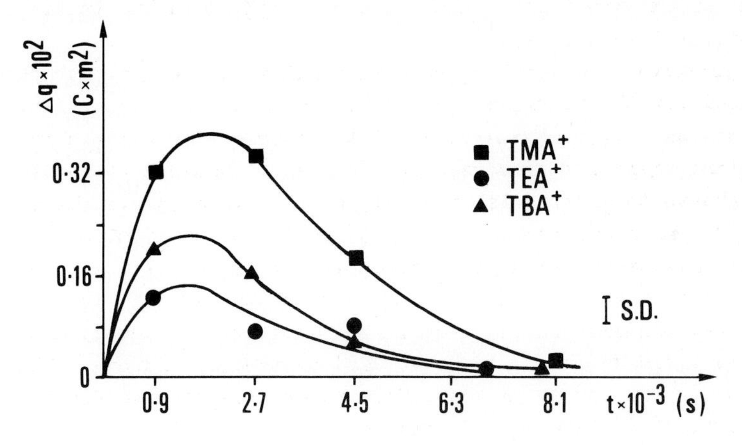

Fig. 1. The surface charge density changes for erythrocytes influenced by 2.5 mM TMA^+, TEA^+ or TBA^+ versus time.

The concentration of investigated ions is 2.5 mM in phosphate buffered saline /PBS standard solution/. As is shown in Fig. 1 these ions induce the transient response of erythrocyte membrane surface charge, to be detected electrophoretically. Initially, the difference Δq between the momentary q/t/ and standard q/0/ values increases to a maximum and then it decreases to reach a plateau. In order to explain the observed results we assumed a model of transport process presented in Fig. 2a:

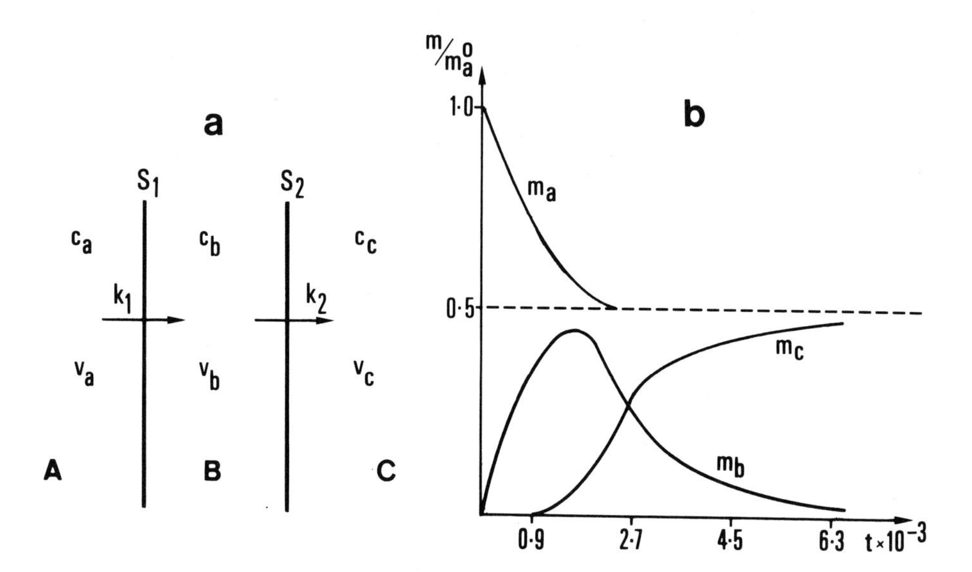

Fig.2 a. The scheme of proposed model /see text/; b. Computer modelling of m_a, m_b, m_c changes versus time for the case $v_a = v_c \gg v_b$.

This model consists of three discrete regions: bulk compartment A glycoprotein coat of cell membrane - compartment B and membrane itself together with inner solution - compartment C. The concentrations of investigated cations and compartment volumes are c_a, c_b, c_c and v_a v_b, v_c. The surface area of the interfaces separting compartment B from A and C are denoted as s_1 and s_2 respectively. We assumed, that the ion's transfer through each of these interfaces is the rate limiting step, i.e. that ion's migration through compartments A and B is much faster than ion's transfer. Thus, the mass flux of quaternary ammonium cation at time $t \gg 0$ is given by the following equations:

$$\frac{dm_a}{dt} = k_1 s_1/c_a - c_b/ \quad ; \quad \frac{dm_c}{dt} = k_2 s_2/c_b - c_c/$$

$$\frac{dm_a}{dt} = -v_a \frac{dc_a}{dt} \quad ; \quad \frac{dm_c}{dt} = +v_c \frac{dm_c}{dt}$$

$$\Delta q = z \cdot F \int_0^t / \frac{dm_a}{dt} - \frac{dm_c}{dt} / \, dt$$

where: k_1- rate constant of ion transfer through the interface s_1,
k_2- rate constant of ion transfer through the interface s_2,
z, F- have their usual meanings.

The mass conservation requires that:

$$v_a c_a + v_b c_b + v_c c_c = m_o.$$

Computer simulation of these equations leads to the curves which are shown in Fig. 2b. The shape of resultant curve describing the changes of m_b vs. time is similar to that obtained from microelectrophoretic measurements /Fig. 1/. Further computer modelling should lead to the values of rate constants of ion transfer through each of the interfaces. Then it will be interesting to compare them with the results of similar studies of the erythrocyte ghosts to distinguish the role of cell interior in the permeability behaviour of red blood cell membrane.

4 REFERENCES

/1/ A. W. Preece and D. Sablovic /Ed./, Cell Electrophoresis: Clinical Application and Methodology, North Holland, Amsterdam, 1979.

/2/Cell electrophoresis,Symp. Brit. Biophys. Soc., J. and A. Churchill Ltd., London, 1965.

/3/ D.H. Heard, G. V. F. Seaman, J. Gen. Physiol. 43 /1960/ 635-654.

/4/ K. Dołowy, Z. Godlewski, J. Theor. Biol. 84 /1980/ 709-723.

/5/ E. Donath, V. Pastushenko, Bioelectrochem. Bioenerg. 7 /1980/ 31-40.

/6/ E. Donath, D. Lerche, ibid., 7 /1980/ 41-53.

/7/ S. Minc, P. Krysiński, ibid., 5 /1978/ 247-251.

/8/ P. Krysiński, S. Minc, J. Electroanal. Chem. 100 /1979/ 71-76.

/9/ P. Krysiński, S. Minc, Bioelectrochem. Bioenerg. 10 /1983/ 261-267.

/10/ A. Monnier, J. Gen. Physiol. 51 /1968/ 26s-36s.

/11/ R. Deves, R. M. Krupka, Biochim. Biophys. Acta 556 /1979/ 524-532.

ISOENZYME ELECTROPHORESIS IN BOVINE THEILERIOSIS

T.R. Melrose

Centre for Tropical Veterinary Medicine, Easter Bush, Roslin, Midlothian, EH25 9RG, U.K.

Theileria parva and T. annulata are economically important members of a group of tick-borne intracellular pathogenic parasitic protozoa which infect domestic and wild ruminants. These parasites, characteristically reproduce by schizogony in the lymphocytes of the vertebrate host and produce further developmental stages which appear as pleomorphic non pigmented bodies, known as piroplasms, in erythrocytes. Theilerial parasites complete their life cycle in certain ticks by processes which are not fully understood but which terminate in the formation of sporozoites in the salivary glands of the vector ticks.

At a practical level there is little difficulty in distinguishing between the major pathogenic species of Theileria, T. parva and T. annulata as their geographical distributions are such that there is no significant overlap between these parasites, with the exception of the Southern Sudan. Problems arise, however, in trying to distinguish between strains of the same species. Such strains, as well as being morphologically identical, may show a considerable degree of immunological similarity particularly in the case of T. annulata. With T. parva the degree of antigenic similarity between stocks is less marked and strains of the parasite can be distinguished by using in vivo cross-immunity trials and in vitro characterisation by monoclonal antibody profiles.

The examination of parasite enzyme constitution using electrophoretic methods has proved to be of value in the differentiation of species and subspecies of other protozoa and it was considered to have a possible role in identification and characterisation of Theileria, and certain preliminary observations on isoenzyme polymorphism in Theileria parva and T. annulata have been made.

Enzymes were examined at three stages of the parasite's life cycle: (a) intraerythrocytic piroplasms: (b) intralymphocytic schizonts, both from the vertebrate host and (c) sporozoites from the salivary glands of the arthropod vector. In a preliminary survey using both piroplasms and infected bovine lymphoblastoid cell lysates twenty two enzymes were examined by thin layer starch gel electrophoresis. Only one enzyme, glucose phosphate isomerase (GPI) E.C.5.3.1.9. was of taxonomic value and clearly distinguished between the host cell and parasite enzyme activities, obviating the need for a definitive separation of these intracellular forms of the parasite from the host material. The staining method used for GPI involved the use of an improved intermediate electron acceptor, Meldola blue, which is photostable and reduces the background staining of gels to a minimum.

Biochemical studies conducted with intracellular parasites necessitate the careful assessment and control of the host-cell components if valid results are to be obtained. During the initial studies into the enzyme complement of theilerial parasites, methods were devised to cope with the particular problems presented by the different stages of these parasites.

Host platelet and leucocyte levels were very effectively reduced by defibrination of infected blood and subsequent treatment with cellulose powder. Piroplasms were then liberated from the erythrocytes by ammonium chloride lysis, washed and used to prepare lysates for electrophoresis. Host leucocyte controls were obtained by omitting the cellulose powder treatment. Piroplasms from T. annulata (Hissar) and T. annulata (Ankara) and from T. parva (Muguga) were examined for enzyme polymorphism.

When examining the intralymphocytic schizonts, no attempt was made to separate the schizonts from the lymphoblastoid cells but the host cell component was effectively controlled by studying lymphoid cell lines, established by infecting in vitro, lymphocytes from a single cow with the three different stocks of Theileria. These produced GPI isoenzyme patterns characteristic of the parasite which infected the cells. As a corollary, identical parasite isoenzyme patterns were obtained in 4 cell lines from different cows infected with the same parasite. When the GPI isoenzyme patterns of lysates prepared from stocks of T. annulata were examined the patterns exhibited by all the stocks were different.

Experimental results show that the Hissar stock of T. annulata from India exhibited an isoenzyme pattern distinct from that of the Ankara stock from Turkey and three stocks of T. annulata from Tehran, Iran. Extensive variation in GPI isoenzyme patterns was also detected in six stocks of T. annulata from Sudan.

In complete contrast, lysates from twelve cell lines infected with T. parva representing nine stocks and three clones of one parasitised cell line, collected from Kenya and Malawi produced isoenzyme patterns which, allowing for the minor differences inherent in the method, were identical with each other.

Lysates prepared from salivary glands dissected from fed and unfed ticks infected with Theileria showed bands of parasite-associated GPI enzyme when compared with uninfected ticks of the same species. These sporozoite enzyme patterns correlated well with those of piroplasms and schizonts of the same parasite stock. Parasite-associated enzyme activity was seen in both unfed and fed infected ticks but was far greater in ticks exhibiting predominantly mature sporozoites.

The value of enzyme polymorphism as an aid to classifying and characterising theilerial parasites, especially T. parva, would be greatly increased if other parasite-associated enzymes could be found. Recent studies by other workers using isoelectric focusing and balanced-charge agarose has established lactate dehydrogenase activity associated with piroplasms of T. parva but the taxonomic value of this observation has yet to be assessed.

Starch-gel electrophoresis and isoelectric focusing rely on charge differences in the protein molecules and it is possible that other separation methods might be necessary which, along with the wide range of specific and non-specific protein staining methods now available, should provide the means of identifying theilerial parasites especially if they are reinforced with serological and immunological methods.

SUBUNITS OF GLUTENIN AND GLIADIN SERVING AS MARKERS TO DETERMINE THE BREAD-MAKING QUALITY OF WHEAT

Inge Paradies, Johannes-Peter Ohms

Landwirtschaftliche Untersuchungs- und Forschungsanstalt Hameln
Postfach 2 95, D-3250 Hameln 1, Bundesrepublik Deutschland

1 INTRODUCTION

The high-molecular-weight subunits of glutenin seem to play an important role in controlling wheat quality (1.2). A relationship is shown between gliadin banding patterns and quality characteristics like grain protein content, grain hardness and dough strength (3 - 5). The possibility of using the electrophoretic patterns of both glutenins and gliadins as markers to recognize the baking quality of wheat is discussed.

2 MATERIAL AND METHODS

Wheat varieties of both known and unknown quality were tested. The glutenin fraction was submitted to one- and two-dimensional electrophoretic methods (SDS-PAGE and IEF x SDS-PAGE) (6). The gliadins were fractionated by disc-electrophoresis at pH 9.2 (7).

3 RESULTS

By 1D-electrophoresis the high-molecular-weight glutenin is fractionated into 11 subunits with molecular weights from 145,000 to 62.000. Five groups are obtained each of them showing a characteristic banding pattern (Fig. 1.1). A loss of bread-making quality is indicated with changing protein patterns from group 1 to 5.
Some glutenin subunits serve as markers for good or poor baking quality depending on their pattern shown by 2D-electrophoresis (Fig. 1.2). The gliadin patterns AI and BI (Fig. 1.3) are generally related to good quality whereas the patterns AII and BII often indicate poor dough quality
To determine the bread-making quality of wheat the electrophoretic patterns of both glutenins and gliadins have to be taken into consideration, for quality differences are reflected by both of them.

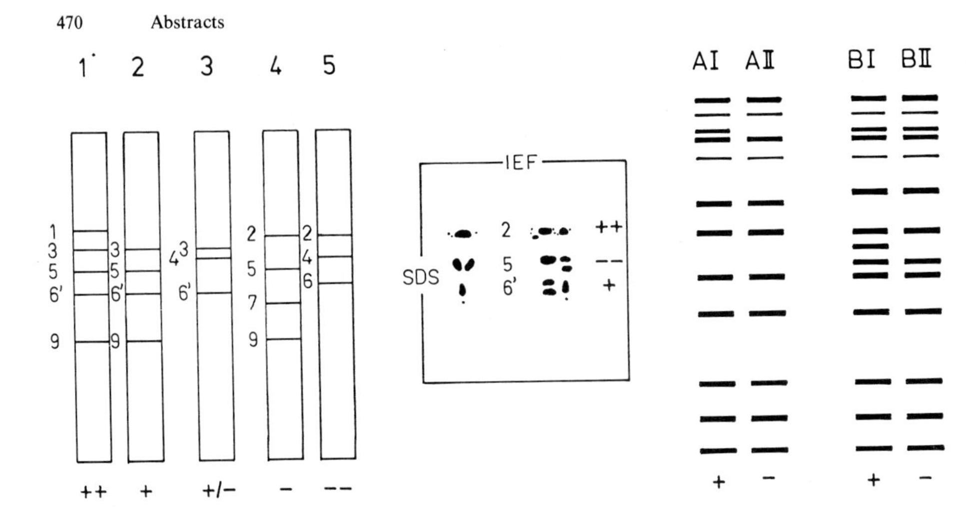

Fig. 1. Glutenin and gliadin banding patterns
1. 1D-electrophoresis of glutenin (SDS-PAGE)
2. 2D-electrophoresis of glutenin (IEF x SDS)
3. Disc-electrophoresis of gliadin

+/- Signs indicating banding patterns or protein spots with good or poor baking quality

4 REFERENCES

(1) T. Burnouf, R. Bouriquet, Theor. Appl. Genet. 58 (1980) 107-111.

(2) P. I. Payne, K. G. Corfield, L. M. Holt, J. A. Blackman, J. Sci. Food Agric 32 (1981) 51-60.

(3) C. W. Wrigley, P. J. Robinson, W. T. Williams, J. Sci. Food Agric 32 (1981) 433-442.

(4) V. M. Bebyakin, N. A. Dushaeva, Fi Ziol. Biokhim. Kul't. Rast 14 (6) (1982) 561-567

(5) A. Sasek, J. Cerny, A. Hanisova, Sb. UVTIZ. Genet. Slechteni 18 (4) (1982) 241-255

(6) I. Paradies, J. P. Ohms, Landwirtsch. Forsch. 37 (1984) i. print

(7) J. P. Ohms, Landwirtsch. Forsch. SH 37 (1980) 287-293

FISH SPECIES IDENTIFICATION BY ISOELECTRIC FOCUSING OF SARCOPLASMATIC PROTEINS: CHANGES OF THE SPECIES SPECIFIC PROTEIN PATTERNS IN DEPENDENCE OF THE FISHING GROUND AND THE CONDITIONS OF FROZEN STORAGE OF THE SAMPLES

Hartmut Rehbein

Institute of Biochemistry and Technology, Federal Research Centre for Fisheries, Palmaille 9, D-2000 Hamburg 50, Federal Republic of Germany

1 INTRODUCTION

Isoelectric focusing of sarcoplasmatic proteins has proven to be the most reliable technique for fish species identification (1). This work describes the application of a fast, reliable and cheap variant of this technique, ultrathin-layer isoelectric focusing in 50 μm polyacrylamide gels on polyester films (2), for the study of two problems: 1. Do specimen of cod (Gadus morhua) and saithe (Pollachius virens) from various fishing grounds of the Northeast Atlantic exhibit differences in the protein patterns, as reported for some other species (3-5)? 2. Are there changes in the patterns during frozen storage due to reactions between formaldehyde (FA), a degradation product of trimethylamine oxide, and proteins?

2 MATERIALS AND METHODS

2.1 Samples of Cod and Saithe from Various Fishing Grounds

The fishes were caught during several cruises of the FRVs "Walther Herwig" and "Anton Dohrn" into NE Atlantic waters between Norway, Island and the Faroers. Immediately after hauling the fishes were measured, bleeded and filleted. Parts of the white muscle were stored at -25/-30°C for further analysis.

2.2 Preparation and Storage of Fish Minces

Minced fish was made from the white muscle (or from fillet in the case of herring and mackerel) of the following species: cod (Gadus morhua), whiting (Merlangius merlangus), blue ling (Molva dipterygia d.), haddock (Melanogrammus aeglefinus), hake (Merluccius merluccius), saithe (Pollachius virens), redfish (Sebastes mentella), mackerel (Scomber scombrus) and herring (Clupea harengus). Portions of the minces were mixed with 1 % of blood or kidney of the appropriate species or with formaldehyde (13 mmoles FA/kg mince); the samples were stored at -8/-10°C for 6 - 8 months.

2.3 Analytical Methods

The samples were extracted with the 4-fold amount of double-distilled water; if necessary, the extracts were concentrated using the Minicon B-15 concentration cell (Amicon). Ultrathin-layer IEF was performed as described by Radola (2). The protein content of the extracts was determined by the biuret method (6). For the estimation of free and bound FA the minces were mixed with sulfuric acid and steam distilled according to Antonacopoulos (7). The FA content of the distillates was measured according to Nash (8).

3 RESULTS AND DISCUSSION

3.1 Protein Patterns of Cod and Saithe from Various Fishing Grounds

3.1.1 Cod

The muscle extracts were analyzed using 2 gel compositions: (I) Servalyt T 4-9 3 %; (II) Servalyt AG 4-6 0.8 %, Servalyt T 4-9 1.6 %, Servalyt AG 8-10 0.8%. With system (I) fishes from all fishing grounds gave nearly identical protein patterns; sometimes variations in the intensity of single bands occurred. Cod from the Baltic Sea was not available which was reported to have a different pattern in the anodic region (9). When gels of the composition (II) were used, the separation of the bands was improved, but the 2 most anodic bands run out of the gel. Some minor variations were observed in the protein patterns of cod from a given fishing ground, but the pattern for all regions was more or less the same.

3.1.2 Saithe

The muscle extracts of saithe were studied using gel composition (II); no differences between the protein patterns of saithe from the various fishing grounds could be detected, but small variations within the fishing grounds happened occasionally.

3.1.3 Conclusions

The polymorphism of species characteristic protein bands leading to difficulties in fish species identification in some cases (3-5) was not observed for the commercially important species of cod and saithe from various NE Atlantic fishing grounds.

3.2 Changes of the Protein Patterns during Frozen Storage

Informations about the changes of the protein patterns during frozen storage of fish muscle are important for food inspection for 3 reasons: 1. In most cases frozen fish products have to be analyzed. 2. Reference samples are stored deep-frozen. 3. From changes in the protein patterns conclusions may be drawn about the degree and the mechanism of protein denaturation during frozen storage.

Fish species with and without FA formation during frozen storage have been compared (Table 1); minces producing large amounts of FA showed a diminished protein content in their extract. Proteins with high isoelectric points are attacked by FA preferentially. Thus, if a fish species has specific protein bands in the anodic region, unknown samples of that species may be identified by IEF even if heavily deteriorated by FA (Figure 1); if necessary, the extracts may be concentrated. In contrast to the results obtained for fishes of the order gadiformes, the patterns of redfish, mackerel and herring remained nearly unchanged during frozen storage.

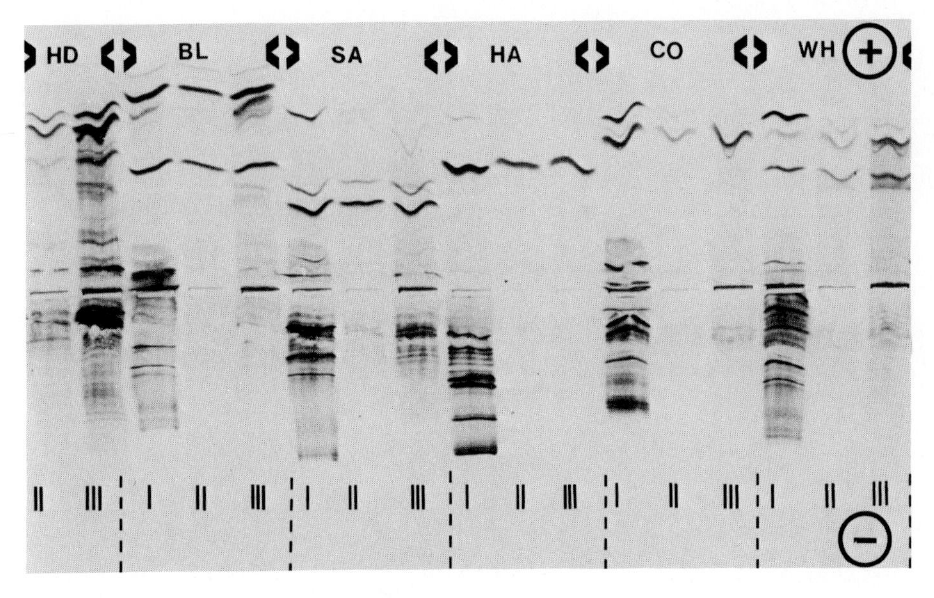

Figure 1: Protein patterns of frozen stored minces of fishes from the order gadiformes. For each species mince without additions (I) and with the addition of kidney (II) was analyzed; (III) shows the effect of concentrating the extracts 5-fold, Haddock, HD; blue ling, BL; saithe, SA; hake, HA; cod, CO; whiting, WH.

Table 1. FA production in fish minces during frozen storage.

Fish sample		FA content (mmoles/kg wet weight)	protein content (mg/ml extract)
Cod mince	without additions	0.94	5.58
	+ kidney	35.7	1.61
Whiting mince	without additions	1.8	6.82
	+ kidney	29.2	2.11
Blue ling mince	without additions	2.4	6.05
	+ kidney	24.2	1.70
Haddock mince	without additions	1.9	7.24
	+ kidney	17.6	n.d. [a]
Hake mince	without additions	1.5	6.00
	+ kidney	34.8	1.98
Saithe mince	without additions	2.2	5.78
	+ kidney	23.9	1.88
Herring mince	without additions	<0.6	6.26
	+ kidney	<0.6	6.98
Mackerel mince	without additions	<0.6	6.22
Redfish mince	without additions	<0.6	5.47
	+ kidney	<0.6	5.90

[a] n.d. = not determined

4 REFERENCES

(1) R. C. Lundstrom, J. Assoc. Off. Anal. Chem. 62 (1979), 624-629.

(2) B. J. Radola, Electrophoresis 1 (1980), 43-56.

(3) R. C. Lundstrom, J. Assoc. Off. Anal. Chem. 64 (1981), 32-37.

(4) N. Taniguchi, K. Sumantadinata, A. Suzuki, J. Yamada, Bull. Jap. Soc. Sci. Fish. 48 (1982), 139-141.

(5) J. Yamada, A. Suzuki, Bull. Jap. Soc. Sci. Fish. 48 (1982), 73-77.

(6) E. Layne in S. P. Colowick, N. O. Kaplan (Eds.), Methods in Enzymology, Vol. III, Academic Press, New York, London 1957, pp. 450-451.

(7) N. Antonacopoulos in W. Ludorff, V. Meyer, Fisch und Fischerzeugnisse, Paul Parey, Berlin und Hamburg 1973, p. 231.

(8) T. Nash, Biochem. J. 55 (1953), 416-421.

(9) J. Gjerde, Fisk. Dir. Skr., Ser. Ernaering 11 (1982), 45-51.

ABNORMAL EXPRESSIONS OF EQUINE PROTEASE INHIBITORY ALLELES, Pi^F AND Pi^L

Scott D. Patterson, Kevin T. Bell

Department of Physiology and Pharmacology, University of Queensland, St. Lucia, Queensland, Australia. 4067.

1 INTRODUCTION

The major proteins of the equine protease inhibitory system (Pi) have been characterized by ISO-DALT electrophoresis in terms of pI, M.W. and inhibitory spectra (1). In the Thoroughbred, the Pi proteins appear to be controlled by eight alleles, Pi $^{F, G, I, L, N, S_1, S_2}$ and ^{U} (2), although two loci have been postulated on the basis of M.W. and inhibitory spectra differences (3). An additional ten alleles have been described in Standardbred horses (4).

Abnormal expressions of both Pi^F and Pi^L have been encountered and the nature of the abnormalities were investigated by IEF (pH 3.5 - 6.0 and 4.2 - 4.9), alkaline and acid 1D - and 2D - polyacrylamide gel electrophoresis and treatment of normal and abnormal plasmas with neuraminidase (V. cholerae). The abnormalities appear to have been caused by variations in the sialylations of some of the proteins.

2 RESULTS

2.1 Normal Expressions of Pi^F and Pi^L

Equine Pi^F controls five major proteins with pIs ranging from 3.74 - 4.27 and molecular weights of 55,500 - 69,000(1). The two most acidic proteins which were of interest in this study, have ISO-DALT co-ordinates of 3.74; 69,000 and 3.92; 62,500 and inhibit only trypsin. The remaining proteins inhibit both trypsin and chymotrypsin.

Pi^L consists of four major proteins with pIs in the range 3.90 - 4.38 and molecular weights of 56,500 - 68,000 (1). All four proteins exhibit anti-trypsin and anti-chymotrypsin activities. The Pi^L protein of interest in this study has ISO-DALT co-ordinates of 4.38; 56,500.

On 1D-acid PAGE the affected proteins of Pi^F and Pi^L were the second and third most anodal proteins and the most cathodal protein respectively (2).

2.2 Abnormal Expression of Pi^F

One case of abnormal expression of Pi^F (in combination with Pi^N) has been found with the abnormal F type being transmitted to two offspring, both with Pi^L.

The two proteins of Pi^F which appeared to have been lost in the 1D-acid PAGE patterns of FL and FN were shown by 2D-electrophoresis to exhibit basic pI shifts of 0.16 and 0.15 for the most acidic and second most acidic proteins respectively with negligible molecular weight changes. Neuraminidase treatment demonstrated that the most acidic protein contained eight sialic acid residues when normally expressed while the abnormal protein contained only six. The second most acidic protein had six and four residues in the normal and abnormal types respectively. The basic pI shifts are also consistent with a loss of two sialic acid residues from the corresponding normal proteins (5). The identical inhibitory spectra in both states of expression suggest that the two proteins (3.74 and 3.92) are closely related.

The smaller, less acidic protein could be derived from the larger, more acidic protein by proteolysis of a 6,500 M.W. portion containing two sialic acid residues. The abnormal expression of Pi^F could then be simply explained by the loss of a bi-antennary carbohydrate sidechain by either an amino acid substitution at the site of attatchment or one which causes a conformational change which prevents the attatchment (cf. human M and Z variants (6)). Either would result in two less sialic acid residues in both proteins.

2.3 Abnormal Expression of Pi^L

An abnormal expression of Pi^L has been found in only 6 of a total of 46 offspring from the same stallion. The abnormal pattern was observed with Pi G, L, N and U while the remaining 40 offspring inherited the normal Pi^L pattern from the sire. The stallion which also possessed the normal Pi^L allele, did not exhibit all the characteristics of the abnormal expression.

On 1D-acid PAGE the loss of the most cathodal Pi L zone in the abnormal type coincided with the appearance of an anodal zone of slightly lower concentration but with the same inhibitory spectrum. This was reflected in the 2D-pattern by an acidic pI difference of 0.08 pH units (normal 4.38; abnormal 4.30) with negligible M.W. difference. Neuraminidase treatment of normal and abnormal Pi L plasmas and the pI shift of 0.08 indicated that most, but not all, of the difference between the two proteins could be accounted for by the addition of one sialic acid residue in the abnormal L protein.

A mechanism such as that postulated for the conversion of bi-antennary to tri-antennary sidechains during stressed synthesis (7) may be applicable in the case of the abnormal Pi^{L}. However, the cause of this abnormality would appear to be genetic as offspring in two mating seasons (1977/78) were affected. The reason for the biased transmission of the abnormal Pi L is being investigated.

3 REFERENCES

(1) C.C. Pollitt, K. Bell, Anim. Blood Grps. biochem. Genet. 14 (1983) 83-105.

(2) C.C. Pollitt, K. Bell, Anim. Blood Grps. biochem. Genet. 11 (1980) 235-244.

(3) K.R. Juneja, B. Gahne, K. Sandberg, Anim. Blood Grps. biochem. Genet. 10 (1979) 235-251.

(4) K. Bell, S. Patterson, C.C. Pollitt, Anim. Blood Grps. biochem. Genet. In press (1984).

(5) J-O Jeppsson, C-B Laurell, M. Fagerhol, Eur. J. Biochem. 83 (1978) 143-153.

(6) A. Yoshida, J. Liebeman, L. Gaidulus, C. Ewing, Proc. nat. Acad. Sci. U.S.A. 73 (1976) 1324-1328.

(7) L. Vaughan, M.A. Loyier, R.W. Carrell, Biochem. Biophys. Acta. 701 (1982) 339-345.

THE INFLUENCE OF HEPARIN AND THROMBIN ON THE BEHAVIOUR OF ANTITHROMBIN III IN IMMUNOELECTROPHORESIS

Chieko Miyashita, Gerhard von Blohn, Ernst Wenzel

Department of the Clinical Haemostaseology and Transfusion Medicine, University of Saarland, D-6650 Homburg/Saar, Federal Republic of Germany

1. INTRODUCTION

Antithrombin III (AT-III) binds thrombin stoichiometrically and irreversively, and thereby inhibits thrombin activity. In the presence of heparin the inhibition occurs immediately because heparin enhances the AT-III-thrombin binding in the form of AT-III-heparin complex. AT-III-heparin- and AT-III-thrombin-complexes can be electrophoretically differentiated (1,2,3). We studied the mobility of AT-III alone and after incubation with heparin, thrombin or both of them at the same time with immunoelectrophoresis.

2. MATERIALS AND METHODS

We utilized AT-III from normal human plasma and human AT-III that was chromatographically purified from AT-III-concentration (Behringwerke, Marburg) at a concentration of 0.5 U/ml. Heparin (Liquemin, 5 - 50 USP U/ml) and Thrombin "Roche" (from bovine, 6.75 and 13.5 NIH U/ml) were from Hoffmann - La Roche, Grenzach-Wyhlen. Isotonic tris-HCl buffer (pH 8.0) was used for dilution of compounds. AT-III was first mixed with buffer, heparin, thrombin and heparin solution containing thrombin, and incubated for 30 min at 37 ^{o} C. Crossed immunoelectrophoresis, "Laurell"-rocket-immunoelectrophoresis, and radial immunodiffusion (RID) were the methods employed in this study. Agarose L as gel material, Clotimmun Antithrombin III as antibody, and Partigen M-Plate Antithrombin III for the RID were from Behringwerke, Marburg. The field intensity was 2.5 V/cm using barbiturate buffer (pH 8.6, u=0.02).

Thus, erroreous results may be obtained when the plasma of a heparin-substituted patient undergoes rocket immunoelectrophoresis for determination of certain plasma proteins. For example heparin substitution of 1.0 USP U/ml plasma may cause a determination of 1.6 U/ml AT-III (160%) instead of 1.0 U/ml (100%). This difference ist clinically relevant. Further investigations need to be conducted to ascertain whether this phenomena also occurs in vivo.

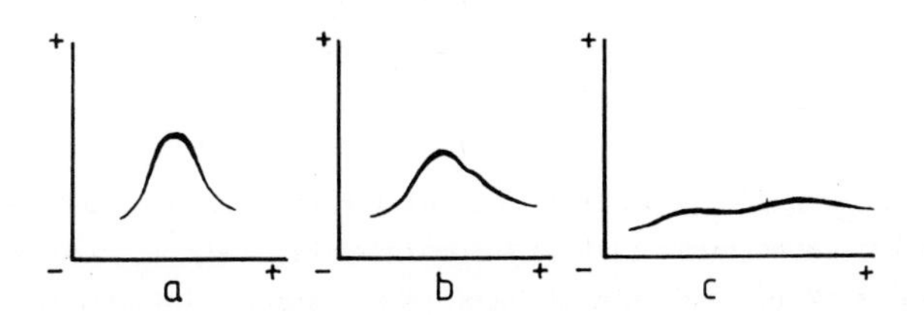

Figure 1. Electrophoresis pattern of a) AT-III only, b) with heparin 5 USP U/ml, and c) 25 USP U/ml in crossed immunoelectrophoresis

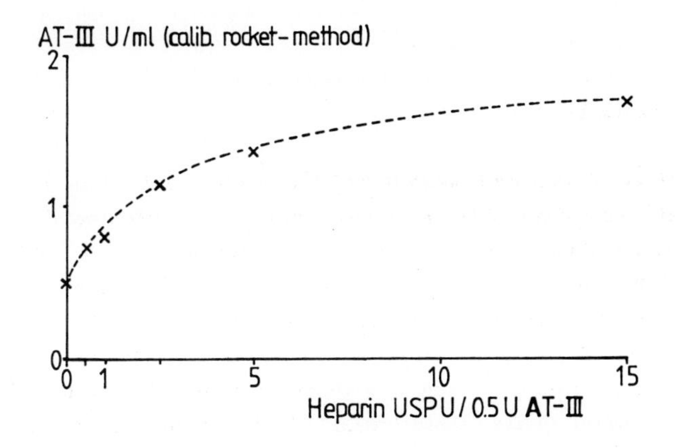

Figure 2. Influence of heparin on AT-III-rocket electrophoresis

5. REFERENCES

(1) R.D. Rosenberg, P.S. Damus; J. Biol. Chem. 248, 6490-6505 (1973).

(2) T.W. Barrowcliffe; Thrombos. Hemostas. 42, 1434-1448 (1979).

(3) J. Kera, K. Yamasawa; Electrophoresis 3, 157-161 (1982).

3. RESULTS

No difference was observed between human plasma AT-III and the purified form.

Influence of thrombin: Thrombin hardly influenced AT-III mobility in the crossed immunoelectrophoresis at all. The almost symmetrical peak of AT-III (Fig. 1-a) was deformed after incubation with thrombin in a form similar to Fig. 1-b. AT-III mobility did not change by adding thrombin in rocket electrophoresis and RID. Thrombin-AT-III binding was demonstrated enzyme assay of thrombin activity using chromogenic substrates.

Influence of heparin: The effect of heparin on AT-III mobility was obvious and much greater than that of thrombin. In the crossed immunoelectrophoresis (Fig. 1a-c) the highest concentration of heparin divided the AT-III single peak into two; the first peak was that of the slower running AT-III alone and the other of the faster running heparin-AT-III complex. The height of the peaks were reduced. Surprisingly, in rocket electrophoresis we found increase in the precipitation peak proportional to an increase in heparin, although the concentration of AT-III was the same (Fig. 2). Thus, heparin appears to influence the precipitation rate of AT-III antigen-antibody complexes. No effect was observed in the RID.

Influence of heparin and thrombin: The effect of both at the same time was similar to that of heparin only. Thrombin had no influence on the heparin effect in all three methods.

4. CONCLUSION

Heparin-AT-III complex moves faster than AT-III alone because of heparin's strongly negative charge. In rocket electrophoresis, the quantitative reaction of antigen and antibody determines the height of the precipitation. When heparin forms a complex with a protein it can cause a higher precipitation peak.

DETECTION OF FACTOR VIII - RELATED ANTIGEN BY MEANS OF IEF IN UREA - AGAROSE GELS AND AN ENZYME LINKED ANTIBODY

R. Schneppenheim, H. Plendl, W. Grote

Abt. Humangenetik, Universität Kiel, Schwanenweg 24, D-2300 Kiel, FRG

1 INTRODUCTION

Diagnosis of certain variants of von Willebrand's disease (vWd), a lifelong bleeding disorder due to a deficiency or abnormality of the factor VIII complex has recently been carried out by SDS electrophoresis (1) and IEF in agarose - urea gels (2) with subsequent detection of the factor VIII related antigen (F VIII R:Ag) by radioactive labeled antibodies. Since radioactive labeled F VIII R:Ag - antibodies are not commercially available, such studies are confined to only a few scientific laboratories. Being of considerable diagnostic value, we tried to alter this method with respect to its applicability in routine coagulation laboratories using a commercially available enzyme linked antibody.

2 MATERIALS AND METHODS

15 µl of citrated plasma (diluted 1 : 16) from 28 individuals with mild to moderate vWd, 4 individuals with hemophilia A and 20 normal individuals were applied at the cathodic end of the gel. Preparation of agarose - urea IEF gels (pH range 3 - 10 and 5 - 8) and running conditions were according to instructions given by Pharmacia (3).

Demonstration of F VIII R:Ag by using an enzyme linked immunosorbent assay (Asserachrom(R) VIII R:Ag, Diagnostica Stago) (2,4) with a subsequent histochemical staining method (5,6) was done as follows:

Fixing: 1 h in 500 ml fixing solution (250 ml ethanol, 100 ml glacial acetic acid, 650 ml distilled water).
Washing: 3 h in 1 l distilled water with 3 changes of the water.
Equilibration: 30 min in 200 ml of 0.02 M phosphate buffer pH 7.2 containing 0.15 M NaCl, 0.02 % NaN_3, 0.1 % bovine albumine.
Incubation: 12 h at 4°C in 100 ml of equilibration buffer, adding 5 mg of freeze dried Anti F VIII/Peroxidase (Diagnostica

Stago).

Washing: 3 h at 4°C in 1 l 0.5 M NaCl with 4 changes of the solution.

Staining: agar overlay - 0.3 g agar noble, 30 ml 0.05 M phospate buffer pH 7.2, 0.5 ml 0.1 M $CaCl_2$, 12.5 mg Amino - 9 - ethyl - carbazole dissolved in 0.5 ml dimethyl formamide, 250 µl 3% H_2O_2. Red - brown bands appeared on a yellow background after 5 to 10 minutes.

3 RESULTS AND DISCUSSION

Subsequent to IEF, F VIII R:Ag could be demonstrated by using an enzyme linked antibody in combination with a histochemical staining method. F VIII R:Ag from all individuals focused as one single band at a pH of about 6.0 on both gels (pH range 3 - 10 or 5 - 8), which agrees with former isoelectric point determinations (2).

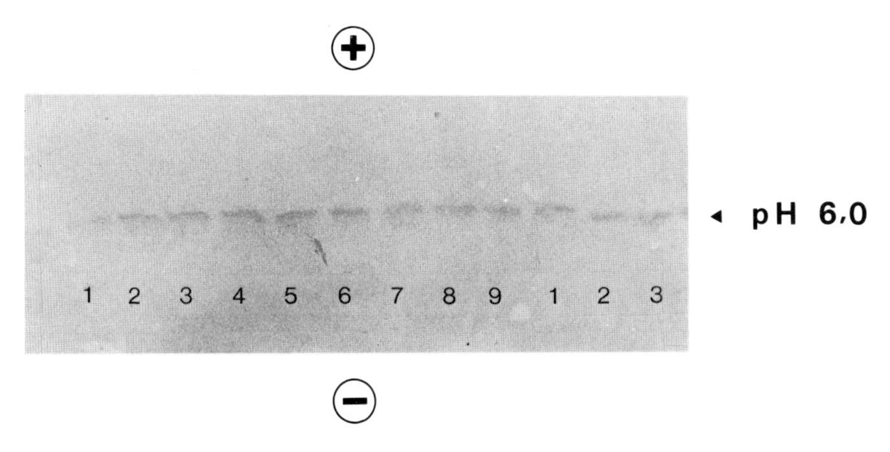

Figure 1. IEF of human F VIII R:Ag in agarose-urea gels (pH 3- 10) demonstrated by ELISA technique using anti-F VIII / Peroxidase. 1, 2, 3, 7, 9: vWd; 4, 5, 8: normals; 6: hemophilia A.

No differences between the various groups of patients and normals were observed (fig. 1), possibly because our material did not contain comparable variants of vWd as were analyzed by others (2).

Nevertheless IEF in agarose - urea gels in combination with ELISA and a histochemical staining procedure is a sensitive method for the detection of F VIII R:Ag. However its value in routine coagulation diagnosis has still to be proved by analyzing further patients.

4 REFERENCES

(1) Z. M. Ruggeri, T. S. Zimmermann, J. Clin. Invest. 65 (1980) 1318 - 1325.

(2) C. A. Fulcher, Z. M. Ruggeri, T. S. Zimmermann, Blood 61 (1983) 304 - 310.

(3) Pharmacia Fine Chemicals (Ed.), Isoelectric Focusing - principles and methods, Uppsala 1982, pp. 92 - 96.

(4) Diagnostica Stago (Ed.), Asserachrom(R) VIII R:Ag, Asnières-sur-Seine 1982, pp. 1 - 2.

(5) H. Harris, D. A. Hopkinson (Eds.), Handbook of Enzyme Electrophoresis in Human Genetics, North Holland, Amsterdam 1976.

(6) C. R. Shaw, R. Prasad, Biochem. Genet. 4 (1970) 275 - 283.

POLYACRYLAMIDE GEL ELECTROPHORESIS OF HUMAN ROTAVIRUS GENOME RNA

Phillip Cash, Eileen Freebairn, Gloria Trallero

Department of Bacteriology, University of Aberdeen, Foresterhill, Aberdeen, Scotland.

1 INTRODUCTION

Polyacrylamide gel electrophoresis (PAGE) of the virion RNA of human rotavirus (HRV) has been used for the diagnosis of HRV infection and in the study of the virus epidemiology (1,2). HRV is an important cause of acute gastroenteritis in young children and causes epidemics in the winter months. The genome of HRV consists of 11 unique pieces of double-stranded RNA which can be separated by PAGE. Virus isolates can be differentiated by variation in the mobility of the RNA segments and are known as electropherotypes. The only correlation consistently observed between serological and RNA typing of HRV has been with the subgroup antigen (3). Subgroup 2 viruses have 'long' electropherotypes and subgroup 1 have 'short' electropherotypes. These two types of RNA profiles are distinguished according to the relative mobilities of the two smallest RNA segments. Since 1981 we have used genome RNA typing to investigate the epidemiology of HRV in north east Scotland.

2 IDENTIFICATION OF HRV ELECTROPHEROTYPES

HRV was concentrated from faecal suspensions by ultracentrifugation and genome RNA extracted from virions by protease K digestion. RNA segments were resolved by discontinuous-PAGE and detected by either ethidium bromide or silver staining (4). For some samples HRV genome RNA was prepared by phenol extraction of the faecal suspension without prior virus concentration. 424 faecal samples which contained HRV (determined by either electron microscopy or ELISA) were processed for RNA analysis; 316 (75%) yielded RNA profiles suitable for typing. These were from 260 individual patients. When compared to electron microscopy, the standard method for HRV diagnosis, 94% were also positive for HRV RNA. For a small number of samples HRV RNA was detected when the samples were scored as negative for HRV by electron microscopy.

Between January 1982 and April 1984 16 virus electropherotypes were identified. 3 electropherotypes were represented by single samples;

in 1 of these cases there was evidence for the child contracting the infection outside our survey area. The major electropherotype was represented by 72 samples. 75% of the typed viruses had long RNA profiles, i.e. subgroup 2, which covered 13 different electropherotypes. The remaining electropherotypes had short RNA profiles. A faecal sample from a single patient gave a RNA profile with 13 rather than 11 pieces of RNA; this has been interpreted by other workers as representing a dual virus infection of the patient (5).

3 EPIDEMIOLOGY OF HRV ELECTROPHEROTYPES

The appearance of the HRV electropherotypes over three epidemic periods has been followed. Co-circulation of HRV electropherotypes was observed with up to 6 types found in one epidemic period. However, there was a succession in the predominant electropherotype between epidemics. Short electropherotypes were confined to two periods of time - September 1982 to January 1983 and November 1983 to January 1984, whereas long electropherotypes were distributed throughout the period of our study. Although the available numbers were limited geographic separation of one short electropherotype was evident. 44 out of 47 (93%) samples of this type were found in the eastern parts of the survey area.

Although PAGE of HRV genome RNA is of limited use in conclusively demonstrating identity of HRV from widely differing localities or periods of time it has been useful in following the spread of virus in local outbreaks of HRV. The method clearly demonstrated the identity of virus isolates which was only suggested by the epidemiological data.

The stability of the RNA profiles as a marker was demonstrated by the fact that the same RNA profile was obtained from virus in duplicate faecal samples from single patients. We have also collected cell-adapted isolates of HRV possessing the same RNA profile as the virus in the original faecal sample when analysed by PAGE.

4 ACKNOWLEDGEMENTS

We are grateful to the members of staff in the diagnostic laboratories at the University of Aberdeen and Aberdeen City Hospital for the HRV positive faecal samples used in this work.

5 REFERENCES

(1) L. F. Avendano, A. Calderon, J. Macaya, I. Prenzel, E. Duarte, Pediat. Res. 16 (1982) 329-331.

(2) S. M. Rodger, R. F. Bishop, C. Birch, B. McLean, I. H. Holmes, J. Clin. Micro. 13 (1981) 272-278.

(3) A. R. Kalica, H. B. Greenberg, R. T. Espejo, J. Flores, R. G. Wyatt, A. Z. Kapikian, R. M. Chanock, Inf. and Immun. 33 (1981) 958-965.

(4) P. Cash, J. Virol. Meth. 4 (1982) 107-115.

(5) M. H. Lourenco, J. C. Nicolas, J. Cohen, R. Scherrer, F. Bricout, Ann. Virol. 132 (1981) 161-173.

GENETIC ALPHA-2-HS GLYCOPROTEIN PHENOTYPES DEMONSTRATED BY ISOELECTRIC FOCUSING AND IMMUNOFIXATION

S. Weidinger, F. Schwarzfischer, R. Burgemeister, H. Cleve

Institut für Anthropologie und Humangenetik der Universität München,
Richard-Wagner-Str. 10/I, D-8000 München 2, Federal Republic of Germany

1 INTRODUCTION

Alpha$_2$-HS glycoprotein (α_2HSG) was described first by Heremans in 1960 (1) and later isolated from human plasma and partially characterized (2, 3). α_2HSG is synthesized in the liver and deposited in mineralising bone (4). Although an opsonising activity of α_2HSG has been suggested (5), the precise biological function of this plasma protein is still unknown. The concentration in the serum of healthy individuals is on the average 60 mg/dl (6). A significant decrease was observed in patients with malignant diseases and inflammatory reactions (6, 7).

In 1977 Anderson and Anderson (8) have described two different electrophoretic variants (N and L) of human α_2HSG using two dimensional electrophoresis. Further genetic studies by silver stain immunofixation indicated the existence of three codominant alleles on the α_2HSG locus (9).

In this paper we describe the distribution of α_2HSG phenotypes and alleles in a German population sample. Using this method a total of seven different α_2HSG types were identified which includes three previously unreported variants.

2 MATERIALS AND METHODS

Serum samples were obtained from blood donors and normal individuals who have been investigated for paternity in our laboratory. Until use sera were stored at - 25°C.

α_2HS glycoprotein was examined by isoelectric focusing (IEF) combined with immunoprinting. Separation by IEF was carried out on 0.5 mm thin polyacrylamide gels (260 x 125 mm) with a pH range from 4-6. Samples of 8 µl were applied with pieces of filter paper near the cathode. A mixture of 0.025 M aspartic acid and 0.025 M glutamic acid was used at the anode, and 2 M ethylenediamine, containing 0.025 M arginine and 0.025 M lysine at the cathode. Electrofocusing was performed in a Multiphor II chamber (LKB) with maximally 1600 V and 25 mA, stabilized at 20 W, for 4 hours. The cooling temperature was kept at 8 °C.

After completion of separation by IEF a cellulose acetate strip soaked with a monospecific anti-α_2HSG antiserum (Behringwerke) was placed for 10 min on the gel in the region of α_2HSG. The strip was subsequently removed and washed overnight. Finally it was stained with Coomassie Brillant Blue R-250.

3 RESULTS AND DISCUSSION

The α_2HSG phenotypes as observed by IEF on polyacrylamide gels and subsequent immunofixation are shown in Figure 1.

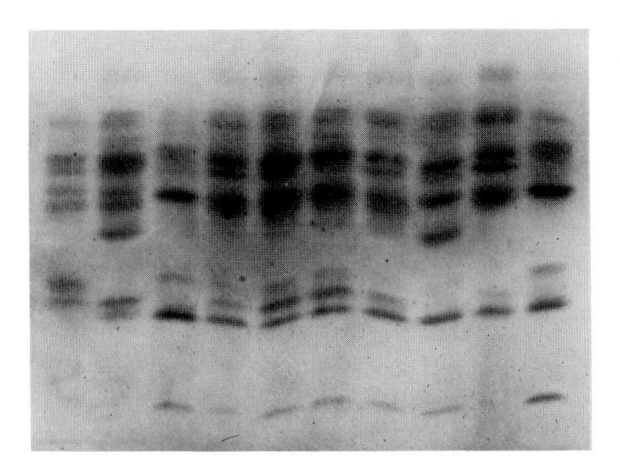

Fig. 1. α_2HSG phenotypes as obtained by isoelectric focusing on polyacrylamide gels (pH range 4-6) and immunoprinting with a monospecific anti-α_2HSG antiserum. From left to right (1) 1-1, (2) 4-1, (3) 2-2, (4, 5, 6, 7) 2-1, (8) 4-2, (9) 2-1 and (10) 2-2.

The band patterns were found in the pH range between 4.7 and 5.0. Figure 2 gives a schematic presentation of seven different phenotypes observed in our study.

The distribution of α_2HSG phenotypes and alleles in our sample of 166 unrelated individuals from Southern Germany is given in Table 1. There is a good agreement between our results and the distribution found in Canadians (9). As shown in Table 2 is the distribution in Japanese apparently different (10).

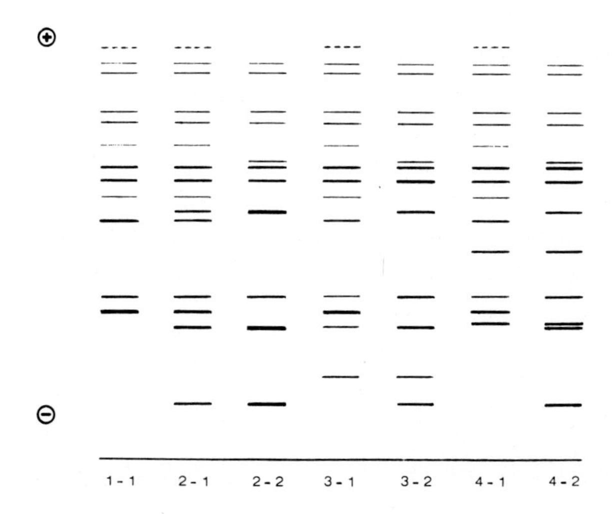

Fig. 2. Schematic representation of seven different observed α_2HSG phenotypes, including two new types α_2HSG 4-1 and α_2HSG 4-2.

Table 1. Frequencies of α_2HSG phenotypes and alleles in a sample from Southern Germany.

	α_2HSG phenotypes							
	1-1	2-1	2-2	3-1	3-2	4-1	4-2	Total
Observed (n)	73	65	20	4	1	2	1	166
(%)	43.98	39.16	12.05	2.41	0.60	1.20	0.60	100.00
Expected (n)	70.94	69.95	17.24	3.26	1.61	1.95	0.96	165.91
χ^2	0.06	0.35	0.44	0.01[a]				0.86

[a] Phenotypes with n (exp) below 10 were combined for χ^2 calculation.

Allele frequencies: HSGA*1 = 0.654 HSGA*3 = 0.015
HSGA*2 = 0.322 HSGA*4 = 0.009

We have studied 17 families with one child in each family; there were no deviations from the expected autosomal codominant mode of inheritance. The new variant α_2HSG 4 was found in two unrelated individuals and also in a mother and her child who both had the phenotype 4-1 indicating a simple mode of transmission. The theoretical exclusion

Table 2. HSGA allele frequencies in three different populations

Populations (Authors)	n	Allele frequencies			
		HSGA*1	HSGA*2	HSGA*3	HSGA*4
Canadian (Cox and Andrews, 1983)	68	0.640	0.345	0.015	-
Japanese (Umetsu et al., 1983)	300	0.725	0.275	-	-
German (This study)	166	0.654	0.322	0.015	0.009

rate for paternity examinations was calculated to be 19.3 %. This system is therefore useful for population studies and for paternity testing.

4 REFERENCES

(1) J.F.Heremans, Les Globulines Sériques du Systéme Gamma, Arscia, Brussel 1960, p. 103.

(2) K.Schmid, W.Bürgi, Biochim. Biophys. Acta 47 (1961) 440 - 453.

(3) H.E.Schultze, K.Heide, H.Haupt, Clin. Chim. Acta 7 (1962) 854 - 868.

(4) J.T.Triffitt, U.Gebauer, B.A.Ashton, M.P.Owne, Nature 262 (1976) 226 - 227.

(5) C.J.Van Oss, C.F.Gillman, P.M.Bronson, J.P.Border, Immunol. Commun. 3 (1974) 329 - 335.

(6) H.Cleve, H.Dencker, Protides of the Biological Fluids, Vol. 14, Elsevier Publishing Company, Amsterdam 1966, pp. 379 - 384.

(7) J.P.Lebreton, F.Joisel, J.P.Raoult, B.Lannuzel, J.P.Rogez, G.Humbert, J. Clin. Invest. 64 (1979) 1118 - 1129.

(8) L.Anderson, N.G.Anderson, Proc. Natl. Acad. Sci. 74 (1977) 5421 - 5425.

(9) D.W.Cox, B.J.Andrews, In D.Stathakos (Ed.) Proc. of the Int. Conference on Electrophoresis, Walter de Gruyter, Berlin-New York 1983, pp. 243 - 247.

(10) K.Umetsu, S.Kashimura, N.Ikeda, T.Suzuki, Z. Rechtsmed. 91 (1983) 33 - 35.

ANALYSIS OF MALIGNANT EFFUSIONS AFTER SELECTIVE ENRICHMENT OF TRACE PROTEINS PRIOR TO TWO-DIMENSIONAL ELECTROPHORESIS

Jeanine Segers, Denis Wulfrank, Marcel Rabaey

Department of Clinical Chemistry, Department of Radiotherapy and Nuclear Medicine and Department of Ophthalmology, University of Gent, Belgium

1 INTRODUCTION

Two-dimensional (2-D) electrophoresis combined with silver staining is a powerful device for the resolution of complex protein mixtures. Most of the studies dealing with plasma proteins and other body fluids, separated by 2-D electrophoresis are restricted to a minority of proteins which are present in relatively high concentration. On the other hand proteins present in trace amounts in body fluids represent a great majority regarding the number. They remain undetected with the 2-D techniques when total body fluid samples are applied, although their pathological significance may be important. Many techniques are now available for the separation of proteins according to either charge or size. General methods allowing separation of proteins according to their concentration are not available. This can only be done by using more specific or preparative procedures. Affinity chromatography is a simple method to remove albumin from samples. An interesting approach was presented by Dermer et al. (1). they used immunoadsorbents to separate serum derived proteins, in several body fluids, from the fluid-specific, non-serum derived proteins. We are exploring several possibilities in the hope of getting a better visualization of trace proteins in pleural and ascitic effusions, especially in malignancy. The enrichment of trace components, as much as possible, on the one side, and elimination of a part of the bulk proteins, on the other hand, are essential. In this paper we will discuss some of our trials. We examined the insoluble proteins after polyethylene glycol (PEG) precipitation at low concentration. Affinity chromatography was used to select and enrich the glycoproteins. In another attempt we combined both techniques. This was a conscious choice of selected methods, because we believed to have a better chance, with this approach, to reveal also cell membrane proteins.

2 MATERIAL AND METHODS

Nine pleural and two ascitic effusions from patients with various malignant tumors, and one benign ascitic fluid were analysed. The fluids were centrifuged and stored at -20°C until use. PEG precipitation was carried out with two concentrations, respectively 2.5 and 5 %. To a volume of 2 to 5 ml of the effusion fluid, an equal volume of PEG solution (at double concentration i.e. 5 and 10 %) in PBS containing 0.1M EDTA, pH 7.2, was added. This mixture was kept overnight at 4°C. After washing, the precipitate was dissolved in 100 to 300 ul (depending on the amount of precipitate) of SDS solution (Ches 50 mM, SDS 1.3 %, 2 Me 3.5 %, glycerol 10 %). Affinity chromatography on Con A-Sepharose (Pharmacia) and Wheat germ Lectin (Pharmacia) was done in small columns (5 and 2 ml), according to the instructions of the manufacturer. DEAE Affi-Gel Blue (Bio-Rad) chromatography was performed according to Quay (2) in a K 9/15 column (Pharmacia). 1 ml of dialyzed pleural or ascitic fluid was applied to the column. Serum depleted effusions were prepared as described by Dermer (1). As immunoadsorbent rabbit anti-human serum (Dakopatts) was used coupled to CNBr-activated Sepharose 4B (Pharmacia) or to Protein A-Sepharose (Pharmacia). After elution, selected fractions were pooled and concentrated in CS-15 or B-15 Minicon concentrators (Amicon). Two-dimensional (2-D) electrophoresis was performed according to Anderson and Anderson (3) with minor modifications (4), and silver staining was according to Wray (5).

3 RESULTS AND DISCUSSION

In the 2-D patterns of serum-depleted effusions, only a very small number of spots are found. One row of polypeptides, with an apparent molecular mass (Mr) near 37,000 and a pI slightly more basic than haptoglobin β-chain, could be a degradation product of fibrinogen, because it co-precipitates with anti-human fibrinogen. If tumor proteins are present in effusion fluids, their concentration will probably be extremely low. In order to obtain a sufficient amount of serum-depleted sample, able to give visible spots after 2-D electrophoresis, excessive amounts of antiserum should be used.

Polyethylene glycol is a known agent for the fractional precipitation of plasma proteins. With the procedure we employed, the proteins insoluble in low concentrations of PEG are redissolved in a small amount of fluid. Up to 100 times more of them can now be analysed by the 2-D system, as compared to the amount present in a few microliter of the original sample. 2-D patterns of PEG treated effusions showed markedly large amounts of fibrinogen and its degradation products. The three different chains (α, β and γ), the Bβ-fragment and the γ-dimer are seen. The above mentioned row of spots (Mr near 37,000) is also visible, but absent in serum and plasma samples after the same PEG treatment. Besides the fibrinogen components and IgG, IgA, IgM, and α_2-macroglobulin, as major components, an unexpected number of small and weak spots are distributed over the 2-D gel pattern. An analogous pattern is seen in all examined cases, except that marked quantitative differences are observed. Spots, not regularly detected, represent a minority. Until now the observed pattern could not be related either to the nature or to the degree of the disease.

After affinity chromatography with immobilized lectins, less protein could be

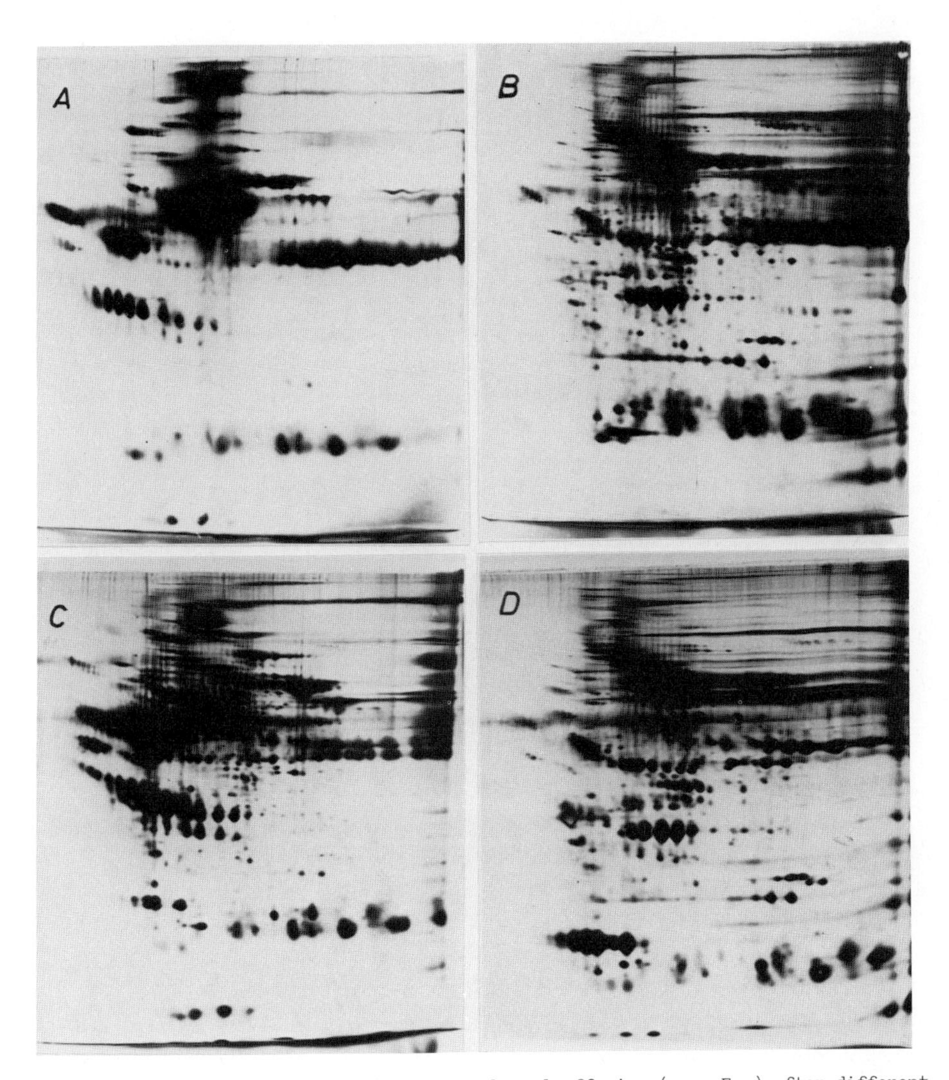

Figure 1. Comparison of 2-D patterns of a pleural effusion (case Fr.) after different treatments. (A) Pattern obtained with 1.5 µl of total pleural effusion. (B) The same sample after 5 % PEG precipitation. Comparison of both maps reveals clearly the increase of weak spots in the area between Mr 50,000 and 25,000. In (C) affinity chromatography on Con A-Sepharose was performed prior to the 2-D analysis. (D) 2-D pattern after combining affinity chromatography and PEG precipitation.

applied to the 2-D gels, due to excess of some glycoproteins such as α_1-antitrypsin and haptoglobin. However, an amount equivalent to 10 - 20 µl of total fluid, reveals a great number of weaker spots, without causing real overloading. Great similarity is observed in all cases. Combination of this affinity step with PEG precipitation, results in considerable enrichment of some glycoproteins, not visible on 2-D gels of the original samples. Indeed, PEG treatment of the isolated glycoproteins, eliminates the interfering α_1-antitrypsin and haptoglobin. 2-D patterns of the proteins eluted in the void volume of a DEAE Affi-Gel Blue column, show essentially IgG, transferrin and α_2-macroglobulin. Besides, a number of smaller more basic components, considerably enriched, are visible.

It is possible that some of the small spots we observed, are derived from tumor tissue, but this remain doubtful. We are now making a catalogue of the minor components found in pleural and ascitic effusions. Probably the trace proteins visible after PEG treatment are only a portion of the total number present in these fluids. Our results illustrate that selective sorting of some proteins prior to 2-D electrophoresis lowers the detectability limit considerably. Unfortunately our techniques still seem to be insufficient, especially for the tumor pathology, and we conclude with Allen (6) that even after all our efforts we are still looking at the surface of an iceberg.

4 REFERENCES

(1) G.B. Dermer, L.M. Silverman, J.F. Chapman, Clin. Chem. 28 (1982) 759-765.

(2) S.C. Quay, A.K. Bhan, Clin. Immunol. Immunopathol. 26 (1983) 309-317.

(3) L. Anderson, N.G. Anderson, Proc. Natl. Acad. Sci. USA 74 (1977) 5421-5425.

(4) J. Segers, M. Rabaey, R. Van Oye, Electrophoresis 5 (1984) 48-53.

(5) W. Wray, T. Boulikas, V.P. Wray, R. Hancock, Anal. Biochem. 118 (1981) 197-203.

(6) R.C. Allen in H. Hirai (Ed.), Electrophoresis '83, Walter de Gruyter, Berlin 1984, p. 3-16.

THE NUCLEAR PROTEINS IN THE HUMAN FIBROSARCOMA CELL LINE HT 1080: SYNTHESIS AND PHOSPHORYLATION.

Gerhard Unteregger

Institute for Human Genetics, University of the Saar, D-6650 Homburg, Federal Republic of Germany

1 INTRODUCTION

In contrast to histones, HMG-proteins and their posttranslational modifications which have been well characterized, less data exist on the heterogeneous group of nonhistone proteins. With the exception of some well known enzymatic functions associated with nuclear proteins the fundamental role of the majority is still unclear. There is however, some evidence that synthesis and phosphorylation of these proteins may play an important part in the regulation of gene activity (1) including those steps involved in the control of proliferation (2). Using two-dimensional polyacrylamide gel electrophoresis we analysed the nuclear protein fraction from the human fibrosarcoma cell line HT-1080, by labelling serum-stimulated cells during G1-phase with ^{35}S-methionine. When the nuclear proteins of serum-stimulated cells were incubated in the presence of ^{32}P-γATP, more than 100 polypeptides were phosphorylated by the endogenous protein kinases.

2 MATERIAL AND METHODS

Confluent cells were starved for 5 days. The medium was then renewed and the cells were labelled for various times in the presence of ^{35}S-methionine (1 100 Ci/mmol, NEN, 10 μl/ml medium). Nuclei were prepared as described earlier (3), but without the sucrose purification step. To obtain total nuclear proteins lacking the histones, the nuclei were extracted for one hour with 5 M urea (4). The remaining chromatin was removed by centrifugation and the nuclear proteins were dialysed, lyophilized and finally dissolved in IEF-sample buffer at 0.15 x 10^6 cpm/μl. In the phosphorylation experiments, starved cells were stimulated for 15 hours without ^{35}S-methionine. In order to achieve an enhanced resolution when phosphorylated proteins were applied to the gel, the nuclei were treated with 5 M urea following an extraction step in reduced salt buffer (10 mM Tris-HCl, pH 7.4-1.5 mM $MgCl_2$-10 mM NaCl-1 mM PMSF). Both solutions were dialysed against 30 mM Tris-HCl, pH 7.4. The nuclear proteins (1mg/ml) were mixed with 45 μl of a solution containing 10 mM DTE-0.1mM ATP-50 mM $MgCl_2$ and ^{32}P-γATP (3 000 Ci/mmol, 50μCi/500μg protein) and phosphorylation was carried out at 37° for 15 min in a final volume of 0.5 ml. The reaction was stopped by chilling on ice and the proteins were precipitated with acetone. Dried proteins were suspended in distilled water, lyophilized and dissolved in IEF-sample buffer at 0.15×10^6 cpm/µl. Two-dimensional gel electrophoresis was performed on linear gradient gels from 10-20% as previously described (3). Fixed gels containing methionine or phosphorus labelled proteins were stained either with Coomassie Blue or by the silver staining method (5). The dried gels were subjected to autoradiography. To obtain the precise molar mass of some phosphoproteins the spots were cut out from the gel and applied to electrophoresis on 15% SDS-gels with the appropriate marker proteins.

3 RESULTS AND DISCUSSION

In an attempt to confirm events occurring during the prereplicative phase of the cell cycle, we used starved cells which can be stimulated to proliferate by fresh serum. Fig. 1 shows the nuclear protein pattern obtained after a labelling period of 12 hours. Most proteins are located on the neutral-acidic region with M_rs from 10 to 60 kilodalton. Some proteins which are represented by prominent spots show comparable incorporation of radioactivity independent from the labelling period (arrowheads). They were also present in cell lines from human fibroblasts and meningiomas (3). In contrast, some nuclear proteins exhibit a time-dependent synthesis, including a set of 5 polypeptides with an apparent molar mass of 24 000 (arrows 3,4,5,6). In a previous study we reported the phosphorylation of this group in cell cultures from different tissues (6). They could also be detected on stained gels exhibiting a strong yellow color when the silver staining method developed by Sammons et al.(5) was applied. But we could not determine if this was due to the phosphorylation of the proteins or to the amount of acidic amino acids present.

As mentioned above, <u>in vivo</u> phosphorylation of HT 1080 cells yields only a small number of phosphorylated nuclear proteins. We thus studied the phosphorylation pattern after incubation of isolated nuclear proteins with ^{32}P-γATP. Under these conditions more than 100 proteins were modified by the enzymatic activity of endogenous nuclear protein kinases. Fig. 2 shows a schematic illustration of the resulting two-dimensional pattern. There is only a small overlap between the phosphorylated proteins extracted with RSB (open circles) and 5 M urea (dark spots) and most phosphoproteins seem to be associated with the DNA. Some prominent phosphoproteins are located in the acidic region (arrows 3-6)

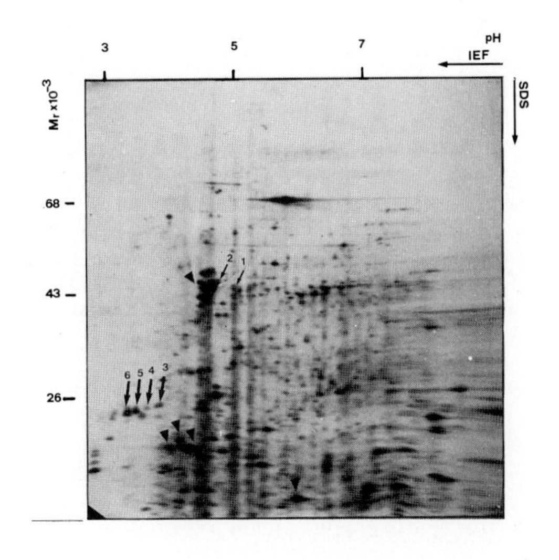

Fig.1
Two-dimensional pattern of total nuclear proteins labelled for 12 h with ^{35}S-met. 3 x 10^6cpm were loaded on the basic side of the gel. Arrowheads indicate the position of some major proteins lacking variation in their synthesis with respect to the labelling period. Proteins exhibiting greater variation in their synthesis within the G1-phase are marked with arrows. Numbers refer to phosphoproteins in Fig. 2. Autoradiography.

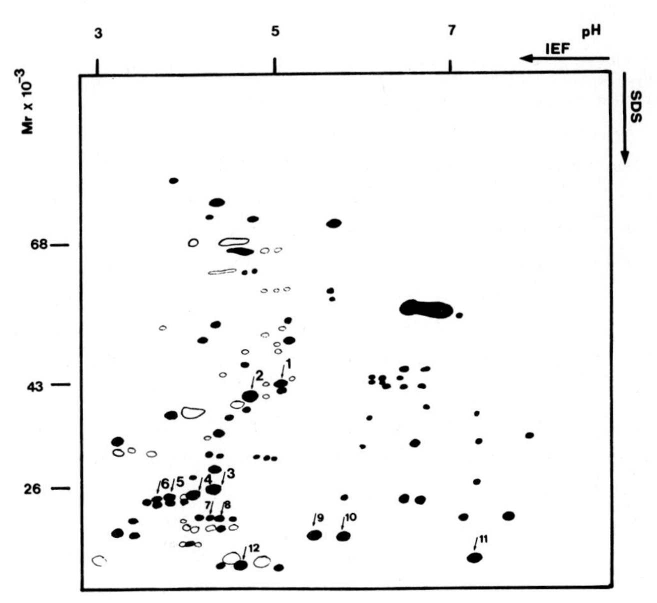

Fig. 2
Schematic illustration of the major nuclear phosphoproteins from HT 1080 cells: Nuclear proteins were either extracted with RSB or subsequently with 5 M urea and were labelled with ^{32}P-γATP for 15 min. Open circles-phosphoproteins from nuclei treated with RSB, dark spots-phosphoproteins in the 5 M urea sample following RSB treatment. Numbers indicate phosphoproteins which were further characterized.

with M_r 26 000 (no.3) and 24 000 (no.6). The composition of this group shows major variations with respect to their synthesis and phosphorylation. It is remarkable that treatment of nuclei with high salt (5 M urea) did not destroy the enzymatic activity of the protein kinases. Additionally, this activity is increased 3-5 fold by the serum-stimulation when compared to starved cells.
These results indicate that the phosphorylation of nuclear proteins as well as their synthesis during the prereplicative phase may be one of the crucial events in the interphase nucleus prior to the onset of proliferation.

4 REFERENCES

(1) G.S. Stein, J.L. Stein, J.A. Thomson, Canc.Res. 38 (1978) 1181-1201.

(2) E.W. Gerner, M. Costa, D.K. Holmes, B.E. Magun, Biochem. J. 194 (1981) 193-207.

(3) G. Unteregger, K.D. Zang, O.G. Issinger, Electrophoresis 4 (1983) 303-311.

(4) J.F. Chiu, H. Fujitani, L.S. Hnilica in D.M. Prescott (Ed.), Methods in Cell Biology XVI, Academic Press, New York 1977, pp. 283-297.

(5) D.W. Sammons, L.D. Adams, E.E. Nishizawa, Electrophoresis 2 (1981) 135-141.

(6) G. Unteregger, K.D. Zang, O.G. Issinger, Eur. J. Cancer Clin.Oncol. 19 (1983) 1321.

Abbreviations:
HMG: High mobility group; DTE: Dithioerythritol; RSB: Reduced salt buffer ; IEF: Isoelectric focusing; M_r: Relative molar mass; PMSF: Phenylmethylsulfonyl fluoride.

PARTICLE ELECTROPHORESIS STUDY ON THE LECTIN BINDING OF PURPLE MEMBRANE FRAGMENTS IN RELATION TO THE IONIC STRENGTH OF THE SUSPENDING MEDIUM

Nezabravka G. Popdimitrova, Maria R.Kantcheva[x], Stoyl P.Stoylov, Dimiter E.Kovatchev

Medico-Biological Institute at the Medical Academy,
[x]Biological Faculty, Sofia University, 1431 Sofia, Bulgaria

1 INTRODUCTION

Binding of lectins to cell surfaces is of considerable interest, since it plays an important role in initiation and modulation of functional activity.Lectins can be used also as a tool for investigation of changes in membrane glycoconjugates.Isoated membrane systems examination is an approach which can permit less ambiguous interpretation of specific details in lectin binding. Purple membrane fragments containing one protein component - bacteriorhodopsin, are widely used as a simple membrane system. PHA-P and Con A are both phytohemagglutinins extracted from beans. Concanavalin A is supposed to be a tetramer stabilized by metals(1).

2 PRINCIPLES OF OPERATION AND POSTULATES

Purple membrane fragments was isolated from Halobacterium halobium described by Oesterhelt and Stoeckenius (2).Electrophoretic mobility measurements of purple membrane clusters were carried out at 20°C in phosphate buffer, pH=6,0, in cylindrical chamber apparatus - Cytopherometer "Opton"(3). Native Con A was obtained from Boehringer Manheim GmbH.Ionic strength of the suspending medium was adjusted with NaCl.

3 Ionic strength effects on Con A binding

Changes in PHA-P binding to purple membrane particles have already been investigated in dependence of ionic strength of the suspending medium (4).Membrane surface electric charge dencity was monitored in order to obtain information about dose dependence of lectin binding.Table 1 indicates the electrophoretic mobility changes at different ionic strengths of the suspending medium after Con A treatment of purple membrane fragments.

Table 1. Decrease of the electrophoretic mobility of purple membrane particles after 150 $mg.ml^{-1}$ Con A- treatment at different ionic strengths, pH = 6,0

Con A /mg/	Ionic strength /M/	Electrophoretic mobility $u.10^{-8}m^2.V^{-1}.s^{-1}$	E /%/
Control	$0,15.10^{-2}$	2,727	-
150	"	0,914	66,5
Control	$0,15.10^{-1}$	2,809	-
150	"	1,300	53,7
Control	0,15	1,628	-
150	"	1,261	22,54

The ionic strength of the suspending medium modifies the reductin of the membrane surface charge dencity, similarly to the effectivity of PHA-P at the same experimental conditions. The less prononced effectivity of Con A binding could be related to the specific membrane components of the purple membrane.

4 REFERENCES

(1) C. F. Brewer, R. D. Brown, S. H. Koenig, Biochemistry, 22 (1983) 3691-3702.

(2) D. Oesterhelt, W. Stoeckenius, Methods Enzimol.(1974),667-678.

(3) M. Kantcheva, N. G. Popdimitrova, S. P. Stoylov, Studia Biophys. 90, (1982),125-126.

(4) M.Kantcheva, N. G. Popdimitrova, S.P.Stoylov, D. E. Kovatchev, Electrophoresis,1984, in press.

STUDIES ON ASTROGLIAL CELL MATURATION USING BIDIMENSIONAL POLYACRYLAMIDE GEL ELECTROPHORESIS

Brigitte Pettmann, Marc Weibel, Gérard Labourdette, Monique Sensenbrenner

Centre de Neurochimie du CNRS - 5, rue Blaise Pascal - 67084 Strasbourg Cedex - France

1 INTRODUCTION

Differentiation and maturation of cells are mainly characterized by modifications of the biosynthesis of specific proteins, usually by the synthesis of new proteins which are known or thought to be related to the physiological function of the differentiated, mature cells.

For a long time only a few specific proteins (markers) have been detected and identified for each cell type. Their levels or enzymatic activities were used as measure of the differentiation or maturation state of the cells. However it was found that in one cell type the various markers do not behave as a whole, indeed treatments of cells in culture by differentiation-maturation agents like db cAMP, hormones or growth factors do not modulate in parallel the biosynthesis of some markers.

2 WORKING HYPOTHESIS

From the last observations we propose that the proteins whose biosynthesis is modulated during the cell maturation, can be grouped into sets which are regulated more or less independently. In each set the proteins are regulated as a whole, i.e. biosynthesis of every protein is under a coordinated control. During cell maturation the various protein sets will be activated. Degrees of maturation could be defined according to the number of sets activated.

3 EXPERIMENTAL PRINCIPLE

Since different, physiological or non physiological, agents are able to modulate differently the biosynthesis of specific markers, these agents might activate some different sets of proteins. Astroglial cell cultures will be treated with such agents and synthesized proteins will be analyzed by bidimensional polyacrylamide gel electrophoresis.

Comparisons of the electrophoretograms will allow to test the hypothesis and, if it is confirmed, to determine the composition of some of the protein sets.

4 METHODS

Primary cultures of astroblasts were prepared from newborn rat cerebral hemispheres as described (1). Agents of maturation used were : 1) the AGF (Astroglial Growth Factor) purified in our laboratory from bovine brain (2), and which also stimulates the astroblasts proliferation ; 2) db cAMP ; 3) the lectin Concanavalin A.

Cultures were treated from day 5 to day 20 after seeding. Cells were harvested and frozen. Then they were lysed and their proteins analysed by 2-D-electrophoresis according to O'Farrell (3) with slight modifications. Silver containing was performed as described by Wray et al. (4) with some modifications.

5 PRELIMINARY RESULTS

In our present experimental conditions around 350 spots were visible on the electrophoretograms, and about 270 could be compared. Proteins of untreated cultures were analysed as a function of time in culture at day 7, 15, 21 and 28. Changes affect less than 10 % of the proteins, mainly between days 7 and 15.

The three applied treatments resulted in the modification of 60 % of the spots compared to the control untreated cultures. In half of these spots staining intensity increases and in the other half it decreases. These proteins could be tentatively classified into 7 sets ; proteins modified identically by the three agents (1 set), by two agents (2 sets), by only one of the agent (3 sets). The number of proteins in the various sets ranged from 5 to 15 % of the total number (i.e., 270 proteins). These preliminary results are compatible with our working hypothesis.

6 REFERENCES

(1) J. Booher, M. Sensenbrenner, Neurobiology 2 (1972) 97-105.

(2) B. Pettmann, M. Weibel, G. Daune, M. Sensenbrenner, G. Labourdette, J. Neurosci. Res. 8 (1982) 463-476.

(3) P.Z. O'Farrell, J. Biol. Chem. 250 (1975) 4007-4021.

(4) W. Wray, T. Boulikas, V.P. Wray, R. Hancock, Anal. Biochem. 118 (1981) 197-203.

A METHOD FOR LOW COST PREPARATION OF POLYACRYLAMIDE GELS FOR VARIOUS ELECTROPHORESIS TECHNIQUES

Alexander Lapin, Hillard J. Zyman, F. Gabl

Institute of Clinical Chemistry and Laboratory Diagnostics
University of Vienna
Lazarettgasse 14, A-1090 Wien, Austria

Sophisticated electrophoretic techniques are very slowly introduced into the clinical laboratory. It is still difficult to obtain within a practicable time sufficient quantity of gels with satisfactory quality. Industrially made gels are costly and not available for every application.

Using plastic package material we constucted in a very simple way a device for simultaneous production of more than 20 gels suitable for isoelectric focusing, SDS electrophoresis and for two dimensional electrophoresis. The gels of 110 x 205 mm in size are supported on 1mm thick glass plates. The thickness of gels is variable from 0,8 to 2 mm and one gel can be used for analysis of more than 25 samples. One batch of 20 gels can be prepared by one person within one hour (completed by overnight polymerization). It is also possible to prepare gels with each kind of gradient with satisfactory reproducibility (linear density gradient better than 97% reproducible).

Gel plates were sealed in polypropylene foil using a frozen food bag sealer and stored at 4°C. The gels stored in this manner showed no deterioration for at least 5 weeks and some were used up to 3 months. Fast documentation of runs was achieved by photocopying the gel plates with somwhat darker contrast than usual. Cost for one gel do not exceed 1 US$.

Example of each technique will be shown.

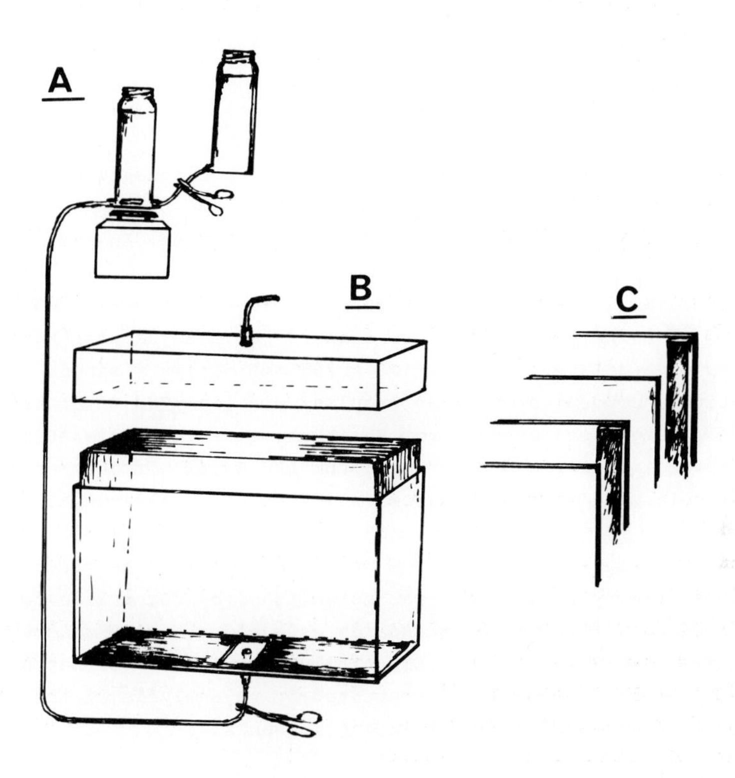

Fig.1 : Gel production apparatus

A- Gradient former device

B- Gel casting box with glass plates (1 x 110 x 205 mm)

C- Detail of glass plates arranged in alternate order: gel former plates (with spacer) and gel supporting plates (treated by "Bind Silan®")

SDS ELECTROPHORESIS OF URINARY PROTEINS IN PATIENTS SUFFERING FROM MULTIPLE MYELOMA AND IN KIDNEY TRANSPLANT PATIENTS

Alexander Lapin, Hillard J.Zyman, Jan Zazgornik[+], Franz Gabl

Institute of Clinical Chemistry and Laboratory Diagnostics
[+]I.University Clinic of Medicine
University of Vienna. Lazarettgasse 14, A-1090 Wien, Austria

Self made SDS density gradient gels (T= 10 - 20%) were used for analysis of urinary proteins.More than 20 patients samples were analyzed on a gel plate (0.8 x 110 x 205 mm) during a single overnight run.Native unconcentrated urine samples were analyzed together with molecular weight standards (from Pharmacia Fine Chemicals AB,Sweden) by horizontal electrophoresis using the LKB Multiphor chamber.After the run gels were stained by Coomassie Blue and evaluated as follows:

In the patients suffering from multiple myeloma the molecular weight of urinary paraprotein was established by comparison to the pattern of molecular weight standards as a additional characterization to the immunological analysis.Especially dimerization of paraprotein molecules could be clearly demonstrated by re-analysis of the same sample after addition of dissociating reagents.

In the case of samples from kidney transplant patients (n = 49) urinary protein patterns were evaluated visually in order to establish four main groups of proteinuria :

A-no protein detectable by electrophoresis
B-albuminuria no other protein than albumin detectable
C-tubular proteinuria occurance of protein with lower molecular weight than albumin (67.000 Dalt)
D-mixed proteinuria occurance of protein with higher molecular weight, albumin and low molecular weight protein

These four groups of samples were compared with following parameters:

-protein concentration in urine
-serum creatinine level
-serum level of immunsuppressant "Cyclosporine A"(when administered)

When all the groups are compared whith each other, different kinds of kidney damage can be pointed out according to type of proteinuria (glomerular,tubular,mixed).

I

N

O

P